D1302254

James McKeen Cattell

Man of Science

James McKeen Cattell, 1860–1944.

1860 – 1944

James McKeen Cattell

Man of Science

VOLUME I

PSYCHOLOGICAL
RESEARCH

1947

THE SCIENCE PRESS

Lancaster, Pennsylvania

Copyright, 1947
By
THE SCIENCE PRESS

The Maple Press Company
York, Pa.

Foreword

The scientific work and writings of James McKeen Cattell—his researches, addresses, formal and informal papers—span the whole history of modern psychology. He listened to lectures by Lotze and Helmholtz, served as assistant in the laboratories of Wilhelm Wundt and of Francis Galton, was a founder of the American Psychological Association and of early psychological journals. He was the world's first Professor of Psychology. And in 1943 he was to have (the meetings were cancelled) participated in the celebration of the 50th Anniversary of the American Psychological Association. His interests comprehended both theoretical and applied psychology from the very beginning of his career and in both these realms he made original and lasting contributions. Many of them, though not all, have been preserved in his numerous publications.

The assembling and presentation of these documents in a form convenient for reference should have a unique historical value. This volume comprising a collection of his researches is the first of two, the second being devoted to formal papers and addresses. The appreciation of Dr. Cattell written after his death by R. S. Woodworth and reprinted as the opening article will afford a brief but effective survey of his scientific work. A complete bibliography at the end of the book, arranged in chronological order, will give access to certain articles which are not to be reproduced in either volume.

The twenty-nine research papers printed here are arranged in chronological order and with no editorial changes, except in the case of 1, 10, and 13, which have been translated from the original German. The reader will find some repetition of material, some variations in the use of terms and some changes over the years in the use of statistical terms and in the organization of tables and charts. It seemed best not to tamper with these, but rather to let them stand as a part of the historical record.

The contents of this volume have more than a mere historical value. In it will be discovered fruitful suggestions for research, important problems attacked in a preliminary way but never completely solved, and the original description of methods and techniques which have never in the succeeding years been exploited to the full. There is reproduced here, too, a considerable body of data which are frequently referred to by research students, such as those contained in the study: "On the Perception of Small Differences." Their easier accessibility should be welcomed.

A survey of the contents of the book will reveal much material of practical import even though some of it was written more than sixty years ago. Of particular interest, in the midst of the current dearth of young scientists, is the series of studies inquiring into the factors that make for scientific productivity. Any far-seeing program for the discovery and development of scientific talent in our population could profit from a careful examination of the several "Studies of American Men of Science."

Over and above whatever contributions may be made to the historian of the science of psychology, to the research student and to those concerned with the problems that come near to everyday life, this compilation of the work of James McKeen Cattell gives the editor, as one of his former students, and as a representative of all of those former students, a means of expressing in a tangible way his respect and affection for a great man of science.

A. T. Poffenberger

Contents

VOLUME I

JAMES McKEEN CATTELL
1860–1944

Written by R. S. Woodworth for the *Psychological Review*, in appreciation of James McKeen Cattell, who was the joint founder of that journal with James Mark Baldwin in 1894, and co-editor with Baldwin until 1904, each serving as editor on alternate years. Printed in the *Psychological Review*, **51**: 201–209, 1944.

In the history of American psychology very few figures are so outstanding as that of James McKeen Cattell whose long and active life has just come to a close. He did not, indeed, belong to the first generation of American scientific psychologists—consisting mainly of William James, G. Stanley Hall and George Trumbull Ladd—but he was probably the most influential of the second generation which included Titchener, Münsterberg, James Mark Baldwin, Jastrow, Sanford, and Scripture, with others coming along just a little later. Though Cattell was not a systematist and did not found a school in that sense, he was the leader in what became a widespread and distinctive movement in American psychology. His interest from the very outset of his career was in introducing quantitative methods into psychology and especially in using such methods for the measurement of individual differences.

Cattell graduated in 1880 from Lafayette College, of which his father was the president. His undergraduate interests had centered largely on literature. His first step toward a professional career, however, was to go to Europe for the study of philosophy. He heard Wundt lecture at Leipzig and Lotze at Göttingen and was much impressed by both of these men. A paper on Lotze won for Cattell a fellowship in philosophy at Johns Hopkins, where he spent the year of 1882–83, with John Dewey and Joseph Jastrow as fellow students. It was during this year that Stanley Hall set up his psychological laboratory at Johns Hopkins, with some assistance from this group of students, and it was there, apparently, that Cattell began his "psychometric investigations," concerned with the timing of various mental processes. He took his data and his designs for improved apparatus back to Germany the following year and remained in Wundt's laboratory for the three years, 1883–1886, being for part of this time Wundt's first laboratory assistant.

From the outset Cattell seems to have been impressed with the variability of human performance and the consequent need for long

1

series of observations in order to reach reliable results. He set up his apparatus in his own rooms at Leipzig so that he could work longer hours than Wundt permitted in the laboratory, and carried out an extraordinarily thorough and extensive study of reaction times, ranging all the way from the simple reaction through the reactions with discrimination and choice up to free and controlled association. Reaction time was of course no novelty in the Leipzig laboratory, being in fact a line of experiment on which Wundt was pinning great hopes. Cattell's conception of reaction time studies, however, differed radically from that of Wundt. Wundt hoped by variation of the experiment, with certain introspective controls, to tease out the time constants for elementary mental processes such as perception, choice and association. Cattell found that he could not himself carry out the required introspections and subjective controls, and he came to doubt the ability of others to do so. It seemed to him that the simple reaction became with practice a "prepared reflex" and that in the more complex reactions the constituent processes overlapped in time and so could not be measured. Yet the reaction time experiment, he still held, was of great value as a tool for determining the speed and difficulty of many everyday mental processes. He could show, for example, that the time required to read a short familiar word was no greater than that required to read a single letter, so that the practice then coming into vogue of teaching the child to read whole words before the single letters had a scientific basis. Without pretending to analyze the complex processes into their elements, Cattell used the total reaction time obtained under various conditions for studying attention, fatigue and practice, for comparing the legibility of the different letters of the alphabet and for many other practical and scientific purposes.

Cattell's Leipzig studies were all concerned with time, but they were not limited to reaction time.[1] He used his "fall tachistoscope" also for determining the exposure time necessary for perceiving colors, pictures, letters and words.[2] He also made an interesting use of a serial exposure apparatus[3]—a type of experiment which has not been followed up as much as it deserves.

Cattell continued to use the reaction time method in important later studies[4] and directed quite a number of his Columbia students in similar work.

[1] Psychometrische Untersuchungen. *Philos. Stud.*, 1886, **3**, 305–335, 452–492; 1887, **4**, 241–250. Also: *Mind*, 1886, **11**, 220–242, 377–392, 524–538; 1887, **12**, 68–74.

[2] Über die Trägheit der Netzhaut und des Sehcentrums. *Philos. Stud.*, 1885, **3**, 94–127. Also: *Brain*, 1885, **8**, 295–312.

[3] Über die Zeit der Erkennung und Benennung von Schriftzeichen, Bildern und Farben. *Philos. Stud.*, 1885, **2**, 635–650. Also: (Abridged) *Mind*, 1886, **11**, 63–65.

[4] (With Dolley, C. S.) On reaction-times and the velocity of the nervous im-

Not during his years at Leipzig, but shortly afterward, Cattell carried on extensive work in another of the classical fields of experimental psychology, psychophysics.[1,2] Here, as well as in reaction time, he broke away from the older view of these experiments as being concerned with the measurement of consciousness and substituted a more objective and operational conception. Experiments using the method of right and wrong cases or of constant stimuli, for example, are not directed operationally toward the measurement of intensity of sensation. They are experiments in observation and judgment and the results come out as measurements of the error of observation. Psychophysics, accordingly, should be conceived as a study of accuracy of observation under different conditions—a study of obvious practical importance. It seemed to Cattell more in accordance with the theory of probability (a theory in which he took much interest) to expect the error of observation to increase as the square root of the observed magnitude, rather than in direct proportion to that magnitude as asserted in Weber's law. As a matter of fact, the data usually come out between these two formulas. That is, the error of observation usually increases less rapidly than Weber's law would predict but more rapidly than predicted by Cattell's square root law.

A little later,[3] by combining his interests in psychophysics and reaction time, Cattell invented a new psychophysical method, the discrimination time method for indicating the difference between magnitudes or qualities—the larger the effective difference, the quicker the discrimination.

Though differing with Wundt on some matters of theory, Cattell always retained a warm personal affection for his master and a high respect for his services as a founder of experimental psychology. After leaving Leipzig Cattell soon came into personal contact with Francis Galton—"the greatest man whom I have known"—and was confirmed by Galton in his own long-held view that the measurement of individual differences would be one of the most fertile fields for the new psychology. Cattell was perhaps the first (1890) to use the term mental tests, and he thus expressed his high hopes regarding them:

Psychology cannot attain the certainty and exactness of the physical sciences, unless it rests on a foundation of experiment and measurement. A

---

pulse. (Abstract) *Psychol. Rev.*, 1894, **1**, 159–168. Also: *Natl. Acad. Sci. Memoir*, 1896, **7**, No. 2, 393–415.

[1] (With Fullerton, G. S.) On the perception of small differences with special reference to the extent, force, and time of movement. *Publ. Univ. Pa.*, 1892, No. 2. Pp. 159.

[2] On errors of observation. *Amer. J. Psychol.*, 1893, **5**, 285–293.

[3] The time of perception as a measure of differences in intensity. *Philos. Stud.* 1902, **19**, 63–68.

step in this direction could be made by applying a series of mental tests and measurements to a large number of individuals. The results would be of considerable scientific value in discovering the constancy of mental processes, their interdependence, and their variation under different circumstances. Individuals, besides, would find their tests interesting, and, perhaps, useful in regard to training, mode of life or indication of disease ([1], p. 373).

At this time he described a series of ten tests which he apparently was using at the University of Pennsylvania. Shortly afterwards, at Columbia, he developed a more extensive list, known for many years as the Freshman Tests, though they had nothing to do with the admission of freshmen to college.[2] They were given to 50 or more volunteers from each successive freshman class, in order to obtain data for the study of individual differences and the factors on which the differences depend. When the sample of freshmen had grown to a sufficient size, the Pearson method of studying correlation having meanwhile become available, these data were subjected to correlational analysis. Though the low correlations obtained were surprising and rather disappointing to Cattell—they suffered from attenuation, as Spearman soon pointed out—this study has considerable historical importance in the development of the correlational method in psychology.[3]

Cattell's plan of testing separate functions—the senses, quickness of movement, perception of time, memory, imagery, etc.—was rather left behind with the appearance of Binet's method of testing intelligence, though it is more in line with recent efforts to develop tests for specific mental abilities.

Reaction time, psychophysics, and tests were thus the main lines of Cattell's early researches. A minor extension of his work on errors of observation is of historic interest as being probably the first study of the reliability of testimony. He wrote:

. . . we do not know how likely it is that a piece of testimony is true, or how the degree of probability varies under different conditions. If we could learn this by experiment the result would be a contribution to psychology, and would at the same time have certain important practical applications ([4], p. 761).

His experiment consisted in asking college students questions about distances on the campus, the weather a week before, the dates of certain historical events, etc. He found wide individual variation in the

[1] Mental tests and measurements. *Mind*, 1890, **15**, 373–381.
[2] (With Farrand, L.) Physical and mental measurements of the students of Columbia University. *Psychol. Rev.*, 1896, **3**, 618–648.
[3] WISSLER, C. The correlation of mental and physical tests. *Psychol. Rev Monogr.*, 1901, **3**, No. 16. Pp. 62.
[4] Measurements of the accuracy of recollection. *Science*, 1895, **2**, 761–766.

students' answers. In some cases the average of the answers was close to the truth while in other cases there was a large constant error.

When students were asked what was said during the first two minutes of the lecture in the same course given one week before, the accounts were such that the lecturer might prefer not to have them recorded. From the testimony of the students it would appear that two minutes sufficed to cover a large range of psychological and other subjects, and to make many statements of an extraordinary character ([1], p. 764).

A major contribution, besides those already mentioned, was the invention of the order of merit or ranking method for use both in psychophysics and in aesthetics and other judgments of value. Cattell first employed it in a psychophysical problem. Having prepared a series of over 200 shades of gray ranging by imperceptible steps from black to white, he asked his subjects to arrange them as well as possible in order of brightness. The observer's errors could be determined by reference to the objective scale of brightness.[2] He soon extended the use of the method to the broad field of value judgments. The first value considered was the scientific standing of American men of science, that is, the relative standing of the men in any given branch of science. In the case of psychology, for example,[3] he first prepared a list of all who could be regarded as scientific psychologists, and then induced ten leading psychologists to serve as judges and rank the listed individuals in order of scientific merit. The ten judges worked independently and Cattell combined their rankings and computed the average position assigned to each individual, with the variation from judge to judge. The average ranks were not published till thirty years later ([4], 5th edition, 1933, pp. 1269 ff.;[5] p. 11). Meanwhile, however, accepting the average ranks as furnishing an approximation to a true order of merit, he was able to use the results in two ways. By comparing each judge's arrangement with the average of all, he had an estimate of the accuracy of each judge. From the average ranks combined with other data he was able to make what might be called an ecological study of *Homo scientificus Americanus* with respect to parentage, place

[1] Measurements of the accuracy of recollection. *Science*, 1895, **2**, 761–766.

[2] The time of perception as a measure of differences in intensity. *Philos. Stud.*, 1902, **19**, 63–68.

[3] Statistics of American psychologists. *Amer. J. Psychol.*, 1903, **14**, 310–328.

[4] *American Men of Science*. New York: Science Press. First edition, 1906, pp 364; sixth edition, 1938, pp. 1608.

[5] Psychology in America. (Address of the President of the Ninth International Congress of Psychology.) *Science*, 1929, **70**, 335–347. Also published separately with supplementary material, New York: Science Press, 1929. Pp. 32.

of birth and of education, and present geographical distribution;[1] and by repeating this study at about seven-year intervals he brought to light changes and trends of considerable interest.[2] The ranking method was quickly applied by his students and colleagues to a great variety of value judgments related to literature, education and business. Cattell himself made some progress in the difficult task of working out the relations between rank order and quantitative measurement.

As was said before, Cattell did not found a school of psychological theory. He was open-minded towards all kinds of psychological research and application, provided they were serious and scientific, and was willing to have many sorts of experiment going on in his laboratory. His own preference was definitely for the objective type of experiment. He no doubt prepared the way for behaviorism and felt considerable respect for it when it emerged but he was not willing to rule out of the science those who preferred the introspective method. There was a great difference between the types of work done in his laboratory and in Titchener's, yet he had a high respect for Titchener as a scientist. Certain statements in Cattell's address at the St. Louis World's Fair in 1904 have often been quoted and deserve to be quoted again:

Sciences are not immutable species, but developing organisms. Their fundamental conceptions and methods at any period can only be approached by a research into work actually accomplished. . . The task has been assigned to me of considering the scope, conceptions and methods of psychology, and it is my business to define the field of psychology or to acknowledge my inability to do so. I must choose the latter alternative. I can only say that psychology is what the psychologist is interested in *qua* psychologist. . . . I am not convinced that psychology should be limited to the study of consciousness as such. . . . I admire . . . the ever-increasing acuteness of introspective analysis . . . but the positive scientific results are small in quantity when compared with the objective experimental work accomplished in the past fifty years. There is no conflict between introspective analysis and objective experiment—on the contrary, they should and do continually coöperate. . . . Let us take a broad outlook and be liberal in our appreciation. . . . As I claim for psychology the freedom of the universe in its subject-matter, so I believe that every method of science can be used by the psychologist. The two great achievements of science have been the elaboration of the quantitative method on the one hand and of the genetic method on the other. . . . It would be an irreparable limitation if either of these methods did not apply in psychology. . . . I see no reason why the application of systematized knowledge to the control of human nature may not in

[1] A statistical study of American men of science. *Science*, 1906, **24**, 658–665, 699–707, 732–742.

[2] A further statistical study of American men of science. *Science*, 1910, **32**, 633–648, 672–688.

the course of the present century accomplish results commensurate with the nineteenth century applications of physical science to the material world. . . . In the end there will be not only a science but also a profession of psychology ([1], pp. 176, 179, 180, 182, 186).

If we try to bring before us the young Cattell who emerged from Leipzig in 1886 with the degree of Doctor of Philosophy, the picture is one of a man of great initiative and energy, eager for large enterprises, and filled with missionary zeal for the advancement of a psychology which should be experimental, quantitative and practical, with great emphasis on the study of individual differences. For two years this young man divided his efforts between England and America, working in Galton's Anthopometric Laboratory in London, lecturing in Cambridge University and making a start toward a laboratory there, and lecturing also at Bryn Mawr College and the University of Pennsylvania. In 1888 he became a professor at the latter institution, and he was always proud of the fact that he was Professor of Psychology and that this was the first professorship of psychology as distinguished from philosophy that was ever established anywhere.[2] Cattell was never hostile in the least to philosophy or philosophers; he was especially appreciative of John Dewey; but he believed that psychology should align itself with the sciencies. His laboratory at Pennsylvania was the first one to provide not only for research but also for the initiation of the college student into the methods of experimental psychology. After a few years at Pennsylvania he accepted a call from Columbia University where he started the laboratory in 1891. Here his influence was felt by many students, including over fifty who took their doctor's degree with him up to 1917 when his connection with the university ceased. The majority of these graduates became active psychologists in various parts of the country, and they look back to Cattell with loyalty and with gratitude for his helpful stimulation and guidance.

Besides his research and teaching, Cattell's enterprising activity branched out in several directions. He took quite an interest in designing improved and simplified forms of psychological apparatus and in having it manufactured in the laboratory shop, so making a conttibution, as he felt, to the development of experimental psychology in the laboratories that were springing up throughout the country. This was one of his earliest enterprises, continued for a couple of decades at Columbia.

[1] The conceptions and methods of psychology. *Pop. Sci. Mo.*, 1904, **46**, 176–186.
[2] Early psychological laboratories. *Science*, 1928, **67**, 543–548. Also: *Feelings and emotions: the Wittenberg Symposium.* (Edited by C. Murchison.) Worcester: Clark University Press, 1928, 427–433.

Another early enterprise was the editing and publishing of scientific journals, and this continued as a major activity for the rest of his life. In 1894 he joined forces with James Mark Baldwin, then professor at Princeton, in establishing the PSYCHOLOGICAL REVIEW series. In the same year he acquired the weekly journal, *Science*, which had just suspended publication because of financial difficulties. He secured the coöperation of an eminent editorial board while taking on himself the arduous tasks of managing editor and business manager. He set up an editorial and publishing office at his country home on the mountain top in Garrison, N. Y., fifty miles from the university, and with the able assistance of Josephine Owen Cattell, his wife, produced an extremely well-edited journal which after a few years became a financial success and was accepted as an indispensable service to American science. A few years later he similarly took over the *Popular Science Monthly* and made a success of it, later renaming it the *Scientific Monthly*, and in 1915 he started a comprehensive educational weekly, *School and Society*. All this editorial work took him away from active research, but such services of a psychologist to the causes of science and education redounded greatly to the credit of psychology.

The same was true of his active participation in the general organization of American scientific men. First we should notice that he was one of the small group that started the American Psychological Association in 1892.[1] He was a member of the Council from the beginning, Secretary the third year and President the fourth year.[2] Soon after coming to Columbia he became a member of the New York Academy of Sciences and soon induced the Academy to set up a Section of Anthropology and Psychology, so winning recognition for our science from this local scientific body. He was President of the New York Academy in 1902 and set forth in his presidential address his ideas on the appropriate organizational scheme for American science. He said:

The organization of science in America toward which I believe we are moving is this: We shall have a national society for each of the sciences; these societies will be affiliated and will form the American Association for the Advancement of Science. . . . Our national societies will consist of local sections, and these sections will unite to form an academy of sciences. . . . This kind of organization may appear to be almost too logical for a world that is somewhat careless of logic, but it is in part already realized ([3], p. 972, 973).

[1] Our psychological association and research. *Science*, 1917, **45**, 275–284.
[2] Address of the president before the American Psychological Association, 1895. *Psychol. Rev.*, 1896, **3**, 134–148.
[3] The academy of sciences. (Address of the President of the New York Academy of Sciences.) *Science*, 1902, **16**, 965–974.

In accordance with this idea of local branches of the national societies, Cattell had already in 1900 secured permission from the American Psychological Association to establish a New York Branch, which maintained a continuous and useful existence till it expanded to become the Eastern Psychological Association of today.

Cattell's interest in the American Association for the Advancement of Science (the A.A.A.S.) evidently began very early, for we find him in 1898 Vice-President of that Association and Chairman of Section H, then the Section of Anthropology but soon to become for many years the Section of Anthropology and Psychology. His vice-presidential address at that time made a definite claim for the recognition of psychology as a science.[1] He said:

From our present point of view science in its history appears to have followed a necessary course. The phenomena of the physical world are stable and readily subject to experiment and measurement; their control is essential to material progress. It is therefore no wonder that the physical sciences should have preceded the biological sciences in their development. Far more complex, transient and inaccessible to experiment even than the phenomena of living beings are men, they themselves and their deeds—sciences of these things must come later. . . . Psychology has become an integral part of modern science; it gives and takes with a free hand. A parvenu among the sciences, it is self-conscious and knows its obligations and its limitations; but its position in the body scientific is henceforth secure. . . . When we regard the fifty years of this Association or the century now ending, we cannot fail to see that it has been an era of science. . . . The older sciences have been reformed and new departments have been established. But amid all this scientific progress nothing has been more notable—at least from my own partial point of view—than the development of psychology into a science rivaling in activity and fruitfulness the other great sciences.

From 1900 on Cattell's main interests were probably his journals, especially *Science*, his directory of men of science along with his already mentioned studies of these men, and the A.A.A.S. In 1900 *Science* became the official medium for the Association, greatly to the advantage of both, and from that time till the end of his life he was a leader in the Association and probably more influential than anyone else in its affairs.[2] He was Vice-President again in 1913, this time for the Section

[1] The advance of psychology. (Address of the Vice-President for Anthropology of the American Association for the Advancement of Science.) *Proc. Amer. Ass. Adv. Sci.*, 1898, **47**, 3–15.

[2] CONKLIN, E. G., THORNDIKE, E. L., LIVINGSTON, B. E., CARLSON, A. J., WOODWORTH, R. S., ACHILLES, P. S., DAVIS, W., HOWARD, L. O., PARKER, G. H., RUSSELL, H. N., and SWANN, W. F. G. James McKeen Cattell—In Memoriam. *Science*, 1944, **99**, 151–165.

of Education,[1] and President of the Association in 1924.[2] He was the first psychologist to receive this distinguished honor, as he had also been the first (in 1901) to be admitted to the National Academy of Sciences. As an active member of the National Academy he was influential in building up the representation of psychology in that body. With his extremely wide acquaintance among scientific men and his varied services to American science in general, as well as by his direct efforts in behalf of psychology, he undoubtedly contributed more than any other one man to win recognition for our science among the group of natural sciences.

Promotion of applied psychology was one of Cattell's ambitions from the very beginning of his career, and one which he emphasized repeatedly in his addresses and writings. He encouraged his students to pioneer in finding applications to education, industry and medicine. Coupled with this desire to make psychology a force for the betterment of mankind was a strong democratic spirit which made him resentful of the necessity of appealing humbly to wealthy donors and foundations, or even to the Government, for the support of scientific research. He pointed to the enormous economic gain resulting from research and urged that a fraction, if only a small fraction, of this gain ought to be turned over to the scientists as a matter of right and of public policy for the support of further research. It was quite in line with these predilections that he organized the Psychological Corporation in 1921, putting into it funds from his own pocket and securing a liberal charter which permits the Corporation to earn money by applying psychology but provides that a large share of the profits shall be plowed in for further research. In spite of his other responsibilities he helped greatly to direct the policy of the Corporation during its early years of struggling existence, and when it began to have some financial success he turned his own stock into a fund to be used for the support of research in applied psychology.

Even yet we have not mentioned all of Cattell's organizational activities. One of the most important during his last twenty years was an active participation in the development of Science Service. He contributed much to the success of this effort to improve newspaper coverage of scientific events and discoveries, and thus to bring science home to the general public.

He set up the Science Press Printing Company in 1923 for specializing in the printing of scientific journals and books.

[1] Science, education and democracy. (Address of the Vice-President for Education of the American Association for the Advancement of Science.) *Science*, 1914, **39**, 443–454.

[2] Some psychological experiments. (Address of the President of the American Association for the Advancement of Science.) *Science*, 1926, **66**, 1–8.

His lifelong interest in problems of university organization and management was strongly tinged with the democratic spirit already mentioned.[1] His outspoken views on these problems brought on some of the most exciting episodes of his career and led up to his eventual dismissal from Columbia during the excitement of the first World War. His pacifist leanings and his particular antipathy to any form of compulsion even during war did not prevent him from contributing of his best to the war effort of the psychologists in the development of the Army tests.

Unfortunately Cattell could never be persuaded to write even a brief autobiography. His excuse was that an autobiography such as he would write would land him in the position of defendant in a number of libel suits. He felt sure he could not bring himself to delete all the pungent comments that would occur to him, and he had found by long experience that such comments were not always accepted in the spirit of raillery that motivated them in his conversation and in his more polemic writings. Autobiographical material bearing mostly on his early career can be found in some of his writings,[2,3,4] and considerable material on his life is available in other sources.[5,6,7]

The crowning honor of Cattell's life came when, at the age of nearly seventy, he was chosen by the votes of American psychologists to represent them as President of the Ninth International Congress of Psychology, held at New Haven in 1929. His presidential address on Psychology in America, with the supplementary materials, makes an important historical document.[4]

The present attempt to convey to the younger generation some impression of the life and work of one of our leaders in American psy-

[1] *University control.* New York: Science Press, 1913. Pp. 484.

[2] Some psychological experiments. (Address of the President of the American Association for the Advancement of Science.) *Science*, 1926, **66**, 1–8.

[3] Early psychological laboratories. *Science*, 1928, **67**, 543–548. Also: *Feelings and emotions: the Wittenberg Symposium.* (Edited by C. Murchison.) Worcester: Clark University Press, 1928, 427–433.

[4] Psychology in America. (Address of the President of the Ninth International Congress of Psychology.) *Science*, 1929, **70**, 335–347. Also published separately with supplementary material, New York: Science Press, 1929. Pp. 32.

[5] BORING, E. G. *A history of experimental psychology.* New York: Century Co., 1929. Pp. 519–528.

[6] CONKLIN, E. G., THORNDIKE, E. L., LIVINGSTON, B. E., CARLSON, A. J., WOODWORTH, R. S., ACHILLES, P. S., DAVIS, W., HOWARD, L. O., PARKER, G. H., RUSSELL, H. N., and SWANN, W. F. G. James McKeen Cattell—In Memoriam. *Science*, 1944, **99**, 151–165.

[7] HENMON, V. A. C., DEARBORN, W. F., WELLS, F. L., WOODWORTH, R. S., HOLLINGWORTH, H. L., and THORNDIKE, E. L. The psychological researches of James McKeen Cattell: a review by some of his pupils. *Arch. Psychol.*, N. Y., 1914, No. 30. Pp. 101.

chology may be brought to a close by taking note of the hearty appreciation expressed by his numerous friends. His associates on numerous committees and governing boards speak gratefully of Cattell's broad vision and wise foresight, of his initiative and courage, of his keen sense for effective and yet democratic organization, of his sound judgment of men, of his great power of work and his willingness to give unsparingly of time and thought to the problems confronting an organization, of his ability to integrate the divergent views of a group of men and lead them to a unanimous decision, of his lively wit, and of his warm friendship and personal unselfishness.[1]

Visitors to his home, where the latch string seemed to be always out for his colleagues, remember the easy, friendly atmosphere of that home, with his evident love of children and family life and his delight in the beauty and freedom of the great outdoors.

His old students would certainly be eager to join in a personal tribute to his unfailing interest and generosity. He met the student halfway in the choice of a problem, and while insisting on sincere work by sound methods, he was satisfied with a reasonable achievement. His more promising students were a matter of personal concern to him. He assisted them in many ways, tangible and intangible: guiding them into fellowships and assistantships, supporting their efforts to secure academic positions, and providing employment at scientific work during summer vacations for those who were far from home or in financial need. Of the intangible assistance he gave them, most important was the inspiration that came to the budding young scientists from the kindly interest of one who was clearly a great man and an important figure in the scientific world.

[1] CONKLIN, E. G., THORNDIKE, E. L., LIVINGSTON, B. E., CARLSON, A. J., WOODWORTH, R. S., ACHILLES, P. S., DAVIS, W., HOWARD, L. O., PARKER, G. H., RUSSELL, H. N., and SWANN, W. F. G. James McKeen Cattell—In Memoriam. *Science,* 1944, **99,** 151–165.

ON THE TIME REQUIRED FOR RECOGNIZING AND NAMING LETTERS AND WORDS, PICTURES AND COLORS

The experiment reported in this paper was begun while he was a Fellow at Johns Hopkins and before he returned to Leipzig. The subjects who served in the experiment were indicated by their initials in Table I. Those whom the editor has identified are: Joseph Jastrow (J. J.), James Cattell (J. C.), John Dewey (J. D.), and G. Stanley Hall (G. H.).

The research was published in *Philosophische Studien*, 2: 635-650, 1885, and bore the title: "Ueber die Zeit der Erkennung und Benennung von Schriftzeichen, Bildern und Farben." It was translated into English by R. S. Woodworth for inclusion in this volume.

Apparently a short statement in English appears in "The Time it Takes to See and Name Objects," *Mind*, 11 (41): 63-65, 1886.

The experimental methods hitherto employed for measuring the duration of mental processes involve two difficulties which impair the accuracy and the whole value of the results obtained. The first difficulty lies in the apparatus used which seldom presents the stimulus in a completely satisfactory manner and seldom measures the times with complete accuracy. It has to be so finely constructed and at the same time so complicated that much time and labor are required for setting it up, using it and keeping it in order. The experimenters have usually found that the greatest part of their time had to be expended on the apparatus. The second difficulty lies in the fact that the time measured gives the duration of an artificial process and not that of a mental process such as occurs in actual life. Through the methods employed the person who serves as subject in the experiment is put into an abnormal state, especially in respect to attention, fatigue and practice, and the obtained times are often too short because the entire mental process is not measured, or too long because some extraneous factor is included. When these defects of the apparatus and this artificiality and inaccuracy of the experimental methods are considered, the suspicion arises that the results obtained by the psychologist in his laboratory do not give the time which a person really consumes in a process of perception, will, and thought. Wundt has contributed much to the overcoming of these difficulties, both by simplifying and improving the registering apparatus and by bringing the experimental conditions nearer to the conditions of real life. Yet it has seemed to me not a superfluous task to set up a number of experiments which require no complicated apparatus at all, and which aim to determine the time that we ordinarily need for recognizing and pronouncing words and letters.

After the sensory impression elicited by a printed letter has arrived in consciousness, it takes a certain time to decide whether any letter is there, and an additional amount of time to discern which letter it is. Further it takes a certain time to select the movement of the speech organs which corresponds to the printed character. These times, to use Wundt's terminology, are the discrimination time and the choice time. In the present study, which embraces only a part of a more extensive investigation, I cannot consider more closely the various physiological and psychophysical factors which make up the measured time, but I plan to do so in the next number of the *Studien* in connection with other experiments.

I

The experiments which I have first to describe were so designed as to make use of a kymograph such as is customarily employed for physiological purposes. It consists essentially of a rotating cylinder driven by a clockwork at a speed which can be regulated at will. In order to determine the speed of rotation I at first used a tuning fork writing on the smoked surface of the cylinder; later, however, since the speed of rotation proved to be perfectly constant, I determined it simply by aid of a chronoscope. The cylinder of the kymograph used had a circumference of 50 cm. and was covered with white paper on which were pasted letters at 1 cm. intervals. These letters, taken from Snellen's test materials, were lower case Roman letters of the size $D = 1.75$. The cylinder was concealed from the experimental subject by a black screen in which there was a horizontal slit 1 cm. in height and adjustable in width. The axis of the cylinder was vertical, the rotation was clockwise. When the subject fixed his eyes on the surface of the cylinder, through the slit, the letters passed through his field of view. With a slit width of 1 cm. there was always one letter in sight which disappeared just as another came into view; with a slit width of 2 cm. two letters were always visible at the same time, and so on. With a slit width of less than 1 cm., the first letter passed through the visible field and then there was a pause during which no letter was visible before the second letter appeared; and so on. The procedure was very simple: The slit was made 1 cm. wide, for example, and the cylinder put into rotation. The subject, looking through the slit, fixated the surface of the cylinder and read the letters aloud as they passed through the visible field at a speed which at first was moderate. Then the speed was gradually increased and the maximum speed determined at which the subject could still read 30–40 consecutive letters without error.[1] From this known speed of rotation of the cylinder it was possible to compute the time required by the subject to recognize and pronounce each single letter. This time is given in Table I for 9 persons (who were university teachers and students) and for different widths of the slit. For unit of time 0.001″ is chosen, so that 200 denotes 0.2 = $\frac{1}{5}$ sec. I give also the curves for subjects H. T. and J. C. and for the group average. The abscissas are proportional to the slit width, the ordinates to the minimum time per letter.

The Table shows that, up to a certain point indicated by a heavy vertical line in the body of the table, a widening of the slit results in a shortening of the time required for reading a letter aloud, and the curves show that the relation between these two variables is a simple one.

When the slit was 1 cm. wide, each letter was in sight for the same length of time as was required for reading it aloud ($\frac{1}{4}$ sec. on the average); but this is not the whole time which is required for recognizing and pronouncing a separate letter. The whole time, according to experiments in which I have sought to determine it, is approximately $\frac{1}{10}$ sec. longer. This apparent discrepancy is not surppising. In the experiments here described the processes of apperception and choice overlap to a certain extent. While one letter is being pronounced the following one is already being apperceived. The second part of the present study will illustrate this relationship further. The time required to recognize a letter amounts to about $\frac{1}{4}$ sec,. and the time required to pronounce it is about $\frac{1}{10}$ sec. During the quarter-second required for recognizing a letter, therefore, the preceding letter is pronounced. Pronouncing the letters is a completely automatic act and the same is often true for recognizing them. No conscious act of will is necessary in oral reading in order to select the vocal symbols that correspond to the printed symbols, and we can even read correctly without knowing what we read. When the slit is 2 cm. wide so that two letters are visible at once, not only does the pronouncing time disappear but there is also a shortening of the recognition time for the single letter amounting to $\frac{1}{40}$ sec. That means that while the reader is apperceiving one letter he is already preparing or even beginning to apperceive the next following letter and so shortening the time required for its apperception. With a slit width of 3 cm. and three letters simultaneously in sight, the time per single letter is further shortened by $\frac{1}{60}$ sec., but this shortening produced by the third added letter is less in amount than that produced by the second letter when it was added to the first.

[1] As experimenter I had a list of the letters in my hand so as to know when a letter was omitted or misread.

So is explained the above-mentioned regular course of the curves. With two of the 9 subjects there was no further shortening of the time when four letters were simultaneously visible; with the others the

TABLE I

Width of slit in mm.	1	2,5	5	10	20	30	40	50	60	10
J. J..............	420	360	245	210	190	170	150	145	145	260
J. C..............	400	312	274	228	200	178	166	160	160	252
J. D..............	738	370	274	208	196	184	178	166	166	240
J. B..............	400	320	260	220	200	185	180	175	175	220
E. H..............	600	342	274	260	240	228	214	214	214	342
G. H..............	534	354	312	252	240	228	224	224	224	
M. T..............	564	480	364	292	252	228	224	224	224	370
A. Y..............	418	300	274	252	224	204	204	204	204	248
H. T..............	418	364	352	312	282	274	274	274	274	332
Average..........	499	356	292	248	225	209	202	198	198	283

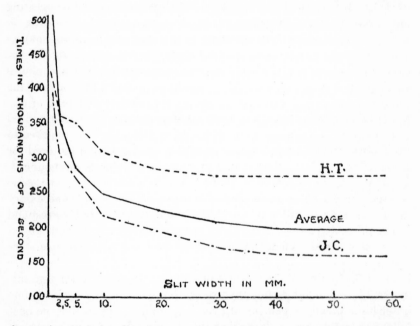

shortening amounted to $\frac{1}{100}$ sec., and with four of them the time was still further shortened (though only by $\frac{1}{200}$ sec.) when a fifth letter was simultaneously visible. When 6 or more letters were simultaneously visible there was no further shortening with any of the subjects. The results show that besides the idea present at the focus of consciousness there were in some subjects 2, in some 3, in some 4 other ideas present in the conscious field.

When, on the contrary, the slit in the screen is made narrower than 1 cm., the processes of recognizing one letter and of apperceiving the next one cannot so well occur simultaneously. Since each letter goes out of sight before it is completely apperceived, attention has to be concentrated more exclusively upon it than in the above-mentioned cases, in order to recognize it; and the shorter the time it is visible, the more are apperception and enunciation forced to become successive processes. When the slit was only 1 mm. wide, each letter was visible only $\frac{1}{10}$ of the time necessary for its apperception and enunciation. Accordingly it is first apperceived and then enunciated. Besides, it is quite probable that the time consumed in apperception or in enunciation or in both is somewhat prolonged. The precision of the numbers given in the Table will be admitted when the fact is added that, while the letters were recognized and spoken in the time stated, this was no longer the case if the time allotted per letter were diminished by $\frac{1}{500}$ sec.

The last column of the Table gives the maximum speed of counting either letters or 3 mm. squares of black paper pasted on the cylinder in place of the letters.[1] The slit width in this part of the experiment was 1 cm., and the letters were counted singly, not in groups. The result is that in general it takes more time to count the letters than to read them aloud. I found that widening the slit gave only a little shortening of the counting time, and that narrowing it gave only a little lengthening of this time, the change in both cases amounting to about $\frac{1}{50}$ sec., somewhat more or less with different individuals. The letters or squares could be counted more rapidly if grouped by twos and still more rapidly if grouped by threes. For subject J. C. the following times were obtained:

	Slit width, cm.	Measured time
Counted singly...............	1	252
In groups of 2.................	1	188
In groups of 3.................	2	134

The rhythm of the passing letters or squares can be grasped and registered more rapidly than one can count them.

II

In the second series of experiments which I have to report the apparatus was still simpler and the measured processes approached still more closely to those of real life. The problem is to determine the

---

[1] The time measurement was more difficult for the counting than for reading aloud, and the results were less constant.

time required for reading letters and words aloud; also the time for naming aloud colors and pictures of objects. For the time measurement a pocket chronoscope (stop watch) was used; it was started as soon as the subject began to read, and stopped as soon as he finished. Naturally the starting and stopping of the watch were not instantaneous; in each case they followed the event to be registered after a short time, the experimenters' reaction time to the sound of the subject's voice. However, the running of this chronoscope, once it is in motion, is extraordinarily exact. Besides, in this serial method the time taken by 100 or 500 homogeneous mental processes is included in a single measurement, so that, when the time for the single process is computed, the error is at least as small as it is in any chronographic method which measures the time of a single process separately. The objection might perhaps be raised that in these experiments as in those previously described I am measuring not the time of each single mental process but only the time elapsing during a considerable number of homogeneous processes, and then computing the time for the single process—but this is exactly the method employed for determining psychophysical times. These times are not constant, like most physical times, but have a normal variation. For this reason (and to eliminate the error of the registering apparatus) a large number of measurements have to be made and their average computed, which is exactly the same thing that I have done in the experiments here described.

The purpose of the experiments next to be described was to determine the time required for recognizing and pronouncing letters and words, first when the letters form words and the words sentences, and second when that is not the case. In order to attack the first task I selected passages from 6 different authors, written in the 6 languages most familiar to my subjects: English, German, French, Italian, Latin, Greek. The following selections were used:

English: Swift's Gulliver's Travels. A voyage to Lilliput. Chapter VI.

German: Goethe's Egmont. Egmont's Monologue in prison. Act V, Scene 2.

French: Rousseau's Émile. Book I.

Italian: Boccaccio's Decameron. Novella I.

Latin: Tacitus' Vita Agricolae. Cap. I.

Greek: Plato's Apologia. Cap. I.

The subjects read in each case the first 100 and the first 500 words, and also the first 100 and the first 500 letters, of the selection. The words and letters were to be read as rapidly as possible, and the words were also to be read at a normal rate. In order to have series of words that made no sentences, and of letters that made no words, we read these same passages backward as well as forward. After some practice the reversed direction of reading does not by itself produce any considerable lengthening of the reading times. However, I also had special lists printed of 100 English or German words and letters, the words being much-used monosyllabic nouns, printed as on an ordinary page. One series of letters consisted of the 100 initial letters of these same nouns, but in reverse order and printed in lower-case Roman (or German) type with such spacing as to give 20 letters in a line 12 cm. long. The second series of letters was printed in capitals, Roman or German, and contained the 100 initial letters of the above-listed English or German selection, again in reverse order.

Table II

Language	English	German	French	Italian	Latin	Greek	Average
			B				
100 words..................	344	196	308	502	418	496	377
500 words..................	407	209	356	514	428	453	395
100 words normal...........	482	292	364	524	534	574	462
500 words normal...........	513	336	443	580	590	591	509
100 words backward.........	504	370	434	499	476	504	465
500 words backward.........	677	414	438	498	517	483	505
100 letters forming words....	340	258	202	249	300	298	275
500 letters forming words....	344	292	234	235	320	300	288
100 letters backward.........	338	388	276	294	354	384	339
500 letters backward.........	370	398	292	302	375	371	351
			C				
100 words..................	138	250	167	327	434	484	300
500 words..................	143	297	196	293	406	391	288
100 words normal...........	240	330	218	380	666	552	398
500 words normal...........	250	401	292	461	638	633	446
100 words backward.........	288	380	300	334	432	507	374
500 words backward.........	292	356	305	319	423	444	357
100 letters forming words....	102	110	118	136	124	186	129
500 letters forming words....	115	121	116	143	131	174	133
100 letters backward.........	264	290	248	252	286	324	277
500 letters backward.........	288	310	273	289	329	306	299

The times obtained are contained in the accompanying Tables. Here again the time unit is $\frac{1}{1000}$ sec., and the numbers give the average time required to recognize and pronounce each single letter or each single word. When the reading was at normal instead of maximum speed, that fact is specially noted in the Tables.

Table III

Subject	H. W.	C. W.	J. R.	Mrs. S.	Miss H.	Average	F. P.	P. P.	C. L.	Frl. K.	Frl. T.	Average
Lists of English Words and Letters												
100 words.....................	352	331	332	380	296	338	534	396	568	298	410	441
Backward...................	382	329	376	352	308	349	480	341	528	331	398	416
100 letters forming words........	152	218	177	138	142	166	342	222	398	220	354	307
Backward...................	420	444	362	463	302	398	368	348	474	386	432	402
100 lower case letters...........	318	236	249	312	212	266	258	246	436	210	286	287
100 capital letters..............	348	212	231	279	216	259	256	261	353	228	304	280
Lists of German Words and Letters												
100 words.....................	447	422	468	656	389	476	364	322	444	266	304	340
Backward...................	414	396	441	596	369	443	417	351	420	284	366	368
100 letters forming words........	212	244	212	236	186	218	318	204	348	209	326	281
Backward...................	468	349	361	442	316	387	362	364	441	321	346	367
100 lower case letters...........	378	248	269	340	251	297	288	240	321	214	260	265
100 capital letters..............	547	456	576	732	580	578	297	317	357	244	290	301
Swift's Gulliver's Travels												
100 words.....................	179	178	178	186	179	180	392	222	416	178	231	288
500 words.....................	193	184	211	221	167	195	410	228	460	194	226	304
100 words normal...............	252	252	256	236	230	245	360	256	379	262	280	307
500 words normal...............	268	259	287	293	243	270	404	278	661	275	298	383
100 words backward.............	394	356	398	520	368	407	565	394	660	310	406	467
500 words backward.............	418	366	431	463	362	408	530	386	622	352	433	465
100 letters forming words........	174	206	186	226	149	188	297	248	372	214	268	280
500 letters forming words........	176	206	190	155	171	180	312	233	382	223	308	292
100 letters backward............	379	320	313	398	283	339	363	322	450	320	394	370
500 letters backward............	408	357	349	398	306	364	422	367	432	368	449	408
Goethe's Egmont												
100 words.....................	324	450	494	726	484	496	190	180	304	190	224	218
500 words.....................	409	445	536	806	343	508	196	200	286	194	206	216
100 words normal...............	430	480	614	649	422	519	292	255	302	249	332	286
500 words normal...............	487	494	601	768	442	558	331	266	341	322	374	327
100 words backward.............	461	424	579	666	440	514	377	302	454	273	366	354
500 words backward.............	459	456	611	782	439	549	420	355	474	338	397	397
100 letters forming words........	180	246	191	236	186	208	280	171	329	164	274	244
500 letters forming words........	203	229	190	278	168	214	262	193	321	176	261	243
100 letters backward............	384	324	306	454	304	354	362	318	439	304	256	336
500 letters backward............	406	334	357	398	318	363	386	343	436	315	387	373

TABLE IV

Date	Oct. 23	Nov. 1	Nov. 4	Nov. 12	Dec. 5	Dec. 11	Jan. 4	Jan. 9	Jan. 12	Jan. 12	Average
B											

Lists of English Words and Letters

Date	Oct. 23	Nov. 1	Nov. 4	Nov. 12	Dec. 5	Dec. 11	Jan. 4	Jan. 9	Jan. 12	Jan. 12	Average
100 words..............	484	530	458	436	428	380	434	418	412	422	440
Backward............	482	472	448	450	451	411	502	476	460	451	460
100 letters forming words.	254	238	210	169	186	186	194	182	179	164	196
Backward............	312	292	266	250	249	247	264	228	249	229	259
100 lower case letters....	288	288	264	298	254	249	239	230	247	233	259
100 capital letters.......	296	308	286	298	269	260	265	251	281	279	279

Lists of German Words and Letters

Date	Oct. 23	Nov. 1	Nov. 4	Nov. 12	Dec. 5	Dec. 11	Jan. 4	Jan. 9	Jan. 12	Jan. 12	Average
100 words..............	342	336	316	306	286	289	322	279	304	289	307
Backward............	398	396	376	368	362	350	414	361	380	386	379
100 letters forming words.	256	242	214	202	208	186	195	188	200	174	206
Backward............	366	316	297	271	282	264	274	246	278	248	284
100 lower case letters....	290	306	261	245	278	258	264	254	267	251	267
100 capital letters.......	344	326	336	317	323	346	384	306	334	314	333

C

Lists of English Words and Letters

Date	Oct. 23	Nov. 1	Nov. 4	Nov. 12	Dec. 5	Dec. 11	Jan. 4	Jan. 9	Jan. 12	Jan. 12	Average
100 words..............	262	246	274	260	247	240	276	237	246	264	255
Backward............	312	286	316	320	292	276	304	298	304	325	303
100 letters forming words.	102	94	98	96	84	79	83	76	84	98	89
Backward............	278	266	250	264	250	219	212	214	212	220	239
100 lower case letters....	254	242	234	258	224	205	212	206	195	206	224
100 capital letters.......	246	240	242	221	224	200	217	212	208	228	224

Lists of German Words and Letters

Date	Oct. 23	Nov. 1	Nov. 4	Nov. 12	Dec. 5	Dec. 11	Jan. 4	Jan. 9	Jan. 12	Jan. 12	Average
100 words..............	298	296	282	311	272	260	296	260	274	274	282
Backward............	324	328	336	356	306	307	336	314	302	321	323
100 letters forming words.	110	110	100	99	93	90	93	94	87	86	96
Backward............	304	284	282	304	277	250	264	246	224	243	268
100 lower case letters....	264	270	274	272	239	224	267	247	255	262	257
100 capital letters.......	412	450	436	462	419	414	426	421	388	444	427

Close examination of the Tables yields the following facts: The maximum speed of reading letters that compose words, and words that compose sentences, changes in direct relation with the reader's knowledge of the language or selection in question. For subject *B* (Dr. G. O. Berger, German) the average time taken to read a single

TABLE V

Date	Oct. 30	Nov. 12	Dec. 3	Dec. 15	Jan. 4	Average	Oct. 31	Nov. 3	Nov. 21	Dec. 23	Jan. 4	Average
	Swift's Gulliver's Travels						Goethe's Egmont					
B												
100 words.....................	312	274	306	282	279	291	186	192	182	184	174	184
500 words.....................	349	307	323	331	334	329	206	205	204	205	191	202
100 words normal...............	428	402	443	439	408	424	310	312	324	316	318	316
500 words normal...............	487	465	463	453	457	465	352	347	346	373	352	354
100 words backward.............	416	388	409	412	419	409	324	318	316	317	291	313
500 words backward.............	457	432	425	435	446	439	369	348	347	340	318	344
100 letters forming words........	268	232	241	219	208	234	218	200	194	186	172	194
500 letters forming words........	260	255	216	243	236	242	250	240	226	222	212	230
100 letters backward............	306	292	299	271	255	285	364	316	290	276	272	304
500 letters backward.............	330	319	304	314	307	315	336	331	299	300	291	311
C												
100 words.....................	132	122	133	127	109	125	220	198	185	170	159	188
500 words.....................	141	126	140	134	130	134	254	217	214	209	192	217
100 words normal...............	226	234	238	234	232	233	312	338	298	307	308	313
500 words normal...............	238	235	249	252	251	245	375	399	332	371	332	326
100 words backward.............	264	262	240	247	250	253	324	300	325	286	286	304
500 words backward.............	287	286	282	267	262	277	331	318	316	310	320	319
100 letters forming words........	100	82	77	84	87	86	112	100	94	93	80	96
500 letters forming words........	103	95	89	94	92	95	111	103	104	102	99	104
100 letters backward............	252	268	227	217	202	233	280	256	274	246	236	258
500 letters backward............	272	274	259	251	262	264	279	286	301	247	259	274

word in the German selection was 184 or 202, according as he read 100 or 500 words; in reading English words his corresponding times were 291 and 329; and in reading the other languages likewise his results gave a measure of his acquaintance with those languages.[1] The same holds good for subject *C* (the author himself, United States, speaking English therefore) and for the other persons who took part in the experiments. Of these the first 5 presented in Table III spoke English as their mother tongue, the last 5 German. The relative speed at which the two languages are read indicates the degree of familiarity of the foreign language. For example, Frl. K. is almost as familiar with English as with German, while Mrs. S. knows only a little German.

[1] This simple method of determining anyone's acquaintance with a language could perhaps find an application in school examinations.

This law holds good not only for words that make sentences but also for letters that make words, though the less exact knowledge of a given language does not lengthen the reading time so much in the case of the letters. The law holds good for normal as well as for maximal reading speed. The subject imagines he is reading the foreign language just as fast as his own, while in reality his speed is a definite function of his knowledge of the languages in question. Thus is explained the well-known fact that it seems to us as if foreigners were talking much more rapidly than we do ourselves.

With words that do not make sentences, and with letters that do not make words, the time required for reading is approximately doubled. For example, subject C read the first 100 words of the English selection at a rate of 125 per word, while he read the same words in reverse order at a rate of 253 per word, and the list of 100 monosyllabic English nouns at a rate of 255 per word. Examination of the Tables (in spite of the individual differences revealed in them) verifies this assertion both for words and for letters. One sees also that the time is a little shorter for recognizing and pronouncing letters than words, but the difference is not large enough to be important. Subject C's time, for example, was 253 and 255 for English words, while for lower-case Roman letters in the three series presented it was 233, 238 and 224 respectively, for capital Roman letters 224, for lower-case German 258 and 257, for German capitals 427. The result is, then, that C takes exactly the same time for lower-case and capital Roman letters, a somewhat longer time for lower-case German, and a significantly longer time for German capital letters. The time for these last was long even with the German readers. The difference between the numbers 224 and 224, as against 233, 238, shows how much less time C required for reading in the customary way from left to right and from above downward on the page, than in the opposite direction, the letters to be read being in both cases the same and in the same sequence.

In the already-mentioned experiments which are not being described here I have found that the time required for recognizing and pronouncing a single, separate word is considerably longer than the times found in the present experiment. The explanation, as already set forth, is that in the present experiment the times taken for recognizing and for pronouncing a word or letter overlap in part with the result that the recognition time is shortened and the enunciation time completely eliminated. Each letter or word is pronounced automatically while the next one is already being apperceived. When the letters make words and the words sentences, the time is very strikingly shortened, because the words and letters are not singly apperceived, one after another, but a whole group of them is grasped in one mental process. The speed at which one reads them is therefore limited only by the maximal speed of speaking.

The less familiar a language, the smaller the difference between the speeds of reading a selection forward and backward. In reading the Italian and Greek selections for the first time and as fast as possible, the subjects were not much helped by the meaning, and their time for reading forward was almost as long as for reading backward. Tables II and III give the results obtained when the selections were read for the first time; at the second reading the times were shorter and more regular. The influence of practice and increasing familiarity with the passage can be seen in Tables IV and V which comprise the results of ten readings of the same selection. The effect of fatigue can be seen from the fact that, in almost all cases, the average time for reading 500 letters or words was greater than that for only 100 mental processes of the same kind. Table III shows that the female sex read somewhat more rapidly than the male, but as between the two nationalities represented there was no difference worth noticing, except that in spelling out the words a significantly longer time was taken by the German than by the English-speaking subjects. Perhaps it is more than a coincidence that the normal speed for reading a selection from a book (which is the same as the speed of speaking and, I believe, of ordinary thinking) is approximately the same as the maximum speed for reading words that do not make sentences. I need not call the reader's attention to the further inferences which he can draw himself from the foregoing Tables, though I will append to them a brief addition: In order to count words singly, B took 343 and C 253; these times agree with those found for the reading of words that do not make sentences. These numbers, like the others reported in this Part II, might well be compared with the corresponding data of Part I.

TABLE VI

Trials	1	2	3	4	5	6	7	8	9	10	Average
B											
100 colors	551	520	524	548	524	519	541	518	513	497	526
100 pictures in German	534	522	501	539	486	484	482	490	449	526	501
100 pictures in English	638	602	600	596	622	584	534	550	528	546	580
C											
100 colors	654	662	760	634	648	587	654	648	586	544	638
100 pictures in English	623	586	626	717	545	523	574	558	556	568	588
100 pictures in German	597	604	626	600	670	637	597	587	598	626	614

By the same method as we have applied to words and letters, the time was determined that is required for recognizing and naming colors and pictures. We selected the following 10 colors: red, blue, green, yellow, orange, violet, rose, black, gray and brown. Ten 3 mm. squares of each color were pasted on a card in random order; they were 1 cm. apart and 10 of them in a row. The sequence of the colors to be named could be changed by turning the card. In a similar way we drew on a card 100 pictures of 26 common objects, hands, trees, ships, etc. The pictures were about 1 cm. square and were drawn 10 to a line of 15 cm. length. The sequence of the pictures, too, could be changed. The pictures were named in English and in German. The refults of this experiment are contained in Table VI.

These times for recognizing and naming colors or pictures are surprisingly long, being about twice as long as the corresponding times for recognizing and naming letters or words. My other experiments, already referred to several times in the course of this report, showed that the recognition time is *shorter* for a color or picture than for a word or letter. The time for recognizing and naming a color or picture, therefore, is so long because of the difficulty of finding the right names, not because of any great difficulty in recognizing the objects. We are so accustomed to read words and letters that the association between the appearance and the name is completely automatic; whereas, as these experiments show, the corresponding association is not so close in the case of colors or pictures. Subject *B* required 79 more time to name the pictures in English instead of his native German; for subject *C* the corresponding excess time was 26. These and similar experiments could probably find use in the investigation of aphasia.

In conclusion I will state explicitly that in computing the averages I have not discarded any measurement nor repeated any. For the benefit of those who doubt the possibility of measuring the duration of mental processes, I call attention to the great regularity of the obtained times, a regularity which is scarcely inferior to that of certain physical observations.

2

THE INERTIA OF THE EYE AND BRAIN

Prepared while he was Assistant in the Psychological Laboratory at the University of Leipzig. Printed as "Ueber die Trägheit der Netzhaut und des Sehcentrums" in *Philosophische Studien*, **3**: 94–127, 1885.

Printed in translation, as given here, in *Brain*, **8**: 295–312, 1885.

Inertia is a property of our sense organs. The molecules of the cells are only set in motion after they have been worked upon by a stimulus of a certain strength and for a certain time, and the motion continues after the stimulus ceases. In the case of sight, the lasting of the motion in the retina, and consequently of the sensation, after the stimulus ceases has long been known, and the phenomena of rotating discs and after-images have been carefully investigated. Less attention has been paid to inertia in the retina and in the brain when the sensation is excited. In considering this subject we must distinguish four operations, the time taken up by each of which we might seek to determine; (1) The time a light must work on the retina, in order that a sensation may be excited. (2) The time a light must work on the retina in order that the maximum intensity of the sensation may be brought about. (3) The time required for the light to be changed into a nervous impulse; and (4) The time taken up in the nerve and brain before the light is seen. Confusion has resulted because these operations and the times taken up by them have not been hitherto distinguished.

Plateau[1] incidentally remarked, fifty years ago, that a certain time is necessary "for the complete formation of an impression produced by a light"; but the subject was first taken up by Fick and Bruecke. Fick,[2] by an analysis of the law of Talbot and a few experiments, showed that a light must work on the retina for some time in order to call forth the maximum intensity of the sensation, and Bruecke[3] found this time to be .186 s. Exner,[4] with ingenious but complicated apparatus and methods, found the time to vary between .119 and .287 s., decreasing in arithmetical progression as the intensity of the light increased in geometrical progression. Kunkel[5] found this time to be

[1] "Bulletin de l'Acad. de Bruxelles," 1835.
[2] "Archiv f. Anat. und Physiol.," 1863.
[3] "Berichte d. Wiener Acad.," 1864.
[4] "Berichte d. Wiener Acad.," 1868.
[5] Pflüger's "Archiv," ix.

different for different colours; with a moderate light, the colours being of about the same intensity, the time was, for red, .057; for blue, .092; and for green, .133 s. All these experiments tend to determine the time of the operation above numbered (2), but the experimentors did not always understand what time they were seeking to measure. Exner, for example, calls his paper "Ueber die zu einer Gesichtswahrnehmung nötige Zeit," confusing the operations (2) and (4). Experiments made by Baxt,[1] under the direction of Helmholtz, should also be mentioned here. Baxt calls his paper "Ueber die Zeit, welche nötig ist, damit ein Gesichts Eindruck zum Bewustsein kommt," etc. (operation (4)), but does not at all determine this time. He allowed letters and curves to work upon the retina for a short time (.005 to .017 s.) and found that if soon afterwards a bright light was thrown on the retina, the letters or curve could not be distinguished. He found the interval which must elapse in order that the letters or curve could be distinguished depends on their nature and on the intensity of the second light, and thinks the length of this interval represents the time taken up in seeing the object, in which mistake he is followed by Tigerstedt and Bergqvist.[2] The impression made by the object first presented may be erased on the retina by the strong light following; but if the times given are correct, it is probably erased in the brain centre, and the times determined represent about the difference in the apperception times of a letter or curve and a bright light.

I shall shortly print an account of experiments I have made, looking to determine the time taken up by the operations above numbered (3) and (4); in this paper I consider the operation (1): the time a light must work on the retina in order that a sensation may be excited. It has been found that about ten vibrations are necessary to excite the sensation of a tone, and perhaps twice that many to enable us to distinguish that tone.[3] In the case of sight, experiments are not necessary to prove that this time depends on the intensity of the light. We can distinguish an object illumined an extremely short time by the electric spark; on the other hand, the astronomer can see a faint star only after he has for a considerable time fixated the point at which he expects to find it. We may consequently assume that the greater the magnitude of the light vibrations, the less is the number necessary to excite the retina. It remains, however, a question of considerable scientific and practical interest to determine the time an object must be looked at, in order that it may be possible to see it, considering (1) the nature of the object, and (2) the intensity of the light.

[1] Pflüger's "Archiv," iv.
[2] "Zeitsch. f. Biologie," 1883.
[3] Wundt, "Phys. Psy.," ii. 260.

I. Apparatus and Methods

The apparatus I used, which may be called a gravity chronometer, is quite simple.[1] It consists (Fig. 1) of two heavy brass columns (*A*, *A*), 30 cm. high and 10 cm. apart. They are set exactly perpendicular by means of the three screws on which the base stands. Wedge-shaped grooves are worked into the columns, and in these a heavy soft-iron screen (*S*, *S*) slides without appreciable friction. The screen is 13 c.

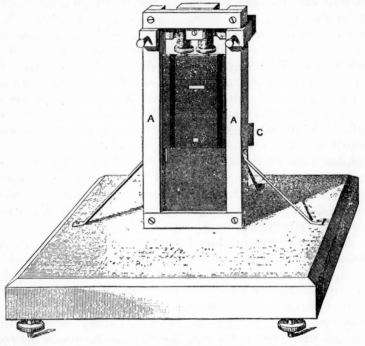

Fig. 1.

high, and has an opening 5 cm. wide, placed 5 cm. from the bottom. This screen is held up by an electro-magnet (*M*), which can be adjusted at any height desired. When the current flowing through the spiral of the electro-magnet is broken, the screen falls, falling always through the same distance in an exactly constant time. The object to be seen is fixed on a card (*C*), 15 × 3 cm., and this card is held in position on the columns by two springs, so that it is hid from the observer by the screen. A grey spot (*P*) on the black screen exactly covers the object to be seen, the spot being 3 mm. in front of the object. After a card, on

---

[1] Carl Krille, Leipzig, has made the apparatus several times after my model, and charges about 4*l*. It may be examined at Leipzig, or at the Army Medical Museum, Washington, U. S. A.

which, for example, a letter has been printed, has been placed in the springs, the observer fixates the grey spot on the screen, and by breaking the current which had been flowing through the spiral of the electro-magnet, lets the screen fall. The letter is seen at the point fixated, while the slit passes and is again covered by the screen. To determine the time the object has been in view, the screen is covered with smoked paper, and a tuning-fork is allowed to write on it as it falls. As the screen falls with the most perfect constancy, the determination with the tuning-fork need only be made so often that we are sure there has been no error. The theoretical time for a body falling in vacuo is scarcely shorter than the actual time for the screen as determined by the tuning-fork. In my experiments the slit in the screen was to be taken 1.3 mm., in order that the object should be in view .001 s. As I could regulate the width of the slit in the screen to .1 mm., the times were accurate to .0001 s.[1] I did not use a screen with a slit the width of which could be regulated; but, for practical reasons, the screen above described, with an opening 5 cm. wide. The entire screen was covered (as shown in the figure) with black cardboard, in which was a slit of the desired width. There was nothing in the method of the experiments to annoy or distract the observer. He fixated the grey spot on the black surface, and at the instant most convenient to him allowed the screen to fall. The object was in view the time desired, at the point fixated, and illumined with a light to which the eye was adapted, and the observer found himself looking at a black surface, an impression having been made by the object on the retina. The object was illumined by daylight from a clear sky, or by lamplight; the latter being the more convenient as it can be secured at pleasure, and its intensity can be accurately regulated. I used a carefully-made petroleum lamp with circular wick. The centre of the flame was 18 cm. from the object, the rays striking the surface at an angle of 55°. Of course no direct light from the lamp was allowed to fall in the eyes of the observer.

These experiments, though begun in America, have been carried out in the psychological laboratory of the University of Leipzig. Most of the determinations were made on *B.* (Dr. Oskar Berger), and *C* (the writer). Care was taken not to strain the attention, or fatigue the retina. The retina was slightly more sensitive after a pause, but this and other possible sources of variation were avoided, and they are thoroughly eliminated by the large number of observations taken.

---

[1] If greater accuracy than this is required, it would only be necessary to make the columns taller, and let the screen fall from a greater height. On the other hand, levers can be applied decreasing, to any extent desired, the rate at which the screen falls; the same result can be reached by an application of the principle of Atwood's gravity apparatus.

II. The Sensitiveness of the Retina for Colours

I find that the time a coloured light must work upon the retina, in order that the colour may be seen, is different for the several colours. I used lights reflected from pigments. The colours were not, of course, fully saturated, but in these experiments it would have been difficult, and in many experiments it is impossible to use the sun's spectrum. It might further be suggested that it is quite as interesting to investigate the eye's relations to colours such as we find them in nature and art, as to the saturated colours of the spectrum. The colours taken were red, orange, yellow, green, blue and violet. They correspond most nearly to rouge 0, rouge orange 5, orange jaune 3, vert 0, bleu 1, bleu violet 4, in the 1er cercle chromatique given by Chevreul in his "Exposé d'un moyen de définir et de nommer les couleurs d'après une méthode précise et expérimentale."[1] It seems most difficult to secure good red and violet in pigments: the red used was slightly dark, and the violet reflected some red light. The coloured surface was 3 × 1 cm. on a white background. As explained above, the card was placed on the springs of the gravity chronometer, the observer fixated a point immediately before the centre of the coloured surface and allowed the screen to fall. The coloured light worked on the retina for a period depending on the width of the slit in the screen. To determine how long the time must be taken, in order that a sensation may be excited, each of the several colours was taken separately, and, in addition, seven intensities of grey, including white and black. When the colour is looked at for an extremely short time it appears grey, yellow approaching the shade of the white card, violet appearing black, the other colours of various shades of grey. Series were made in which the colour to be investigated was placed about five times in the springs, shades of grey approaching in intensity the colour about five times; the observer of course did not know in any single case whether the colour or grey had been taken. After the light had worked on the retina the time desired, he decided whether he had seen the colour or not. When the time was taken sufficiently long he always named the colour, and when it was not there, said correctly "grey." On the other hand, when the time was taken very short, the observer saw no colour, and either always said "grey," or if he imagined he saw colour, was wrong as often as right. Thus it is easy to determine the time at which the colour is usually seen; a point at which it is seen about nine out of ten trials. This point is quite constant, and can be determined to the ten-thousandth of a second. Table I gives the results of the determination made on seven individuals with daylight from a clear sky, as

[1] Paris, 1861; also "Mém. de l'Acad.," xxxiii.

also determinations made on B and C under various conditions to be explained below. In all the tables, as well as in the text, $\sigma = .001$ second is taken as the unit of time.[1]

TABLE I

		Red	Orange	Yellow	Green	Blue	Violet
B	Clear sky..............	1.1	0.7	0.6	1.1	0.75	1.75
C	Clear sky..............	1.6	1.1	1.25	1.6	1.5	2.5
H	Clear sky..............	1.0	0.6	0.75	1.25	1.0	2.25
L	Clear sky..............	1.25	0.75	1.0	1.25	1.5	2.5
P	Clear sky..............	0.75	0.6	0.6	1.25	0.75	2.0
S	Clear sky..............	1.75	1.1	1.25	1.5	1.5	2.75
T	Clear sky..............	1.5	1.25	1.25	2.0	1.5	2.5
		1.28	0.82	0.96	1.42	1.21	2.32
B	White following.........	10.0	6.0	6.0	7.5	7.5	12.5
C	White following.........	7.5	5.0	6.0	7.5	7.5	12.5
B	Orange following........	10.0	10.0	5.0	15.0	4.5	15.0
C	Orange following........	10.0	10.0	7.5	15.0	7.5	12.5
B	Blue following..........	3.5	2.25	2.25	7.5	6.0	7.5
C	Blue following..........	4.0	2.5	3.0	7.5	6.0	7.5
B	Lamp..................	1.0	0.9	1.25	1.4	2.0	1.6
C	Lamp..................	1.6	1.25	1.75	2.75	5.0	3.0
B	¼ intensity.............	.....	1.2	.....	.....	2.75	
C	¼ intensity.............	.....	1.4	.....	.....	6.0	
B	$\frac{1}{16}$ intensity.............	.....	1.25	.....	.....	4.0	
C	$\frac{1}{16}$ intensity.............	.....	1.6	.....	.....	7.5	
B	$\frac{1}{64}$ intensity.............	.....	1.75	.....	.....	6.0	
C	$\frac{1}{64}$ intensity.............	.....	2.0	.....	.....	10.0	
B	$\frac{1}{256}$ intensity.............	.....	2.5	.....	.....	9.0	
C	$\frac{1}{256}$ intensity.............	.....	2.75	.....	.....	15.0	

The table shows that light reflected from a coloured surface must work on the retina from .6 to 2.75σ in order that it may be possible to see colour. The time varies with the several colours and with the different observers; the order of the colours is, however, almost constant.[2] The retina is most sensitive to orange light but nearly equally so to yellow. Blue must work on the retina about $.25\sigma$ longer than yellow, in order that it may be recognised. Next come red and green, red

[1] In psychometric experiments the times are usually given in thousandths of a second, and it would be convenient to have a symbol representing this unit: σ is analogous to $\mu = .001$ m.

[2] It would be of interest to make these experiments on persons who are colour-blind.

requiring about .1 and green .2σ longer than blue. The retina is least sensitive to violet light, the time for which is two to three times as long as for orange. Undoubtedly the brightness of the colour has an influence on these times, but the brightness is a property not an accident of the colour, a saturated orange being brighter than a saturated violet. The time must be taken slightly longer if it is necessary to distinguish a colour from another lying near it in the spectrum, as orange from yellow, or blue from violet. I need not, however, give the results of the experiments I have made, as the times are but little longer than when the colour was to be distinguished from grey, and depend on the shade of the colours.

In these experiments, after the excitation by the colour the retina was allowed to rest, being only irritated by the amount of light reflected from dull black paper. If white paper (being illumined naturally by light from a clear sky) is substituted for the black, the light reflected from it washes away the impression on the retina, so the colour must work on the retina much longer (as shown in the table), in order that it may be distinguished. A coloured light following, lengthens in like manner the time, and the order in which the colours are seen is changed, as is shown in the table when orange or blue immediately follow the colour to be distinguished. B's retina is decidedly more sensitive than C's; his time is shorter for all the colours when the retina is not afterwards irritated; his retina is, however, also more sensitive to the irritating light, so that when this is present he must be given as long a time as C, in order that he may be able to recognise the colour.

When lamplight is substituted for daylight, the time for most of the colours becomes longer and the order is changed. The red light from the lamp makes orange considerably easier to distinguish than yellow, and places red next to orange. The time for violet, owing to the red rays it reflects, becomes shorter than for blue. I have given above (Sect. I) the normal illumination with the lamp; if the lamp is placed twice as far from the coloured surface (the angle of incidence for the rays being the same), the objective intensity of the light is reduced to one-fourth. I thus arranged five intensities of light, 1, $\frac{1}{4}$, $\frac{1}{16}$, $\frac{1}{64}$, $\frac{1}{256}$, and determined the time for orange and blue (the easiest and most difficult colours to distinguish). The results are given in the table, and the curves (Fig. 2) are drawn, in which the abscissas are taken proportional to the intensity of the light, the ordinates to the time.

The curves approach both axes, but can reach neither of them, for on the one hand we can assume that even with an indefinitely strong light a certain number of vibrations would be necessary to excite the sensation, on the other hand we know that colour ceases to be visible before the light becomes indefinitely weak. The portion of the curve I have investigated follows the formula,

$$t = c \log i(+c')$$

in which t is the necessary time and i the intensity of the light: that is, the time coloured light must work on the retina in order that it may be seen, increases in arithmetical progression, as the intensity of the light decreases in geometrical progression.

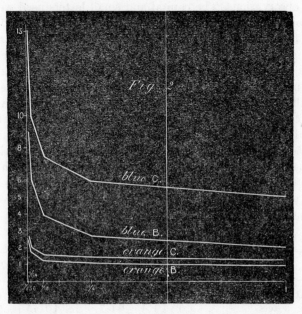

III. THE SENSITIVENESS OF THE RETINA FOR LETTERS AND WORDS

Substantially the same method as for colours was used to determine the time the light reflected from a letter or word must work on the retina in order that the letter or word may be distinguished. After a card had been placed in the springs of the gravity chronometer, the observer fixated the grey spot on the black surface, and allowed the screen to fall. The light from the letter or word worked on the retina the time desired, and the observer either tried to name it, or said he did not know what it was. As in the case of colours, a point is found at which all the letters and words can be read correctly, another at which none of them can be seen, these two points being about half of a thousandth of a second apart. I tried to determine the interval at which half of the letters or words are correctly read. The time is quite constant, the normal variation being less than $.1\sigma$. The sensitiveness of the retina is not, however, always the same; indeed, these experiments bear witness to a striking change. At the end of this investigation, the time for both B and C was about $.25\sigma$ longer than at the beginning. This decrease in the sensitiveness of the retina was not gradual, but quite sudden. The change took place first in B's retina, so that for a time it was not more sensitive than C's. Then a corresponding and equally sudden decrease in the sensitiveness of C's retina took place. The following table contains the times for various classes of letters and words, the results being drawn from over fifteen thousand separate observations. The capital and small letters used were of the size in which this is printed. Twenty-six English and German words of four and five letters, and twenty-six of over eight letters were chosen. Each letter or word of the same class was placed five times in the springs, as a series (except in case of the German letters) was made up of one hundred and thirty observations. The table gives the times at which half of the letters and words are correctly read; the times being in some cases judged, from series in which more or fewer than half were read. The times given in the table are for lamplight, they are about $.25\sigma$ shorter for daylight from a clear sky. On the right-hand side of the table are given the results of experiments made on five sizes of letters taken from Snellen's "Optotypi." D is the distance in meters at which the letters fill an angle of $5'$, and is consequently proportional to the linear size of the letters.

TABLE II

	B	C	H	W	D =	B	C
Capital Latin letters	1.1	1.4	1.6	1.2	4	.6	.7
Small Latin letters	1.1	1.4	1.7	1.3	1.75	.75	.9
Capital German letters	1.25	1.7	1.7	...	1.25	1.1	1.35
Small German letters	1.15	1.5	1.7	...	.8	1.4	1.75
Short English words	1.1	1.4	...	1.1	.5	3	4
Long English words	1.2	1.5					
Short German words	1.1	1.5	1.5				
Long German words	1.1	1.55	1.6				

The table shows, that in order that a letter or word may be read, the light reflected from it must work on the retina from 1 to 1.7σ. There is a decided difference in the sensitiveness of the retinas of the four persons experimented upon, but the times for the several classes of letters and words do not vary greatly. The time is longer for the German (especially the capital) than for the Latin letters. This is due to the unnecessary complication of the German type and the similarity of certain letters. The time is slightly shorter for words than for letters. Children are now generally taught to read words as words, and are not required to spell out the letters; but it is well to prove that we read a word as a whole. The time is longer for long or rare words, and for words in a foreign language.

As in the case of colours, the impression left by the letter or word on the retina is washed away if it is followed by a white light, the time must consequently be taken longer in order that it may be possible to distinguish the letter or word. The times are given in Table III, when the capital Latin letters were followed by a white light lasting 1, 3, and 5σ and indefinitely. If the process started by the letter is allowed to work on for 5σ, the effect of the disturbing stimulus is not so great, as the table shows. On the right-hand side of the table are given the results of experiments made to determine the relation of the intensity of the light to the time under consideration. Capital Latin letters were used, the method being substantially the same as that described above for colours. It will be noticed that the general form of the curves is the same as for colours, but the portion investigated does not follow the formula $t = c \log i(+c')$, the ordinates t increasing more rapidly.

TABLE III

	B	C	Intensity =	B	C
White 1σ	1.6	1.7	1	1.1	1.4
White 3σ	2.3	2.4	¼	1.4	1.75
White 5σ	4	4.3	$\frac{1}{16}$	1.85	2.5
White indefinitely	6.5	6.5	$\frac{1}{64}$	4	6
Black 5σ, white 1σ	1.5	1.5	$\frac{1}{256}$	10	20
Black 5σ, white indefinitely	3.2	3			

IV. The Relative Legibility of the Letters of the Alphabet

In the foregoing section we considered the time various classes of letters and words must work on the retina in order that they may be seen, and found that some alphabets are harder to see than others. In this section it will be shown that the different letters of the same alphabet are not equally legible. These are both circumstances of the greatest practical importance. Reading is one of the largest factors in our modern life, but at the same time a thoroughly artificial act. Here, as everywhere in nature, the organism shows its power of accommodating itself to its environment, but the large percentage of children who become shortsighted and weak-eyed, and suffer from headaches, gives us sharp warning, and puts us on our guard, lest these diseases become hereditary. Considering the immense tension put of necessity upon eye and brain, it is of the most vital importance to relieve them by using the printed symbols which can be read with the least effort and strain. Experiments are not necessary to show that books (especially school-books) should be printed in large clear type, but experiments, such as I have described, may lead us to determine the most favourable type. It seems probable that the use of two varieties of letters, capital and small, is more of a hurt than help to the eye and brain. All ornaments on the letters hinder, consequently the German type is injurious. The simplest geometrical forms seem the easiest to see. The lines must not be too thin; we seem to judge the letters from the thick lines, and it is doubtful whether it is advantageous to use thin and

Fig. 5.

thick lines in printing. From all these considerations it seems that our printing-press has not improved on the alphabet used by the Romans. Our punctuation marks are hard to see, and, I think, quite useless. It seems to me far better to replace (or at all events supplement) them by spaces between the words, corresponding in length to the pauses in the thought, or, what is the same thing, to the pauses which should be made in reading the passage aloud. Such a method of indicating to the eye the pauses in the sense would not only make reading easier, but would teach us to think more clearly.

As I have already stated, not only are some types harder to see than others, but the different letters in the same alphabet are not equally legible. It was found in making the experiments described in the foregoing section that certain letters were usually correctly read, whereas others were usually misread or not seen at all. Fifty-four series were made with the capital Latin letters, consequently each letter was used 270 times. Out of this number of trials, *W* was seen 241 times, *E* only 63 times. The relative legibility of the different letters is clearly shown in the curve (Fig. 3), in which the ordinates are taken proportional to the number of times each letter was read correctly out of the 270 trials.

I shall publish hereafter tables giving the number of times each letter was not seen at all, and the number of times it was misread, together with the letters for which it was taken. These tables show that certain letters, as *S* and *C*, are hard to recognize in themselves; others are mistaken for letters similar in form, as in the case of *O*, *Q*, *G* and *C*. The great disadvantage of having in our alphabet letters needlessly difficult to see will be evident to every one. If I should give the probable time wasted each day through a single letter as *E* being needlessly illegible, it would seem almost incredible; and if we could calculate the unnecessary strain put upon eye and brain, it would be still more appalling. Now that we know which letters are the most illegible, it is to be hoped that some attempt will be made to modify them. Our entire alphabet and orthography needs recasting: we have several altogether useless letters (*C*, *Q* and *X*), and there are numerous sounds for which no letters exist. In modifying the present letters, or introducing new forms, simplicity and distinctness must be sought after, and experiments such as these will be the best test.

Experiments made on the small letters show a similar difference in their legibility. Out of a hundred trials, *d* was read correctly 87 times, *s* only 28 times. The order of distinctness for the small letters is as follows: *d k m q h b p w u l j t v z r o f n a x y e i g c s*. As in the case of the capital letters, some letters are hard to see (especially *s*, *g*, *c* and *x*) owing to their form; others are misread, because there are certain pairs and groups in which the letters are similar. A group of this sort is made up of the slim letters *i j l f t*, which are constantly mistaken the one for the other. It would not perhaps be impossible to put λ in the place of *l*, and the dot should certainly be left away from *i* (as in Greek). It seems absurd that in printing, ink and lead should be used to wear out the eye and brain. I have made similar determinations for the capital and small German letters, but these should be given up. Scientific works are now generally printed in the Latin type, and it is to be hoped that it will soon be adopted altogether. At present, however, it is impossible to get the books most read, Goethe's works, for example, in Latin type.

V. The Limits of Consciousness

So far I have been speaking of inertia in the retina. I began by saying that the molecules of the cells are only set in motion after they have been worked upon by a stimulus of a certain strength and for a certain time; the experiments described, however, determine not merely the time necessary to set the molecules of the cells in motion, but the time the light reflected from a coloured surface or printed sign must work on the retina in order that it may be perceived. We found, for example, that a red light must work on the retina over .001 s. in order that the red may be seen. When, however, a red light works on the retina only .001 s., we have a right to suppose that the molecules in the cells are set in motion, and that a nervous impulse corresponding to the red light is sent to the centre for sight in the brain, but is too weak to excite there the sensation. We thus have to do with inertia in the brain, and the difficult subject of the threshold of sensation (minimum visible).[1] It is not necessary to enter into a discussion of this subject in a paper, the object of which is to describe experiments, not to set up theories. I need only say that these experiments determine what may be called the threshold of consciousness.

There is not only a threshold of sensation, but also a maximum intensity of the sensation beyond which an increase in the strength of the stimulus does not increase the intensity of the sensation; analogous to this is a limit to the number of objects, or complexity of the object, consciousness can at one time attend to.

Whether the mind can attend to more than one thing at a time was a disputed question in the scholastic philosophy, under the form of the proposition: "Possitne intellectus noster plura simul intelligere"; and the subject has been discussed by a number of modern philosophers.[2] As the several philosophers reached their results chiefly through theoretical considerations, we need not be surprised that the number of ideas consciousness can hold at one time has been placed at from one to an indefinitely large number. Light is thrown on this subject by the number of feet of which a verse of poetry may be made up, and by the construction in music. Special experiments have been made by Wundt and his pupils,[3] from which it seems that when twelve to sixteen beats follow one another at intervals of .2 to .3 s. the number can be correctly judged, the separate beats not having been counted. In this case, however, it is probable that the beats are combined into groups, so that not sixteen simple, but fewer slightly complex impressions are at the same time present in consciousness. I have made experiments which show that the number cannot be correctly judged

[1] See Wundt, "Physiologische Psychologie," i. 321. Fechner, "Psychophysik," ii. 431. Exner, in Hermann's "Physiologie," iii. 2, 324. Funke, id. ii. 215.

[2] See references given by Wundt, "Phys. Psy." ii. 214; and Hamilton, "Metaphysics," i. ch. xiv.

[3] Wundt, "Phys. Psy." ii. 213; id. "Philos. Studien," ii. 3.

when more than four or five sound-impressions follow one another with great rapidity.

Experiments on the limits of consciousness can, however, be made to better advantage through the sense of sight. I have shown in a previous paper[1] that from three to five (varying with the person) letters can be considered by consciousness at one time. This result is confirmed by an extended series of experiments I have made with aid of the gravity chronometer above described. In the first of these experiments, short perpendicular lines, 2 m. apart, were printed on a card, and, as above described with colours and letters, were allowed to be seen for .01 s.[2] Eleven cards were used, containing from four to fifteen lines, and the observer tried to give the number of lines on the card he had seen. The determination was carefully made on eight persons, and it was found that two could judge the number of lines correctly up to six, two up to five, three four, and one not four. This gives the number of simple impressions consciousness can at one time attend to. When the number of lines is larger than consciousness can grasp, it is estimated, those persons who can grasp the largest number estimate, as a rule, the most accurately. There seems to be a tendency to under-estimate the number of lines, and the mean error seems to follow the psycho-physical law, being directly proportional to the number of lines. Practice does not seem to improve the accuracy of the judgment.

In the same manner numbers, letters, words and sentences were exposed to view for .01 s., and it was determined how much consciousness can attend to at one time. The numbers and letters were printed with an American type-writing machine (Remington No. 4), five letters taking up 1 cm. The words were taken from a printed page, not more than two were put on a line, and they fell in all cases within the field of distinct vision. The sentences (likewise from a printed page) were divided into two lines when over three or four words in length, but extended in some cases beyond the field of distinct vision. The determinations made on eight individuals show a considerable personal difference, but on an average consciousness can at one time grasp four numbers, three to four letters, two words, or a sentence composed of four words. The letters are slightly more difficult to grasp than the numbers, every combination of numbers making a number that gives "sense." Not as many words as letters can be grasped at one time, but three times as many letters when they make words as when they have

---

[1] Wundt, "Philos. Studien," ii. 4.

[2] An object exposed to the retina for .01 s. can be seen very distinctly; if longer time is allowed, there is a danger that the impressions may be taken up by consciousness successively instead of simultaneously.

no connection. Twice as many words can be grasped when they make a sentence as when they have no connection. The sentence is taken up as a whole; if it is not grasped, scarcely any of the words are read; if it is grasped, the words appear very distinct; this is also the case when the observer constructs an imaginary sentence from the traces he has taken up.

In making these experiments I notice that the impressions crowd simultaneously into my consciousness, but, beyond a certain number, leave traces too faint for me to grasp. Though unable to give the impression, I can often tell, if asked, whether a certain one was present or not. This is especially marked in the case of long sentences; I have a curious feeling of having known the sentence and having forgotten it. The traces of impressions beyond the limits of consciousness seem very similar to those left by dreams.

The individual difference is a matter of special interest. *B* out of forty trials read correctly five times a card containing seven numbers, and could always read five numbers correctly. He could grasp six letters, four disconnected words, or a sentence of seven words, whereas others could grasp but three letters, two words, or a sentence of four words. The latter numbers are the limits for one of the four students experimented on, and for the two women, one an educated young lady, the other the wife of a mechanic. The limit for a boy nine years old was somewhat higher. I tried to make the determinations on two rather obtuse porters, but their consciousness did not seem able to take up at all such delicate impression. They required three times as long as educated people to read a letter or word.

3

THE TIME TAKEN UP BY CEREBRAL OPERATIONS

The research recorded here comprises the first two parts of an extended project containing six parts and entitled: "Psychometrische Untersuchungen." The first five of these made up the author's "Inaugural-Dissertation zur Erlangung dos Doctorgrades der Philosophischen Facultät der Universität Leipzig" with the above title.

Parts I and II were published in German in *Philosophische Studien*, **3**: 305–335, 1886, under the titles "Apparate und Methoden" and "Die Reactionszeit" respectively.

The English version reproduced below was published in *Mind*, 11: 220–242, 1886, under the title "The Time Taken up by Cerbral Operations," Part I, "Apparatus and Methods," and Part II, "The Reaction Time."

Mental states correspond to physical changes in the brain. The object of this paper is to inquire into the time needed to bring about changes in the brain, and thus to determine the rapidity of thought. When waves in the luminiferous ether of a particular length strike the retina a red light is seen, but a certain time passes after the waves have struck the retina before the light is seen:—(1) It takes time for the light waves to work on the retina, and generate in the cells a nervous impulse corresponding to the nature of the light; (2) it takes time for the nervous impulse to be conveyed along the optic nerve to the brain; (3) it takes time for the nervous impulse to be conveyed through the brain to the visual centre; and (4) it takes time for the nervous impulse to bring about changes in the visual centre corresponding to its own nature, and consequently to the nature of the external stimulus. When these changes are brought about a red light is seen. It does not take any time for a sensation or perception to arise after the proper changes in the brain have been brought about. The sensation of a red light is a state of consciousness corresponding to a certain condition of the brain. The chemical changes in a galvanic battery take time, but after they are brought about, no additional time is needed to produce the electric current. The current is the product of chemical changes in the battery, but at the same time the immediate representative of these changes; and the relation is so far analogous between states of consciousness and changes in the brain. Again, as it takes time to see a light, so it takes time to make a motion. Changes in the brain, the origin and nature of which we do not understand (physiologically they are part of the continuous life of the brain,

41

mentally they are often given in consciousness as a will-impulse), excite the centre for the coordination of motions. The impulse there developed is conveyed through the brain (and it may be spinal cord) to a motor nerve, and along the nerve to the muscle, which is contracted in accordance with the will-impulse. We have here in the reverse direction the same four periods as in the case of a stimulus giving rise to a sensation. In each case there is the latent period in the sense-organ or muscle, the centripetal or centrifugal time in the nerve, the centripetal or centrifugal time in the brain, and the time of growing energy in the sensory or motor centre. Besides these two classes of processes, the one centripetal, the other centrifugal, there are centrimanent cerebral operations, some of which are given in consciousness, and make up the mental life of thought and feeling. These cerebral changes all take time, and, as I shall show, the times can in many cases be determined.

I. APPARATUS AND METHODS

The time taken up by cerebral operations cannot be directly measured. It is necessary to determine the time passing between the production of an external stimulus, which excites cerebral operations, and the making of a motion after these operations have taken place. The apparatus needed to determine this time must consist of three parts:—(1) An instrument producing a sense-stimulus to excite cerebral operations and registering the instant of its production; (2) an instrument registering the instant a motion is made, after the cerebral operations have taken place; and (3) an instrument measuring the time passing between these two events. The first two instruments must vary with the sense-stimulus to be produced and the motion to be registered; to measure the times, I have used the Electric Chronoscope made by Hipp in Neuchatel. When properly controlled, this chronoscope measures the time as accurately as any of the chronographic methods which have been proposed, and it is much simpler and more convenient in its application.

The Chronoscope is a clockwork moved by a weight and regulated by a vibrating spring. The spring vibrates a thousand times a second, and at each vibration the tooth of a wheel is allowed to pass, somewhat on the principle of the escapement in a watch. This method of regulating the clockwork is ingenious and accurate, but, especially in the new form of the chronoscope, is apt to get out of order. The value of the chronoscope consists in the application of an electromagnet. The hands recording the time are not in connexion with the clockwork, and consequently do not move when it is set in motion; but, when an electric current is sent through the coil of the electromagnet, the armature is attracted, a system of levers throws the hands into connexion with the clockwork and they are set in motion; and, again, when the current flowing through the coil is broken, a spring draws back the armature and the hands stand still. Thus the time the current flowed through the coil of the electromagnet is measured.[1] The hands record thousandths of a second.[2] The chronoscope works with great accuracy; the only serious difficulty in its application being that the length of the times recorded by the hands varies with the strength of the current passing through the coil of the magnet. Supposing the strength of the spring holding back the armature to remain constant, if the current sent through the coil is very weak, the soft iron is only completely magnetised after a considerable interval, and it takes longer for the magnet to attract the armature after the current has been closed, than for the spring to draw back the armature after the current has been broken; consequently the time recorded by the hands is shorter than the time the current flowed through the coil of the magnet. If, on the other hand, the current used is very strong; the soft iron is rapidly magnetised and the armature attracted. But the magnetism lasts a considerable interval after the current has been broken. Thus, it takes longer for the spring to draw back the armature after the current has been broken than it took the magnet to attract it after the current had been closed, and the time recorded by the hands is longer than the time the current flowed through the coil of the magnet. If the strength of the current is not properly adjusted, the times recorded may be over $\frac{1}{10}$ sec. too long or too short, an error as large as the whole length of the reaction-time. It is, however, possible so to adjust the relation between the strength of the spring and the strength of the current that it takes exactly as long for the magnet to attract the armature after the current has been closed as it takes the spring to draw it back after the current has been broken, and in this case the hands record the exact time the current flowed through the coil of the magnet. This can be done empirically by determining the time the current has been closed, and then so adjusting the strength of the spring and the current that the hands record the correct time. For this purpose (as well as for others later to be described) I have used an instrument, which, with reference to the use for which it was first devised,[3] I call a Gravity-Chronometer.

It consists (Fig. 1) of two heavy brass columns 30 cm. high and 10 cm. apart, standing perpendicular to the base. The columns can be set exactly perpendicular by means of the three screws on which the apparatus stands. Wedge-shaped grooves are worked in the columns, and in these a heavy soft iron screen slides without appreciable friction. This screen is held up by an

---

[1] A second electromagnet makes it possible to reverse this process, and measure the time a current has been broken.

[2] Throughout this paper, both in the text and in the tables .001 second is taken as the unit of time. I use σ as a symbol to represent this unit: σ is analogous to $\mu = .001$ mm.

[3] See *Philosophische Studien*, iii. 1; *Brain*, Oct., 1885. The apparatus described in this paper was made under my direction in the workshop of Carl Krille, Leipsic, and he can supply duplicates. The apparatus can be examined in the Psychological Laboratory, Leipsic, or in the Army Medical Museum, Washington.

electromagnet, which can be adjusted at any height desired. When the current passing through the coil of the magnet is broken, the screen falls, falling through the same distance in an exactly constant time. On one of the columns small keys (Figs. 2 and 3) can be fastened, which respectively close and break a current. They each consist of a hard rubber basin filled with mercury, the

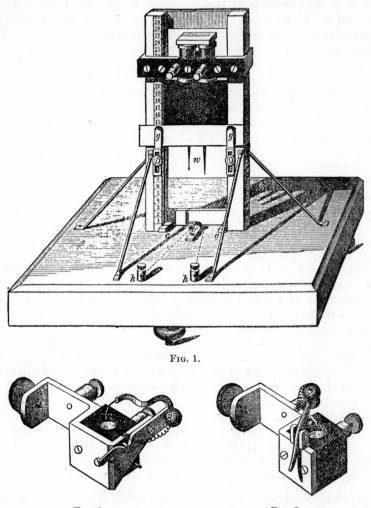

FIG. 1.

FIG. 2.   FIG. 3.

mercury being in connexion with a binding screw; a lever with a platinum point, connected by a wire with a binding screw, dips into the mercury. In the one key (Fig. 2) the lever is so adjusted that the point does not touch the mercury, but when the key is fastened to the column of the gravity-chronometer and the lever is struck by the falling screen, the point is thrown into the mercury. In the other key (Fig. 3) the lever dips into the mercury, but is thrown out (as shown in the figure) when struck by the screen. The keys are fastened to one of the columns, as at x and y (Fig. 1), the key (Fig. 2) at which the current is interrupted being above. The current controlling the chronoscope passes through both of these keys, the connexion, however, being interrupted at the upper key. The screen is now allowed to fall by breaking a current (not the chronoscope current) which through the electromagnet had been holding it up. After the screen has attained a considerable velocity it strikes the lever of the upper key, and throws it into the mercury; thus the current controlling the chronoscope is closed and the hands are set in motion. After the screen has fallen the distance between the keys (xy) it strikes the lever of the second key and throws it out of the mercury; the current controlling the chronoscope is consequently broken and the hands stand still. The screen always falls through the distance between the keys in exactly the same time, and the times recorded by the hands of the chronoscope are constant, but may be over $\frac{1}{10}$ sec. longer or shorter than the time the current was really closed. The time required for the screen to fall through the distance xy (the time the current has been closed) is determined by means of a tuning-fork which writes on smoked paper covering the screen. The time can also be calculated; the theoretical time for a body falling in a vacuum being but little shorter than the actual time as determined by the tuning-fork. When we know the time between the closing of the current at the upper key, and the breaking at the lower, the strength of the current attracting the armature and of the spring holding it back can be so adjusted that the hands record the correct time. The stronger the current and spring are taken, the shorter is the time required for the armature to be attracted after the current has been closed and drawn back after the current has been broken. The determination with the tuning-fork need only be repeated so often that we are sure no error has been made; it is well to change the distance between the keys and see that the times given by the chronoscope and the tuning-fork are the same. The chronoscope must, moreover, be controlled every day by the gravity-chronometer (or by a sensitive electrometer; the apparatus itself is a very sensitive electrometer) to see that the current has remained constant, and to readjust it if it has become stronger or weaker. For this purpose the gravity-apparatus supplied by Hipp can be used if proper precautions are taken. The strength of the current is adjusted by means of a rheostat, (R, R', Fig. 8) and its direction changed (to avoid permanent magnetism) by means of a commutator. It is evident that a battery must be used giving as constant a current as possible. After considerable experiment I have adopted a form of the zinc-copper gravity-battery. I use six large cells, renewing them about once a month.

If the chronoscope is properly controlled it measures the times very accurately. With the same current the mean variation of the chronoscope (including sources of error in the gravity-chronometer) is less than $\frac{1}{500}$ sec. This small variation corrects itself completely in a series of measurements. A second variation about equal to the first is caused by the current not being accurately adjusted, or changing after it has been so adjusted. This error also tends to eliminate itself. A third source of error lies in the chronoscope's running too fast or too slow. This is, however, no greater than in any chronographic method where the time is measured by a vibrating tuning-fork; the chronoscope can indeed be regulated with great accuracy as it runs a minute (60,000 vibrations).

The gravity-chronometer (Fig. 1) was used in nearly all my experiments to produce the sense-stimulus, and to close at the same instant the current controlling the chronoscope. When the reaction-time for light was to be determined, the space between the columns was filled up with black pasteboard, so that the screen was completely hid from the observer. In the pasteboard (below the screen, the magnet being higher than in the figure) a hole 3×2 cm. was cut, and the observer fixated a black surface several mm. back of the hole. The experimenter allowed the white screen to fall by breaking the current which had been flowing through the coil of the magnet. Suddenly and without warning, at the point fixated by the observer a white surface 3×2 cm. appeared; at the same instant (to $\frac{1}{1000}$ sec.) the screen struck the lever of the key (Fig. 2) and closed the current controlling the chronoscope. No noise is made by the falling screen until it is stopped by striking the spring f and the rubber cushions $c\ c$, and this noise comes too long after the light to either shorten or lengthen the time of the reaction. The spring f is so adjusted as to partially stop the falling screen and to prevent it from rebounding after it has struck the cushions. If cerebral operations other than those included in the reaction-time were to be investigated, the object exciting these operations, a printed word for example, was pasted on a card 15×3 cm. This card is held in position by the springs $g\ g$, and is hid from the observer by the black screen. The observer fixated a grey spot on the screen, which exactly covered the object on the card (the figure shows of course the back of the apparatus). A bent copper wire w, one side longer than the other, is fastened to the screen, as shown in the figure. When the screen falls the amalgamated points run into two holes bored in the base and filled with mercury. These basins are connected with the binding screws hh, and these respectively with the battery and chronoscope, so that the current is interrupted at this point. When the screen falls, however, the copper wire connects the two basins of mercury, and the apparatus is so adjusted that the instant (to $\frac{1}{1000}$ sec.) the object on the card is uncovered to the observer, the shorter limb of the wire touches the mercury and the current controlling the chronoscope is closed. This method is in every way better than that hitherto used of illumining the object by an electric light. It avoids altogether the great inconvenience and difficulty of using an induced current, as keeping the light constant, closing simultaneously an induced and galvanic current and other difficulties best known to those who have tried to overcome them. Further, it eliminates the time required to adapt the eye to a light of unexpected intensity, placed by experimenters as quite large. Lastly, it enables the observer to fixate exactly the point at which the object appears, so that words, &c., can be used.

Three instruments were used to break the current controlling the chronoscope at the instant the observer made a motion. The first of these was a telegraphic key, which the observer held closed with his finger or fingers, and let go by a motion of the hand. The key used should be very sensitive; it should break the current instantaneously, yet should not require much pressure to hold it closed. The other two instruments were devised to break the current when the organs of speech are moved. The first of these (Fig. 4) we can call a lip-key. The binding screws *BB* are connected respectively with the battery and the chronoscope. The platinum contact at *c* is closed when the observer holds the ivory tips *TT* between his lips; but as soon as the lips are moved the spring *S* breaks the contact, and, consequently, the current which had been flowing through the chronoscope. The only difficulty in the way of using this lip-key is that it is possible for the observer to move his lips before he makes the motion to be registered. This difficulty is avoided by

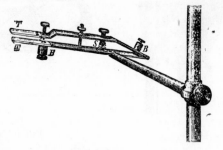

FIG. 4.

means of the apparatus shown in Figures 5, 6 and 7, which we can call a sound-key. The current controlling the chronoscope is broken when the observer speaks into the mouth-piece *M* (Fig. 5). An additional galvanic current is needed to work this apparatus. I used four Daniel cells. The current flowed through a commutator (*C''*, Fig. 8), the coil of the electromagnet (Fig. 7), and the instrument shown in Figures 5 and 6. This latter consists of a mouth-piece, a funnel, and a ring (Fig. 6) fitting into the funnel, and covered with kid leather. When the observer speaks into the mouth-piece, the sound waves throw the membrane into vibration, and the platinum contact at *c* is broken; the breath accompanying speech also breaks the contact. The current making the electromagnet (Fig. 7) flows through this contact; so when it is broken, if only for an instant, the soft iron looses its magnetism, and the armature is drawn back by means of the spring *F*. The strength of this spring can be regulated by means of the screw *N*. The binding screws *BB'* are connected respectively with the chronoscope and its battery, so that the current flows through the contact at *C*. This contact is closed as long as the armature is held by the magnet, but is broken the instant the magnetism in the soft iron disappears or is weakened so that the spring can draw away the armature. The armature is not held against the magnet, the contact being at the point *C*. The pressure is kept constant by regulating the strength of the spring *F*. It will be seen that after the contact in the funnel is broken, no appreciable time elapses before the current controlling the chronoscope is broken; but the contact in the funnel is broken by the slightest motion of the speech-organs, so the instant of this motion is registered.

In Fig. 8 I give the arrangement of the apparatus when it is wished to determine, for example, the time it takes to see and name a word. It is a matter of no small importance so to arrange the apparatus that it can be conveniently operated on, and the figure will further make clear the connexion of the different instruments and the several batteries. The observer sits at A., the light coming over his left shoulder. His head is held naturally, and

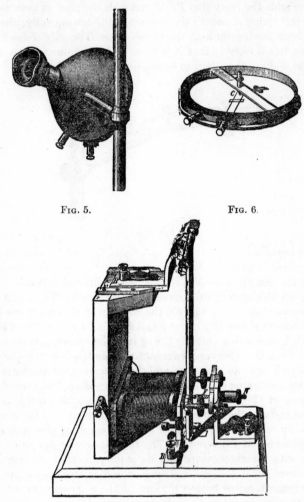

Fig. 5.   Fig. 6.

Fig. 7.

at the distance of most distinct vision for the word. He can conveniently speak into the mouth-piece of the sound-key F, or hold the telegraphic key at K closed. The experimenter[1] sits at B., within easy reach of all the apparatus he has to control. The current belonging to the chronoscope flows from the positive pole of the battery B to the commutator C, thence through the rheo-

---

[1] I call the person having charge of the apparatus the experimenter; the person on whom the experiments were made the observer.

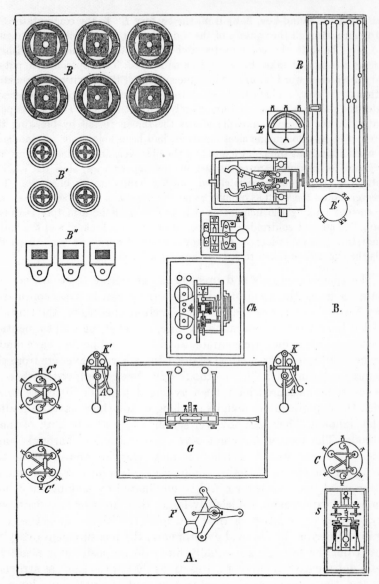

Fig. 8.

stat *RR'* (if desired, also through the electrometer *E*) and chronoscope *Ch* to the gravity-chronometer *G*, where the connexion is interrupted when the mercury in the two basins is not connected, thence the current flows through the contact of the sound-key at *F* back to the commutator and battery. The current making the electromagnet of the gravity-chronometer flows from the battery *B'* to the commutator *C'*, and thence through the key *K''* and the gravity-chronometer back to the commutator and battery. The third current, controlling the sound-key, flows from the battery B'' to the commutator C'', and thence through the contact of the sound-key at F and coil of the magnet at S, and back to the commutator and battery. Suppose now we wish to measure the time it takes to see and name a word. The experimenter puts a card on which a word is printed into the springs of the gravity-chronometer; he then says 'now,' and starts the clockwork of the chronoscope. The observer fixates the point on the screen immediately before the word. Then the experimenter (or the observer himself) allows the screen to fall by breaking the current which, through the electromagnet, had been holding it up. Suddenly the word appears at the point fixated by the observer, and at the same instant the basins of mercury are connected by the copper wire; thus the current controlling the chronoscope is closed and the hands are set in motion. The observer names the word as quickly as possible. As soon as he begins to speak, the current making the magnet at S is broken and the armature is drawn away. The current controlling the chronoscope is thus broken, and the hands stand still. The experimenter then stops the clockwork and reads from the dials the exact time taken to see and name the word.

The special methods and precautions necessary to secure correct results in using the apparatus here described can best be considered when I come to treat of the different cerebral operations, the times of which I have tried to determine. It may, however, be well to mention here two points, which are common to all the experiments I have made. The first of these is the method of deducing a correct average from the separate experiments. Two methods have been employed: either all the reactions measured have been averaged together, or those times which the experimenter thought too long or too short have been altogether ignored. There are however serious objections to both of these methods. The former does not give correct results. Through some abnormal circumstance, a reaction may vary so greatly from the average of the others, that the whole series gets a false value. It might be supposed that this error could be eliminated by making the whole number of experiments sufficiently large; this, however, makes necessary a great expenditure of time and labour, without altogether correcting the error. In physical experiments, the measurements varying most from the average are equally likely to be positive or negative; this is not the case in our work. Reactions that are so short as seriously to affect the average can scarcely occur, but through some inner or outer disturbance the reactions are sometimes abnormally long. Thus, even though the average of an indefinitely large number of reactions is taken, the result is not correct, but somewhat larger than the average of the reactions made under normal circumstances. The method introduced by Exner of simply ignoring the reactions which seem to be too long or too short may give correct results, but is undoubtedly unreliable. The experimenter thinks he has found the proper worth, and

PIEDMONT COLLEGE LIBRARY

then almost unconsciously leaves out of his reckoning the reactions which would invalidate it. For example, Merkel[1] gives fifteen averages in which his 'perception time' is between 22 and 25σ, and the times in a hundred and twenty other series, made on eight different persons, correspond exactly with this, varying only between 19 and 26σ. These averages correspond to an altogether impossible extent; we need not therefore be surprised at finding the time quite false. The work of v. Kries and Auerbach[2] loses much of its value from the fact that so many of the determinations have been omitted in calculating the results.

I have used a different and, as far as I am aware, new method. If the apparatus did not work properly, of course no reaction was measured; but the average of all the reactions measured was calculated. Either 13 or 26 reactions were made in a series; the average of these reactions was calculated, and the variation of each reaction from this average. Then the reaction having the largest variation was dropped, the average of the remaining 12 or 25 reactions was calculated, and the reaction varying most from this average was again dropped. This process was continued until the 3 or 6 worst reactions had been dropped, I then having the 10 or 20 best reactions, and the variation of each of these from the average. In practice we need not calculate so many new averages, it being only necessary to drop the 3 or 6 reactions varying most from the corrected average, which can usually be foreseen. In this paper I give the average of all the reactions made, as well as the average corrected by the method I have described. It will be seen that the two values do not differ greatly; this is owing to the fact that the conditions of the experiments were such that really abnormal reactions seldom occurred.

The second point to be mentioned here is the influence of practice, attention and fatigue on the length of the times determined. In a later section of this paper I shall give an account of experiments I have made on this subject. In other cases it was sought to eliminate as far as possible these sources of variation. The two subjects (Dr. G. O. Berger and the writer) on whom the determinations were made had already had much practice in psychological work. They were in good health and lived regularly, not even using coffee. The experiments were made every morning (except Sunday) from eight to one o'clock. After each series of 26 reactions, a considerable and constant interval elapsed before the same subject again reacted. The subject held his attention as constant as possible, and was not disturbed by noise or the presence of others in the room.

[1] *Philosophische Studien*, ii. 1.
[2] *Du Bois-Reymond's Archiv*, 1877.

These experiments, though begun in America, have been carried out in the psychological laboratory of the University of Leipsic. Professor Wundt, the founder and director of this laboratory, has earned the gratitude of all those interested in the scientific study of the mind. I owe him special thanks for the constant help and encouragement he has given me in my work.

II. The Reaction-time

The reaction-time can be determined with ease and accuracy, but it is difficult to decide what operations take place when a reaction is made, quite impossible to determine how the time is divided among the several operations. We shall see that under favorable circumstances the reaction-time for light is about 150σ. It seems to me probable that this period is divided about equally between the processes occurring within and without the brain. The latter are: (1) the latent period in the sense-organ; (2) the time of transmission in the afferent nerve; (3) the time of transmission in the spinal cord and efferent nerve; and (4) the latent period in the muscle. Physiologists have attempted to determine these times separately, but they must be far more constant than the discordant results would lead us to suppose. The experiments I am about to describe show that when the reaction-time is measured the mean variation of the separate times from the average is only $\frac{1}{20}$ of the whole time; and we may attribute this small variation chiefly to changing states of the brain. If these times were not constant it is probable that we could not distinguish colours and tones.

The velocity at which a nervous impulse is transmitted has been a favourite subject for physiological research,[1] but the results as yet reached are unsatisfactory. Exner, in Vol. ii. of Hermann's *Handbuch der Physiologie*[2] gives, as result of the "perfectly irreproachable measurements" of Helmholtz and Baxt, the rate of transmission in a motor nerve as 62m. the second; whereas, in the same volume[3] and likewise as the result of experiments by Helmholtz and Baxt, Hermann gives the rate as 33.9005m. the second. The fact seems to be that the rate depends on the temperature and other conditions, chiefly brought about by the method of experiment. Determinations made on the sensory nerve give results still more discordant and unsatisfactory. We can for the present do nothing better than assume the average rate of transmission in both motor and sensory nerve to be 33m. the second. It is probable that the rate is slower in the spinal cord, and that the nervous impulse is delayed in entering and leaving the cord,

[1] See for references Hermann, *Handb. d. Physiol.* II., ii., 14 ff.
[2] ii., 272.
[3] i., 22.

as also in passing through a ganglion.[1] As a temporary hypothesis we can suppose that when the reaction, lasting 150σ, is made, 50σ is used in transmitting the nervous impulse from the retina to the brain, and from the brain through the spinal cord to the muscle of the hand. The latent period when the muscle of the frog is stimulated by means of an induction-shock, is between 5 and 10σ;[2] and is perhaps the same when the muscle of the hand is innervated by means of a will-impulse. There is also undoubtedly a latent period in the sense-organ while the stimulus is being converted into a nervous impulse. In the so-called mechanical senses this period is very short, but when the retina is stimulated by light a chemical process (as we suppose) takes place, and the time may be quite long.[3] We know that a light must work on the retina for a considerable time in order that the maximum intensity of the sensation may be called forth; from this time, however, we can draw no exact inferences as to the length of the process here under consideration. I have shown[4] that a coloured light of medium intensity must work on the retina .6 to 2.75σ (varying with the observer and colour) in order that a sensation may be excited; the time becomes however much longer when a white light follows the colour, the second light washing away, as it seems, the impression made on the retina by the first light. Under these circumstances a violet light had to work on the retina 12.5σ, if it were to be distinguished. It seems, therefore, probable that the violet light had not been converted into a nervous impulse within this interval, and if this is the case it would give us a minimum time for this process. The familiar experiment with rotating discs shows that light-impressions of moderate intensity following one another at intervals of 25σ are just fused together. It seems, therefore, that the retina is excited, and begins to resume its normal condition in about 25σ. If this assumption is correct we have the maximum time for the period under consideration. We may be tolerably sure that the time passing before a light is converted into a nervous impulse varies with the intensity of the light, and may perhaps assume the time to be $15-20\sigma$ for daylight reflected from a white surface.

These considerations lead us to suppose that, when a reaction is made on light, only about half the time, that is 75σ, is taken up by

---

[1] Exner, *Pflüger's Archiv*, viii., *Archiv. f. Anat. u. Phys.*, 1877; François-Franck et Pitres, *Gazette Hebd.*, 1878; Wundt, *Mechanik der Nerven*, ii., 45.

[2] Tigerstedt, *Archiv. f. Anat. u. Physiol.*, 1885, and references there given.

[3] V. Wittich (*Zeitschr. f. Rat. Med.*, xxxi.) and Exner (*Pflüger's Archiv*, vii.) found the reaction-time to be shorter when the optic nerve was stimulated by an electric current than when the retina was stimulated by light. This difference may, however, be due to other factors of the reaction-time as well as to the latent period in the sense-organ.

[4] *Philosophische Studien*, iii., 1; *Brain*, Pt. 31.

the cerebral operations. We naturally ask what happens in the brain after the nervous impulse reaches it. It has generally been assumed that the largest factors of the reaction-time are taken up by the processes of perception and willing. I think however, that if these processes are present at all they are very rudimentary. Perception and volition are due, we may assume, to changes in the cortex of the cerebrum, but reflex motions in answer to sense-stimuli, as in contraction of the pupil and in winking, can be made after the cortex has been removed, and an animal in this condition can carry out motions adapted to the nature of the stimulus. If a pigeon from which the cerebral hemispheres have been removed is thrown into the air, it will not only fly, but also avoid obstacles and alight naturally on the ground. It seems to have consequently sensations of light, but apparently no perceptions, either because it does not see colour and form, or because it lacks the intelligence needed to understand their meaning. In the same way a reaction such as we are considering can probably be made without need of the cortex, that is, without perception or willing. When a subject has had no practice in making reactions (in which case the reaction-time is usually longer than 150σ) I think the will-time precedes the occurrence of the stimulus. That is, the subject by a voluntary effort, the time taken up by which could be determined, puts the lines of communication between the centre for simple light sensations (in the optic thalami probably), and the centre for the co-ordination of motions (in the corpora striata, perhaps, connected with the cerebellum), as well as the latter centre, in a state of unstable equilibrium. When therefore a nervous impulse reaches the thalami, it causes brain-changes in two directions; an impulse moves along to the cortex, and calls forth there a perception corresponding to the stimulus, while at the same time an impulse follows a line of small resistance to the centre for the coordination of motions, and the proper nervous impulse, already prepared and waiting for the signal, is sent from the centre to the muscle of the hand. When the reaction has often been made the entire cerebral process becomes automatic, the impulse of itself takes the well-travelled way to the motor centre, and releases the motor impulse.[1]

I now go on to give the results of my experiments. I only give the

[1] This theory concerning the nature of the reaction would be none the less probable, though we suppose the centres for sensation and perception not to be distinct, or indeed that in the reaction the brain, in some mysterious way, "acts as a whole." In this paper I take it for granted throughout that mental states are due to changes in the brain. We know, however, but little as to the functions of the brain. I therefore make as few assumptions as possible, and these must be kept apart from the positive results, which it is the object of this paper to make known.

determinations made on B (Dr. G. O. Berger) and C (the writer); I have made similar determinations on other subjects of different age, sex, occupation, etc., but these can be better considered after we know the results of careful and thorough experiments on practised observers. We have first to consider the simple reaction-time for light. When this was to be measured, all being in readiness, as described in the foregoing section, the experimenter said "Jetzt," and the observer fixated the point at which the light was to appear, and put himself in readiness to make the reaction. The experimenter then set the clock-work of the chronoscope in motion, and about one second afterwards caused the light to appear by means of the apparatus described. The observer lifted his hand as soon as possible after the appearance of the light, and the interval that had elapsed between the occurrence of the light and the commencement of the muscular contraction was read by the experimenter directly from the chronoscope. In no single case, as far as I can remember, did the observer make a premature reaction, that is, lift his hand before the necessary physiological operations had had time to occur. The only disturbance was caused by the clock-work of the chronoscope sometimes not being properly controlled by the vibrating spring. If the experimenter noticed this in time he did not produce the light. This occasional failure of the chronoscope was always noticed, so does not interfere with the accuracy of the times here given, but the observer was sometimes disturbed so that his reactions may have been made less regular. Throughout this paper I give every series and every reaction made; I give, however, in addition to each series, a corrected value reached by the method above described. This correction simply excludes all abnormal values. In the Tables I give the average of the variation of each reaction from the average of the series to which it belongs (V); that is, if A is the average of the n reactions making up the series, and a_1, a_2, a_3, . . . a_n are the values of the several reactions, then

$$V = \frac{(A - a_1) + (A - a_2) + (A - a_3) + \cdots + (A - a_n)}{n}$$

all the differences being taken as positive. The averages under R in the Tables (except when expressly stated) are taken from the 26 observations which made up the series, the averages under R' from the 20 reactions of the corrected series. Table I gives the results of twenty series, made at intervals during a period of six months.

The Table shows that the average of 520 reactions on daylight reflected from a white surface was, for B 150, for C 146σ; or, if the series are corrected by the method explained, the averages for both B and C become 1σ longer. The average of the mean-variation of the reac-

TABLE I

1885	B				C			
	R	V	R'	V'	R	V	R'	V'
12. I............	140	10	141	8	144	12	143	8
	145	10	143	6	136	9	138	5
16..............	137	16	139	11	133	16	128	11
	156	10	155	7	147	15	150	11
30..............	131	13	131	9	149	9	151	6
	152	13	149	9	143	11	143	9
27. II..........	148	14	147	8	146	10	144	7
	160	13	162	8	144	9	144	6
28..............	139	13	142	11	149	9	149	6
	161	15	163	9	146	9	146	5
	152	13	149	7	144	9	143	6
31. III..........	164	14	164	8	163	9	163	6
	151	10	153	6	150	8	151	5
3. IV..........	133	16	132	11	143	8	144	5
	157	9	159	6	138	11	136	7
4..............	165	13	170	9	161	9	163	5
5..............	144	13	147	9	147	9	148	6
7..............	168	9	170	5	148	17	148	9
2. VII..........	137	16	140	11	158	12	158	6
4..............	152	13	155	9	140	14	145	9
A..............	150	13	151	8	146	11	147	7

tions from the series to which they belong was for B 13, for C 11σ; in the corrected series it becomes respectively 8 and 7σ. It will be seen from the Table that the series made at different times do not differ greatly from each other; the mean-variation of the twenty series is B 9, C 5. The reaction-time for practised observers is consequently quite a constant quantity; when a reaction is made it will only differ about $\frac{1}{100}$ s. from those preceding and following it, and less than $\frac{2}{100}$ s. from reactions made on different days and under changed circumstances. I do not however lay much weight on the third decimal; if this investigation were to be repeated it is not likely that we should obtain the same results to $\frac{1}{1000}$ s. When B's reaction-time for light is given as 150σ, I only mean that this was the result of these 520 reactions; in comparing this with other determinations where we wish to know the absolute length of B's reaction-time, we can best limit ourselves to saying that it is .15 s., or perhaps better still, between .14 and .16 s.

In these experiments the reaction was made with the right hand. The time is the same with the left hand.[1] I give in Table II the average

[1] Tischer, *Phil. Studien*, i., 534; Merkel, *Ib.*, ii., 88. Prof. G. S. Hall and Dr.

of five series (130 reactions) made with the left hand on light and also on sound.[1]

TABLE II

		B				C			
		R	V	R'	V'	R	V	R'	V'
Light...	3–7. IV	153	12	156	8	147	11	148	6
Sound..	3–7. IV	126	8	126	6	122	11	122	7

It is a matter which the later sections of this paper will show to be of special interest to us that the time is longer when the reaction is made with the speech-organs. To determine this time I used both the lip-key and the sound-key above described. In either case the observer said "Jetzt" as soon as possible after the appearance of the light, and the motion of the speech-organs stopped the hands of the chronoscope in the way I have explained. The results of these experiments are given in Table III.

TABLE III[1]

	Sound-key				Lip-key			
	B		C		B		C	
	R	R'	R	R'	R	R'	R	R'
3. IV.......	164	167	177	176	199	199	172	171
	161	159	165	165	185	187	173	173
5...........	175	176	175	176	199	201	172	173
	170	168	175	172	189	186	177	177
7...........	168	168	157	159	166	165	185	176
A...........	168	168	170	170	188	188	176	174
AV.........	19	10	16	10	11	6	13	8

[1] To save space in this and some other Tables, I only give the average of the mean-variation for the several series (AV).

We thus find that it takes about 30σ longer to make the reaction with the speech-organs than with the hand.

I used an additional method of determining the reaction-time with the speech-organs. The observer as quickly as possible after the appear-

Hartwell (MIND, ix. 93) do not seem to have known of the work published by Tischer and Merkel.

[1] The sound (as in all cases where the reaction-time for sound was measured) was made by a stone ball 22 gr. in weight, falling from a height of 33 cm. on the wooden base of the Hipp gravity-apparatus.

ance of the light simply said "Jetzt"; a second observer as soon as he heard the sound let go the telegraph-key, and this stopped the hands of the chronoscope. The hands recorded the time of a double reaction, that of the first observer on the light with his speech-organs, and that of the second observer on the sound with his hand. But we can determine the time of the second observer's reaction on the sound, and by subtracting this from the entire time, we have the reaction-time of the first observer with his speech-organs. When the average of several series is taken the error becomes very small. A further application of this method will be found below. For our present purposes it was to a large extent superseded by the use of the lip-key and sound-key. There are however certain difficulties in the way of using these instruments, especially in the case of inexperienced persons, children or the insane, for example. The method could further be applied to determining the reaction-time, etc., of the lower animals, and also the length of certain reflex processes where the motion can with difficulty be registered. I give in Table IV the results of four series of reactions made in this way, Mr. H. Wolfe making reactions on the sound.

TABLE IV

	B				C			
	R	V	R'	V'	R	V	R'	V'
7. 1.........	349	30	346	20	328	32	321	17
	330	37	332	23	327	24	326	14
30..........	380	30	372	20	392	27	392	18
	357	32	349	19	393	25	393	16
A..........	354	32	350	20	360	27	358	16

Mr. Wolfe's reaction-time on sound was about 150σ. The series made on 30 I. seem to have given rather long times, the others correspond to those where the motion of the speech-organs was directly registered.

The length of the reaction-time depends on conditions which can be classified as belonging, partly to the sense-stimulus, partly to the reacting subject. It was my object in the experiments here under consideration rather to eliminate these sources of variation than to investigate them. I used therefore the same sense-stimuli and the same subjects. The only varying conditions were the changing states of the subject due chiefly to different degrees of attention, fatigue and practice. It seemed desirable thoroughly to investigate these owing (1) to the light they throw on the nature of the cerebral operation, and

(2) to the necessity of knowing what influence they exert on the lengths of the processes investigated, before we can judge of the accuracy of our results. I can best postpone the full consideration of this subject until the end of the paper, but it will be of advantage before going further to consider the relation of attention to the length of the reaction-time. It has always been assumed that the length of the reaction varies greatly with different degrees of attention, and this is a natural supposition, when it is believed that the time is mostly taken up by the processes of perceiving and willing. If however the reaction is automatic, the changes not penetrating into the cortex of the cerebrum, then the time would not be greatly dependent on the concentration of the attention during the reaction. The reaction would however be delayed if the conditions were such as to make it difficult for the subject to hold the path of communication and motor centre in a state of readiness. The simplest way of distracting the attention is to cause a noise while the reactions are being made. I let three metronomes beat and ring rapidly. The results of these experiments are given in Table V for both light and sound.

TABLE V

	Light				Sound			
	B		C		B		C	
	R	R'	R	R'	R	R'	R	R'
2. IV.......	149	150	162	159	122	120	121	118
3..........	159	159	146	147	124	127	120	119
	152	152	144	142	126	124	128	127
4..........	146	148	162	161	132	131	137	138
5..........	155	155	168	170	119	119	125	124
A..........	152	153	156	156	125	124	126	125
AV........	8	5	10	6	10	6	10	6

If these results are compared with those given in Table I it will be seen that B's reaction-time for light was lengthened 2, C's 10σ. These increments are very small, falling in the case of B within the limits of the natural variation. The reaction time for sound was the same as when no distracting noise was present. Wundt[1] found the reaction-time to be considerably lengthened by a distracting noise. This was probably because the subjects had not learned to make the reaction as automatically as B and C. The experiments by Obersteiner[2] are scarcely such as to give accurate results.

[1] *Physiol. Psych.*, ii., 243.
[2] *Brain*, 1879.

The attention can be more thoroughly distracted if the brain is busied with some other operation while the reactions are being made. A good way to accomplish this is to let the subject beginning with any number add as rapidly as possible 17 after 17 to it. The attention can on the other hand be concentrated to a maximum degree by a voluntary effort of the subject. Many experimenters seem to have attempted this in all their reactions; Exner, for example, says[1] that although sitting quietly on his seat he would sweat with the exertion. In my experiments the attention was held in a state which I shall describe as normal; the subject expected the stimulus and reacted at once, but did not strain his attention or make special haste. We have thus three grades of attention: concentrated, normal and distracted.

TABLE VI

Concentrated				Normal				Distracted			
R	V	R'	V'	R	V	R'	V'	R	V	R'	V'
12.—25. II. 1884. *B* Light											
189	15	187	8	201	17	197	9	245	28	242	13
C											
158	17	156	10	132	16	133	9	153	19	151	10
27. II.—6. III. 1884. *B* Electric Shock											
160	13	161	7	165	12	164	7	190	16	189	9
C											
147	14	147	8	150	15	150	9	184	21	184	11

The first experiments on this subject were made in the winter of 1883–4, before the chronoscope was properly controlled; the absolute times may be as much as 10σ wrong, but the relative times are correct. As a stimulus I used the electric light produced in a Puluj's tube, and an induction-shock of moderate intensity on the left forearm. In these experiments 15 reactions were made in a series, 5 being dropped in the corrected series. The numbers in Table VI give the average from 10 series.

Similar experiments were made in 1885, daylight and sound being used as stimuli. The averages given in Table VII are as usual taken from 26 reactions.

[1] Hermann's *Handb. d. Physiol.*, II., ii., 287.

I put together the results of these experiments in Table VIII, the time when the attention was normal being taken as 0.

TABLE VII

	Concentrated				Normal				Distracted			
	R	V	R'	V'	R	V	R'	V'	R	V	R'	V'
					B Light							
27. II.......	144	16	147	7	148	14	147	8	196	26	185	12
	131	11	130	8	160	13	162	8	186	26	183	19
28..........	141	10	143	7	139	13	142	11	178	15	180	11
	137	8	139	4	161	15	163	9	179	16	179	10
	143	8	144	6	152	13	149	7	194	14	190	9
A..........	139	11	141	6	152	14	153	9	187	19	183	12
					C							
27. II.......	149	13	150	9	146	10	144	7	166	12	167	7
	149	7	150	4	144	9	144	6	154	16	156	11
28..........	146	8	144	5	149	9	149	6	157	13	159	8
	146	12	144	8	146	9	146	5	154	9	155	6
	140	8	139	5	144	9	143	6	163	14	160	9
A..........	146	10	145	6	146	9	145	6	159	13	159	8
					B Sound							
2. II........	132	7	132	5	157	11	157	8	193	26	189	13
	129	6	129	5	158	19	149	8	188	28	191	19
3..........	127	14	129	4	155	14	152	7	174	12	173	8
	123	9	122	6	147	10	145	6	169	24	163	17
4..........	127	7	126	5	138	9	139	6	188	24	183	17
A..........	128	9	128	5	151	12	148	7	182	23	180	15
					C							
2. II........	129	12	126	8	145	10	140	6	166	18	162	12
	135	11	135	8	133	12	132	9	156	19	148	14
3..........	125	12	127	6	141	11	140	8	158	15	161	9
	123	12	123	8	142	11	139	6	155	17	155	12
4..........	131	11	126	8	136	10	133	5	157	15	153	9
A..........	129	11	128	8	139	11	137	7	159	17	156	11

It will be noticed that when the brain is otherwise occupied the reaction is lengthened, though not to a great extent. The time is however but little shorter when the subject makes a great exertion to react quickly than when he makes the reaction easily and naturally. These experiments support the hypothesis that a reaction is an automatic act, only needing the activities seated in the cortex to prepare its way. A noise did not in the case of B and C so disturb the subject as especially to interfere with the placing in readiness of the parts of the brain concerned in making the reaction. If the brain was busied by adding 17 after 17, it could not so well put the lower centres in readiness, and the time of the reaction was lengthened. On the other hand a great effort of the will could only slightly shorten the reaction by holding the path of communication and motor centre in a state of more unstable equilibrium.

TABLE VIII

	B		C	
	Concen.	Distr.	Concen.	Distr.
Electric light..................	−12	+44	+26	+21
Electric shock.................	− 5	+25	− 3	+34
Daylight......................	−13	+35	0	+13
Sound........................	−23	+31	−10	+20
A..........................	−13	+34	+ 3	+22

TABLE IX

	B				C			
	R	V	R′	V′	R	V	R′	V′
27. II...........	148	10	149	7	155	9	155	5
	136	9	139	6	147	11	148	6
28.............	139	9	139	6	143	12	142	6
	156	10	154	6	157	11	158	7
4. IV...........	146	16	145	10	162	12	159	8
A.............	145	11	145	7	153	11	152	6

There is still another way of distracting the attention. When the time of normal reactions was measured the stimulus came about a second after the signal (*i.e.*, the starting of the chronoscope), so the brain parts could be put in a state of complete readiness. It might be expected that we could not hold these parts very long in a state of unstable equilibrium, and experiments show this to be the case. Instead of always letting the stimulus occur from $\frac{3}{4}$ to $1\frac{1}{4}$ sec. after the signal, I let the maximum interval be about 2 secs., and obtained the results given in Table IX.

The averages show that the attention can be held strained, that is, the centres kept in a state of unstable equilibrium for 1 sec. *B*'s time is slightly shorter than normal; this is probably because he strained his attention more, and thus held the centres in more unstable equilibrium than usual in spite of the longer interval. *C*'s time, on the other hand, is slightly lengthened, concentrated attention not shortening his times, and the delay interfering with the maximum of readiness. In like manner the interval between signal and stimulus was varied at the pleasure of the experimenter between normal and fifteen seconds. The experiments recorded in Table X were made with both light and sound.

TABLE X

	Light				Sound			
	B		*C*		*B*		*C*	
	R	*R'*	*R*	*R'*	*R*	*R'*	*R*	R^1
27. II.......	200	198	170	168	184	173	174	169
28..........	204	196	164	164	176	173	167	166
	168	161	wanting		168	164	154	147
4. IV.......	159	158	184	181	171	171	173	166
5..........	178	174	174	176	158	159	170	166
A..........	182	177	173	172	171	168	168	163
AV.........	22	14	16	11	23	13	22	13

It will be seen that the times are considerably longer than normal; the mean variation is also large.[1] The first series made on *B* gave especially long times; afterwards he learned to accommodate himself better to the conditions. All these experiments show that in the case of *C* the reaction is more thoroughly reflex than in the case of *B*. Contrary to my expectation the reaction on sound seems to be more lengthened by distracting the attention than the reaction on light; it requires less effort to react on the sound, the reaction seeming to take place quite of itself, and we know that it is easy to make motions in time to sound-rhythms.

I made further series of experiments in which "Jetzt" was said and the chronoscope was set in motion as usual, but the light was

[1] On two occasions with *B*, I varied the series on sound with results worth noting. I let towards the end of the series the interval between signal and stimulus become regular and normal. *B* did not notice that any change in method had taken place, but his reaction-time after the first two trials became 40σ shorter. That is, without any conscious effort, the brain-parts concerned were put in the usual maximum state of unstable equilibrium.

produced only half the time. My thought was that the subject could not put his brain-centres in the maximum state of unstable equilibrium, lest the motor impulse should be discharged in the case where no stimulus was forthcoming. The averages in Table XI are from 13 and 10 reactions, as measurements were only made in half the experiments of the series.

TABLE XI

	B				C			
	R	V	R'	V'	R	V	R'	V'
27. II...........	153	18	147	10	174	22	165	8
	148	10	148	6	166	18	160	8
28..............	154	23	148	15	142	6	143	8
	165	20	157	10	154	12	156	6
	157	9	156	7	153	12	150	8
A...............	155	16	151	10	158	14	155	7

The delay here caused is related to the will-time to be considered later on.

From these experiments we see that ordinary degrees of attention do not greatly affect the length of the reaction time. We find, further, grounds for assuming that the cortex is not concerned and that perception and willing are not factors of the reaction-time. It is not necessary to perceive the stimulus before the motor centre can be excited; and the willing—not of necessity given in consciousness—is done before the stimulus occurs, and consists in setting the brain-parts concerned in a state of readiness.

III. THE PERCEPTION TIME

This third portion of "Psychometrische Untersuchungen" entitled "Die Unterscheidungszeit," was printed in *Philosophische Studien*, **3**: 452–472, 1886. An English version entitled, "The Perception Time," printed in *Mind*, **11**: 377–392, 1886, is reproduced here.

We have found the simple reaction-time on daylight for *B* and *C* to be about 150σ, and I have given my reasons for assuming that a perception-time is not included in this interval. The perception-time can be defined as the interval between sensation and perception (or between indefinite and definite perception, apperception), that is, the time passing after the impression has reached consciousness before it is distinguished. The impression is perhaps in the back-ground of consciousness when it reaches the optic thalami; before it is in the centre of consciousness it must probably travel to the cortex of the cerebrum and excite there changes corresponding to its nature. The method used by Wundt[1] to determine this time is to let the subject react as quickly as possible in one series of experiments, and in a second series not to react until he has distinguished the impression, the difference of the times in the two series giving the perception-time for the impression. I have not been able myself to get results by this method; I apparently either distinguished the impression and made the motion simultaneously, or if I tried to avoid this by waiting until I had formed a distinct impression before I began to make the motion, I added to the simple reaction, not only a perception, but also a volition. The method for determining the perception-time suggested by Donders[2] and since used by a number of others, is to let the motion depend on the nature of the stimulus. It has been thought by Donders, v. Kries and Auerbach and others, that if the subject reacts on one of two impressions and makes no motion when the other occurs, only a perception has been added to the simple reaction. This is however, not the case, it being necessary after the impression has been distinguished to decide between making a motion and not making it. This question, which has been much discussed, becomes quite simple if we consider the cerebral operations that probably take place. I assume that the changes do not penetrate into the cortex at all when a simple reaction is made. When, however, lights of two different colours (say red and blue) are used, and the subject may only lift his hand if the light is blue, the motor impulse cannot be sent to the hand until the subject knows that the light is blue. The nervous impulse must therefore probably travel from the thalami to the cortex and excite changes there, causing in consciousness the sensation or perception of a blue light; this gives a perception-time. In the cortex after the light has been distinguished a nervous impulse must be prepared and sent to the motor centre discharging a motor impulse there held in readiness; this gives a will-time. I do not think it is possible to add a perception to the reaction without also adding a will-act. We can however change the nature of the perception without altering the will-time, and thus investigate with considerable thoroughness the length of the perception-time.

The object most quickly perceived through the sense of sight is a simple light. In order to investigate the time required I took two cards, one entirely black, the other having on the black a white surface. One of the cards, the observer not knowing which, was placed by the experimenter in the springs of the gravity-chronometer, and the clockwork of the chronoscope was set in motion. The observer fixated the grey spot on the screen immediately before the centre of

---

[1] *Physiol. Psych.*, ii., 247 ff.; *Phil. Studien.*, i., 25 ff.

[2] De Jaager, *De physiologische Tijd Bij psychische Processen*, Utrecht, 1865; Donders, *Archiv. f. Anat. u. Physiol.*, 1868.

the white surface (supposing this card to be there), and with his left hand broke an electric current and let the screen fall. The card appeared at the point fixated, and at this same instant the current controlling the chronoscope was closed. The observer either saw nothing, or at the point fixated a white surface. If the light appeared he lifted his hand as quickly as possible, if there was no light he did not let go the key, and the hands of the chronoscope ran on until the clockwork was stopped by the experimenter. Twenty-six experiments were made

TABLE XII

	B				C			
	R	V	R'	V'	R	V	R'	V'
14. I............	203	8	203	6	239	14	246	7
19.............	217	18	213	12	219	13	217	10
20.............	222	22	222	15	226	13	226	9
31.............	234	35	217	11	238	13	241	10
2. II...........	219	21	214	13	215	16	217	11
	214	30	206	18	216	12	219	7
3.............	207	20	203	7	256	20	254	10
25. III.........	239	28	234	21	250	19	253	15
	212	19	205	6	263	22	259	9
31.............	215	34	205	15	244	16	248	9
	189	13	186	6	245	10	242	7
	191	16	189	7	251	11	252	5
	183	12	185	8	246	17	242	12
2. VII..........	213	13	212	7	262	7	262	4
4.............	209	13	210	8	251	11	251	6
A.............	211	20	207	11	241	14	242	9

in a series, the white light occurring thirteen times. Determinations were only made when the light occurred, so the averages in this section are from thirteen reactions (in the corrected series from ten). It will be seen that, as the observer tries to make the reaction as quickly as possible, he may lift his hand when the light is not present. If this happens often the times measured are not correct, but too short, since we may assume that the observer lifts his hand as often when the white light is present before he has seen it, as he makes the motion when no light comes. We must however expect such a false reaction occasionally to occur, otherwise we might assume that the reaction is not made in the minimum time when the light is present. In these experiments such false reactions scarcely happened except when the observer was disturbed, or when the impressions to be distinguished were similar (*E* from *F*, for example). In the first case the average is not seriously affected, as the reactions are as apt to be unduly retarded as unduly hurried. In the second case false reactions lead us to suppose that some of the reactions on the stimulus are too short. The method I have introduced of giving a corrected average eliminates all premature reactions. I give in the Tables the number of false reactions made;[1] it would have been well if v. Kries and Auerbach, Merkel and others had done the same.

We can now examine Table XII giving the time needed to perceive and react on a white surface.

The simple reaction-time for B and C is about 150σ, therefore (on our hypothesis as to the nature of the cerebral operations, and assuming, though not without hesitation, that the corresponding physiological processes take up the same time as in the simple reaction) the time needed for the nervous impulse to travel from the thalami to the centre for sight in the cortex and excite the cells there so as to call forth the sensation of a light, and for a will-impulse to be prepared there and sent thence to the motor centre, was for B 61, for C 95σ. We may suppose that the time of the centripetal and centrifugal progress through the brain is about the same, and that the time used in the cortex is about equally divided between the perception of the light and the preparation of the motor impulse; at all events the whole time is so short that, if we divide it equally between the processes of perception and volition, the error cannot be great. We therefore set the perception-time for light, where the nature of the light need not be distinguished, at 30σ for B, 50 for C, and the will-time in these and similar experiments at the same.

The reaction was made with the speech-organs in quite the same manner. When the white surface was seen the observer said "Weiss" and the hands of the chronoscope were stopped by means of the lip-key or sound-key. When no white surface was present the observer

TABLE XIII

	Sound-key				Lip-key			
	B		C		B		C	
	R	R'	R	R'	R	R'	R	R'
3.I V.......	246	241	282	281	236	241	276	275
4...........	255	247	302	308	241	246	281	276
5...........	234	237	274	268	233	235	256	250
	247	244	264	264	243	248	263	263
7...........	248	246	274	268	244	245	256	256
A...........	246	243	279	278	239	243	266	264
AV........	20	11	18	12	14	9	18	12

[1] After "false," the entire number made during the series given in the column under which it stands.

said nothing, and the hands ran on until the experimenter stopped the clockwork.

We have seen that the motor-time is longer when a simple reaction is made with the speech-organs than when it is made with the hand. There is no reason why the perception and will-time found by subtracting the simple reaction-time (Table III) from the time here measured should not be the same as when the reaction was made with the hand. If we average together the determinations with the sound-key and lip-key we get 65σ for B, 100 for C, which agrees very well with the determinations made with the hand.

If instead of two black cards on one of which there is a white surface, we take two white cards on one of which there is a black surface, and let the observer react only when the black is present, the conditions are substantially as before; the perception may require slightly longer, the will-time is probably the same. The results of such experiments are given in Table XIV.

If, instead of black, we place a colour on the white card, the perception becomes slightly more difficult; it is not quite so easy to see that something is there when it is yellow as when it is black, the will-time however presumedly remains the same. In one series of experiments (to the left in Table XV) only one colour was used at a time, in a second series (right in Table XV) ten colours, the observer not knowing which was to come, but not needing to distinguish it before making the motion.

TABLE XIV

	B				C			
	R	V	R'	V'	R	V	R'	V'
6. I............	250	20	253	15	236	21	233	16
14............	227	19	226	7	236	13	234	10
19............	245	21	249	13	231	14	230	8
20............	215	20	212	14	244	12	243	7
31............	227	10	227	7	246	21	241	13
A............	233	18	233	11	239	16	236	11

It thus takes a little longer to recognise the presence of a colour (even though the colour need not be distinguished) than of a white light. It is to be noticed that B's times became shorter in 1885 than they were in 1884.

We next determine the perception-time when it is necessary to distinguish the colour. Two cases were considered; in one the colours were taken in pairs, and one colour was distinguished from the other; in the second each colour was distinguished from ten colours. With blue and red electric lights (the above-mentioned Puluj's tube seen through coloured glasses) I got as perception- and will-time 75σ for *B*, 109 for *C*.[1] In most of my experiments however, with aid of the gravity-chronometer, I used daylight reflected from coloured surfaces, these exciting the processes with which our brain is occupied in our daily life. Red and blue and green and yellow were taken in pairs, the coloured surface being 3 × 30 mm. The numbers in Table XVI give the average of six series.

TABLE XV

		B		C			B		C	
		R	R'	R	R'		R	R'	R	R'
Orange.....	22. XII	291	296	258	261	22. XII	289	293	245	237
Violet......	......	262	269	251	255	......	260	254	259	263
Black......	......	250	253	236	233	......	263	255	250	253
Pink.......	6. I	268	263	270	266	6. I	238	242	245	240
Brown.....	7	295	290	267	263	7	278	282	241	244
Gray.......	9	291	280	267	265	9	234	237	276	277
Red........	10	277	282	264	265	2. II	230	230	232	239
Blue.......	......	265	263	284	279	......	219	223	242	237
Green......	......	262	264	268	268	......	229	219	245	244
Yellow.....	......	264	262	280	286	......	230	228	254	257
A..........	......	272	272	264	264	......	247	246	249	248
A V........	......	20	13	18	13	......	25	17	24	17
False.......	......	1	...	0	...	......	0	...	2	

Ten colours were further taken in pairs, as indicated in Table XVII, and the time required to distinguish the one from the other determined.

[1] These are the only experiments described in this section which had been previously made; Donders (*Archiv. f. Anat. u. Physiol.*, 1868) found the time to be 184σ, Wundt (*Physiol. Psych.*, 11, 251) 210 to 250σ, v. Kries and Auerbach, working ucder the direction of Helmholtz (*Archiv. f. Anat. u. Physiol.*, 1877), 12 and 34σ. In annot accept the results reached by these latter experimenters. The times seem to be too short to be correct. I do not know where the error lies, the experiments having apparently been made with great care, but the simple reactions are very long, the reactions with perception and volition very short. The latter may have been made unduly short through the frequent occurrence of premature reactions (the number of false reactions is not given); at all events I consider their method of calculating the averages dangerous, they ignoring what reactions they saw fit. They do not give the number of measurements made in the series, but in the model series given in the appendix, we find that in one 22 reactions were used, in one on the perception of light only 9; we may therefore assume that in the latter series over half of the reactions were ignored. If the mean variation of the reactions used in this series be calculated, it will be found to be 6 (smaller, I imagine, than the mean error of the recording apparatus); the mean variation of the corresponding series of simple reactions (from which determinations had also been omitted) is 12σ. When averages are made up in this way any results desired can be obtained.

If we average together the results given in Tables XVI and XVII, and subtract the reaction-time and supposed will-time, we find that it took *B* 100, *C* 110σ, to distinguish one colour from another.

TABLE XVI

		B				C			
		R	V	R'	V'	R	V	R'	V'
27. XI.-2. XII..	Red	278	22	272	11	232	40	324	26
	Blue	287	19	280	17	291	24	288	16
I.-5. XII........	Green	268	26	265	18	313	32	312	21
	Yellow	276	26	273	16	297	31	300	20
	A	277	23	272	15	306	32	306	21
	AV	2	..	...	..	8			

TABLE XVII

		B				C			
		R	V	R'	V'	R	V	R'	V'
22. XII................	Orange	308	21	309	11	316	47	299	21
	Violet	258	23	262	15	289	16	297	8
	Black	267	35	262	26	278	16	275	9
6. I...................	Pink	288	19	284	14	302	26	303	18
7.....................	Brown	308	20	294	15	340	31	323	16
9.....................	Gray	283	12	287	6	397	80	367	31
10.....................	Red	278	22	272	11	322	40	324	26
	Blue	287	19	280	17	291	24	228	26
	Green	268	26	265	18	313	32	312	21
	Yellow	276	27	273	16	297	31	300	20
	A	282	22	279	15	314	34	303	20
	False	1	..	...	..	5			

In the series of experiments next to be given, I determine the time it takes to distinguish a colour from nine others, that is the real perception-time for a colour. The results of ten series in which the motion was made with the hand, and of five in which it was made with the speech-organs, are given in Table XVIII.

This gives as the time needed to distinguish a colour 105σ for *B*, 117 for *C*; respectively 5 and 7σ longer than it took to distinguish one colour from another, and 26 and 41σ longer than it took to see that a colour was present when it was not necessary to distinguish it.

The results given in Table XVIII (where the reaction was made with the hand) were obtained at the beginning of the investigation; the determinations were repeated after four months of constant practice, and again after a pause of three months, the results being given in Table XIX.

TABLE XVIII

		B				C			
		R	V	R'	V'	R	V	R'	V'
					Hand				
17. XII.........	Red	317	19	310	10	341	31	340	20
	Green	298	19	291	10	330	31	338	22
	Gray	302	29	295	20	316	33	319	22
18..............	Blue	289	28	276	9	316	7	315	3
	Yellow	260	12	261	9	317	24	310	14
	Black	283	22	284	14	289	15	293	9
19..............	Orange	309	51	290	23	285	20	279	12
	Violet	302	16	299	11	312	34	308	24
	Brown	318	12	314	8	313	30	313	18
	Pink	293	30	282	12	312	22	305	12
	A	297	24	290	13	313	25	312	16
	False	1	..	...	..	4			
					Sound-key				
17. II...........	Red	306	35	297	18	359	25	360	19
19..............	Green	293	11	289	7	360	12	364	7
21..............	Black	286	34	279	17	306	16	311	11
24..............	Violet	271	30	265	22	309	20	304	14
26..............	Brown	296	18	291	11	359	46	347	32
	A	290	26	284	15	339	24	337	17

Practice therefore shortened the perception- and will-times about 30σ for B and 20 for C, and this decrease in the length of the times was not lost by an interruption in the practice.

With the same methods I found the time it takes to see or distinguish a letter. I tried in my experiments to determine the time taken up by those operations which are constantly going on in the brain; the letters chosen therefore were such as we usually have to read (of the size in which this is printed). The time for larger letters is somewhat shorter. In the first experiments it was not necessary to distinguish the letter, only to know that a letter was present; the conditions were consequently the same as in the first experiments (Table XV) on colours.

It therefore (making the same assumptions as above) took B 47, C 58σ, to see that a small object was on a white surface.

The next case to be given is where it was necessary to distinguish

TABLE XIX

| | | B | | C | | | B | | C | |
		R	R'	R	R'		R	R'	R	R'
Red........	4. IV	244	237	294	287	2. VII	283	267	292	286
Green......	......	247	239	311	309	4	247	252	277	278
Gray.......	7	270	258	283	279	31	264	257	325	314
Blue.......	......	246	246	273	275	......	253	257	286	279
Yellow.....	8	290	249	304	302	......	245	245	267	264
A.........	......	259	246	293	290	......	258	256	289	284
AV........	......	35	13	16	10	......	30	17	24	15
False.......	......	5	...	2	...	......	0	...	0	

TABLE XX

| | B | | | | C | | | |
	R	V	R'	V'	R	V	R'	V'
3. II............	261	31	260	18	268	12	266	11
27. III..........	234	21	228	12	235	23	229	11
1. IV...........	205	37	194	23	261	32	255	25
	230	38	220	25	251	24	255	19
	206	18	208	6	277	23	218	16
A..............	227	29	222	17	258	23	257	16

one of two letters from the other, A and Z being taken. The averages given are taken from six series.

It thus took B 142, C 137σ, to distinguish one letter from another, respectively 45 and 31σ longer than to distinguish one colour from another.

We now come to consider the time needed to distinguish one letter from all the others; that is the time it takes to see a letter. This is a process with which our brain is constantly busy; the time taken up by it is therefore of special interest. If for example the time is different for the several letters, it is a matter of the greatest practical importance, for those letters which it takes the longest to see might be so modified as to shorten the time. If it takes 20σ longer to see E than it would to see a symbol that might be taken in its place, say Δ, it is startling if we calculate how much time is being wasted and how much unnecessary strain is being put on eye and brain. I have published[1] extended series of experiments, determining the time the light reflected from a printed letter must work on the retina in order that it may be possible to see the letter. These experiments show that there

[1] *Phil. Studien,* ii. 4; *Brain,* No. 31.

is a great difference in the legibility of the several letters; out of 270 trials W was read correctly 241, *E* only 63 times. In this case the whole time was short, 1 to 1.5σ, and the difference in the time for the several letters correspondingly small. When however we determine the entire time needed to recognise the letter, we may expect to find the time considerably shorter for a simple and distinct symbol than for one complicated or easily confused with others, just as the time is shorter for a colour than for a letter.[1] The speech-organs as well as

TABLE XXI

		B				C			
		R	V	R'	V'	R	V	R'	V'
4.—10. XII...	A	315	26	319	16	327	31	323	18
	Z	330	31	325	21	348	29	348	21
	A	322	28	322	18	337	30	335	19
	False	3	..	...	..	5			

the hand were used in these experiments. Here however a slight complication is added, as we cannot be sure that a difference in the time for the several letters is to be referred only to the perception-time, it being possible that the time needed to name the several letters or to register the different motions may be different. This difference in time can however only be very small, as the observer knew what letter he had to name, so there was no choice between different motions, as in the experiments to be considered in the next section of this paper. Tables XXII–XXIV (placed, with others, at the end of this paper) give the results obtained at different times, the motion being made both with the hand and the speech-organs.

A shortening in the time through practice will be noticed in these Tables; if we take Table XXIII, which contains the most determinations and times representing about the average of the three Tables, we find the perception-time for a capital letter of the size in which this is printed to be 119σ for *B*, 116 for *C*. The Tables contain the results of a great many experiments, but not enough to determine finally the time for the several letters; if however the four series made

[1] I have not been able to determine accurately and finally the perception-time for different alphabets and for the several letters. In these experiments the different letters cannot well be used in the same series, and further in half the cases no measurement is made. As the difference in the times is small and the variation of the series not inconsiderable, a large number of experiments must be made before the difference in the time for the several letters can be determined with certainty. This is however not only a subject of scientific interest, but also of great practical importance; it is to be hoped that it will be thoroughly investigated by independent experimenters.

with the hand on E and M are averaged together, we find that it took B 19, C 22σ longer to see E than to see M. The order for the five letters on which four series were made is $M\ A\ Z\ B\ E$, which (except the position of Z) agrees with the order of legibility established in the paper referred to.

Similar determinations were made with the small letters, the results being given in Table XXV. It seems from this Table that the perception-time is about the same for the large and small letters, which agrees with experiments I have made by an entirely different method (see MIND 41).

We now come to consider the time it takes to see a word, a process with which the brain is constantly occupied. Twenty-six words were taken, and when the expected one was seen the observer lifted his hand. The perception-time so determined is the time needed to distinguish the word from the other twenty-five; the time is slightly longer when it is necessary to distinguish words from others very similar in form; for example, hand from band. Indeed we must remember that perception is not a sharply defined process. As I have shown, we see a letter before we see what letter it is; in like manner a further time passes before we see the letter in all its details, that it is not perfectly printed, for example. The perception-time for a painting by Raphael is indefinitely long. The results of experiments with English and German words are given in the Tables XXVI–VII.

The Tables give us a perception-time for short English words B 132, C 141σ; for short German words B 118, C 150σ; for long English words B 154, C 158σ. The time was therefore slightly shorter (B 22, C 17) for a short than for a long word, and for a word in the native than in a foreign language (B 14, C 9). It will be noticed that the perception-time is only slightly longer for a word than for a single letter; we do not therefore perceive separately the letters of which a word is composed, but the word as a whole. The application of this to teaching children to read is evident; I have already in connexion with other experiments called attention to it.

The only other perception-time we have to consider is for a picture. It takes, we may suppose, about the same time to recognise the picture of a tree as it takes to see the tree itself; this is consequently a process nearly always going on in the brain. I had carefully drawn twenty-six pictures of common objects, tree, hand, ship, etc., about one square cm. in size, the method of determining the perception-time being as before.

We thus find that the perception-time for a picture, and we may assume for the objects we are continually seeing in our daily life, was 96σ for B, 117 for C, about the same as for a colour and shorter than for a letter or word.

TABLE XXII

		B				C			
		R	V	R'	V'	R	V	R'	V'
		Hand							
11. XII.......	B	358	25	354	18	342	28	346	17
12...........	Z	345	24	350	18	370	33	353	20
	A	327	31	314	14	337	22	342	16
16...........	M	338	36	345	20	329	15	324	7
	E	360	31	345	9	343	28	326	9
17...........	S	333	22	326	11	341	25	338	17
	P	339	24	332	14	329	32	318	18
	T	330	29	320	16	323	30	330	18
18...........	O	293	19	297	11	302	25	301	18
	L	338	15	339	10	350	37	333	16
	A	336	26	332	14	337	27	331	16
	False	5	..	...	..	4			
		Square-key							
17. II........	A	330	27	337	17	406	16	401	11
19...........	M	336	36	332	30	410	29	412	17
21...........	E	308	36	310	22	359	35	354	28
24...........	P	311	22	307	13	321	13	325	8
26...........	O	303	21	307	16	380	33	372	27
	A	318	28	319	20	375	25	373	18
	False	1	..	...	..	1			

Table XXIII

		Hand					Lip-key			
		B		C			B		C	
		R	R'	R	R'		R	R'	R	R'
A..........	13. I	309	312	323	328	15. I	288	295	338	332
B..........	12	307	311	353	350	13	348	353	362	363
C..........	17	304	306	319	322	17	307	310	333	325
D..........	....	342	309	332	341	....	320	324	346	354
E..........	14	328	334	341	345	15	333	345	340	330
F..........	17	322	324	358	344	20	307	310	317	321
G..........	....	326	321	331	327	....	309	308	311	309
H..........	19	323	320	320	317	....	305	308	338	333
I..........	....	294	293	295	301	....	271	275	296	290
J..........	....	329	326	299	288	21	342	338	330	335
K..........	....	330	335	305	297	....	334	334	315	314
L..........	14	296	304	302	299	29	320	302	357	353
M........	13	311	316	320	322	15	342	330	373	366
N..........	20	318	317	333	330	21	318	321	323	328
O..........	14	263	266	292	288	13	315	319	355	352
P..........	....	288	284	337	326	29	321	324	338	339
Q..........	20	317	315	315	319	21	312	314	312	302
R..........	....	311	313	322	317	....	334	340	322	315
S..........	14	285	281	327	332	15	318	325	313	313
T..........	....	319	295	310	305	29	318	315	366	363
U..........	20	311	298	329	331	24	320	320	335	331
V..........	22	322	330	334	330	....	324	327	333	338
W..........	....	278	283	338	332	....	312	314	343	345
X..........	....	315	297	349	341	....	292	297	362	366
Y..........	....	303	307	341	337	....	318	313	339	339
Z..........	12	323	319	347	345	13	350	343	331	324
A..........	....	310	308	326	324	....	318	319	336	334
AV........	....	22	15	22	14	....	22	14	25	16
False.......	....	13	..	13	..	....	18	..	4	

TABLE XXIV

		B		C			B		C	
		R	R'	R	R'		R	R'	R	R'
B..........	5. IV	275	262	321	319	31. VII	307	308	304	306
Z..........	....	272	273	310	301	......	313	314	311	303
A..........	....	276	281	292	288	2	295	295	309	302
M.........	7	293	291	302	306	4	298	299	307	306
E..........	8	316	316	337	331	......	313	306	315	319
A..........	....	286	285	312	309	......	305	304	309	307
AV........	....	25	16	20	13	......	22	14	26	18
False.......	....	2	...	3	...	......	0	...	0	

TABLE XXV

		Hand					Lip-key			
		B		C			B		C	
		R	R'	R	R'		R	R'	R	R'
b..........	5. I	301	306	314	306	22. I	313	317	327	321
z..........	....	307	298	324	325	....	305	300	336	322
a..........	7	316	320	327	320	23	330	328	313	309
m..........	....	310	312	311	313	....	310	304	313	315
e..........	12	337	342	356	356	....	331	321	330	322
s..........	....	322	325	368	359	....	297	290	338	343
p..........	13	323	320	341	337	28	345	345	370	372
t..........	....	311	310	139	315	....	305	300	346	342
o..........	14	293	290	306	304	....	299	299	335	332
l..........	....	303	300	306	304	....	311	314	344	339
A..........	....	312	312	327	324	....	315	312	335	332
AV........	....	19	13	28	19	....	20	11	25	16
False.......	....	4	...	8	...	....	7	...	2	

TABLE XXVI

| | | Hand | | | | | Lip-key | | | |
| | | B | | C | | | B | | C | |
		R	R'	R	R'		R	R'	R	R'
Mind	12. XII	353	352	337	329	31. I	360	366	374	364
Life	15	348	351	373	377	....	366	367	363	365
Time	16	333	330	375	372	15	311	312	371	366
House	......	377	366	383	389	....	331	324	355	361
Child	......	345	343	328	339	17	347	341	370	375
Year	18	353	359	369	360	....	337	336	354	358
Truth	......	352	329	376	367	29	302	311	360	353
Name	......	341	339	392	393	....	313	315	374	380
Light	19	332	328	327	323	....	325	332	372	372
Ship	......	318	313	336	332	....	294	302	340	340
A	......	345	341	360	358	....	329	331	363	363
AV	......	24	13	26	17	....	23	12	28	20
False	......	2	...	4	...	....	7	....	0	
Education	5. I	331	331	346	348	17. I	349	345	382	386
Philosophy	......	330	322	349	354	....	347	351	376	377
Knowledge	7	341	337	366	360	22	353	348	329	319
Architecture	......	377	375	382	377	....	357	355	336	340
Literature	10	339	320	363	354	23	333	332	377	382
Temperance	......	341	333	399	404	....	339	330	377	376
Ignorance	......	300	297	380	369	....	325	319	378	382
Physician	......	325	329	380	375	26	339	333	351	346
Enthusiasm	12	334	337	405	409	....	353	349	409	400
Imagination	......	321	317	384	375	....	342	337	395	391
A	......	334	330	375	373	....	344	340	371	370
AV	......	25	16	28	19	....	23	15	27	17
False	......	8	...	8	...	....	6	...	9	
Buch	24. I	290	294	367	363	23. I	315	318	359	355
Zahl	......	309	311	380	378	....	310	319	370	378
Kunst	......	307	309	369	374	....	310	314	362	352
Welt	......	308	307	361	353	....	308	305	362	362
Haus	26	295	292	354	353	24	299	297	339	344
Licht	......	324	323	354	359	....	330	329	356	350
Kind	......	323	323	377	380	....	303	308	352	356
Land	29	309	307	363	365	26	316	321	373	365
Traum	......	321	316	377	376	....	324	325	368	373
Jahr	......	319	318	365	368	....	321	325	374	378
A	......	311	310	367	367	....	314	316	362	361
AV	......	14	9	20	13	....	17	12	31	20
False	......	6	...	5	...	....	10	...	7	

TABLE XXVII

| | | Hand | | | | | | Sound-key | | | |
| | | B | | C | | | | B | | C | |
		R	R'	R	R'			R	R'	R	R'
6. IV.	Mind	266	269	312	306	14. II.	Mind	311	307	380	391
	Life	302	292	340	340	19....	Life	338	333	400	409
7.....	Time	307	303	325	330	24....	Child	319	326	360	364
	House	299	296	321	317		Truth	317	318	339	345
8.....	Child	282	284	327	322	26....	Ship	320	326	361	367
	A	291	289	325	323	......	.....	321	322	368	375
	AV	18	10	22	14	......	.....	27	19	25	16
	False	5	...	0	...	......	.....	3	...	4	

TABLE XXVIII

| | Picture of a | B | | | | C | | | |
		R	V	R'	V'	R	V	R'	V'
		Hand							
12. II......	Watch	262	23	249	15	295	21	292	14
	Ship	264	19	268	13	324	31	320	16
	Eye	271	17	266	11	313	24	316	9
20. III.....	Hand	297	20	294	15	282	37	266	10
	Tree	246	12	244	7	296	28	302	23
	Bird	289	28	297	15	310	43	291	10
	Fish	290	19	293	17	301	23	294	13
	Leaf	267	12	265	9	321	31	317	26
24..........	Hat	270	28	277	22	306	21	312	10
	Shoe	283	17	286	12	341	23	346	18
	A	274	19	274	14	309	28	306	15
	False	8	..	...	..	8			
		Sound-key							
17. II......	Watch	308	32	302	14	364	44	357	34
19..........	Eye	341	30	336	25	408	40	408	25
21..........	Tree	283	27	276	17	374	32	361	17
24..........	Fish	309	38	315	22	304	23	296	15
26..........	Hat	305	42	296	24	367	59	348	36
	A	309	34	305	20	363	40	354	25
	False	2	..	...	..	2			

IV. The Will-time[1]

The fourth part of "Psychometrische Untersuchungen" was first published under the title "Die Wahlzeit" in *Philosophische Studien*, **3**: 472–485, 1886.

It was rewritten in English by the author and printed as reproduced here, with the title "The Will-Time," in *Mind*, **11**: 524–534, 1886.

In the experiments described in the foregoing section the motion to be made was always the same, and took up the same or about the same time. In this section the nature of the motion depends on the nature of the impression. The experiments about to be described will throw further light on the Perception-time, but we shall find in addition a variable Will- (or Motor) time. The perception-process, further, is different from what we considered in the foregoing section: then the observer expected a certain impression and saw whether it was present or not; in the experiments now to be described the observer, not awaiting a given impression, had to identify the one occurring. We might perhaps expect the perception to be more difficult and consequently to last longer in the latter case; the experiments however show that there can be no great difference in the time.

Experiments have been made in this direction by Donders[2] and others, they letting the observer lift his right hand if (for example) the light is red, the left if it is blue. Under Wundt's direction Merkel[3] extended this method, the observer lifting a different finger for each of ten different impressions. My first experiments (carried out in the winter 1883–4) were made with aid of electric lights, as above described, and were similar to those of previous experimenters; they gave as the time for distinguishing the colour and choosing the motion 120σ for *B*, 168 for *C*. Afterwards I used the gravity chronoscope, which enabled me to use daylight reflected from coloured surfaces. The current controlling the chronoscope was led through two keys (*K* and *K'* Fig. 8, Mind 42), the observer holding one closed with his right, the other with his left hand. Two colours, say red and blue, were used in the same series of experiments. If red appeared the observer lifted his right hand, if blue his left. The times are given in Table XXIX, the pairs of colours used being red and blue, and green and yellow. The reaction on red and on green was made with the right hand, on blue and on yellow with the left. Each number gives the average of six series (78 reactions in the uncorrected series).

[1] I use the term "Will-time" for lack of a better; in Germany "Wahlzeit" is used. The motion is in most cases simply the result of the perception, and "Association-time" might be used, were it not already taken up. "Motor time" would perhaps best explain the process, but might cause confusion.

[2] *Arch. für Anat. u. Physiol.*, 1868.

[3] *Phil. Studien.* ii. 1.

TABLE XXIX

		B				C			
		R	V	R'	V'	R	V	R'	V'
27. XI.—2. XII..........	Red	291	27	289	18	342	39	322	32
	Blue	296	27	296	18	332	25	320	22
1.—5. XII..............	Green	289	25	286	17	354	32	351	18
	Yellow	303	28	306	20	334	34	332	23
	A	295	27	294	18	340	32	331	24
	False	9	..	...	..	3			

If from the average time for the four colours we substract the simple reaction-time, we find that it took B 145, C 190σ to distinguish the colour and find the proper motion. If these times are compared with those given in the preceding section (Table XVI) we find that it took B 18, C 34σ longer to send out the proper and corresponding motion, than the command sending out a motion already determined. As I have already remarked, the perception-process is slightly different in the two cases; it being necessary in the first to see whether the light is red or blue, in the second only to recognise the red light. The results of the experiments show that there can scarcely be a difference in the times taken up by the two processes.

Quite a similar method was used with letters, the observer lifting his right hand if A was present, his left if Z. The numbers given in the Table are taken from six series.

TABLE XXX

		B				C			
		R	V	R'	V'	R	V	R'	V'
4.—10. XII..............	A	328	27	324	18	379	42	370	30
	Z	339	23	336	15	382	34	379	22
	A	333	25	330	16	380	38	374	26
	False	8	..	...	..	3			

The perception-time was thus for B 38, for C 40σ longer than for colours, and the will-time for B 11, for C 43σ longer for the choice between two motions than for the choice between making a motion and not making it.

In most of my experiments the motion corresponding to the impression was made with the organs of speech. I consider the time of special interest, as we are constantly reading a word, naming a colour, &c. In the experiments first to be considered two impressions were used; the observer did not know which was to come, but named the one occurring as soon as possible after seeing it. The motion was registered by means of the sound-key. These experiments are an extension of those given in Tables XVIII, XXII, XXVII and XXVIII. There the observer made a determined motion (*i.e.*, named an expected object), here the motion had to be found after the impression had been distinguished. The relation between the processes is exactly the same as when the motion is made with the hand, the only difference being that we are constantly giving the name blue (for example) to a certain colour, whereas the association between a motion of the left hand and the colour blue must be made for the experiments. The impressions were taken in pairs as indicated in Table XXXI. 26 reactions were made as usual in a series, 13 on each of the two impressions.

These results in Table XXXI, when compared with those given in Tables XVIII, XXII, XXVII and XXVIII, give the increased will-times shown in Table XXXII.

We have already seen that with the hand *B* needed less additional time than *C* to make the choice between two motions: the difference between the two observers is still more marked when the motions are made with the speech organs. Table XXXII is further interesting in showing a difference between letters and words on the one hand, and colours and pictures on the other. The association between a printed letter or word and its name requires less time, and is consequently closer than between a colour or picture and its name. We can understand this, as the former association is being more continually practised; still we could not have foreseen it, as the association between a colour or object and its name is formed long before we learn how to read.

In the experiments now to be described there were not two objects and two corresponding motions, but a large number of objects; the one occurring to be named by the observer. In this case we determine the time it takes to see and name an impression, as a word or a colour. We have in the preceding section determined approximately the time taken to see an object: the difference between the two times gives us the time it takes to name the object. We shall first consider the time needed to see and name a letter. All the letters of the alphabet (capital letters of the largest size in the text of MIND) were used, each occurring once in the course of the series. After thirteen series had been made, the times for the separate letters were averaged together, so that we get the average of thirteen determinations on each letter; these series were corrected in the usual way, the three reactions varying most from the corrected average being dropped. As the determinations for the same letter were made at different times we find the mean variation larger than usual. Table XXXIII gives besides the results obtained

TABLE XXXI

		B		C				B		C	
		R	R'	R	R'			R	R'	R	R'
17. II.	A	346	353	439	440	19.II.	Mind	339	332	432	355
	Z	338	341	398	390		Life	294	298	406	401
19.....	B	366	366	415	420	21....	Time	296	305	379	382
	M	338	332	435	434		House	285	291	368	363
21.....	E	326	321	384	383	24....	Child	355	350	410	415
	S	300	294	391	386		Year	361	364	409	411
24.....	P	354	352	387	382		Truth	303	297	392	390
	T	350	341	436	429		Name	329	324	397	399
26.....	O	292	296	425	421	26....	Light	339	339	421	424
	L	323	308	412	408		Ship	294	298	396	395
	A	333	330	412	409	.....	.....	319	320	401	401
	AV	24	17	28	19	.....	.....	24	16	21	14
17. II.	Red	342	329	472	479	17.II.	Watch	350	343	458	447
	Blue	317	322	441	447		Ship	376	387	424	422
19.....	Green	303	298	484	474	19....	Eye	369	367	495	488
	Yellow	309	301	499	502		Hand	346	333	455	445
21.....	Black	347	354	386	382	21....	Tree	340	336	455	459
	Pink	298	305	394	376		Bird	343	339	451	447
24.....	Violet	293	288	395	370	24....	Fish	337	345	382	376
	Orange	276	270	433	441		Leaf	333	339	430	424
26.....	Brown	323	325	421	431	26....	Hat	336	344	407	412
	Gray	331	337	453	446		Shoe	346	342	415	403
	A	314	313	438	435	.....	.....	348	347	437	432
	AV	27	18	41	36	.....	.....	31	20	44	31

TABLE XXXII

	B	C
Letters.....................................	+15	+ 37
Words......................................	− 2	+ 33
Colours....................................	+24	+101
Pictures...................................	+39	+ 74

with aid of the sound-key, series made with aid of a second observer. The first observer simply named the letter as quickly as possible, and the second observer made the reaction on the sound in the manner above described. Mr. Wolfe acted as second observer; in the Table

I have subtracted his reaction-time on sound (150σ) and his mean variation (10σ).

TABLE XXXIII

| | Second observer. 9.—30. I | | | | | | Sound-key. 5.—19. II | | | | | |
| | B | | | C | | | B | | | C | | |
	R	V	R'	R	V	R'	R	V	R'	R	V	R'
A.........	398	25	405	458	43	440	430	18	396	462	38	476
B.........	444	30	436	471	53	457	414	26	406	418	30	413
C.........	466	36	477	450	22	453	417	29	417	421	28	424
D.........	421	18	417	454	31	454	394	51	400	412	15	411
E.........	400	11	402	445	9	447	396	30	397	425	28	424
F.........	432	31	434	442	21	446	405	30	412	414	26	420
G.........	453	31	446	483	24	474	402	48	395	427	14	426
H.........	435	20	441	423	13	417	356	20	352	429	26	422
I.........	395	26	403	433	25	429	394	24	394	449	36	451
J.........	408	29	417	473	44	472	399	42	410	417	21	415
K.........	432	18	438	474	34	463	395	25	401	415	27	409
L.........	412	20	418	463	47	457	393	22	397	427	34	423
M.........	421	44	400	435	16	425	389	21	395	418	26	422
N.........	429	38	419	453	19	460	384	32	390	415	36	422
O.........	410	15	404	440	32	436	395	19	392	411	15	409
P.........	459	64	442	462	23	455	392	19	398	395	15	393
Q.........	446	28	461	480	22	469	428	34	438	413	22	418
R.........	422	20	435	462	20	469	385	28	389	443	18	446
S.........	431	33	431	471	38	479	391	27	394	412	22	410
T.........	425	25	432	446	34	454	398	36	390	414	18	409
U.........	428	22	434	461	47	471	391	22	396	439	14	441
V.........	463	32	450	465	29	461	383	20	378	428	26	423
W.........	421	42	405	485	16	481	353	26	364	435	24	432
X.........	465	46	471	452	25	460	381	31	388	405	29	412
Y.........	433	20	446	501	26	493	405	44	415	458	33	463
Z.........	431	12	432	499	37	507	393	19	392	426	22	421
A.........	430	..	431	461	..	459	395	..	396	424	..	424
AV.......	...	28	14	...	29	16	...	29	19	...	25	17

We thus see that it takes the observers about four-tenths of a second to see and name (*i.e.*, read) a letter. In this connexion results I have already published[1] should be considered. I there determined by two distinct methods the time it takes to see and name letters. In most of the experiments, however, the observer while seeing and naming one letter could begin to see and name the one or ones following, so that the processes overlapped and the times became much

[1] *Phil. Studien*, ii. 4; MIND 41.

shorter, namely 279σ for *B*, 224 for *C*. The times were still further shortened (becoming 96σ for *B*, 89 for *C*) when the letters made words. Why *B*'s times should be longer than *C*'s under these circumstances and shorter for a single letter I do not know. We found in the preceding section that it took *B* 119, *C* 116σ to perceive a letter. Supposing the perception-time to be the same in both cases, *B* needed 143σ *C* 176 to find the name belonging to a letter. It should be added that in later series of experiments *B*'s time became shorter. This method of determining the relative legibility of the several letters has an advantage over that in the previous section in so far as all the letters occur in the same series; but it is greatly complicated by the fact that the time of pronouncing the several letters may be different, as also the motion registered by the sound-key or second observer.

Series were made on the German capital letters with the results given in Table XXXIV

TABLE XXXIV

	B				C			
	R	V	R'	V'	R	V	R'	V'
14. II...........	423	36	420	23	554	63	538	32
16.............	446	30	439	18	573	58	549	33
18.............	377	30	382	20	531	60	519	38
23.............	363	34	357	23	464	30	461	21
25.............	369	31	389	24	507	33	510	20
A...............	396	32	397	22	526	49	515	29
F...............	3	..	...	..	1			

Numbers of one, two and three places were further used, and the time it takes to see and name them was determined. I did not take numbers of more than three places, fearing that they might not be seen and read as wholes. The results are given in Table XXXV; from which it will be seen that it took *B* 33, *C* 38σ longer to see and name a number of two places than of one, and *B* 57, *C* 47σ longer for a number of three than of two places.[1]

The time it takes to see and name a word was determined in the same way. Experiments were made on long and short English and German words, 26 of each sort being taken. In the case of the short words I made thirteen series, and found the time for the separate words as with the letters (Table XXXVII). On the long words only five series (130 determinations) were made, and the times for the separate words were not calculated (Table XXXVI).

[1] See Friedrich, *Phil. Studien*, i. 1.

An examination of the Tables shows that it took longer (in English *B* 52, *C* 46σ, in German *B* 39, *C* 46σ) to see and name a long than a short word. In both cases, of course, the beginning of the motion was registered; so the time occupied in pronouncing the word does not come into consideration. We further learn that it takes longer (for

TABLE XXXV

	One place				Two places				Three places			
	R	*V*	*R'*	*V'*	*R*	*V*	*R'*	*V'*	*R*	*V*	*R'*	*V'*
B												
30. III......	318	14	317	9	357	26	358	16	413	39	417	20
2. IV.......	316	28	312	16	344	18	343	10	381	25	377	15
A..........	317	21	314	12	350	22	350	13	397	32	397	17
C												
30. III......	390	28	397	18	424	32	423	22	476	31	503	24
2. IV.......	418	24	419	13	460	39	460	21	502	39	499	24
A..........	404	26	408	15	442	35	441	21	489	35	501	24

TABLE XXXVI

	English				German			
	B		*C*		*B*		*C*	
	R	*R'*	*R*	*R'*	*R*	*R'*	*R*	*R'*
14. II.......	493	484	451	450	419	409	501	498
16...........	481	475	490	488	451	454	533	527
18...........	447	440	451	457	424	418	507	500
23...........	391	383	430	434	379	370	433	432
25...........	391	378	431	431	381	376	473	475
A...........	441	423	451	452	411	405	489	486
AV.........	37	21	20	13	20	20	24	15

short words *B* 17, *C* 35σ, for long words *B* 30, *C* 38σ) to see and name a word in a foreign than in one's native language.[1] Comparing the results here reached with those given in the foregoing section, we find that to name a short word in his native language *B* needed 104, *C* 114σ. We find further that *B* named a word in 39, *C* in 62σ less time than a letter. This is not surprising; we are constantly reading and

[1] See Cattell, *Phil. Studien*, ii. 4; MIND 41.

using words, much more than letters; so the association between the concept and the name has become closer and takes place in less time.

The same method was used to determine the time it takes to see and name a colour. The ten colours taken occurred two to three times in a series, and the times for the separate colours (13 determinations) were afterwards averaged together. Table XXXVIII gives the times as measured with aid of a second observer, and as directly registered. The order of the colours is that of the average time needed to name them, beginning with the colour most quickly named.

TABLE XXXVII

5.—25. II.....	B		C		5.—26. II.....	B		C	
	R	R′	R	R′		R	R′	R	R′
Bond.........	393	397	407	405	Baum.........	367	367	423	423
Cause.........	395	394	423	428	Berg..........	382	385	414	417
Chair.........	398	390	415	411	Bild..........	366	365	428	424
Child.........	396	385	414	411	Brief..........	367	362	444	440
Death........	397	399	410	405	Buch.........	377	381	441	443
Earth.........	405	414	409	406	Ding..........	380	379	432	435
Fact..........	358	355	389	385	Fluss.........	356	362	425	424
Faith.........	374	367	388	379	Form.........	350	354	407	409
Force.........	359	362	371	373	Gold.........	378	385	452	450
Head.........	366	368	367	362	Haus........	326	322	405	403
House........	366	367	385	388	Jahr..........	362	354	455	454
King..........	393	389	414	408	Kind........	392	401	444	450
Life..........	388	394	430	424	Kunst.......	397	400	456	461
Light.........	396	394	418	414	Land........	381	386	440	441
Love..........	386	375	409	404	Licht........	363	379	441	441
Mind.........	421	426	422	418	Mann........	396	403	447	439
Name.........	402	401	405	410	Nacht........	401	392	451	447
Plan..........	395	390	388	396	Recht........	333	327	446	445
Ship..........	380	384	385	390	Stadt........	399	402	451	449
Slave.........	407	413	409	402	Stern........	417	413	436	432
Song.........	385	387	387	389	Teil..........	375	370	430	424
Style.........	431	435	435	442	Tisch........	381	385	446	449
Time........	381	388	411	408	Traum.......	366	372	453	454
Truth........	380	372	426	424	Volk.........	348	346	429	428
World.......	381	370	411	408	Welt.........	341	340	447	445
Year.........	393	384	415	412	Zahl.........	374	381	459	469
A............	389	388	405	404	....	372	374	439	438
AV..........	30	20	21	14	....	25	18	22	14

These results are interesting and were not foreseen. We found in the preceding section that it takes less time to perceive a colour than a letter or word; we now find that it takes comparatively a very long time (B 286, C 400σ) to find the name of the colour. This was especially the case at first and for certain colours. The colour was recognised with ease, but the name could only be found (more especially by C) with great difficulty. The colours most frequently seen and named in our daily life, red, yellow, green, blue and black, were named with greater ease and in decidedly less time (B 61, C 150σ) than the other five colours, pink, violet, orange, gray and brown. In the case of these latter colours the time was considerably shortened by practice.

The twenty-six pictures already described were in like manner seen and named (by B in German, by C in English), the times for the several pictures (13 determinations) being given in Table XXXIX.

TABLE XXXVIII

| | Second observer. 9.—30. I | | | | | | Sound-key. 5.—25. II | | | | | |
| | B | | | C | | | B | | | C | | |
	R	V	R'	R	V	R'	R	V	R'	R	V	R'
Blue.............	551	47	530	633	40	643	443	56	438	518	34	515
Green.............	535	59	539	663	25	658	433	36	440	539	29	532
Red.............	503	37	491	638	46	658	492	57	504	576	61	559
Black.............	641	82	618	589	34	583	473	41	464	515	54	505
Yellow.............	575	33	563	660	17	656	481	70	490	588	54	575
Pink.............	614	105	615	714	62	699	503	75	485	614	92	578
Violet.............	621	52	613	688	73	659	552	56	558	603	32	611
Gray.............	568	57	586	860	119	841	447	63	426	714	91	697
Brown.............	641	104	630	978	130	990	532	83	515	625	85	603
Orange.............	669	56	659	910	122	876	584	96	566	718	76	730
A.............	592	..	584	733	...	726	494	..	489	601	..	591
AV.............	...	63	39	...	67	42	...	63	42	...	61	38

We find in the foregoing section that pictures (and, we may assume, the objects themselves) can be seen in about the same time as colours; we now find that they can also be named in about the same time (by B in 251, by C in 278σ) as the colours most frequently used. The difference in time for the several pictures is interesting; both B and C named the picture of a hat in the shortest time; B required the longest time to name "bird" and "teapot," C to name "teapot" and "moon." It is an interesting fact that the picture of a chair can be recognised in less time than the word "chair," but that it takes over a tenth of a second longer to name it.

It will be useful to collect together certain of the results of these experiments. In the following Table I do not give to the thousandth

TABLE XXXIX

Picture of an	B		C			B		C	
	R	R'	R	R'		R	R'	R	R'
Anchor.....	489	463	552	535	Leaf........	497	497	578	567
Bird........	515	507	569	566	Moon.......	496	504	588	587
Bottle......	489	479	572	561	Picture.....	475	486	587	574
Candle......	493	494	563	552	Scissors.....	447	453	558	558
Chair.......	498	510	539	534	Ship	445	438	493	486
Cross.......	485	470	586	591	Shoe.......	437	430	492	493
Eye........	496	476	500	503	Star........	481	488	496	498
Fish........	462	454	497	487	Table.......	486	496	544	547
Flower......	495	479	568	586	Teapot.....	499	486	612	600
Glass.......	480	466	585	596	Tree.......	457	449	524	517
Hand.......	484	476	500	490	Umbrella...	466	472	567	556
Hat........	419	415	454	446	Watch......	461	462	567	562
Hatchet....	469	454	526	513					
Key........	477	467	561	560	A..........	477	472	545	541
					AV.........	46	30	40	25

14.—26. II

of a second the averages of the determinations made, but what from
the experiments seems to be the time it takes B and C to perceive
and find the name of the objects we have been considering.

TABLE XL

	B	C
Reaction-time for light.........................	150	150
Perception-time for light.......................	30	50
Perception-time for a colour....................	90	100
Perception-time for a picture...................	100	110
Perception-time for a letter....................	120	120
Perception-time for a (short) word..............	120	130
Will-time for colours...........................	280	400
Will-time for pictures..........................	250	280
Will-time for letters...........................	140	170
Will-time for words.............................	100	110

We have thus found the time it takes us to see and name the objects which we spend a great part of our life in seeing and naming.
We have not been dealing with artificial processes or things outside
the circle of our natural interests. If in the course of evolution, as is
probable, the molecular arrangement of the nervous system becomes
more sensitive and delicately balanced, we may suppose that the times
taken up by our mental processes become shorter, and we live so
much the longer in the same number of years. It will therefore be of

great interest to make experiments such as these on the lower races, as well as on persons of different age, sex, occupation, &c.

V. The Influence of Attention, Fatigue and Practice on the Duration of Cerebral Operations

This fifth portion of "The Time Taken up by Cerebral Operations" was first published under the title "Einflus der Aufmerksamkeit, Ermüdung und Uebung auf die Dauer psychischen Processe," in *Philosophische Studied*, **3**: 486–492, 1886.

The German version was the final section of the author's doctoral dissertation, published in 1886, under the title "Psychometrische Untersuchungen." It was rewritten by the author and printed as reproduced here with the title "The Influence of Attention, Fatigue and Practice on the Duration of Cerebral Operations," in *Mind*, **11**: 534–538, 1886.

We have seen that while the time of a reaction is somewhat lengthened when the brain cannot so well prepare itself, it does not vary greatly with different degrees of Attention. I have made similar determinations for cerebral operations in which complications have been

TABLE XLI

	Concentrated				Distracted			
	B		C		B		C	
	R	R'	R	R'	R	R'	R	R'
White surface								
4. IV.......	192	194	236	234	333	321	273	278
5..........	196	193	235	237	250	233	256	254
6..........	186	191	230	231	244	234	234	229
7..........	192	194	246	249	239	239	246	248
A..........	191	193	237	238	266	257	252	252
AV........	13	6	13	10	38	23	16	9
Letters								
4. IV.......	334	335	395	398	387	388	441	442
	336	333	397	402	371	366	403	411
5..........	335	337	404	410	373	377	432	435
6..........	333	336	395	397	343	350	422	418
7..........	331	333	410	408	340	339	427	426
A..........	334	335	400	403	363	364	425	426
AV........	29	20	21	13	33	20	26	16

added to the simple reaction-time. I chose as typical cases the time it takes to see a white surface and show this by a motion of the hand,

and the time it takes to see and name a letter. On the one hand the observer tried by great concentration of the attention and effort to react as quickly as possible; on the other hand the impression was produced at irregular intervals (three-fourths to fifteen seconds), so that the brain could not be held in a maximum state of readiness.

We find, from Table XLI, under the two degrees of attention or preparation a difference in the times of seeing and reacting on the white surface of 75σ for B, 15 for C; in the time of seeing and naming a letter 29σ for B, 25 for C.

As I have given throughout this paper the dates on which the series were made and have not omitted any series, the results of continued Practice can be studied to advantage. B and C had previously had considerable practice in making simple reactions, but none in the other processes here considered. In the twenty series of reactions on light (Table I) made during a period of six months, no reduction in the time is to be noticed. B's reaction-time was however shorter in 1884–5, as can be seen from Table VI, where his times, especially for light, are considerably longer than C's. I repeated at the close of the investigation the determinations made at the beginning in which the observer reacted on one of a number of colours, letters or words (the results are given in Tables XIX, XXIV, XXVII), and found that the times had become shorter. I give the decrease in time.

	B	C
Colours..................................	28	20
Letters...................................	50	25
Words....................................	54	35

As I have already mentioned, the time of naming the colours and pictures became shorter through practice. In some cases where the attention was distracted the brain accommodated itself to the changed conditions. It can be stated as a law that the times of cerebral operations become shorter as they become more automatic, but that a limit is reached beyond which further practice has little or no effect.

The investigation was concluded in April; in July, after an interval of three months during which no reactions were made, the times of the more important processes were again measured. The Table gives the results of five series of simple reactions on light and sound, of five series in which the observer showed by a motion of the hand that he had perceived a white surface, a letter and a colour, and of three series in which he perceived and named a letter, a word and a colour. The increase or decrease of the time is given in the column headed Df.

TABLE XLII

	B					C				
	R	V	Df	R'	V'	R	V	Df	R'	V'
Light..............	139	12	−10	140	8	167	13	+17	167	9
Sound.............	122	7	− 3	121	5	141	9	+16	139	6
White.............	212	12	+ 1	211	6	254	13	+13	254	8
Letter.............	305	22	+19	304	14	309	26	− 3	307	18
Colour............	258	22	− 1	256	17	289	24	− 4	284	15
Letter.............	354	25	−41	353	17	425	22	+ 1	428	14
Word.............	331	17	−58	330	12	410	20	+ 5	410	14
Colour............	402	33	−92	400	23	609	71	+ 8	600	50

We now come to the effects of Fatigue. These, like the effects of attention, have been greatly overestimated, experimenters having made but few reactions in a series or at a sitting, fearing lest the observer should become fatigued and the times unduly long. In order to determine the influence of fatigue in successive reactions, I took thirty series of simple reactions on light and averaged all the first reactions (as also the mean variation of these reactions) together, all the second reactions, and so on through the twenty-six reactions of which the series was made up. In the same way I took two hundred series where the subject had to react (with the hand) after distinguishing an impression, and averaged all the first, second, &c. reactions together. The impressions were different in the different series, but of course the

TABLE XLIII

	B		C			B		C			B		C	
	R	V	R	V		R	V	R	V		R	V	R	V
I.........	136	18	139	15	XIV......	147	9	151	10	I........	277	30	306	29
II........	146	14	155	13	XV........	147	9	151	8	II......	287	25	308	22
III.......	144	11	150	9	XVI......	149	12	148	8	III.....	294	25	308	23
IV.......	145	16	149	10	XVII.....	152	12	154	12	IV.....	298	22	316	28
V.........	143	9	149	10	XVIII.....	152	8	152	10	V.....	297	25	314	23
VI.......	142	13	149	13	XIX......	151	9	154	13	VI.....	300	25	317	22
VII.....	147	10	151	13	XX.......	148	10	151	12	VII.....	292	21	318	24
VIII.....	148	10	150	11	XXI......	150	13	146	9	VIII....	298	23	319	23
IX.......	155	13	149	7	XXII.....	152	12	150	10	IX.....	299	20	319	23
X........	145	9	151	9	XXIII.....	147	8	148	12	X......	297	23	322	24
XI.......	143	13	147	9	XXIV....	152	13	144	10	XI.....	297	23	319	22
XII......	154	14	147	13	XXV......	150	13	144	11	XII....	293	20	322	23
XIII.....	153	16	152	11	XXVI....	150	15	150	10	XIII....	295	22	317	23
A........	...	..	...	..	....	148	12	149	11	....	294	23	316	24

same throughout each series. In these series only thirteen determinations were made, but twenty-six mental processes took place, it being as fatiguing to see that the object was not there and keep from reacting, as to distinguish the object and react.

It will be seen that, though the difference is not great, the first reactions of a series are the shortest. It seems that in the first experiments the observer involuntarily strains his attention more, and so gives shorter times. This is the more marked the less automatic the process is; that is, with the white light than in the simple reaction, and in the case of B than in the case of C. The further course of the series shows no lengthening in the times or increase in the mean variation; so the brain is not considerably fatigued by making (or refraining from making) twenty-six reactions in succession.

In order further to investigate the effects of fatigue, I made extended series of experiments in which 1950 reactions were made in succession, the observer reacting almost continuously from early in the morning until late into the night. Three series (78 reactions) were made with light, then three series (39 determinations, but 78 mental processes) in which white light was distinguished, and reacted on, then

TABLE XLIV

	Light		White surface		Letters		Assoc.		Sound	
						B				
31. III. 7.30 a.m..........	157	12	198	21	344	25	733	103	139	9
9.40 a.m..........	−1	−1	−1	−4	+10	+2	−98	−17	−3	−1
1 p.m..........	−14	−2	+9	−4	−7	+9	−59	−11	+11	+10
2.50 p. m..........	−10	−3	+9	+4	+4	+1	−2	−8	−7	−2
6.55 p.m..........	+1	−2	+34	−3	+12	+6	−81	−39	+3	+2
8.50 p.m..........	+5	+1	+20	−2	+37	+5	−228	+121	+10	+1
1. IV. 8.30 a.m..........	+17	−2	−10	+1	+21	+9	+83	+2	−16	−2
8 p.m..........	+7	+3	+2	−5	+ 1	+10	+153	+68	−2	+5
						C				
26. III. 7.30 a.m..........	156	10	247	12	439	23	827	125	144	13
10.55 a.m..........	+10	+3	−17	+4	−8	−4	+9	+8	+2	−3
2.40 p.m..........	+28	+5	+1	+9	+9	0	+12	+43	+15	+1
7.20 p.m..........	+19	+1	−10	+7	+19	−3	+58	+5	+15	+3
9 20 p.m..........	+33	+7	+6	+9	+37	+3	+163	+23	+19	−4
11.40 p.m..........	+34	+8	+2	+4	+30	0	+111	+10	+11	0
27. III. 8-30 a.m..........	+27	+1	+6	+7	−3	+5	+19	+7	wanting	
8 p.m..........	+20	+5	−2	+2	+11	−3	−12	−41	+23	−2
28. 8.30 a.m..........	+25	+12	−1	+5	−5	−3	42	+44	−6	−1

three series in which letters were seen and named, then two series in which associations were made, lastly three series of reactions on sound. This entire combination of series was repeated six times. The experiments were begun both days at 7.30 a.m. and were concluded in the case of *C* at 1.30 a.m., in the case of *B* at 11 p.m., short pauses being made for meals. One series of each variety was made the following morning and again in the evening; in the case of *C* a further set of series the day after. In the Table I give the average time and mean variation of the first set of series, afterwards the increase or decrease as compared with these. I do not take up space to give the corrected series, as they scarcely differ from the others.

The first result to be noted from the Table is the very slight effects of fatigue; in no case is the time lengthened more than a couple of hundredths of a second, and the mean variation is but little increased. We reach the unexpected result that the processes which are the most automatic (naming the letters, and *C*'s simple reaction-time) are the most affected by fatigue. The determinations made on the following day show that *B* had recovered from all fatigue; in the case of *C*, however, the brain substance concerned in the simple reaction seems to have been so far exhausted that his reaction-time remained abnormally long for two days.

I think these experiments show that it is possible to apply scientific methods to the investigation of mind. We have determined the times required for those processes which make up a great part of our mental life, and found these times to be constant; they are no more arbitrary, no less dependent on fixed laws than, for example, the velocity of light. I shall soon print an account of experiments going a step farther and determining the times of mental processes more removed from psychophysical operations having to do with sensation and motion.

4

EXPERIMENTS ON THE ASSOCIATION OF IDEAS

This sixth portion of "The Time Taken up by Cerebral Operations" was first published under the title: "Die Association unter willkürlich begrenzten Bedingungen," in *Philosophische Studien*, **4**: 241–250, 1888. It was not included as a part of his doctoral dissertation.

An English version of this study printed in *Mind*, **12**: 68–74, 1887, with the title "Experiments on the Association of Ideas" is reproduced here.

The Association of Ideas has been a favourite subject with psychologists from Aristotle on, yet the results have not been very definite from the scientific point of view. An important paper by Mr. Galton[1] first applied experimental methods to the subject, and put it in a way where scientific advance was possible. Professor Wundt at once saw the importance of this work, and took it up in his laboratory with improved apparatus and methods.[2] Nothing further has, however, been published on the subject, which is a pity, as experimental psychology seems to have its most hopeful outlook in this direction.

Experiments I described in a paper contributed to MIND, Nos. 42–4, on "The Time taken up by Cerebral Operations," showed that about $\frac{2}{5}$ sec. was needed to see and name a word. When the physiological factors and the time taken up in seeing the word were eliminated, it was found that about $\frac{1}{10}$ sec. was spent in finding the name belonging to the printed symbol. The time was longer for letters, which we do not read as often as words and still longer (about $\frac{1}{4}$ sec.) for colours and pictures. I called the time passing, while the motor expression was being found, a "Will-time." The process is, however, largely automatic, and consists in carrying out an association previously formed between the concept and the expression. There is no break between such a process and the other processes I am about to describe.

I

If an object is named in a foreign instead of in one's native language, the association between concept and expression is less intimate and takes up more time. It is an open question as to how far concepts are formed without the aid of words, and it is not evident what mental

---

[1] *Brain*, 1879; cp. MIND, iv. 551.

[2] *Physiologische Psychologie*, c. xvi; *Philosophische Studien*, i. 1.

process takes place when an object is named in a foreign language, it depending, of course, on the familiarity of the language. It need scarcely be said that we know almost nothing as to the physical basis of memory and thought; we may hope that psychometric experiments, such as I am about to describe, will contribute something toward the study of this subject. In the paper above mentioned I showed how we can determine the time it takes to see and name the picture of an object; in like manner the time we need to name the picture in a foreign language can be measured. I must refer the reader to that paper for a detailed account of apparatus and methods. .001 sec. is taken as the unit of time, σ being used as its symbol. B (Dr. G. O. Berger) and C (the writer) are the two subjects; after these designations there is given the average time taken in all the experiments made, and the mean variation of these measurements from the average; after this is given a second average and mean variation, found by dropping the most irregular times in accordance with the method I have described.[1] The number of experiments made on each subject is given in parenthesis. The experiments were made at Leipsic during the first half of the year 1885.

I give first the time it took the subjects to recognise the pictures of twenty-six familiar objects, and name them in a foreign language— B in English, C in German.

PICTURES NAMED IN FOREIGN LANGUAGE (78)

B	649	104	632	49	C	694	87	682	43

It has been shown[2] that B took 477, C 545σ to see and name these same pictures in their native languages. B consequently needed 172, C 149σ in addition to find the name in a foreign language. C talks German readily, B English less so. These should be compared with other experiments I have made showing that the rate at which a person can read a foreign language is proportional to his familiarity with the language.[3]

We go a step further when a word must be translated from one language into another. The mental operation is again obscure, the processes of translating and naming not being sharply defined; but if

[1] MIND, xi. 229. It will be noticed that the corrected averages are usually smaller than the averages from all the determinations; this is because the subject found difficulty in a few cases. The uncorrected value gives the average time taken up by associations; the corrected average more nearly the time usually taken up by associations.

[2] MIND, xi. 533.

[3] Phil. Studien, ii.635; Abstract in MIND, xi. 63. I hope shortly to print an account of experiments showing the increasing rapidity with which the classes of a German gymnasium can read Latin.

we subtract the time it takes to see and name a word from the time
it takes to see a word, to translate it into a foreign language and name
it, we get approximately the time of translation. This time I give for
translating from a foreign into the native language, and in the reverse
direction. I have subtracted the time it takes the subjects to see and
name words (B 390, C 428σ), and the mean variation (B 28, C 20; in
the corrected series, B 19, C 13σ).

ENGLISH-GERMAN: SHORT (COMMON) WORDS (78)

B	240	77	199	36	C	258	59	237	29

ENGLISH-GERMAN: LONG (LESS FAMILIAR) WORDS (78)

331	96	309	67	388	101	367	62

GERMAN-ENGLISH: SHORT WORDS (78)

303	148	237	53	152	17	153	13

GERMAN-ENGLISH: LONG WORDS (78)

593	281	573	116	411	85	389	55

These numbers show that foreign languages take up much time
even after they have been learned, and may lead us once more to
weigh the gain and loss of a polyglot mental life.

II

A great part of our time is spent in calling to mind things we already know. Memory is no transcendental process outside of space
and time; this paper shows just how much time it takes to remember,
and we have every reason to believe that the time passes while certain changes in the brain call forth other changes. I give below the
time it took B and C to remember certain facts, examples of the necessary associations with which the mind is continually busy. A well-
known city was given, and the subject named the country in which it
is situated; a month was given, and the season to which it belongs
was named, and in like manner the preceding or following month; an
eminent author was given, and the subject named the language in
which he wrote; a distinguished man, and his calling was named. In
the last two cases below, the subject respectively added and multiplied numbers of one place. At first sight this mental operation may
seem to consist of a mathematical calculation, and to be altogether
different from the others; it is however not unlike them, being essentially an act of memory.

CITY-COUNTRY (52)

B	348	53	333	35	C	462	120	413	65

MONTH-SEASON (26)

415	55	410	31	310	63	306	16

MONTH-FOLLOWING MONTH (26)

345	45	327	25	389	172	384	61

MONTH-PRECEDING MONTH (26)

763	245	619	129	832	233	815	160

AUTHOR-LANGUAGE (78)

417	80	402	53	350	57	337	32

MAN-CALLING (78)

465	89	440	62	368	95	326	53

ADDITION (52)

221	46	223	23	336	77	299	36

MULTIPLICATION (52)

389	71	369	38	544	225	507	158

The mental processes considered above are by no means invented for the sake of experiment, but are such as make up a considerable part of life. We see that it took the subjects $\frac{2}{5}$ to $\frac{4}{5}$ sec. to call to mind facts with which they were familiar. The times needed in the different cases are of interest. The time of addition was the shortest of all; B needed 168, C 208σ longer to multiply than to add; it took twice as long to call to mind the foregoing as the following month. It will be noticed that the times of the two subjects correspond closely (the average time in the eight examples given is 420σ for B, 436 for C); the differences of time in the several cases are explained by the character and pursuits of the subjects, and in turn throw light back upon these. For example, B is a teacher of mathematics, C has busied himself more with literature; C knows quite as well as B that $5 + 7 = 12$, yet he needs $\frac{1}{10}$ sec. longer to call it to mind; B knows quite as well as C that Dante was a poet, but needs $\frac{1}{10}$ sec. longer to think of it. Such experiments lay bare the mental life in a way that is startling and not always gratifying.

The numbers given are the averages from many measurements; the mean variation shows how greatly the separate determinations vary from the average. This variation is partly owing to changing conditions of the brain, so that the same process never takes exactly the same time; it is, however, largely due to the fact that the mental operations under the same class are not equally simple, and consequently require different times. Just as it takes less time to add 2 to 3 than to multiply 2 by 3, so it takes less time to add 2 to 3 than to add 6 to 7. Owing to the normal variation in the time of the same mental process, we should not place too much reliance on a small number of measurements; it will, however, be worth our while to notice a few examples. In giving the country in which the city is situated, as average of three trials, both B and C took the shortest

time for Paris (212, 278σ), and the longest time for Geneva (403, 485σ).
In giving the language in which an author wrote, as average of the
three trials, *B* took the shortest time for Luther (227) and Goethe
(265), and the longest for Aristotle (591) and Bacon (565); *C* took
the shortest time for Plato (224) and Shakespeare (258), the longest
for Chaucer (503) and Plautus (478). In the case of Luther *B* took
244, in the case of Goethe 102σ less time than *C*; in the case of Shakespeare *C* took 186σ less time than *B*. It should be borne in mind that
B is a German, *C* an American. In giving the calling of eminent men
the order was as follows, the shortest times being placed first:—*B*—
Poet (355), Warrior, Historian, Philosopher, Artist, Reformer, Man
of Science (657); *C*—Poet (291), Artist, Historian, Warrior, Philosopher, Reformer, Man of Science (421). With both subjects Poet comes
first and Man of Science last. It is easier to think of Homer as a poet
than of Darwin as a man of science.

III

In the experiments so far considered a question was asked which
admitted but one answer: the association was necessary, and the
interval passing while it was being formed might be called a "Recollection-time." A question can, however, be so arranged that beside
the act of recollection a certain choice as to the answer must be made,
and in this case a little more time is needed. Below is given the inverse
of several of the cases we have considered; a country being given,
some city situated in it had to be named, &c. The last line gives the
time needed to think of a work by a given author.

COUNTRY-CITY (26)

| *B* | 400 | 72 | 357 | 45 | *C* | 346 | 75 | 340 | 48 |

SEASON-MONTH (26)

| | 561 | 92 | 548 | 36 | | 435 | 99 | 399 | 54 |

LANGUAGE-AUTHOR (78)

| | 663 | 200 | 702 | 110 | | 519 | 137 | 523 | 83 |

AUTHOR-WORK (26)

| | 1076 | 397 | 1095 | 287 | | 763 | 308 | 596 | 127 |

It will be seen that it took no longer to name a city when the
country was given than the reverse; in this case there was but little
choice, as there is in each country one particular city which was named
almost as a matter of course. It took, however, considerably longer to
name a month when the season was given and an author when a
language was given than the reverse. A choice had in the former case
to be made, and further, as Steinthal has before remarked,[1] the mind

[1] *Einleitung in die Psychologie und Sprachwissenschaft*, p. 161.

moves more readily from the part to the whole than from the whole to the part. It will be noticed that the naming a work by a given author is one of the most difficult associations considered in this paper. As to the time taken up by the separate associations, I must again call attention to the fact that it is laigely deteimined by accidental variation. This variation could only be eliminated by making a large number of experiments, and in this case we should no longer have the time taken up by associations in our daily life, but the minimum recollection-time, which would tend to become the same for different classes of associations as they became equally familiar. In naming a city, C needed the longest time for Brussels (1042) and Pekin (1001); the shortest time for Athens (214) and Philadelphia (222), his home. In naming an author, less time was needed for English, German and Italian, where Shakespeare, Goethe and Dante at once occurred, than in the three other languages used, French, Latin and Greek. In naming a work by a given author C needed the longest time for Chaucer (*Canterbury Tales* 1898), Aristotle (*Logic* [*sic*] 1522), and Bacon (*Novum Organum* 1388); the shortest time for Milton (*Paradise Lost* 328), Dante (*Inferno* 373), and Goethe (*Faust* 393).

IV

We now come to consider certain classes of associations in which the mind is allowed a larger degree of liberty. The times required in eight such cases are given. A noun representing a class of objects was given and a particular example was named (river-Rhine); a picture of an object was shown, and instead of naming the entire picture the subject was required to select some part of the object and name it (picture of a ship-sail); a concrete noun was in the same way given and a part of the object was named: both the pictures and names of objects were shown, and the subject said what the thing is used for or what it does (horse-ride or trot); a substantive had to be found for an adjective (blue-sky,) a subject for an intransitive (swim-fish) and an object for a transitive verb (write-letter).

THING-EXAMPLE (52)

B 727	216	663	102	C 537	179	457	95

PICTURE-PART OF OBJECT (52)

399	96	368	40	447	162	415	69

SUBSTANTIVE-PART OF OBJECT (26)

578	128	568	85	439	135	404	82

PICTURE-PROPERTY (52)

358	105	325	49	372	121	370	78

SUBSTANTIVE-PROPERTY (26)

| 436 | 157 | 390 | 109 | 337 | 100 | 291 | 69 |

ADJECTIVE-SUBSTANTIVE (26)

| 879 | 278 | 823 | 186 | 351 | 86 | 307 | 41 |

VERB-SUBJECT (26)

| 765 | 366 | 584 | 166 | 527 | 171 | 497 | 107 |

VERB-OBJECT (26)

| 654 | 242 | 561 | 139 | 379 | 122 | 317 | 86 |

The times given need no long comment. The most difficult associations seem to be the finding of a special example when the class is given, and the subject for a verb; in both of these cases the times needed were irregular, as is shown by the large mean variation. B took 111, C 146σ longer to find a subject than to find an object for a verb, the mind moving logically in the latter direction. In identifying a particular object the mind was inclined to choose either one immediately at hand or to go back to the home of childhood. Thus out of the 52 cases B thought of an object in the room 8, C 20 times;[1] of objects identified with the early home B 22, C 19 times. In the other cases this was mostly impossible, but also here either a very recent or an early association was formed in all except 6 out of the 104 cases.

V

We have lastly to consider the time it takes to form a judgment or opinion. I choose three cases in which the results could conveniently be averaged. In the first case the subject estimated the length of a line drawn horizontally on a card 10 cm. long, 50 lines being used varying in length from 1 to 50 mm. In the second case the subject estimated the number of short perpendicular lines on a card,[2] the number varying between 4 and 15. In the third case the names of two eminent men were shown, and the subject decided which of them he thought to be the greater.

LENGTH OF LINE (150)

| B | 1124 | 242 | 1127 | 154 | C | 664 | 124 | 664 | 88 |

NUMBER OF LINES (26)

| | 183 | 57 | 180 | 35 | | 319 | 74 | 313 | 45 |

EMINENT MEN (104)

| | 667 | 143 | 604 | 80 | | 558 | 171 | 522 | 112 |

I made rather a large number of determinations with the lines, as

---

[1] The experiments were made in C's room.

[2] For experiments on the Limits of Consciousness see Cattell, *Phil. Student,* iii. 94.

I wished to find the ratio between the length of the line and the average error (psychophysical law), and between the error and the time taken up in coming to a decision. I think it however desirable to still further increase the number of experiments before publishing the results. In judging as to the relative greatness of eminent men, as might be foreseen, the times were shortest where the judgment was easiest, more especially if the subject had already compared the men together (Homer, Virgil). The nature of the judgments is not without interest, but can better be considered when I come to print similar experiments which I have made on a larger number of subjects.

The associations we have been considering in this paper are in their nature fixed or limited, and we have concerned ourselves chiefly with the time taken up. The conditions of the experiment can however be so arranged that one idea is allowed to suggest another somewhat as in our ordinary thinking. I shall shortly have ready experiments in this direction in which both the time and the nature of the association will be considered.

5

THE INFLUENCE OF THE INTENSITY OF THE STIMULUS ON THE LENGTH OF THE REACTION TIME

Prepared while he was Assistant in the Psychological Laboratory at the University of Leipzig. Printed in *Brain*, **9**: 512–515, 1886.

During the past two years, Dr. G. O. Berger and I have been carrying on a series of experiments in the Psychological Laboratory of the University of Leipsic, looking to determine the relation between the intensity of the stimulus and the length of the reaction time. Wundt, Exner, and others had already made experiments on this subject, but it seemed to need a more thorough investigation.[1] We undertook to determine the influence of various intensities of the electric shock, and of light on the length of the simple reaction time, and on the reaction time complicated by the addition of simple cerebral operations.

The term "reaction time" is now generally understood. If one lifts one's hand as soon as possible after the sudden appearance of a light, the interval between the application of the stimulus and the beginning of the muscular contraction is a reaction time. In order to investigate the influence of various intensities of light on the length of this time, we used a light produced in a Geissler's tube by an induction current from six Daniell cells. This light we took as normal, and kept constant. We then arranged five weaker intensities by putting smoked glass before the light. The amount of light transmitted through the smoked glass we determined photometrically. If we set the intensity of the normal light VI = 1000, then the intensities of the lights would be

I	II	III	IV	V	VI
1	7	23	123	315	1000

We further obtained two still brighter lights (vii and viii) by means of lenses, but could not determine with our photometer the relation

[1] Wundt, "Physiologische Psychologie," 2. xvi.; Exner, "Hermann's Physiologie," 2. 2. iv.; Kries u. Auerbach, "Archiv f. Anat. u. Physiol.," 1877; Vintschgau u. Hönigschmied, "Pflüger's Archiv," xii.; Wittisch, "Zeitschr. f. Rat. Med.," xxxi.

of these to the normal intensity. The observer sat in the dark, and looked through a telescopic tube at the point where the light was to appear. The following table gives the average of 150 reactions made by each of us with the several intensities. No reactions at all were omitted in taking the average. The second line, marked M, gives the average of the variation of each from the average of all the reactions; that is, if A is the average of n reactions a, b, c, d, then

$$M = \frac{(A - a) + (A - b) + (A - c) \cdots}{n}$$

all the differences being taken as positive. M shows us how much the reactions differ from one another, and when we know the number of reactions, we can find the probable error of the average. In the table .001 s. is taken as the unit of time.[1]

TABLE I

					B				
Intensity	I	II	III	IV	V	VI	VII	VIII	Average
Time.......	308	235	208	200	192	195	177	168	210
M..........	26	18	16	15	15	17	18	16	18
					C				
Time.......	251	175	160	148	147	143	135	128	161
M..........	30	17	16	14	15	13	16	19	18

It will be seen from the table that when the light is taken very weak, just strong enough to be seen, the times are the longest and (with one accidental exception, B between V and VI) the greater the intensity of the light, the shorter the time of the reaction. I cannot, however, formulate a general law from the table.

In substantially the same manner the relation between the strength of an electric shock and the length of the reaction time was determined. The shock was received on the left forearm, and the reaction made with the right hand. We used four intensities; the strongest, IV,

[1] It should be mentioned that in our first experiments the absolute time is not certain. The times were measured with aid of an electro-magnet, and we assumed that when a current was sent through the coil, the armature was attracted instantaneously. This is not the case, and I have made an allowance for the error, but the times may be as much as .01 s. wrong. At all events the relative times are correct, as the error was constant.

somewhat painful, the weakest, I, just enough to be felt. The two intermediate intensities made up, as far as we could judge, four equal steps. The averages of 150 reactions by each observer and on each intensity are given in the table.

TABLE II

Intensity	I	II	III	IV	Average
B					
Time............................	182	163	158	160	166
M............................	17	14	12	11	13
C					
Time............................	164	155	132	131	145
M............................	19	18	14	14	16

It will be noticed that with the electric shock, as with light, the time of the reaction becomes shorter as the stimulus becomes stronger. The differences are not, however, so great, and for the intensities III and IV, the times are about the same; with IV the reaction was probably retarded, because the shock was painful.

In connection with the experiments on the intensity of the light, we made others to determine whether or not the quality of the stimulus, that is, the colour of the light, has any influence on the length of the reaction time. The averages of 180 reactions made by each of the observers, and on each of the six colours used, are given in the table.

TABLE III

	White	Red	Yellow	Green	Blue	Violet	Average
B..........	196	203	192	199	199	201	198
C..........	155	162	160	156	161	153	158

The table does not show any decided difference in the times for the several colours. Violet and green, which I have found (see last number of "BRAIN") must work longer on the retina than the other colours, in order that a sensation may be called forth, do not seem to cause a longer reaction time; this is because the reaction is made on the light, without waiting until the colour has been distinguished.

The time is longer when it is necessary to distinguish the colours before the reaction is made. We can determine this time, if instead of always reacting as quickly as possible we use two lights of different colours, say blue and red, and let the subject react only on one of them. The subject does not know which light is to come, but is to lift his hand as quickly as possible if it is red, but not at all if it is blue. We thus add to the simple reaction the time it takes to see whether the light is blue or red, and complicate somewhat the process of volition in the simple reaction time. We can further let the subject lift his right hand if the light is red, his left hand if it is blue; we then have, besides the time necessary for the simple reaction and for distinguishing the colour, the time it takes to make a choice between two motions. The results of experiments made with three intensities of light (V, III, and I) are given in the table.

TABLE IV

	B			C		
	V	III	I	V	III	I
Reaction time..........................	189	218	273	189	209	303
Reaction with Perception time............	238	293	373	274	328	417
Reaction with Perception and Will time....	287	320	393	356	388	495
Perception time.........................	49	75	100	85	119	114
Will time...............................	49	27	20	82	60	78

It seems from the table that the time it takes to see or perceive a colour becomes shorter as the intensity of the light becomes stronger, but that the will time is not a function of the intensity of the stimulus.

6

THE TIME IT TAKES TO SEE AND NAME OBJECTS

This research was originally published in greater detail as: "Ueber die Zeit der Erkennung und Benennung von Schriftzeichen, Bildern und Farben" in *Philosophische Studien*, **2**: 635–650. Printed in its present form in *Mind*, **11**: 63–65, 1886.

The relation of the sensation to the stimulus and the time taken up by mental processes are the two subjects in which the best results have been reached by experimental psychology. These results are important enough to prove those to be wrong who with Kant hold that psychology can never become an exact science. It would perhaps be convenient to call the work done by Weber, Fechner and their followers in determining the relation of the sensation to the stimulus Psychophysics, and to confine the term Psychometry to the work done by Wundt and others in measuring the rapidity of mental processes. Psychometry seems to be of as great psychological interest as Psychophysics, but it has not been nearly so fully and carefully worked over. This is partly due to the difficulties which lie in the way of determining the time taken up by mental processes. Such a time cannot be directly measured; the experimenter can only determine the period passing between an external event exciting mental processes and a motion made after the mental processes have been completed. It is difficult or impossible to analyse this period, to give the time required for the purely physiological operations, and to decide what mental processes have taken place, and how much time is to be allotted to each. Experimenters have also met with two other difficulties. The physical apparatus used seldom produces the stimulus in a satisfactory manner or measures the times with entire accuracy, and must be so delicate and complicated that it requires the greatest care to operate with it and keep it in order. The other difficulty lies in the fact that the times measured are artificial, not corresponding to the times taken up by mental processes in our ordinary life. The conditions of the experiments place the subject in an abnormal condition, especially as to fatigue, attention and practice, and the method has often been such that the times given are too short, because the entire mental process has not been measured, or too long, because some other factor has been included in the time recorded. Considering therefore the difficulty of analysing the period measured, the inaccuracies of the recording apparatus, and the artificial and often incorrect methods of making the experiments, we have reason to fear that the results obtained by the psychologist in his laboratory do not always give the time it takes a man to perceive, to will and to think. Wundt has done much toward obviating these difficulties, carefully analysing the various operations, and improving the apparatus and methods. It has seemed to me, however, worth the while to make a series of experiments altogether doing away with involved methods and complicated apparatus, and looking to determine the time we usually require to see and name an object, such as a letter or a colour.

(1) I pasted letters on a revolving drum (a physiological kymograph) and determined at what rate they could be read aloud, as they passed by a slit in a screen. It was found that the time varied with the width of the slit. When the slit was 1 cm. wide (the letters being 1 cm. apart) one letter was always in view; as the first disappeared the second took its place, &c. In this case it took the nine persons experimented on (university teachers and students) from $\frac{1}{3}$ to $\frac{1}{5}$ sec. to read each letter. This does not however give the entire time needed to see and name a single letter, for the subject was finding the name of the letter just gone by at the same time that he was seeing the letter then in view. As the slit in the screen is made smaller the processes of perceiving and choosing cannot so well take place simultaneously, and the times become longer; when the slit is 1 mm. wide the time is $\frac{1}{2}$ sec., which other experiments I have made prove to be about the time it takes to see and name a single letter. When the slit on the contrary is taken wider than 1 cm., and two or more letters are always in view, not only do the processes of seeing and naming overlap, but while the subject is seeing one letter, he begins to see the ones next following, and so can read them more quickly. Of the nine persons experimented on four could read the letters faster when five were in view at once, but were not helped by a sixth letter; three were not helped by a fifth and two by a fourth letter. This shows that while one idea is in the centre, two, three or four additional ideas may be in the background of consciousness. The second letter in view shortens the time about $\frac{1}{40}$, the third $\frac{1}{60}$, the fourth $\frac{1}{100}$, the fifth $\frac{1}{200}$ sec.

(2) I find it takes about twice as long to read (aloud, as fast as possible) words which have no connexion as words which make sentences, and letters which have no connexion as letters which make words. When the words make sentences and the letters words, not only do the processes of seeing and naming overlap, but by one mental effort the subject can recognise a whole group of words or letters, and by one will-act choose the motions to be made in naming them, so that the rate at which the words and letters are read is really only

limited by the maximum rapidity at which the speech-organs can be moved. As the result of a large number of experiments the writer found that he had read words not making sentences at the rate of $\frac{1}{4}$ sec., words making sentences (a passage from Swift) at the rate of $\frac{1}{8}$ sec. per word. Letters not making words were read in $\frac{1}{40}$ sec. less time than words not making sentences; capital and small letters were read at the same rate, small German letters slightly and capital German letters considerably more slowly than the Latin letters. The experiments were repeated on eleven other subjects, confirming these results; the time required to read each word when the words did not make sentences varying between $\frac{1}{4}$ and $\frac{1}{2}$ sec. When a passage is read aloud at a normal rate, about the same time is taken for each word as when words having no connexion are read as fast as possible. The rate at which a person reads a foreign language is proportional to his familiarity with the language. For example, when reading as fast as possible the writer's rate was, English 138, French 167, German 250, Italian 327, Latin 434 and Greek 484; the figures giving the thousandths of a second taken to read each word. Experiments made on others strikingly confirm these results. The subject does not know that he is reading the foreign language more slowly than his own; this explains why foreigners seem to talk so fast. This simple method of determining a person's familiarity with a language might be used in school-examinations.

(3) The time required to see and name colours and pictures of objects was determined in the same way. The time was found to be about the same (over $\frac{1}{2}$ sec.) for colours as for pictures, and about twice as long as for words and letters. Other experiments I have made show that we can recognise a single colour or picture in a slightly shorter time than a word or letter, but take longer to name it. This is because in the case of words and letters the association between the idea and name has taken place so often that the process has become automatic, whereas in the case of colours and pictures we must by a voluntary effort choose the name. Such experiments would be useful in investigating aphasia.

7

MENTAL ASSOCIATION INVESTIGATED BY EXPERIMENT

The experiment reported here was published with the collaboration of Sophie Bryant, while Cattell was Professor of Psychology at the University of Pennsylvania. The large number of subjects that participated were tested in England, Ireland, Germany and the United States. Among them was G. F. Stout, the British psychologist whose critical comments are appended at the end of the article. The report was published in *Mind*, **14**: 230–250, 1889.

Mental Association has always interested students of psychology. The importance of studying the train of ideas is everywhere admitted, and by the English school association has been put forward as an explanation of mental phenomena. We may, therefore, be glad that it has recently been found possible to investigate the subject by scientific experiment. During the past ten years such research has been undertaken both in England and in Germany,[1] and of this our present work is a continuation.

1. Methods of Experiment

Most of our experiments were made in a way so simple that they may be repeated by anyone. A spoken or printed word was given to an observer (or "subject") who was required to say or write as quickly as possible what it suggested. The experiment thus began with the perceiving and ended with the expressing of a word. The intervening mental process is an association, the name being here taken in a wide signification. We used 20 nouns (given in Table V) with about 500 observers, and 250 or more words with 6 observers. We thus have a large mass of material which we shall consider in regard to (1) the time taken up in the process and (2) the nature of the association.

The time it takes for one idea to suggest another is of scientific and practical interest. It was also of advantage in a first series of experiments to get the observer to give the associated idea as quickly as possible in order to obtain uniformity. Three methods were used to measure the times. (*a*) In the first series of experiments, made by

---

[1] Galton, *Inquiries into Human Faculty*, 182 ff., and *Brain*, 1879, 149 ff.; cp. MIND iv. 551. Wundt, *Physiologische Psychologie*, 3rd ed., 312 ff., 364 ff. Trautscholdt, *Philosophische Studien*, i. 213 ff. Kraepelin, *Tageblatt der Naturforscherversammlung zu Strassburg*, 1885. Cattell, MIND xii. 68 ff.; *Phil. Stud.*, iv. 241 ff. For an account of theories concerning the "Association of Ideas," with references, see Croom Robertson in *Encyc. Britannica*, 9th ed., ii. **730** ff.

C at Leipsic (1885) with the help of Dr. Berger, apparatus[1] was employed which made it possible to measure to the thousandth of a second the time of each association. Such elaborate methods could not, however, be conveniently used with a large number of persons, nor was it necessary to measure so exactly the time. (*b*) We therefore (1885–8) prepared lists containing 10 words, and the observer seeing the words in order said what each of them suggested, the total time for the 10 processes being taken. The average time of association could thus be obtained with sufficient accuracy, but not the time for the separate processes. We were able, however, to get the times for different classes of associations by using lists made up of concrete nouns, abstract nouns, verbs, &c. (*c*) In a third series of experiments, made mostly by *B* (1887–8), a method was used that admitted of a number of persons being tested simultaneously. A word was distinctly spoken, and the observers were required to write in the order suggested as many words as they could until they were stopped after 20 secs. In this case the number of ideas suggested was complicated by the need of writing them down, but the results seem to show that the number of ideas was limited, not by the rate of writing, but by the rate of thought.

While three different methods were used to measure the times, the process of association in the several sets only differed in so far as in the first two sets the starting-word was read and the suggested word spoken, whereas in the third set the former was heard and the latter written. In this third series of experiments we have the train of ideas for 20 secs., and this is in some ways more interesting than the first idea suggested. This latter, however, presents the simpler problem, and gives as much material as can be conveniently considered in the present paper. We may at some future time have experiments on the train of ideas, and we hope that others will also undertake research in this direction.

2. The Time Taken Up in Mental Association

The times we obtained in our experiments do not give merely the duration of the process of association, but include the time required to perceive the original words, and to say or write the suggested ideas. The time, if any, taken up with intermediate ideas which are not expressed in definite words must be considered as part of the association-time. In the cases where the duration of a series of processes was measured, it is not possible to eliminate with any exactness the perception-and movement-times. This is due to the overlapping of the processes; an association may be going on while the foregoing idea is

[1] For description, see Cattell, MIND xi. 220 ff.

being expressed or the following word is being perceived. Experiments, however, show[1] that it takes on the average about ½ sec. to see and name a word; so if this interval be subtracted from the whole time we get approximately the duration of the association. In comparing the time required by different persons and classes of persons the whole interval may be used, the perception-and-movement-time being short as compared with the association-time, and in a general way proportionate to it.

(a) In the first series of experiments, it was possible to eliminate the perception-and-movement-time, and thus to determine with great accuracy the association-time. This is given in thousandths of a second in the following Table. There is also given after the average time the mean variation of the different measurements. 52 words of each class were used, German for Dr. Berger, English for *C*.

TABLE I.—TIME OF ASSOCIATION

	Concrete nouns	Less concrete[1]	Abstract nouns	Verbs
Bg....................	361 (73)	540 (168)	638 (188)	538 (184)
C.....................	380 (108)	384 (108)	508 (171)	465 (144)

[1] The nouns were divided into three classes: *author* and *hour* are not as concrete as *book* and *clock*

The time of association was thus in the neighbourhood of ½ sec. It will be noticed that the time was longer (*Bg* 272, *C* 128σ) when the given noun was abstract than when it was concrete. This is an interesting fact supported by all our experiments. The time of association with verbs was between that for concrete and abstract nouns. According to this method, in all, 832 associations were made by *C* about half of them on new words, the other half on words which had already been used. The average time of association was 475σ, a little less than ½ sec. The mean variation of the different associations from the series in which they were made was 134σ, nearly ⅟₇ sec. If difficult and unusual associations are omitted by dropping the 6 most irregular times from each series of 26, the average time becomes 431σ, the mean variation 69σ. Thus the usual time required by *C* to form an association such as we are here considering is somewhat less than ½ sec., and does not vary greatly from time to time. The longest associations were *deliverance-hope* (1453), *cut-knife* (1085), and *civilization-wilderness* (1064); the quickest *good-bad* (111), *father-mother* (132), and *life-death* (143). With these latter it will be noticed that the relation between the two ideas is so close that the association follows almost as a matter of course.

[1] Cattell, MIND xi 63 ff.; 530 ff.

(*b*) In our second series of experiments associations were made by *B* and *C* on 500 words. Of these words 250 were concrete nouns, 100 abstract nouns, 50 proper nouns, 50 verbs, and 50 adjectives. Associations with the concrete and abstract nouns were also made by Mr. Stout, and with the concrete nouns by Mr. Edgeworth and Miss Hughes. We further selected 10 abstract and 10 concrete nouns (given in Table V), and used these with 17 university graduates (men). With these, also, Miss Dudley tested 25 students of an American women's college (Bryn Mawr), and Dr. Berger 40 students of a German gymnasium. In these cases a list of ten words was first used for practice, the results not being recorded. The average time of association in seconds is given in Table II, the interval including, however, the perception-and-movement-time.

TABLE II.—AVERAGE TIME OF ASSOCIATION

	Concrete	Abstract	Proper	Verbs	Adj.
B	1.53	1.77	2.06	1.68	1.74
C	1.14	1.2	1.28	1.2	1.16
S	1.76	2			
E	1.88				
H	1.19				
University graduates	2.11	2.42			
Bryn Mawr College	3.14	4.1			
Gymnasium II*b*	2.42	4.31			
Gymnasium III*b*	4.46	7.07			

With these observers, consequently, the average time of the mental process varied from a little more than one to about seven seconds. These varying times evidently indicate important personal differences in rate of thought and stage of mental development. The shorter times may be partly referred to clearer understanding of what was to be done and to greater decision in choosing out some special association, as well as to the fact that some think faster than others. Other conditions, such as practice, are also concerned, and the nature and complexity of the process doubtless varies considerably with different observers. But all the factors are psychological; and, while at present we may not be able to define the part played by each, we may hope that such experiments will ultimately throw light on the development and nature of thought. It will be noticed that in all cases the associations on abstract nouns took up more time than those on concrete nouns, but the ratio of the two times varies with the different observers, and shows that the use of abstract thought greatly quickens its relative rate.

(c) Our third series of experiments was made with the three lists of nouns above-mentioned, but the observer, instead of naming a single association for each word, wrote what was suggested during 20 secs. The average time could thus be obtained, but the first association of the series differs somewhat from the following, and the time devoted to writing was a larger part of the whole interval than was the movement-time when the suggested idea was named. Table III contains a summary of our results, the average time for each word being given in secs. The observers were mostly students of a London and a Dublin girls' school. The experiments in the latter were made by Miss Josephine Conan, who also made those on the Irish Royal University graduates.

TABLE III.—AVERAGE TIME OF ASSOCIATION

Form	No. of persons	Average age	On concrete nouns	On abstract nouns	Average of both	Ratio of concrete to abstract
	London School					
VI....................	30	17.8	3.70	4.55	4.13	.81
V.....................	138	16.3	4.26	6.06	5.16	.7
IV....................	111	14.8	4.76	7.41	6.09	.64
III...................	84	12.7	6.90	11.76	9.33	.59
Average..............		15.1	4.76	7.14	5.95	.67
	Dublin School					
	71	14.5	6.25	8.34	7.30	.75
	Bryn Mawr College					
	10		3.51	4.88	4.20	.72
	London Graduates					
	13		3.03	3.85	3.44	.79
	Irish Graduates					
	8		3.08	3.92	3.58	.75

The Table explains itself. A distinct shortening of the mental process accompanies growth and education. The students of the sixth form of the London school required less than half the time of students of the third form. A corresponding result was obtained in the German gymnasium (see above Table II).[1] The girls in the Irish school required

[1] Dr. Berger has recently published experiments on the rapidity of mental processes in the different classes of a German gymnasium. See *Phil. Stud.*, v. 170 ff.

about the same time as girls of the same age in the English school, and the students in the American college the same time as the students in the sixth form of the English school. It will be noted that the relative time for the abstract associations becomes less as the students are older; it is less for the Irish than for the English students. The number of students in the forms of the English school was sufficient to eliminate accidental sources of variation. The times for the separate divisions of the forms are not so regular, but any variation can to a large extent be explained by the character of the class, and in turn throws light on it.

The 363 students of the London school were divided, according to their class-rank, into four parts. The average time of association for each quarter is given in Table IV.

TABLE IV.—AVERAGE TIME OF ASSOCIATION ACCORDING TO RANK

	Concrete	Abstract	Average	Ratio of conc. to abst.
1st quarter.............	4.65	6.90	5.78	.67
2nd quarter............	4.88	7.14	6.01	.68
3rd quarter............	4.76	6.90	5.83	.69
4th quarter............	5	7.41	6.21	.67

This shows an increased rate of association as the class-rank of the students is higher, but the difference is not great. Indeed, it is possible that such experiments measure the alertness of the student's mind more accurately than does the class-rank, which depends largely on diligence and other factors not telling in such experiments. The Table does not show a difference for the several quarters in the relative rate of the concrete and abstract associations; consequently higher class-rank does not seem to be accompanied with greater ease in abstract thought, attention to objective details being equally useful.

We may lastly notice the average number of associations made by the English students in 20 secs. on the several words used. This is given in the next Table, and, for convenience, the amount that it is above or below the average.

The Table shows a tolerably constant decrease in the number of words written as the series was continued. Thus with the first word of the concrete list on the average 4.7 associations were made, with the last word 3.6; with the first word of the abstract list 3.9, with the last 2.7. This bears witness to, and in a way measures, fatigue or decrease in attention as the experiments were continued. The falling-off in the number of associations was not, however, regular, and we may thus see that some ideas lend themselves more readily to associations than others. It was found easier to make associations on *ship* than on *clock*, on *time* than on *virtue*.

TABLE V.—AVERAGE NUMBER OF ASSOCIATIONS WITH DIFFERENT WORDS

Concrete nouns					Abstract nouns				
House	4.7	+.6	Bird	4.1		Time	3.9	+1.1	Love	2.4	−.4
Tree	4.6	+.5	Shoe	3.9	−.2	Courage	2.9	+.1	Strength	2.6	−.2
Ship	4.8	+.7	Hat	3.8	−.3	Form	2.7	−.1	Part	2.4	−.4
Chair	4	−.1	Child	3.7	−.4	Virtue	2.3	−.5	Beauty	2.8	
Clock	3.9	−.2	Hand	3.6	−.5	Art	3.1	+.3	Number	2.7	−.1

Average......................... 4.1   Average......................... 2.8

3. THE NATURE OF THE ASSOCIATION

We have explained the method used to obtain our associations. The observer was given a word and was required to say or write as quickly as possible what other word was suggested by it. For the sake of uniform results and for other reasons, this seemed the best way to begin an investigation into Mental Association, but it by no means concludes it; our experiments being, as we have seen, conditioned by the need of *naming* the suggested idea and doing it *quickly*. The nature of the process can best be gathered from our results, wherefore we give them as fully as is consistent with the reader's convenience. The lists of ten concrete and ten abstract words were used with 465 observers, and in Table VI we give all the associations which occurred ten times or oftener, together with the number of times they occurred.

We shall give below a classified list of all associations made on *house* and *time*. Here it may be worth while to call attention to the frequency of certain associations as shown by the Table. Thus, to nearly half the observers *tree* suggested *leaf* (*ves*) and *hand finger*(*s*). In the above Table an average of less than eight associations with each word is given, and more than half of all the associations made were included within these narrow limits.

Before treating of the classification of our results, we shall give, in addition to Table VI, a selection from the associations made by *B* and *C* on the longer lists of words. The original word is given first in each couple, and after it the associated word.

The associations given in Tables VI and VII illustrate the "Laws of Association" dwelt on by the English psychologists. The majority of them could be classified under Contiguity in space and time,

Similarity and Contrast. Following the best authority, we may at once depose Contrast to a subdivision. We should then have left Contiguity in space and time, and Similarity. These two classes represent fundamental differences which are borne out by our experiments.

TABLE VI.—MOST FREQUENT ASSOCIATIONS
Concrete Nouns

House. 74 room(s), 43 window(s), 39 brick(s), 25 [door(s), furniture], 23 garden, 19 people, 12 chair(s).

Tree. 212 leaf(ves), 45 branch(es), 28 green, 17 flower(s), 11 colour, 10 shrub.

Ship. 111 sail(s), 80 mast(s), 67 sea, 33 water, 19 boat, 16 [sailor(s), wood].

Chair. 115 leg(s), 64 wood(en), 52 seat, 46 table, 35 cane, 14 sitting, 12 stool.

Clock. 157 time, 121 hand(s), 27 watch, 22 pendulum, 18 tick, 14 [face, works].

Bird. 131 wing(s), 69 feather(s), 40 song(s), 23 singing, 15 sings, 14 flying, 12 nest.

Shoe. 86 leather, 74 boot(s), 60 foot(eet), 46 lace(s), 24 sole, 18 heel, 17 button(s).

Hat. 70 head, 46 feather(s), 41 straw, 33 ribbon(s), 32 bonnet, 30 trimming(s), 12 cap, 11 brim.

Child. 35 boy, 29 mother, 21 baby, 20 dress, 18 young, 16 girl, 15 parent, small, 13 age, 12 man, 10 [hair, infant, pretty, toy(s)].

Hand. 219 finger(s), 23 nail(s), 20 arm(s), 15 foot(eet), 13 glove(s).

Abstract Nouns

Time. 102 clock, 56 hour(s), 27 minute(s), 18 tide, 13 watch, 12 year, 11 work.

Courage. 103 bravery, 68 brave, 19 strength, 16 bold(ness), 10 [fear, hero, man].

Form. 74 shape, 10 colour.

Virtue. 127 good(ness), 45 vice, 14 [patience, truth], 10 grace.

Art. 115 painting, 49 drawing, 45 picture(s), 43 science, 18 music.

Love. 34 kind(ness), 24 affection, 36 hate(red), 16 [mother, parents], 15 friendship, 12 like, 11 gentleness.

Strength. 46 strong, 43 weak(ness), 30 power, 26 force, 21 man, 15 courage, 14 health, 13 muscle.

Part. 60 whole, 24 portion, 18 share, 17 half, 13 piece.

Beauty. 55 lovely(iness), 46 pretty(iness), 22 ugly(iness), 16 face, 10 beautiful.

Number. 44 figure(s), 39 many, 34 one, 18 quantity, 17 arithmetic, 10 crowd.

TABLE VII.—EXAMPLES OF ASSOCIATIONS

B. Water—pail, candle—stick, curls—yellow, tooth—wash, rod—spare, elbow—out, at, cloak—blue, jam—raspberry, cap—fur, house—door, hair—golden, watch—clock, heathen—Christian, coat—red, nightingale—bird, philosopher—wise, battle—soldiers.

C. Garden—house, forest—tree, spectator—theatre, rod—child, beast—beauty, melody—tune, queen—king, friend—enemy, affect—effect, building—house, mind—magazine, music—art, farm—food, rib—Eve, water—flow, tea—drink, protection—government, heathen—heath.

Contiguity in space and time defines, perhaps, with sufficient accuracy the nature of the associative link, but the meaning is clearer when we reflect that this class contains such associations as have been given us ready-made by sensation. Contiguity-in-space does not cover all cases of simultaneous contiguity, for example, a melody suggesting the words belonging to it. Contiguity-in-time calls up too much the idea of disconnected and sharply defined events following each other, whereas the associations of this class are probably due to the overlapping rather than to the succession. We prefer to use the terms Objective or Outer to define association due to previous connexion in sensation, and to subdivide it into Co-existence and Succession.

Similarity seems to be an unfortunate term. It gives at the outset an explanation, which is altogether rejected by many psychologists, and it does not naturally include cases of specification, definition and cause. In contradistinction to those associations which are given in sensations, we wish to designate such as are due to thought. These we shall call Logical or Inner. We do not wish to imply that the link of association must be wholly objective or wholly logical, on the contrary the results of our experiments show that in many, if not all, associations both factors are concerned. But in most cases it is easy to see which is predominant. Logical associations we shall subdivide into Specifying and Causal, analogous to the division of objective associations into co-existing and successive.

These four classes may with advantage be further subdivided. In the case of the Objective-Co-existing associations, there is an important distinction as to whether the movement is from Part to Part, from Whole to Part, or from Part to Whole—for example, whether *house* suggests *garden, window* or *street*. There is a quite analogous distinction with the Logical-Specifying associations, the relation in which may be Correlation, Specialisation or Generalisation; thus *house* may suggest *church, villa* or *building*. In Successive associations the direction may be forward or backward, that is, in an order the same as, or the reverse of, the original presentations,—thus, *house* may suggest *top* or *glass*. Analogously Causal associations may be either Final (forward) or Efficient (backward), that is, may give end or means, the terms being used in a sense broad enough to include all causal relations; thus *house* may suggest *shelter* or *builder*. The plan of classification which we obtain is thus as follows:—

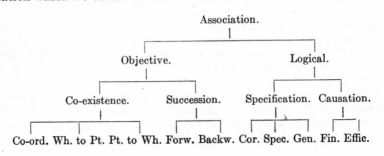

In Table VIII we give all the associations made by 465 observers on the words *house* and *time*, classified according to the method we have proposed.

TABLE VIII.—ASSOCIATIONS WITH

House

Co-ordination—25 furniture, 23 garden, 19 people, 12 chair(s), 7 table(s), 4 trees, 2 bed, pictures, 1 [boy, cat, girls, grounds, lady, master, men, road, servant-girl]; (103).

Whole to Part—74 room(s), 43 window(s), 25 door(s), 13 roof, 7 stairs, 6 bricks, walls, 4 chimney, 3 storey, 2 floor, stones, 1[bedroom, glass, kitchen, street-door, slates]; (190).

Part to Whole—3 [street, town], 2 road; (8).

Forwards—7 -top, 4 -maid, 2 [-dog, -rent, -to let], 1 [-agent, -hold, -of commons, -step, that Jack built, watch, -wife, -work]; (25).

Backwards—1 glass; (1).

Correlation—6 cottage, 5 mansion, 2 cot, 1 church, hut, 3 mouse (*verbal*); (18).

Specialisation—6 tall, 5 [brick, size], 3 [home, large, situation], 2 [dolls, height, high], 1 [big, grey, kind, low, magnificent, Morton Hall, pretty, this house of wood, tool-house, villa]; (41).

Generalisation—7 buildings, 5 dwellings, 2 habitation, 1 abode; (15).

End—3 [home, inhabitants], 2 [inmates, to live in, shelter], 1 [dwelling-place, habitation, live, people]; (16).

Means—33 bricks, 6 builders, 2 built, 1 [build, stones, wood]; (44).

Unclassified—1 [dice, hat, wind]; (3).

Misunderstood—(1).

Time

Co-ordination—(0).

Whole to Part—(0).

Part to Whole—(0).

Forwards—18 tide, 11 work, 7 flies, 2 [be quick, space], 1 [ever-rolling stream, flies fast, how it flies, -keeper, money, o'clock, price, race, reapers, slaves, -table, "time, gentlemen, time," -to do it, -to learn, -up, "waits for no man," -waits]; (57).

Backwards—1 [lose, lost, thief, when Father Time]; (4).

Correlation—8 eternity, 6 place, 5 [age, space], 3 [hurry, speed, to death, quickness, weather], 1 [duration, duty, haste (need for), life, manner, old age, swiftness], 3 thyme; (49).

Specialisation—56 hour(s), 27 minute(s), 12 year, 9 [day, long], 7 [late, lessons], 4 [quick, second(s)], 3 [length of time, scythe, short, when], 2 [early, fast, holidays, how long, how much, lost, night, quickly, seasons, waste], 1 [classes, examination, fast or slow, Father Time, for play, good, image, infinite, leaving school, magazine *Time*, moment, no time now, present, slow, slowness, something o'clock, soon, swift, term, train, twenty-four hours, what, what time, what time now, youth]; (194).

Generalisation—4 length, 3 space, 1 [passing, value]; (9).

End—1 [commerce, employment, not to waste, use, work]; (5).

Means—102 clock, 13 watch, 2 [hands (of clock), works (of clock)], 1 [hour-glass, sun-dial, tick (of clock), vibration]; (123).

Unclassified—1 [poems, temper, water, will]; (4).

Misunderstood—(23).

This classification gives the most convenient divisions which we were able to make of the associations obtained by our experiments. We do not, however, look on the classes as "natural kinds." On the one hand our subdivisions run into each other, and an association is rarely or never due to one only of the relations; on the other hand further subdivisions might be made.

The relation of Part to part, Whole to part, and Part to whole, with the corresponding logical subdivisions, Correlation, Specialisation and Generalisation, are perhaps the most important of the distinctions, but they are not defined with entire sharpness. Thus it depends on the attitude of the observer's mind whether *house—furniture* is a relation of Part to part or of Whole to part, and *house—cottage* of Correlation or Specialisation.[1] It seems possible that in most cases of Co-ordination the mind goes first to a whole and then to a part; thus, *house* may call up the complex *house and garden*, but there being no convenient name for this, *garden* is named. In associations which have been put under Cause and Succession the movement is often from a part to a whole; thus, when *bird* suggests *sings*, the total complex may be a singing bird, and when *house* suggests *top*, the part leads to a verbal whole.

As concerns further subdivisions of the classes, it is evident that the Objective associations might be distributed among the senses by means of which they were originally given. As a matter of fact the associations of Co-existence are almost without exception visual, and the associations of Succession verbal, *i.e.*, a complex of auditory, muscular and perhaps visual sensations (of printed words). The Logical associations might conveniently be further subdivided. Similarity and Contrast are natural subdivisions of Correlation, and there is an intervening class represented by associations such as *king—queen*, *shoe—boot*, &c. Then verbal similarities such as rhymes and alliterations are materially different from the rest. Specialisation includes a general or particular case as, *strength—man*, or *Sampson*, and a qualification, as *hair—yellow*. Generalisation includes associations as different as *snow—white* and *music—art*. An End or Final Cause may be purpose, object or act, as in the examples, *house—shelter*, *love—mother*, and *boy—run*, and in the case of act the given idea may be taken either as active or passive; thus water may suggest *flow* or *drink*. Under Means or Efficient Cause are included source, material, &c.

Returning to our chief divisions, we give in Table IX the percentage

---

[1] In Table VIII such associations are put under Co-ordination, but *C* thinks in the case of young students the relations were most likely of Whole to part and Specialisation. There are also a few other cases in which the writers differ as to the classification.

of associations falling to each. It contains the results of more than 12,000 observations made with 516 observers. The majority of these, however, were school-girls, as their results dominate. An analysis for different classes of observers will be given below.

TABLE IX.—PERCENTAGE OF ASSOCIATIONS

		Con-crete	Abstract	Proper	Verbs	Adject.
	No. of associations........	6120	5310	200	200	200
Objective	Co-ordination.............	10	0	17	0	0
	Whole to part............	34	0	10	0	0
	Part to whole.............	1	0	17	0	0
	Forwards................	4	5	9	15	9
	Backwards...............	2	1	5	1	0
Logical	Correlation...............	10	33	16	18	18
	Specialisation.............	19	31	7	48	68
	Generalisation............	3	8	5	0	1
	Final cause...............	13	4	12	9	0
	Efficient cause............	1	4	2	9	4
	Unclassed................	1	2	0	0	0
	None....................	1	6	0	0	0
	Misunderstood...........	0	6	0	0	0
	Objective................	51	6	58	16	9
	Logical..................	46	80	42	84	91
	Verbal..................	6	6	11	14	6

The Table shows that in the case of concrete nouns the ratio of Objective to Logical associations was 51:46, that is, the link of association was not quite as often supplied by thought as by sensation. As regards subdivisions it will be noticed that Whole to part and Specialisation are favourite categories, whereas Part to whole and Generalisation are not often used.[1] Employing the terms to include both Logical and Objective associations, Co-ordination was the relation in one-fifth of the cases, Whole to part in more than half, and Part to whole in one-twenty-fifth. In Succession, Backwards occurred half as often as Forwards; and in Cause, Efficient was much rarer than Final. In 1 per cent. of the cases the association could not be

[1] Steinthal says (*Einl. in die Psych. u. S.W.*, p. 161) the part more readily suggests the whole than the reverse, because "the mind rests in the thought of a whole." The advantage of experiment to theory is illustrated by comparing this with our results.

classified, and in 1 per cent no association was made. Our classification is not as useful for abstract as for concrete nouns, as with abstract nouns, Objective associations, other than verbal, scarcely occurred. The classes Correlation and Specialisation are about equal in size, each including nearly one-third of the cases, and four times as many as Generalisation. Fewer experiments were made with proper nouns, verbs and adjectives, and these were confined to B and C. In the last line of the Table is given the percentage of cases in which the association seemed to be purely verbal.

The nature of the association differs considerably with different persons and classes of persons. This variation in the case of concrete nouns may be studied in Table X. The first four columns contain the results of experiments made by Mr. Edgeworth, Miss Collet, and the writers; the fifth column by 31 university students and graduates (mostly women); the four following columns by the several forms of the London girls' school; the next column by the Dublin girls' school; and the last column by the boys of a German Latin school.

TABLE X.—PERCENTAGE OF ASSOCIATIONS WITH DIFFERENT OBSERVERS

Observers	E	Ct	B	C	Univ. grads.	London sch.				Dr. sch.	Ger. sch.	Av.
						IV	V	IV	III			
No. of assoc............	250	250	250	250	310	300	1380	1110	840	710	740	
Co-ordination...........	11	8	14	9	7	15	12	10	10	7	3	10
Whole to part...........	4	3	4	1	47	35	41	47	42	30	32	34
Part to whole............	1	6	3	3	0	3	1	0	1	0	4	1
Forwards..............	3	14	14	10	1	1	1	1	0	5	10	4
Backwards..............	5	19	5	2	0	0	0	0	0	0	5	2
Correlation..............	22	19	20	12	9	24	6	4	6	13	17	10
Specialisation...........	33	19	24	21	20	10	18	19	15	23	16	19
Generalisation...........	11	1	5	2	2	1	1	1	2	5	5	3
Final clause.............	7	3	8	37	11	10	15	11	16	12	7	13
Efficient cause..........	1	2	1	3	2	0	1	2	1	0	1	1
Unclassed..............	0	4	0	0	1	1	1	1	1	1	0	1
None..................	0	0	0	0	0	0	1	0	4	4	0	1
Objective..............	24	50	40	25	55	54	55	58	53	42	54	51
Logical................	74	54	58	75	44	45	41	39	40	53	46	46
Verbal.................	8	33	26	12	2	1	2	1	1	8	14	6

The Table shows that Logical and Verbal associations are favoured by the first four observers, who teach and write. With the students

Whole to Part is the favourite category, they seem to visualise the object and name some part of it. With the English school girls less than half the associations are Logical, and very few are Verbal. With the Irish school girls more than half are Logical, and 8 per cent are Verbal; this is perhaps due to the fact that the training in the Irish school is more literary. While the students of the London school made only about 1 per cent of Verbal association, *Ct* and *B*, who teach in the school, made respectively 33 and 26 per cent. The 14 per cent of Verbal associations made by the German students is doubtless due to the nature of the language. The largest proportion of logical associations (34) was made by *E* and *C*, who are engaged in abstract studies.

The nature of the association depends not only on the observer, but also on the word given. The percentage of the several kinds of associations occurring with different words is given in Table XI.

TABLE XI.—PERCENTAGE OF ASSOCIATIONS WITH DIFFERENT WORDS

456 ass. on each word	Tree	Chair	Bird	Clock	Child	Hand	Time	Art	Courage	Love	Number	Beauty
Co-ordination......	4	10	12	1	12	10	0	0	0	0	0	0
Whole to part......	65	40	46	41	11	56	0	0	0	0	0	0
Part to whole.......	2	2	1	0	0	1	0	0	0	0	0	0
Forwards..........	0	0	0	0	3	3	12	2	2	5	2	3
Backwards.........	0	0	0	0	0	0	1	1	0	0	0	0
Correlation.........	8	8	1	8	16	5	10	15	54	36	21	30
Specialisation.......	15	29	13	4	40	9	42	62	16	12	52	37
Generalisation......	5	0	1	1	7	2	2	6	18	15	6	18
Final cause........	1	9	23	42	4	9	1	4	2	18	1	3
Efficient *C*........	0	0	0	0	0	0	26	7	0	2	7	2
Unclassed..........	0	0	2	2	2	1	1	1	2	1	2	0
None..............	0	1	1	1	5	4	5	2	6	11	9	5
Objective..........	71	52	59	42	26	70	13	3	2	5	2	3
Logical	29	46	38	55	67	25	81	94	90	83	87	90

The Table shows that the association is largely determined by the original word. *Tree* and *hand* are natural objects which are easily pictured, and have parts (leaves and fingers respectively) readily named. With *child*, on the other hand, Specialisation was the favourite category. Final Cause was the largest class in the case of *clock*, a thing made and used for the special purpose of measuring time. Conversely *time* often suggested the means of its measurement. Of the other abstract nouns, *art* and *number* were commonly specialised, while *courage* and *love* most frequently suggested a similar or contrasted idea.

We wish to lay special stress on our Tables, as these contain the results of extended series of experiments. In a joint paper it is not convenient to enter into criticism and discussion; we have, consequently, confined ourselves to the exposition of our research. We, however, add a section in which several of the observers discuss the experiments with special reference to the subjective aspect of the association.

IV. REMARKS ON THE EXPERIMENTS

By G. F. Stout

I wish chiefly to draw attention to the nature of the process by which the mind passes from the given idea to that suggested idea which is the first to be definitely recognised and named. In my case the transition seems to be most commonly mediated by a more or less obscure total presentation, including as part of its content both the given and the suggested ideas. At the time when I was subjected to these experiments, I always felt that the word which came first to my lips, and which was therefore set down in Dr. Cattell's list, was a hopelessly inadequate indication of what was actually taking place in my mind. By retrospection following close upon the actual process, I was for the most part able to recover and analyse those contents of my consciousness which I had found it impossible to express in words or to render explicit in thought.

Examples will make my meaning clear. *Smoke* suggested *fire*. The intermediate link in this case was not the picture of a fire smoking. It was the phrase, "Where there is smoke there is fire." Nor was the connexion merely a verbal one. The words were quite indistinct. The first among them to emerge into clear consciousness was the word *fire*. In the intermediate state, what vaguely floated before my mind was the general sense of the saying considered as an example of inference. There was also traceable in my mind a dim and distant reference to a lecturer who had used this illustration in my hearing. *Finger* suggested *heart:* in this instance, transition was mediated by the vague total presentation of the circulation of the blood. I thus came to think of the heart as propelling blood to the extremities. *Cannibal* suggested *Andrew Lang.* Here there loomed before me the massive and blurred presentation of what I now in retrospect name and recognise as "anthropology." In this indistinct totality, the first detail, besides the given one *cannibal*, which acquired sufficient definiteness and salience to be verbally expressed was the name of the well-known author, *Andrew Lang.*

It would be possible for me to analyse a large number of similar examples. The great majority of the suggestions in my case were of the kind described. The transition from *tail* to *the rest* is worth noting, because in this case the process was concluded, so to speak, at an earlier stage than usual. *Tail* revived the obscure presentation of the whole animal. Instead, however, of singling out some special detail within this whole, it occurred to me just to name *the rest* of it without further ado.

The instances in which I proceeded from given whole to a part of that whole, or from a given part to the whole comprehending it, were comparatively few, and I do not think that they require any special discussion. The usual course of reproduction in my case passed from a named and definite partial presentation by the mediation of an unnamed and obscurely defined total to another named and definite partial presentation.

The next point to which I wish to call attention is the limitation imposed on the subject of the experiments by the necessity of finding a verbal expression for his thought as soon as possible. This is certainly a disturbing condition, which interferes with the analogy between the experiments and the normal course of reproduction. There is perpetually present in the mind of the experimentee a voluntary effort to find some word or other, whatever it may be. This circumstance seems to me greatly to augment the influence of merely verbal connexions on the flow of ideas. It might be well to try experiments in which no regard should be paid to the time occupied by the process of suggestion.

In conclusion, I may remark that what interests me most in these experiments is the indication which they seem to afford, when closely examined, of the operation of obscure links in the process of reproduction. The psychological atomism of the English associationists is perhaps mainly due to the neglect of these obscure phenomena. If we lose sight of the indistinct whole which mediates transitions between its component parts, the train of ideas must of necessity appear a separate and exclusive succession.

By F. Y. Edgeworth

With regard to these words I have hardly any explanation to give. I just stuck down, or rather cried out, whatever word came up first. The first word did not always correspond to the first idea. Often there seemed to be a throng of ideas struggling for expression. Thus, in the case of *Saint Matilda*, the word *Saint* raised the ideas of an amiably mild lady, in fact the picture of Saint Cecilia, only I could not remember in time her name; and the first name which occurred was that of the heroine in *Rokeby*, suggested by some similarity of character.

I could have gone a little faster, I think, if I had made an effort; but I thought it best to make as little effort as possible. The most conscious exercise of will occurred after assigning adjectives to several words, such as *beautiful* to *hair, bright* to *lamp*. I felt it would be stupid, and perhaps disappointing to the experimenters, if all the results came out of this type, so I changed my hand and checked the flow of adjectives.

By E. P. Hughes

My attitude of mind during the experiment was this: I did not care at all what words were suggested; my mind was free to suggest any words; but I had decided the words were to come quickly. I *willed* that they should come quickly; I did not *will* as to the kind of words that came.

At first I found nouns suggested nouns, and there was generally a connexion that could be traced. After a little, however, I found the nouns suggested not nouns but whole sentences, and a word out of these sentences was taken, sometimes an adverb, or a verb, or an adjective, and very occasionally a noun. *E.g.*, the word *slave* brought up to my mind many sentences expressing my detestation of slavery, and I said the word *bad*.

I allowed my mind to work in any direction as long as it worked quickly; but all the time I found myself criticising the connexions, and generally recognising whether they were reasonable or not, and being amused at absurd and far-fetched connexions, and also when the word said was in no way connected, as far as I could see, with the word given.

I found a great difficulty in remembering afterwards the words I had said. I found it easier to remember them several minutes later than immediately after I had said them. In one instance I utterly failed to remember what word I said at the time, and remembered it with little effort ten minutes later.

I found it was easy to say words after the first three or four words of the 10 words in a group; it then became difficult, but I felt at the end of the 10 words, if the list had been longer, I should eventually have given the words more quickly.

After two or three groups of 10 words, I came to a word I could not read, and from that time I felt a waste of energy in so far as I continually dreaded meeting a word I could not read. In the fourth group I misread a word, and thought it was a verb and not a noun, and when I learnt my mistake I felt there was a further expenditure of energy to the end of the experiment, because I always dreaded taking a noun for a verb; and once the word *bottle* raised in my mind the question whether it was a verb or a noun, and I said mentally "noun," and ejaculated *Yes.*

When I started by mentioning the "colour" of a noun given I generally gave several colours, and the same with "shape." I found there was a greater inclination to give shape than colour.

Occasionally I remembered the general impression given by a word, *e.g., slave,* but I could not remember the particular word I gave, *viz., bad.*

The word *cow* appeared frequently. I have a special horror of cows.

Hat-good; I had lately made a hat-rack, and one part of it was specially praised; my teacher was a foreigner and used the word "good," and, as he did not speak in English as a rule, the word was very impressive. *Baggage-bandage;* my father, when a surgeon in the militia, kept a supply of bandages in his baggage, which I had rolled up sometimes.

By C. E. Collet

Eight per cent of the words suggested by the 250 concrete nouns selected for experiment were names of things in coexistence; here in nearly every case the idea excited by the name suggested the next idea, and that idea suggested the name: the mental processes were comparatively simple. The word *cavalier* suggested the word *Charles I* having aroused a picture of the times of Charles I in an atmosphere of Sir Walter Scott's novels, with Vandyke's portrait somewhere in space. *Scaffold* suggested confused representations of persons in fiction ascending scaffolds, including Sydney Carton (*A Tale of Two Cities*), Clayton the actor, and, most distinct of all, Strafford, whose name was the one actually uttered. The names of the others did not enter my thoughts, and the whole picture was vague, most prominent being the representation of feelings excited when reading the stories of Carton and Strafford.

Only two per cent of the words suggested were the names of parts of the things denoted by the words read.

Six per cent were names of wholes suggested by names of parts; *e.g., violin* suggested by *string; theatre* by *curtain; Attic* by *philosopher,* this association being partly due to an image of *Le Philosophe sous les Toits,* and partly to the verbal association "Attic philosopher."

Fourteen per cent of the words come under the head of Forwards Associations, nineteen per cent under the head of Backwards Associations; so that thirty-three per cent are classed as Verbal Associations, and of the nineteen per cent classed under Specialisation many are undoubtedly verbally suggested.

As examples of verbal forwards associations, *bell* suggested *bell-horse*, the name given by workmen to men encouraged to spur them on to greater speed; *cap* suggested *cap-à-pie*, neither word raising any representation beyond the printed letters; *mob* suggested *mobilise;* *hand* suggested *hand-maiden*. In these cases the train of thought is started by words, not by ideas. One noteworthy exception to this is the suggestion of the word *sweep* by the word *chimney*. This word at once revived Hans Andersen's story of the China shepherdess; the word was localised in China-shepherdess land, and the whole story reviewed, so far as I can judge, before the word *sweep* came to the lips as the easiest to be uttered.

The 48 words classed as instances of Specialisation, and the 48 words classed as instances of Backwards verbal association resemble each other in being to a great extent the result of verbal association, but the dominating mental process was different. The specialisations were nearly all suggested by words rather than by a specialising process on my own part, but the words did actually suggest to me the special things, and my attention was given to them; *e.g.*, *garden* suggested *kitchen*, and attention was given to the representation of a kitchen-garden. Under the head of Backwards associations I have put words which were verbally suggested but which were not accompanied by representations of the things denoted by them. The instances under this class are the results of a complex process. *E.g.*, *ornament*. The first syllable, together with the meaning of the word, aroused faintly the words, "Beauty unad*orn*ed ad*orn*ed the most," and the first word actually uttered was *beauty*.

Men suggested the title of Stevenson's book, *The Merry Men*, but concomitantly with it rose the representation of the story in which I localised the "men"—the story, not the book. The written word seems always to take up a position in space and to be a kind of keyhole through which the mind passes to an imaginary world. It arises most probably from a constant habit of reading fiction and looking at a world located beyond the printed page which gives admittance to it.

The word *skin* was followed by the name *Nicodemus*. At first, although quite conscious of the mental process preceding the utterance of the word *Nicodemus*, I could not see any connexion that *skin* had with it. As soon as I saw the word, I was looking at the representation of a fairy tale: a little dwarf was jumping before the fire, and I seemed to know all about him and to know his name, but I could not say it; *N*ebuchadnezzar (the last part of the name being very faint) rose as somewhat analogous, but not the word I wanted, and was followed by the utterance of *N*icodemus, which seemed more satisfactory. The word which I wanted to pronounce was Rumpelstiltskin, and the analogy between the names was then and is now quite clear to me; Nicodemus and Rumpelstiltskin seem alike, both rhythmically and in a certain element of ridiculousness which I cannot define. But it was some time before it flashed upon me that *skin* had raised the name and the story of Rumpelstilt*skin* by a backwards association.

Instances of Co-ordination were nineteen per cent of the whole. In this class many of the words suggested were merely different names for the things denoted by the written words; *e.g.*, *brain* suggested *cerveau*. Compared with the others, this class is noticeable for the absence of reference to books, songs, speeches, &c.

There was not one instance of Generalisation.

By S. Bryant

The mental process concomitant with the utterance of the suggested word appears to me of such considerable complexity in many cases as to be by no means expressed or even hinted at in the spoken word. This, in fact, expresses one feature of the whole, because that feature was either most interesting, most prominent, most easy to name or earliest in time. In the case of concrete nouns, such as water, plate, lane, the most conspicuous factor of the whole process in my mind was the definite and varied activity of the pictorial imagination. Into whatever class the expressed association eventually falls, there went with it a picturing out of either the expressed or associated idea, or both, with quite a considerable surrounding of local and other particulars.

The simplest cases were those coming under the first head. Thus *water-pail* means a simple picture to the second element in which the spoken word attaches, and this is classed under Co-ordinate Existence; the picture here appeared to be present before the word and to have caused it. On the other hand, *candle-stick* seemed in the making of it to be verbal only—an auditory and motor sequence in time—but the picture of a candlestick followed so simultaneously that this association also might easily have been taken to mean primarily a case of Co-ordinate Existence. Verbal associations with this pictorial sequence occurred quite commonly, and these as well as others I felt bound to classify as Verbal associations, though if made by other people I should have treated them differently in default of the necessary introspective knowledge. With such a verbal association as *rod-spare*, into which was quite consciously condensed the whole quotation, "Spare the rod and spoil the child," imagination threw up vague pictures of naughty children and irate old dames, while the name at least of Solomon rose also to mind, though passing on in haste to the next word on the list. My verbal associations, including rhymes, amount to the large proportion of 26 per cent, being much the largest that occurs with the exception of Miss Collet's high proportion of 33 per cent.

The favourite class for the majority of those experimented on is that of Whole to Part, and this might seem at first to be the most natural expression of the fact that the meaning of a concrete noun is most commonly realised by the formation of a pictorial image. I make, however, only 4.4 per cent of associations under this head, and only 22 in all the Co-existence classes taken together, while the class of Specialisation alone contains 24.4, and is my most favoured class. But I found the pictorial element very potent in associations of this kind. In *curls-yellow,* for instance, the picture of yellow, curling hair rose distinctly to mind, with attention fixed on its admired character of golden yellowness; and the associated word is simply descriptive of the image seen under a distinct play of aesthetically inspired imagination. Similar remarks apply to *cloak-blue, jam-raspberry, cap-fur;* the image is described as it happens for some reason or other to be particularised, and in the two former cases I was aware of a preferential motive. In such cases it is probable that the image is less generic than when *house* suggests *door,* or *table chair.* In *house-door* the image may be generic, and the attitude of mind is certainly analytic; while in *cloak-blue* the image must be specific up to a certain extent, and the attitude of mind qualitatively descriptive as well as particularising. Thus the two descriptions *hair-face* and *hair-golden* indicate quite different movements of mind, though they might have started from similar images of hair in the first instance.

In calling such results as we have obtained associations it is understood that the word is used in a broad sense, and any discussion of the limits which should be put on its exact use would not be suitable here. I may, however, point out that the forced rapidity of the process by which the subject of experiment linked each word to each must have tended to secure that the most readily suggested word came to hand first, thus excluding, so far as possible, deliberate acts of choice, which would certainly have presented results that were not mere associations. To secure the minimum of thought proper is essential in the production of associations. Nevertheless, it is quite certain that even with all haste a considerable amount of thinking and choosing does get itself done in these experiments; and I believe the introspection of other observers will bear witness with mine on this point. The exact analysis of the processes and their proper classification would require much careful observation and experiment of an introspective character. All that it seemed possible to do in objective experiments, such as ours were in the main, was to eliminate the higher thought activities as much as we could by not giving them time to produce spoken results.

By J. McK. Cattell

I find it extremely difficult to observe by introspection the process of association, whether in the usual course of mental life or in experiments such as are here recorded. If, however, I combine the results of these experiments with introspection, I conclude that, when one idea suggests another, they have previously been associated in a common presentation, and that the suggestion is possible because the idea in distinct consciousness belongs to a larger whole, some of it indistinctly given, the rest below the threshold of consciousness. In conclusion, I should like to emphasise the fact that we have made *quantitative* determinations in two directions: we have measured the time of mental association, and obtained statistics of its nature.

8

MENTAL TESTS AND MEASUREMENTS

Printed in *Mind*, **15**: 373–381, 1890.

Psychology cannot attain the certainty and exactness of the physical sciences, unless it rests on a foundation of experiment and measurement. A step in this direction could be made by applying a series of mental tests and measurements to a large number of individuals. The results would be of considerable scientific value in discovering the constancy of mental processes, their interdependence, and their variation under different circumstances. Individuals, besides, would find their tests interesting, and, perhaps, useful in regard to training, mode of life or indication of disease. The scientific and practical value of such tests would be much increased should a uniform system be adopted, so that determinations made at different times and places could be compared and combined. With a view to obtaining agreement among those interested, I venture to suggest the following series of tests and measurements, together with methods of making them.[1]

The first series of ten tests is made in the Psychological Laboratory of the University of Pennsylvania on all who present themselves, and the complete series on students of Experimental Psychology. The results will be published when sufficient data have been collected. Meanwhile, I should be glad to have the tests, and the methods of making them, thoroughly discussed.

The following ten tests are proposed:

    I. Dynamometer Pressure.
    II. Rate of Movement.
    III. Sensation-areas.
    IV. Pressure causing Pain.
    V. Least noticeable difference in Weight.
    VI. Reaction-time for Sound.
    VII. Time for naming Colours.

---

[1] Mr. Francis Galton, in his Anthropometric Laboratory at South Kensington Museum, already uses some of these tests, and I hope the series here suggested will meet with his approval. It is convenient to follow Mr. Galton in combining tests of body, such as weight, size, colour of eyes, &c., with psychophysical and mental determinations, but these latter alone are the subject of the present discussion. The name (or initials) of the experimentee should be recorded, the nationality (including that of the parents), and the age, sex, occupation and state of health.

VIII. Bi-section of a 50 cm. line.

IX. Judgment of 10 seconds time.

X. Number of Letters remembered on once Hearing.

It will be noticed that the series begins with determinations rather bodily than mental, and proceeds through psychophysical to more purely mental measurements.[1]

The tests may be readily made on inexperienced persons, the time required for the series being about an hour. The laboratory should be conveniently arranged and quiet, and no spectators should be present while the experiments are being made. The amount of instruction the experimentee should receive, and the number of trials he should be given, are matters which ought to be settled in order to secure uniformity of result. The amount of instruction depends on the experimenter and experimentee, and cannot, unfortunately, be exactly defined. It can only be said that the experimentee must understand clearly what he has to do. A large and uniform number of trials would, of course, be the most satisfactory, the average, average variation, maximum and minimum being recorded. Time is, however, a matter of great importance if many persons are to be tested. The arrangement most economical of time would be to test thoroughly a small number of persons, and a large number in a more rough-and-ready fashion. The number of trials I allow in each test is given below, as also whether I consider the average or "best" trial the most satisfactory for comparison.

Let us now consider the tests in order.

I. *Dynamometer Pressure.*—The greatest possible squeeze of the hand may be thought by many to be a purely physiological quantity. It is, however, impossible to separate bodily from mental energy. The 'sense of effort' and the effects of volition on the body are among the questions most discussed in psychology and even in metaphysics. Interesting experiments may be made on the relation between volitional control or emotional excitement and dynamometer pressure. Other determinations of bodily power could be made (in the second series I have included the "archer's pull" and pressure of the thumb and forefinger), but the squeeze of the hand seems the most convenient. It may be readily made, cannot prove injurious, is dependent on mental conditions, and allows comparison of right- and left-handed power. The experimentee should be shown how to hold the dynamometer in order to obtain the maximum pressure. I allow two trials with

---

[1] Sharpness of sight (including colour-vision) and hearing might perhaps, be included in the list. I have omitted them because it requires considerable time to discover the amount and nature of the defect (which is usually bodily, not mental), and because abundant statistics have been published, and are being collected by oculists and aurists. [See Remark (*b*) below, p. 140.]

each hand (the order being right, left, right, left), and record the maximum pressure of each hand.

II. *Rate of Movement.*—Such a determination seems to be of considerable interest, especially in connexion with the preceding. Indeed, its physiological importance is such as to make it surprising that careful measurements have not hitherto been made. The rate of movement has the same psychological bearings as the force of movement. Notice, in addition to the subjects already mentioned, the connexion between force and rate of movement on the one hand and the "four temperaments" on the other. I am now making experiments to determine the rate of different movements. As a general test, I suggest the quickest possible movement of the right hand and arm from rest through 50 cm. A piece of apparatus for this purpose can be obtained from Clay & Torbensen, Philadelphia. An electric current is closed by the first movement of the hand, and broken when the movement through 50 cm. has been completed. I measure the time the current has been closed with the Hipp chronoscope, but it may be done by any chronographic method. The Hipp chronoscope is to be obtained from Peyer & Favarger, Neuchâtel. It is a very convenient apparatus, but care must be taken in regulating and controlling it (see MIND No. 42).[1]

III. *Sensation-areas.*—The distance on the skin by which two points must be separated in order that they may be felt as two is a constant, interesting both to the physiologist and psychologist. Its variation in different parts of the body (from 1 to 68 mm.) was a most important discovery. What the individual variation may be, and what inferences may be drawn from it, cannot be foreseen; but anything which may throw light on the development of the idea of space deserves careful study. Only one part of the body can be tested in a series such as the present. I suggest the back of the closed right hand, between the tendons of the first and second fingers, and in a longitudinal direction. Compasses with rounded wooden or rubber tips should be used, and I suggest that the curvature have a radius of .5 mm. This experiment requires some care and skill on the part of the experimenter. The points must be touched simultaneously, and not too hard. The experimentee must turn away his head. In order to obtain exact results, a large number of experiments would be necessary, and all the tact of the experimenter will be required to determine, without undue expenditure of time, the distance at which the touches may just be distinguished.

IV. *Pressure Causing Pain.*—This, like the rate of movement, is a determination not hitherto much considered, and if other more important tests can be devised they might be substituted for these.

[1] See Remark (c) below, p. 140.

But the point at which pressure causes pain may be an important constant, and in any case it would be valuable in the diagnosis of nervous diseases and in studying abnormal states of consciousness. The determination of any fixed point or quantity in pleasure or pain is a matter of great interest in theoretical and practical ethics, and I should be glad to include some such test in the present series. To determine the pressure causing pain I use an instrument (to be obtained from Clay & Torbensen which measures the pressure applied by a tip of hard rubber 5 mm. in radius. I am now determining the pressure causing pain in different parts of the body; for the present series I recommend the centre of the forehead. The pressure should be gradually increased, and the maximum read from the indicator after the experiment is complete. As a rule, the point at which the experimentee says the pressure is painful should be recorded, but in some cases it may be necessary to record the point at which signs of pain are shown. I make two trials, and record both.

V. *Least Noticeable Difference in Weight.*—The just noticeable sensation and the least noticeable difference in sensation are psychological constants of great interest. Indeed, the measurement of mental intensity is probably the most important question with which experimental psychology has at present to deal. The just noticeable sensation can only be determined with great pains, if at all: the point usually found being in reality the least noticeable difference for faint stimuli. This latter point is itself so difficult to determine that I have postponed it to the second series. The least noticeable difference in sensation for stimuli of a given intensity can be more readily determined, but it requires some time, and consequently not more than one sense and intensity can be tested in a preliminary series. I follow Mr. Galton in selecting "sense of effort" or weight. I use small wooden boxes, the standard one weighing 100 gms. and the others 101, 102, up to 110 gms. The standard weight and another (beginning with 105 gms.) being given to the experimentee, he is asked which is the heavier. I allow him about 10 secs. for decision. I record the point at which he is usually right, being careful to note that he is always right with the next heavier weight.

VI. *Reaction-time for Sound.*—The time elapsing before a stimulus calls forth a movement should certainly be included in a series of psychophysical tests: the question to be decided is what stimulus should be chosen. I prefer sound, on it the reaction-time seems to be the shortest and most regular, and the apparatus is most easily arranged. I measure the time with a Hipp chronoscope, but various chronographic methods have been used. There is need of a simpler, cheaper and more portable apparatus for measuring short times.

Mr. Galton uses an ingenious instrument, in which the time is measured by the motion of a falling rod, and electricity is dispensed with, but this method will not measure times longer than about ⅓ sec. In measuring the reaction-time, I suggest that three valid reactions be taken, and the minimum recorded. Later, the average and mean variation may be calculated.[1]

VII. *Time for Naming Colours.*—A reaction is essentially reflex, and, I think, in addition to it, the time of some process more purely mental should be measured. Several such processes are included in the second series; for the present series I suggest the time needed to see and name a colour. This time may be readily measured for a single colour by means of suitable apparatus (see MIND No. 42), but for general use sufficient accuracy may be attained by allowing the experimentee to name ten colours and taking the average. I paste coloured papers (red, yellow, green and blue) 2 cm. square, 1 cm. apart, vertically on a strip of black pasteboard. This I suddenly uncover and start a chronoscope, which I stop when the ten colours have been named. I allow two trials (the order of colours being different in each) and record the average time per colour in the quickest trial.

VIII. *Bisection of a 50 Cm. Line.*—The accuracy with which space and time are judged may be readily tested, and with interesting results. I follow Mr. Galton in letting the experimentee divide an ebony rule (3 cm. wide) into two equal parts by means of a movable line, but I recommend 50 cm. in place of 1 ft., as with the latter the error is so small that it is difficult to measure, and the metric system seems preferable. The amount of error in mm. (the distance from the true middle) should be recorded, and whether it is to the right or left. One trial would seem to be sufficient.

IX. *Judgment of 10 Sec. Time.*—This determination is easily made. I strike on the table with the end of a pencil, and again after 10 seconds, and let the experimentee in turn strike when he judges an equal interval to have elapsed. I allow only one trial and record the time, from which the amount and direction of error can be seen.

X. *Number of Letters Repeated on Once Hearing.*—Memory and attention may be tested by determining how many letters can be repeated on hearing once. I name distinctly and at the rate of two per second six letters, and if the experimentee can repeat these after me I go on to seven, then eight, &c.; if the six are not correctly repeated after three trials (with different letters), I give five, four, &c. The maximum number of letters which can be grasped and remembered is thus determined. Consonants only should be used in order to avoid syllables.

[1] See Remark (*d*) below, p. 140.

Experimental psychology is likely to take a place in the educational plan of our schools and universities. It teaches accurate observation and correct reasoning in the same way as the other natural sciences, and offers a supply of knowledge interesting and useful to everyone. I am at present preparing a laboratory manual which will include tests of the senses and measurements of mental time, intensity and extensity, but it seems worth while to give here a list of the tests which I look on as the more important in order that attention may be drawn to them, and co-operation secured in choosing the best series of tests and the most accurate and convenient methods. In the following series, fifty tests are given, but some of them include more than one determination.

Sight

1. Accommodation (short sight, over-sight, and astigmatism).
2. Drawing Purkinje's figures and the blind-spot.
3. Acuteness of colour vision, including lowest red and highest violet visible.
4. Determination of the field of vision for form and colour.
5. Determination of what the experimentee considers a normal red, yellow, green and blue.
6. Least perceptible light, and least amount of colour distinguished from grey.
7. Least noticeable difference in intensity, determined for stimuli of three degrees of brightness.
8. The time a colour must work on the retina in order to produce a sensation, the maximum sensation and a given degree of fatigue.
9. Nature and duration of after-images.
10. Measurement of amount of contrast.
11. Accuracy with which distance can be judged with one and with two eyes.
12. Test with stereoscope and for struggle of the two fields of vision.
13. Errors of perception, including bisection of line, drawing of square, &c.
14. Colour and arrangement and colours preferred. Shape of figure and of rectangle preferred.

Hearing

15. Least perceptible sound and least noticeable difference in intensity for sounds of three degrees of loudness.
16. Lowest and highest tone audible, least perceptible difference in pitch for C, C', C'', and point where intervals and chords (in melody and harmony) are just noticed to be out of tune.

17. Judgment of absolute pitch and of the nature of intervals, chords and dischords.

18. Number and nature of the overtones which can be heard with and without resonators.

19. Accuracy with which direction and distance of sounds can be judged.

20. Accuracy with which a rhythm can be followed and complexity of rhythm can be grasped.

21. Point at which loudness and shrillness of sound become painful. Point at which beats are the most disagreeable.

22. Sound of nature most agreeable. Musical tone, chord, instrument and composition preferred.

Taste and Smell

23. Least perceptible amount of cane-sugar, quinine, cooking salt and sulphuric acid, and determination of the parts of the mouth with which they are tasted.

24. Least perceptible amount of camphor and bromine.

25. Tastes and smells found to be peculiarly agreeable and disagreeable.

Touch and Temperature

26. Least noticeable pressure for different parts of the body.

27. Least noticeable difference in pressure, with weights of 10, 100 and 1000 gms.

28. Measurement of sensation-areas in different parts of the body.

29. Accuracy with which the amount and direction of the motion of a point over the skin can be judged.

30. Least noticeable difference in temperature.

31. Mapping out of heat, cold and pressure spots on the skin.

32. The point at which pressure and heat and cold cause pain.

Sense of Effort and Movement[1]

33. Least noticeable difference in weight, in lifting weights of 10, 100 and 1000 gms.

34. Force of squeeze of hands, pressure with thumb and forefinger and pull as archer.

35. Maximum and normal rate of movement.

36. Accuracy with which the force, extent and rate of active and passive movements can be judged.

---

[1] Organic sensations and sensations of motion, equilibrium and dizziness, should perhaps be included in this series.

Mental Time

37. The time stimuli must work on the ear and eye in order to call forth sensations.

38. The reaction-time for sound, light, pressure and electrical stimulation.

39. The perception-time for colours, objects, letters and words.

40. The time of naming colours, objects, letters and words.

41. The time it takes to remember and to come to a decision.

42. The time of mental association.

43. The effects of attention, practice and fatigue on mental time.

Mental Intensity

44. Results of different methods used for determining the least noticeable difference in sensation.

45. Mental intensity as a function of mental time.

Mental Extensity

46. Number of impressions which can be simultaneously perceived.

47. Number of successive impressions which can be correctly repeated, and number of times a larger number of successive impressions must be heard or seen in order that they may be correctly repeated.

48. The rate at which a simple sensation fades from memory.

49. Accuracy with which intervals of time can be remembered.

50. The correlation of mental time, intensity and extensity.

Remarks by Francis Galton, F.R.S.

(a) One of the most important objects of measurement is hardly if at all alluded to here and should be emphasised. It is to obtain a general knowledge of the capacities of a man by sinking shafts, as it were, at a few critical points. In order to ascertain the best points for the purpose, the sets of measures should be compared with an independent estimate of the man's powers. We thus may learn which of the measures are the most instructive. The sort of estimate I have in view and which I would suggest should be noted [? for private use] is something of this kind,—"mobile, eager energetic; well shaped; successful at games requiring good eye and hand; sensitive; good at music and drawing." Such estimates would be far from worthless when made after only a few minutes' talk; they ought to be exact when made of students who have been for months and years under observation. I lately saw a considerable collection of such estimates, made by a medical man for a special purpose. They were singularly searching and they hit off, with a few well chosen epithets, a very great variety of different characters. I could not induce the medical man to consent to the publication of specimens of his excellent analyses, nor even of fancy specimens. Even these would have sufficed to show that if psychologists seriously practised the art of briefly describing characters, they might raise that art to a high level.

(*b*) The method I have long used for testing keenness of eyesight in persons whose powers of eye-adaptation are normal, still seems to me quite effective. It is to register the greatest distance at which numerals printed in diamond type can be read. Strips of paper cut out at random from a small sheet printed all over with these numerals, are mounted on blocks set at successive distances from the eye-hole. They can easily be changed when dirty. Fair light is wanted, but that is all that is needed for ordinary test-purposes.

(*c*) I have constructed an instrument which is not yet quite as I desire, of which the first part would I think greatly facilitate the working with the Hipp chronograph. I had found great trouble in inducing coarse and inexperienced persons to deliver their blows aright. They bungled and struck the instrument wrongly, and often broke it. Then I made it more massive, yet still they broke it and often hurt themselves much in doing so. My present plan is to give them nothing more than one end of a long thread to hold. The other end passes round a spring reel, like the tape in a spring measuring tape. The string when left to itself will reel home much faster than the swiftest blow can travel. All that the experimentee does is to *retard* it; the quickest man retarding it the least. The string travels smoothly and swiftly in a straight line between two eyelet holes. A bead attached to that part of the string would make the necessary breaks of electric contact with great neatness. The thread has a stop to check it when it has run far enough home. My reel is nothing more than a very light wooden wheel with a groove in it, some 3 inches in diameter, and with a brass axis turning freely between fixed points. One thread passes round the axis, and is tied at the other end to an india rubber band. The other thread passes in the opposite direction round the grooved wheel, and then through the eyelet holes. The experimentee is placed well back, quite clear of the apparatus. Nothing can act better than this part of my new instrument.

(*d*) I now use a very neat, compact, and effective apparatus (made for me by Groves, 89, Bolsover Street, Portland Street, W.) which is a half-second's pendulum, held by a detent 18° from the vertical. The blow of a released hammer upon the detent gives the sound-signal and simultaneously lets the pendulum go. An elastic thread is fixed to the pendulum parallel to its axis, but about 1½ inch apart from it. As the pendulum oscillates this thread travels between 2 bars; the one fixed, the other movable. The fixed bar lies horizontally between the pendulum and the thread and is graduated. The movable bar nips the thread when a key is touched. Doing this, constitutes the response. The pendulum itself receives no jar through the act, owing to the elasticity of the thread. The graduations on the bar, that forms the chord to an arc of 18° on each side of the vertical, are calculated and published in the *Jour. Anthrop. Inst.* early last year, 1189, together with my description of the first form of the instrument. I exhibited the revised form of it at the British Association last autumn; a brief description of it will appear in their Journal. The instrument is arranged for sight signals as well. It is also arranged to measure the rapidity with which any given act can be performed. The experimentee touches a key that releases the pendulum; then he performs the act; finally he touches the second key, that causes the thread to be nipped.

9

ON THE PERCEPTION OF SMALL DIFFERENCES

With Special Reference to the Extent, Force and Time of Movement

The research project reported here was done at the University of Pennsylvania with the collaboration of George Stuart Fullerton, Professor of Philosophy at that institution. It was printed as Publications of the University of Pennsylvania, Philosophical Series No. 2, 1892.

CONTENTS

INTRODUCTION

SEC. 1. *The Least Difference Which Can Be Perceived.*—Instruments discover differences which the unaided sense cannot detect. Sensations may appear alike to common observation, while the stimuli differ by amounts which may be measured with the help of rules, clocks, balances, thermometers and other instruments. We thus find a psychological problem which admits of scientific study. How great a difference must there be between two magnitudes in order that it may be perceived, and how does this least noticeable difference vary with varying circumstances? The relation between the intensity of a stimulus and the least noticeable difference is the only problem which has hitherto received much attention. But the intensity of the stimulus is only one of a number of factors affecting the error of observation. The time and space relations of the stimulus are not less essential than its intensity; and the variations of different observers, and of the same observer in different conditions, deserve study. The determination of the relation oï one magnitude to another makes of psychology an exact science, whereas the study of personal differences may find practical applications in medicine and education.

We shall first review the methods which have been used in studying the perception of small differences, as these throw light on the nature of the mental process.

SEC. 2. *Method of the Just Noticeable Difference.*—If it be wished to determine the least difference between two stimuli which can be noticed, the simplest and most natural way would seem to be to make stimuli so different that the difference can just be noticed. This was indeed the method used by Weber[1] and by Fechner[2] in their first experiments on discrimination. It has been elaborated and praised by Wundt[3] and others, but has not escaped criticism.[4] Our own experi-

[1] Ernst Heinrich Weber, Annotationes de Pulsu, Resorptione, Auditu et Tactu, Lipsiæ, 1834; Der Tastsinn und das Gemeingefühl, in Wagner's Handwörterbuch der Physiologie, III. 2, Braunschweig, 1846; Annotationes Anatomicæ et Physiologicæ, Lipsiæ, 1851.

[2] Gustav Theodor Fechner, Zend-Avesta, Leipzig, 1851; Elemente der Psychophysik, Leipzig, 1860; In Sachen der Psychophysik, Leipzig, 1877; Revision der Hauptpunkte der Psychophysik, Leipzig, 1882.

[3] Wilhelm Wundt, Grundzüge der Physiologischen Psychologie, Dritte umg. Aufl., Leipzig, 1887; Preceding editions 1880 and 1874; Das Weber'sche Gesetz und die Methode der Minimaländerungen, Lipsiæ [1882]; Ueber die Methode der Minimaländerungen, Philosophische Studien, Leipzig, 1883, I. 556.

[4] Georg Elias Müller, Zur Grundlegung der Psychophysik, Berlin, 1879. Joseph Jastrow, a Critique of Psychophysical Methods, Am. Journal of Psychology, 1888, I. 271. Both of these writers, however, think that the method can be used in a correct manner—namely, by gradually increasing or decreasing a stimulus until the

ments have led us to the discovery of serious practical and theoretical objections to this method. These cannot be fully discussed in this paragraph. It is, however, evident that if it be left to the observer to say when he can just notice a difference, different observers may attach different meanings to the words. Lotze[1] and others adopt the curious supposition that stimuli seem exactly alike so long as the difference is less than a certain amount, whereas, when the difference is made greater than this amount, it becomes suddenly apparent. This is by no means the case. The clearness with which a difference is distinguished varies gradually from complete doubt to complete certainty. The variation is continuous, and no point can be taken and called the "just noticeable difference," and kept constant for different observers, or even for the same observer at different times. If complete certainty be taken as the standard, a difference in the stimuli will be required much greater than that which can ordinarily be distinguished, and the standard will be found to differ greatly with different observers, measuring, if anything, rather their character than their fineness of sensation. The clearness of discrimination is a continuous function of the amount of difference between the stimuli, but even with a fixed amount of difference it does not remain constant. It depends on many variables, so that a difference which may be distinctly perceived at one time will be indistinguishable at another. It has always been assumed that these variations may be eliminated by using the average of a large number of observations, but as they affect each single observation, they make it extremely difficult for a conscientious observer to come to any decision.

The only means by which scientific results can be obtained with the method of the just noticeable difference would seem to be to keep the observer in ignorance of the real relations of the stimuli, and see to it that when he said he could just notice a difference, the difference was of the sort he thought it to be. If in a long series of trials the observer make no mistake with a given difference, we may, indeed, assume that he can really distinguish this difference. But we should also conclude that he might notice a smaller difference, and have no basis for comparing different observers, or the same observer under different circumstances. If we make the difference smaller until

---

observer notice the direction of the change. This may, in some cases, be an improvement in technique, but does not seem to us to alter the fundamental assumptions of the method.

[1] Hermann Lotze, Metaphysik, Leipzig, 1879 (English translation, Oxford, 1884), § 259, "Ein Intervall bleibt, durch welches hindurch der Reiz sich erfolglos verstärkt, um erst mit dem erreichten Endwerthe einen merklichen Unterschied der Empfindung hervorzubringen."

the observer be sometimes wrong in his judgment, the method is reduced to that of right and wrong cases which we have next to consider.

SEC. 3. *Method of Right and Wrong Cases.*[1]—If two stimuli be taken so nearly alike that an observer cannot always distinguish the difference between them with clearness and certainty, and a series of trials be made, he will sometimes notice the difference distinctly, at other times vaguely or not at all, at still other times a difference will apparently be observed contrary to the real relation of the stimuli. Owing to the complex physical, physiological and psychological antecedents of perception, the same stimulus is not always accompaneid by the same sensation. There is a normal error of observation; it has been treated by mathematicians and students of the physical sciences with a view to elimination, but it can be studied with advantage by the psychologist. Experience has led to the conclusion that small errors of observation are more common than large ones, and that an error is as likely to be positive as negative. The theory of probability further assumes that an error of observation is the algebraic sum of a very large number of small errors due to independent causes. Based on these assumptions, the probability of an error of any size has been determined by mathematical analysis, giving the well-known probability curve and its equation:[2]

$$y = ce^{-h^2x^2}$$

What happens when an observer tries to distinguish a small difference may be illustrated by a diagrammatic figure (Fig. 1). Let the two magnitudes be proportional to the lines xo, XO, their difference would then be PO. Now, when the observer perceives the first stimulus xo, the error of observation will cause him to perceive it as sometimes smaller, sometimes larger than xo. The distribution of his errors is represented by the curve vyu. That is, the probability of any error, say po, is proportional to the corresponding ordinate pq, or the number of errors in one direction not greater than po is proportional to the portion of the area of the curve above this abscissa, $poyq$. The shape of the curve depends on h and c in the equation, and these depend on the average precision of observation. Thus if the curve vyu represent the

[1] This method seems to have been first used by Hegelmayer working under Vierordt's direction (Vierordt's Archiv, XI. 844). Fechner (*op. cit.*), however, deserves the chief credit for its elaboration. See, also, Müller (*op. cit.*).

[2] This paper is not written by mathematicians, nor for mathematicians. We give the commonly accepted formulæ, but our results may be understood by those who are not familiar with their significance. The theory of errors of observation is treated without mathematics by Jevons, Venn and Galton, and with the aid of comparatively simple mathematics by Airy and Merriman.

precision of one observer, the precision of a better observer would be represented by another bell-shaped curve taller and narrower than *vyu.*

This curve may be drawn if any one abscissa and its ordinate be known. An abscissa of such a size that half the errors are smaller and half larger (in the figure this would be *po*) may conveniently be used

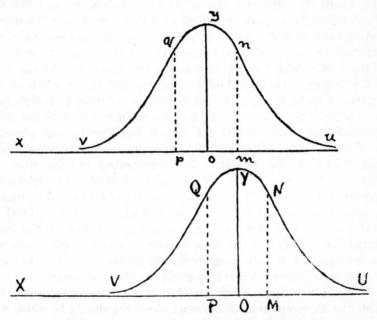

FIG. 1.—The distribution of errors of perception.

as a measure of the accuracy of discrimination. This abscissa or error is called the probable error.[1]

The error of observation cannot, however, be directly determined. After the stimulus *xo* has been perceived, a second (say greater) stimulus, *XO*, is presented to the observer. Supposing the perception of this stimulus to be subject to the same error of observation as the first,[2] the distribution of errors is represented by the curve *VYU*. Now, a consideration of these two curves will show that the first stimulus might be perceived as *xv*, and the second as *XU*, in which case the difference would be perceived with distinctness and certainty. But

[1] The mean error, the error of mean square, and the modulus are all used to measure the error of observation. These quantities are related theoretically. If the probable error be 1.00, the mean error is 1.18, the error of mean square 1.48 and the modulus 2.10.

[2] It would usually be different, but to an inconsiderable degree. (See Müller's criticism, *op. cit.*, p. 21 *seq.*)

more frequently the first stimulus would be perceived as larger than *xv*, say as *xp*, while the second stimulus might be perceived as *XM*; in this case the observer might distinguish the difference, but it would seem smaller than before, and would be noticed with less clearness and confidence. It is further possible that the two stimuli might be perceived respectively as *xo* and *XP*, in which case they would seem alike. Lastly, the first stimulus might be perceived as *xu*, while the second stimulus might be perceived as *XV*, in which case the objectively greater stimulus would appear the less. If the observer could define the amount of difference which he perceives in a series of trials, his curve of precision could be immediately drawn, but he can only do this vaguely.[1] He may, however, be required to say which of the two stimuli seems the greater, and the number of times he is right and the number of times he is wrong may be recorded.[2] If, with the same difference, two observers be right in their decisions the same percentage of times, we conclude that their accuracy of discrimination is the same. If one observer be right a larger percentage of times than another, the difference in the stimuli can be decreased for the better observer, until he be right the same percentage of times, and we regard the accuracy of discrimination of the two observers proportional to the difference which they can discriminate equally well. In the same manner the accuracy of the same observer under varying conditions (for example, when both magnitudes are greater, or when the time between their presentation is increased) may be determined.

It would be tedious to experiment until a difference were found for which the discrimination of different observers should be alike, nor is this necessary. It is evident that the percentage of right cases will increase as the difference is taken greater, and the relation between the two can be determined by mathematical analysis. It follows the formula developed by Gauss for determining the relative area of the

[1] We indeed required the observer to give the degree of confidence which he felt in his judgment, and noted it by the letters *a, b, c, d*—a plan proposed by Peirce and Jastrow (C. S. Peirce and J. Jastrow, On Small Differences of Sensation, National Academy of Sciences, III. [1884]). The great variation in the use of these letters (say "*a*" practically sure) by different observers shows how little reliance can be placed on their judgment of the just noticeable difference, Method I.

[2] As we have seen, the stimuli might appear alike, and most experimenters have recorded right, wrong and doubtful cases. Strictly speaking, however, the two stimuli would never appear exactly alike (except once in an indefinitely large number of trials), and it is theoretically better and practically more convenient to require the observer to come to some decision. "Doubtful cases" are analogous to the just noticeable difference, depending on the judgment (or caprice) of the observer. The assumption that there is no difference in sensation when the observer is doubtful as to its nature has led Fechner, Müller, Wundt and others into many difficulties.

probability curve above any abscissa. Adapted to the percentage of right cases it is

$$\frac{r}{n} = \frac{1}{2} + \frac{1}{\sqrt{\pi}} \int_0^{t\,=\,\frac{\Delta}{\text{P.E.}}} e^{-t^2}\, dt$$

in which P.E. is the probable error and Δ the amount of difference.[1] The values of this integral given in works on probability are the converse of what is needed for the present purpose. We, therefore, give a table in which the entries and arguments have been reversed. This tables gives the values of $\frac{\Delta}{\text{P.E.}}$ for every percentage of right cases above fifty.[2]

TABLE I.—TABLE FOR DETERMINING THE PROBABLE ERROR FROM THE PERCENTAGE OF RIGHT CASES AND AMOUNT OF DIFFERENCE

$\% \ r$	$\frac{\Delta}{\text{P.E.}}$	$\% \ r$	$\frac{\Delta}{\text{P.E.}}$	$\% \ r$	$\frac{\Delta}{\text{P.E.}}$	$\% \ r$	$\frac{\Delta}{\text{P.E.}}$	$\% \ r$	$\frac{\Delta}{\text{P.E.}}$
50	.00	60	.38	70	.78	80	1.25	90	1.90
51	.04	61	.41	71	.82	81	1.30	91	1.99
52	.07	62	.45	72	.86	82	1.36	92	2.08
53	.11	63	.49	73	.91	83	1.41	93	2.19
54	.15	64	.53	74	.95	84	1.47	94	2.31
55	.19	65	.57	75	1.00	85	1.54	95	2.44
56	.22	66	.61	76	1.05	86	1.60	96	2.60
57	.26	67	.65	77	1.10	87	1.67	97	2.79
58	.30	68	.69	78	1.14	88	1.74	98	3.05
59	.34	69	.74	79	1.20	89	1.82	99	3.45

The values of $\frac{\Delta}{\text{P.E.}}$ in this table are inversely proportional to the probable error of an observer, and measure directly his accuracy of discrimination. Thus if two weights be used weighing 100 and 108 gm., and one observer can correctly distinguish the difference ninety-one per cent of the time, while another can distinguish it only seventy-five per cent of the time, the accuracy of the former is about twice

[1] We had in view the testing of this formula by experiment; it had, however, been confirmed by Fechner, by Peirce and Jastrow and during the course of our experiments by Higier (Experimentelle Prüfung der psychophysischen Methoden im Bereiche des Raumsinnes der Netzhaut. Dorpat, 1890. Also Philos. Stud., VII, 232, 1891).

[2] In case the percentage of right cases be less than fifty, which can only occur when there is a constant error larger than Δ or when the number of experiments is limited, use the percentage of wrong cases, and take $\frac{\Delta}{\text{P.E.}}$ negative.

as great as that of the latter, or the observer who could distinguish a difference of 8 gm. ninety-one per cent of the time could distinguish a difference of 4 gm. seventy-five per cent of the time. Thus whatever the difference between the stimuli and whatever the percentage of right cases, the difference with which an observer would be right seventy-five per cent of the time can be discovered.

The equation given above can, of course, only be solved with the aid of the integral calculus, but its meaning may be understood by regarding Fig. 1. Thus if the difference between the stimuli be *PO*, the number of times that *XO* will seem larger than *xo* or *XP* will be to the number of times that it will seem smaller, as the area *PUNQ* is to the area *PVQ*, but in this case the area *PUNQ* is to the area *PVQ* as 3:1; consequently, when the difference (Δ) is equal to the probable error (P.E.), the observer will be right in his decision seventy-five per cent of the time.[1]

We trust the considerations brought forward in this section will throw light on the real nature of the just noticeable difference. It seems to us that it is a difference so large that the error of observation will not often cause the observer to err as to its nature. We learn by experience what difference we can usually distinguish correctly, and regard this as the just noticeable difference. But what point shall be called the just noticeable difference depends on the character and experience of the observer. Some people are sure they are right when they have but little to guide them, whereas others are slow in coming to a decision. If this view of the just noticeable difference be correct, it cannot be regarded as a fixed unit fit for measuring the intensity of sensation, and preceding theories on this subject must be radically altered.

Sec. 4. *Method of Average Error.*—If a stimulus be presented to an observer, and he be required to make a second stimulus as nearly as possible equal to it, the error of observation which we have been considering will lead him to make it sometimes greater, sometimes less. If a series of trials be made and the average error taken, the observer's accuracy of discrimination is directly measured. As (apart from con-

[1] While the probable error seems the best standard for comparison, it is better in making experiments to choose a difference with which the observer will be right about eighty-four per cent of the time, the error of mean square. This is an abscissa about half again as large as *PO* (Fig. 1), where it will be seen there is an inflection point in the curve, and it approaches the horizontal axis most rapidly. Here an alteration in the error makes the greatest difference in the size of the ordinate, and a reliable result is reached with fewest experiments. Near *Y* and near *V*, on the other hand, the curve is nearly parallel to the horizontal axis, and very large (near 100) or very small (near 50) percentages of right cases are the most unfavorable for calculating the probable error.

stant errors) the real errors are known, the average error directly obtained is proportional to the probable error (1.000:0.845), and results obtained by this method may be readily compared with those obtained by the method of right and wrong cases. By the latter method, however, we only determine the number of errors in one direction greater than a given size, and many experiments must be made before we can proceed to calculate the probable error, whereas by the method of average error the amount and direction of error are in each case measured, and a reliable result is obtained more directly and quickly. A single experiment by the method of average error indicates the observer's accuracy of discrimination, and half-a-dozen give a result sufficiently reliable for clinical and anthropometric purposes. This method is therefore to be preferred whenever it can be used. If, however, the observer be required to make a stimulus, such as a weight or light, apparently equal to another, he can only do so with repeated trials, and it is difficult to keep the conditions constant. In such a case it is better to use a fixed difference and the method of right and wrong cases. With movements, on the other hand, the method of average error can be used to great advantage. The observer is required to make one movement and then another movement as nearly as possible equal to it, the error in extent, force or time being measured by suitable apparatus. In this case, however, the error is complex, being partly an error of perception, and partly an error in adjusting the second movement. We do not see how the error of adjustment can be eliminated otherwise than by using the method of right and wrong cases.

The error of an observer is apt to consist of two components— one a variable error dependent on the normal variation in perception, which we have been considering—the other a constant error due to overestimating or underestimating the second stimulus as compared with the first. With the method of average error the constant error is directly determined by the experiments, and it may be subtracted algebraically from each error, and thus the variable error obtained.[1] The precision of observation has usually been measured by the variable error, but the constant error also measures an important error in perception.

SEC. 5. *Method of Estimated Amount of Difference.*—When experiments are made with stimuli of different degrees of intensity, a stronger and a weaker stimulus may be presented to the observer, and he may

---

[1] The theoretical relation of the variable to the constant error is determined by values of P.E. and Δ in the probability integral. See, below, the method of eliminating and determining the constant error, when the method of right and wrong cases is used.

be required to fix on a third stimulus which appears to him midway between the two. This has been called the method of mean gradation.[1] An observer may further be required to double[2] a given stimulus, also to halve it, etc. We regard this method as distinct from the three preceding methods, which rest on the error of observation.[3] It is true, the error of observation is measured in this method, but, in addition, the observer attempts to estimate definite quantitative differences in sensation. If an observer can, in fact, estimate quantitative amounts of difference in sensation, apart from association with known quantitative differences in the stimuli, a relation between mental and physical intensity can be determined. The writers, however, agree in finding that they cannot estimate such quantitative differences in sensation in a satisfactory manner. We can indeed say when one weight seems approximately double another, but this is doubtless because we have often lifted first one volume, and then two, and the like. But we cannot say when one sound seems twice as loud, or one day twice as hot as another. We have made experiments to see how nearly different observers would agree in adjusting one shade of light midway between two others, and have found hesitation in coming to a decision and great divergence of opinion. Most men will think that a just king is happier than a tyrant, but few will agree with Plato in considering him 729 times as happy.

An important distinction in the senses should be kept in mind. In estimating the quantitative relations of weights, for example, we should expect an approach to the true relations. We know when one weight is twice as heavy as another, because two objects of the same sort are twice as heavy as one, and from frequent use of the balance. We are also interested in the objective relations of weights. Two pounds of sugar cost twice as much as one, and go twice as far. Sounds and lights, however, are rarely doubled, and can be measured only with difficulty, if at all. We, therefore, have no association with the real magnitudes of the stimuli. On the other hand, we see the same object, sometimes in a bright light, sometimes in a dim light; we hear the same noise, sometimes near by, sometimes at a distance. We may, therefore, come to regard relative differences as equal differences.

SEC. 6. *The Laws of Weber and of Fechner.*—The methods we have been considering have been used chiefly in studying the relation be-

[1] This method has long been used by astronomers in estimating the apparent magnitudes of the stars. It is said to have been first used for psychological purposes by Plateau (Bull d l'Acad. de Belgique, XXXIII. 376, 1872).

[2] Apparently first done by Merkel, Philos. Stud., IV. 541; V. 245, 499, 1888–9.

[3] The method of just noticeable difference has been used in such a form that the differences should appear not just noticeable, but equal. In this case the method comes under the present head, and is subject to the same criticism.

tween the least noticeable difference and the intensity of the stimulus. Weber[1] observed that the least difference between two stimuli which could be noticed was not the same for stimuli of different magnitudes, but a proportional part of the stimulus. When an observer could just distinguish the difference between 1 and 1.05 kg., he could not distinguish any difference between 4 and 4.05 kg., but could only distinguish the difference when it was about four times as great—*i.e.*, about .2 kg.

Since Weber published this result, an amount of experiment and theorizing has been devoted to this subject, which has probably never been surpassed in the history of any science. It is commonly claimed that the experiments confirm Weber's generalization. At all events, the difference which can just be noticed is usually found to become greater as the stimulus is taken greater. Weber's law can be expressed by the equation

$$N = C \frac{\Delta S}{S}$$

in which N is the least difference which can be noticed, and ΔS the increase in the stimulus S which causes this difference. No objection can be made to this statement of Weber's law so long as the meaning of N be left an open question. We ourselves consider it a physical quantity, dependent on the error of observation, and this indeed, if Weber's law hold, would increase in direct proportion to the stimulus. Fechner, followed by many others, regards N as an equal increase in sensation, always the same whatever value may be given to S. If N be such a unit fit for measuring the intensity of sensation, it follows directly from Weber's law that the sensation increases in arithmetic ratio as the stimulus increases in geometric ratio. Fechner further assumes that the difference between no sensation and the least sensation which can be noticed is a mental quantity equal to the other N's, whence follows the equation:

$$E = C \log S$$

that is, the sensation is equal to the logarithm of the stimulus multi-

[1] *Op. cit.* As long ago as 1730 Daniel Bernoulli (cf. Todhunter, History of the Theory of Probability, Cambridge and London, 1865) maintained that the value of money is relative, so that (to use the terms of Laplace) the *fortune morale* is proportional to the logarithm of the *fortune physique*. The general principle is expressed by Hobbes and Spinoza, and is implicit very early, as in the institution of Mosaic tithes. Bouguer (Traite d'optique, etc., Paris, 1760) seems to have been the first to observe that the just noticeable difference (between lights) is proportional to the magnitude of the stimulus. Lambert (Neues Organon, Leipsic, 1764, II. 268–9) seems to have made the same observation independently, as his least noticeable difference (1⁄30) differs from that of Bouguer (1⁄64).

plied by a constant. This equation, which leads to negative sensations and other difficulties, has been discussed at great length by many writers.[1]

SEC. 7. *Interpretations of Weber's Law.*—According to Wundt and other writers, there are three possible interpretations of Weber's law. These are respectively psychophysical, physiological and psychological. The first is adopted by Fechner, who holds that his development of Weber's law expresses an ultimate relation between mind and matter. Such a functional relation is, of course, only conceivable on the assumption that the sensation is measurable. If this be the case, however, a direct proportion would seem far more natural, and should only be rejected under stress of facts which cannot otherwise be explained. The physiological interpretation of Weber's law is based on the supposition that the sensation is, indeed, directly proportional to the brain changes immediately correlated with it, but that these increase as the logarithm of the physical stimulus. It has been argued that this may be due to resistance,[2] radiation[3] or fatigue[4] in the nervous system. Owing to our complete ignorance of the minute physiology of the nervous system, such hypotheses may be made more easily than proved or disproved. The inertia of the nervous system may account for a very weak stimulus not being perceived, and its exhaustion

---

[1] Some of the more important works not hitherto mentioned in this paper are as follows:

H. Aubert, Physiologie der Netzhaut, Breslau 1865.

H. Helmholtz, Handbuch der Physiologischen Optik, Leipzig 1867. Second edition in course of publication.

J. J. Müller, Sitz. d. Sächs. Ges., Leipzig 1870.

J. Delbœuf, Étude psychophysique, Bruxelles, 1873, and later publications.

F. Brentano, Psychologie, etc., Leipzig 1874.

E. Hering, Ueber Fechner's psychophysisches Gesetz, Sitz. d. Wiener Acad. 1875.

P. Langer, Die Grundlagen der Psychophysik, Jena 1876.

F. A. Müller, Eine Untersuchung etc., Marburg 1882.

J. v. Kries, Ueber die Messung etc., Viertelj. f. wissensch. Philos., VI. Leipzig 1882.

P. Tannery, Revue Philos., Paris 1884.

A. Elsas, Ueber die Psychophysik, Marburg 1886.

A. Köhler, Ueber die hauptsächlichsten Versuche etc.; Philos. Stud., Leipzig 1886.

A. Grotenfelt, Das Weber'sche Gesetz etc., Helsingfors 1888.

H. Münsterberg, Beiträge etc., Freiburg i. B. 1889.

[2] J. Bernstein, Untersuchungen über den Erregungsvorgang im Nerven- und Muskel-Systeme, Heidelberg 1871.

[3] James Ward, An Attempt to interpret Fechner's Law, Mind I. 464, London 1876.

[4] Herm. Ebbinghaus, Ueber den Grund der Abweichungen von dem Weber'schen Gesetz bei Lichtempfindungen, Pflüger's Archiv, XLV. 113, 1889.

or destruction for a very strong stimulus failing to call forth a corresponding sensation, but so long as there is no proof it must be regarded as unlikely that brain changes should vary as the logarithm of the stimulus. A psychological explanation of Weber's law is favored by Wundt, who argues[1] that it is a case of the "relativity of feeling." This principle may account for certain effects of contrast, etc., but scarcely seems relevant to the supposed relation between intensity of sensation and intensity of stimulus. Indeed, Wundt seems to think that the physiological explanation may be combined with his.

Sec. 8. *The Relation between the Error of Observation and the Magnitude of the Stimulus.*—As may be gathered from what has preceded, the writers cannot accept any of these explanations of Weber's law. All the experiments made by the first three methods which we have described seem to us to determine the error of observation under varying circumstances, and not to measure at all the quantity of sensation. The fourth method, it is true, seeks to estimate quantitative relations in sensation, but we find that this cannot be done apart from association with known quantitative relations of the stimuli. Our own experiments by this method, to be described below, show that in such cases we tend to estimate the intensity of sensation as directly proportional to the intensity of the stimulus; consequently, in so far as any deduction concerning quantitative relations in sensation can be made from such estimation, the sensation increases as the stimulus and not as its logarithm. The experiments which we have made by the first three methods (and incidentally by the fourth) show that the error of observation usually increases as the stimulus is taken greater, but more slowly. We therefore believe that Weber's law does not hold for the perception of movement. We believe, however, that the error of observation tends to be related to the magnitude of the stimulus in a simple manner; namely, that the error of observation (and the so-called least noticeable difference) is proportional to the square root of the stimulus. We believe, further, that we can explain this relation in a satisfactory manner. Suppose time to be taken as the physical magnitude. If one second be estimated, a certain error of observation will occur. If the experiment be repeated, an error on the average of the same size will be made. Now, if the two seconds be estimated continuously, each second composing the interval may be regarded as subject to its own error. If these errors were always in the same direction, the error in estimating two seconds would be twice as great as the error in estimating one second, and Weber's law would hold. In half the cases, however, the two errors would be in opposite directions and would partly counterbalance each other, and the average error

[1] Phys. Psy., I. 377 *seq.*

in estimating two seconds would, consequently, be smaller than twice the average error for a single second. It would, indeed, according to the theory of probability (confirmed by our own experiments), be the average error for one second multiplied by the square root of two. Or, generally, the algebraic sum of a number of errors is the average error multiplied by the square root of the number. There seems to be reason for maintaining that this deduction should hold for the estimation of any physical magnitude composed of equal units, although this view has not, we think, been hitherto proposed.

As the result of our own experiments we find that the error of observation varies more nearly as the square root of the magnitude than as the magnitude. An exact correspondence with such a law can indeed only be looked for under the simple conditions assumed by the theory of probability. In actual perception the fractions of the magnitude, physically equal, would seldom or never be subject to exactly the same errors of observation. Every general law is subject to secondary laws, and the greater our knowledge the more do these secondary laws increase. The planets do not, in fact, move in ellipses, but by very complex paths; the volume of a gas does not, in fact, vary inversely as the pressure, but in a very complex manner. It is usually a token of our ignorance rather than of our knowledge when the complex phenomena of nature seem to be related by a simple mathematical formula. The error of observation would, in fact, seldom or never increase as the square root of the magnitude, but the summation of errors would seem to account in an entirely satisfactory manner for the usual increase of the error of observation as the magnitude is taken larger. We, therefore, substitute for Weber's law the following: *The error of observation tends to increase as the square root of the magnitude, the increase being subject to variation, whose amount and cause must be determined for each special case.*[1]

SEC. 9. *The Perception of Bodily Movement.*—The larger part of the experiments described in this paper are concerned with the perception of small differences in movements of the body. We choose this class of sensations, partly because it offers peculiar advantages for studying the perception of small differences, and partly because more knowledge is needed concerning the perception of movement. Movements are convenient for such study, because the observer himself causes the

[1] One of the writers (G. S. F.) gives but a qualified assent to the subject-matter of this section and its application elsewhere in this paper, on the ground that mathematicians are not agreed as to the soundness of the theory upon which the law is based, and also on the ground that the errors in question may not be independent errors. He regards, however, the results obtained by the writers as sufficiently in accord with the law to justify them in holding it tentatively, and subject to criticism.

stimulus which he perceives, while at the same time it can be measured more exactly than light or sound. The complexity of the perception of movement is so considerable that there is much difference of opinion as to its nature, and for its study exact experiments are needed.

Common observation does not tell us what nervous and muscular mechanism is involved in movement, nor what sensory apparatus is used in its perception. In this paper we shall lay stress on the fact that movements differ in their force, in their extent and in their time, and we shall try to show how accurately these different factors are discriminated, and how far they are interdependent. This analysis of movement seems to us natural, as it is in accordance with the magnitudes, energy, space and time, on which physical science is based. But we have still to inquire how we come to perceive the force, extent and time of our movements. The perception of movement was formerly identified with touch, and passive sensations from the skin undoubtedly give us knowledge concerning bodily movements. These sensations may be of two sorts—one due to pressure at the place where force is applied, the other due to contraction, relaxation, etc., of the skin of the moving member and its connections. In addition to these sensations from the skin, sensory nerves ending in the muscles[1] and about the joints[2] have been discovered, and these doubtless play some part in the perception of movement.[3] Then in all movements, and especially in such as are violent and powerful, many parts of the body are concerned. The whole position and balance of the body may be altered, and vital processes, respiration, circulation, etc., are affected. In addition to these sensations from the skin and inner body, important knowledge concerning the movement may be obtained from the other senses, particularly from sight.

It is well known that besides the numerous sensory impressions resulting from the movement, an immediate consciousness of the motor impulse calling forth the movement has been considered an essential factor in its perception. Wundt,[4] Bain[5] and others lay great stress

[1] C. Sachs, Archiv f. Anat. u. Phys., 1874, pp. 175, 491, 645. Sachs' microscopical results have, however, been disputed. See Mays, Zeitsch. f. Biol., XX.

[2] Rauber, Vater'sche Körper der Bänder und Periostnerven und ihre Beziehung zum sogenannten Muskelsinn, München, 1865. See William James, The Principles of Psychology, New York, 1890, II. 189, *seq.*

[3] Wundt (Phys. Psy., I. 464) writes: "Die Annahme eines specifischen Muskelsinnes wurde zuerst, wie es scheint, von Ch. Bell aufgestellt." The distinction was probably known to Aristotle, and is plainly made by Scaliger (1557). See Hamilton's edition of Reid's Works, Edinburgh 1846, p. 867.

[4] Beiträge zur Theorie der Sinneswahrnehmung, Leipzig 1862; Vorlesungen über die Menschen- und Thierseele, Leipzig 1863; Phys. Psy.

[5] Senses and Intellect, 3d ed., 1868. The author's views were gradually elaborated in the preceding editions, 1855 and 1864.

on this "feeling of innervation," holding it to be an important, if not the only ground for belief in matter and space. On the other hand, Bastian,[1] Ferrier,[2] James[3] and others argue that there is no consciousness accompanying the outgoing current. The extended discussion concerning the sense of innervation may be partly confused by misunderstanding. It is evident that we know what movement we purpose to make, but it seems equally evident that we cannot thus know what movement we carry out. We may will to lift a heavy box, and discover from the unexpected movement resulting that the box is empty. Our perception of the movement we have carried out may, however, be affected by our knowledge of the movement we have willed. The box which unexpectedly turns out to be empty seems to fly up of itself.

SEC. 10. *The Importance of Uniform Conditions.*—Before proceeding to describe our experiments, some mention of special methods should be made. One of the most important considerations is the need of keeping all the conditions constant, except the variable to be investigated. This is such an evident precaution in all exact experiments that it would seem needless to mention it, were it not that it has been neglected in many psychological investigations. The resulting confusion has been very great. If experiments are being made on the variation of the error of observation, with the magnitude of the stimulus, care must be taken to keep the time of stimulation, the interval between the stimuli, the place and it may be the area of stimulation, the condition of the observer, etc., constant. This has often been neglected, especially when the methods of just noticeable difference and of average error have been used. But the greatest confusion has been due to the previous knowledge of the observer. If he know the results of preceding experiments, he may seek to distinguish apparent differences in sensation, or he may seek to make his judgment objectively correct, and the difference in result will be great. If the observer know beforehand the real relations of the stimuli in each case, he will find that this will affect the apparent relations of the sensations, and almost any result can be obtained. We regard, therefore, all experiments made by a single observer on himself as provisional. Lastly, many psychological researches have but little value because the author has rejected experiments and series which seemed wrong to him. Under such circumstances even the most conscientious observer may obtain results conforming better to his theory than to the truth.

[1] On the Muscular Sense, Brit. Med. Journ., 1869; The Brain as an Organ of Mind, appendix, 3d ed., London, 1882; Brain, 1887, with discussion.

[2] The Functions of the Brain, 1st ed., London, 1876; 2d ed., 1886, Ch. X.

[3] The Feeling of Effort, Anniv. Mem. of the Boston Soc. of Nat. Hist., 1880. Psy., Ch. XXVI.

SEC 11. *Concluding Remarks.*—The experiments published in this paper were mostly carried out in the psychological laboratory of the University of Pennsylvania during the years 1889, 1890 and 1891. The observers who took part in the experiments are designated by letters: *F* and *C* the writers; *R* and *J*, respectively, their wives; *K*, also a woman, a student of psychology and biology; *D*, *N* and *S*, advanced students of psychology; *L* and *S*, advanced students of biology. The calculations were made by the observers. Most of the apparatus used was given to the University by Dr. Weir Mitchell, Mr. H. H. Houston and Mrs. Matthew Baird. Some part was obtained through an appropriation from the Bache Fund, and is the property of the National Academy of Sciences. The new apparatus was made under our direction by Clay & Torbensen, Camden, N. J. The drawings of apparatus were made by Miss Washington, University of Pennsylvania, and the curves were drawn by *F*, *C* and *J*.

PART I

On the Extent of Movement

SEC. 12. *Introductory.*—Until quite recently but little experimental work had been done on the discrimination of the extent of movements. Wundt[1] gives the results of an investigation concerned with movements of the eyes, and considers them in harmony with Weber's law. Numerous experiments[2] have been made on the perception of small differences in the length of lines; and as the eye in most cases has not been carefully fixed, the movement was doubtless an important factor in the judgment. But it cannot be separated from the influence of the size of the image. Several researches have been published comparing movements made with the right and left hands. Thus Hall and Hartwell,[3] Loeb[4] and Bloch[5] have studied movements of the arm with a view to comparing those made with the right side of the body and those made with the left. Jastrow[6] has investigated the perception of space by disparate senses, and in so doing has made use of various movements, but he is concerned rather with the relations which different senses, or different aspects of the same sense, hold to each other

[1] Phys. Psy., Bd. II. s. 116 ff.

[2] The most recent by Higier (*op. cit.*), who gives references to preceding investigations.

[3] Bilateral Asymmetry of Function, Mind, Vol. IX. pp. 93–109.

[4] J. Loeb, Untersuchungen etc., Pflüger's Archiv, 1887 and 1890.

[5] A. M. Bloch, Experience etc., Rev. Scientifique, 1890.

[6] The Perception of Space by Disparate Senses, Mind, Vol. XI. pp. 539–54.

than with the accuracy with which the extent of movements can be discriminated, in itself considered.[1]

There are peculiar difficulties connected with the study of ocular movements, and it has seemed desirable to the writers to choose for investigation movements of another class. In judging by the eye of the distance between two points, or of the length of a line, active sensations of movement may contribute much to the result; but the passive sensations arising from the extent, the position or the motion of the image on the retina, or in binocular vision, the difference in character of the retinal images, may contribute no unimportant factor. In free movements made by the arm this difficulty is obviated. They are, to be sure, complex, and in so far not wholly satisfactory; but they are at least less unsatisfactory than ocular movements, and offer the special advantage that they enable us to compare directly the judgment of the extent of a movement with the judgment of its force and time.

Our experiments on the extent of movement were undertaken with a view to:

(1) The investigation of psychophysic law in the sphere of bodily movements.

(2) A comparison of the results obtained by the use of the four psychophysical methods.

(3) The determination of the effects of practice.

(4) The determination of the significance of the confidence of the experimentee in relation to objective correctness.

(5) The investigation of constant errors.

Sec 13. *Apparatus and Methods.*—The larger part of the experiments on the discrimination of the extent of movements were made with very simple apparatus. A scale, graduated to millimeters, was fastened along the edge of an ordinary table. At one end of the scale, to the left of the experimentee as he sat facing the table, was a fixed upright which served as point of departure for the movement. A movable upright, which could be placed at any desired point on the scale, determined the extent of the movement chosen as standard of comparison. To allow for the width of the finger used in making the movements, the two uprights were set on flat bases, with bevelled edges projecting in such a way that, when these edges were in contact

---

[1] No less than four inaugural dissertations have recently been published bearing more or less directly on the subject. Those by Cremer and by Ostermann, Würzburg, and by Falk, Dorpat, we have not seen. Ueber Bewegungsempfindungen, by Edmund Burke Delabarre, Freiburg i. B., 1891, we have received since our paper has been written. This dissertation contains interesting experiments on movements of the arm, but the relation of the variable error to the magnitude of the movement is not considered.

at the 0 point of the scale, there was just room for the finger between the uprights above. A seconds pendulum, swinging above the table, gave the time for each movement, and the interval between the movements to be compared. The experimentee sat directly opposite the 10 cm. mark on the scale, with the fixed upright to his left at the 0 point. His body was about 20 cm. back from the edge of the table. The movement was made with the index finger of the right hand, the arm swinging freely and being used as a whole in the movement. The motion was from left to right, and when in motion the finger was from 2 to 6 cm. above the table. Each movement occupied, as nearly as possible, one second, and one second was allowed for recovering position between the two movements to be compared in each experiment. A screen prevented the experimentee from seeing the movements made. The recorder sat to the right of the experimentee and regulated the standard movement in each experiment by placing in position the movable upright. The experimentee then moved his finger over the space between the two uprights, and, having thus gained a standard, made a second movement to which the first served as guide. The point at which the finger rested upon the scale at the end of this second movement was recorded, the finger-nail being cut to a point as a help to the recorder. The experimentee knew nothing of the results of the experiments until after the whole number was completed. The danger of his unconsciously allowing for constant errors, and vitiating the results, was thus avoided.

With this apparatus, and in the manner described, 4400 experiments were made, and all four of the so-called psychophysical methods were employed. The method of just noticeable difference was used in the attempt to mark off a distance just greater and one just less than 500 mm. The method of estimated amount of difference was used in the attempt to halve 500 mm., to double 300 mm., and to find the mean between 300 and 700 mm. The method of average error was used in the attempt to measure off successively 100, 300, 500 and 700 mm. Finally, the method of right and wrong cases was used in the attempt to decide whether the two uprights were nearer together or farther apart in the second of each pair of movements, their distances being as 500:510 mm., or as 510:500 mm.

We have here ten different kinds of experiments; or, since the experiments by the method of right and wrong cases may count double, the second movement in each experiment being half the time longer and half the time shorter than the first, we may say that we have eleven kinds. A complete series, including ten experiments of each kind, or in all 110 experiments, was made at each sitting. Sometimes one and sometimes two series were made in a day. The ten experiments of each kind (except those by the method of right and wrong cases) were made before passing to the next and the eleven different kinds were arranged in the series in the order in which they are given above. Every second series was made in reversed order. Further details of these experiments will be given later, when each class will be discussed by itself. All these experiments were made upon F, the recorder being M, who is not otherwise represented in this paper.

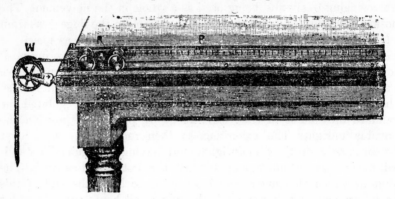

Fig. 2.—Apparatus for measuring the extent of movement.

After these experiments were made, it occurred to the writers that there was a possible source of error in the method of getting the standard movement in most of the experiments. In all the experiments, the first movement was determined by two uprights, while the second movement, except in the experiments by the method of right and wrong cases, was made with the movable upright removed. It would seem to be quite possible that the force expended in the touch against the upright limiting the first movement would have made the movement appreciably greater if the limit had not been there, and that a second movement, made in imitation of the first, but without such an independent limit, would have a tendency to be too great. Eight hundred later experiments were made by the method of average error, upon two subjects, and care was taken to overcome this difficulty. The apparatus used in making them was more elaborate than that employed before, and was constructed partly with a view to discriminating between the force and the extent of movements, and modifying either factor independently of the other.

This apparatus consists of a brass plate one meter long, graduated to millimeters, and grooved for the wheels of a small brass carriage. Along the scale is a wire, carrying an indicator (P) which is moved by a bar attached to the carriage. To the left of the experimentee, as he sits facing the apparatus, are two brass pins, which stop the carriage at the 0 point of the scale. Between the front and back wheels of the carriage, and parallel with the track, is a ring (*R*) into which is to be inserted the finger used in moving the carriage. Attached to the carriage is a cord (*W*) which runs over a pulley to the left of the experimentee, and admits of being weighted to any desired extent. Here, as before, the movement is from left to right. The indicator, which slides along the wire as the carriage moves, and remains at the farthest point reached, makes the readings much easier than in the apparatus used before, where the recorder had to catch the reading during the very brief time before the finger began the return movement. The carriage may be moved alone, or made to raise any weight attached to the cord. Thus one may study the effect of increasing or decreasing the amount of force demanded by movements of a given extent, and see to what degree judgments of distance are conditioned by the amount of force expended. So far, the writers have not found time to carry out such experiments.

Sec. 14. *Experiments by the Method of the Just Noticeable Difference.*—The method of the just noticeable difference has been described. It assumes that the smallest difference between two stimuli that can be consciously noted may be taken as a measure of the fineness of discrimination of any sense—the smaller the just noticeable difference, the greater the fineness of discrimination. But the use of this unit of measurement is, as we have seen, not without its difficulties. We do not find that all things consciously noted are noted with equal clearness. We are clearly conscious of some things, less clearly conscious of others, and still others seem to be on the border-line between consciousness, or at least what usually passes by that name, and the obscure region which has been designated as "sub-consciousness" or "latent thought." And, just as there may be many degrees of objective difference below the level of the least degree that can be consciously noted as such by the unaided sense, so it is quite thinkable that there may be many corresponding degrees of sensation below the level of that which we are accustomed to regard as on the threshold of consciousness. Such sub-conscious mental modifications may differ from those commonly called conscious, simply as the fainter among these latter differ from the clearer. That such is the case, and that we have between the clearest consciousness and a complete cessation, if such there be, of all mental life a descending series, each member of which differs continuously from the one immediately preceding it, and a portion of which lies below what we commonly recognize as the threshold of consciousness, there seems good reason to believe. We do not have, then, two clearly marked divisions, the one lying below and the other above a well-defined threshold or ideal limit between sensations of quite different classes. Neither do we have a series beginning abruptly with what would be recognized as a "conscious" sensation.

If this be the case the just noticeable difference would seem to be a unit arbitrarily taken. Since we can, by varying the objective difference between two stimuli, bring about a varying degree of clearness in the consciousness of difference, the meaning of the words "just noticeable" must necessarily be vague. A larger difference than the one settled upon would be noted with a clearer consciousness, and a smaller with a fainter, the differences between the cases being one of degree and not of kind. And although it is possible that the same observer may at different times give the words approximately the same meaning, there would appear to be no way at all of deciding that the just noticeable difference means the same thing in the case of different persons.

Again, the same degree of difference in the stimuli may, by the same observer, be perceived as a difference much more clearly at one time than at another. Many causes concur to produce at times a heightened consciousness and at times a less vivid one. Suppose that the difference between two weights is so small as to be distinguished with some clearness at one moment, and not thus distinguished at the next. Is it to be called a noticeable difference? If it be distinguished in nine cases out of ten, may we call it the *just* noticeable difference? Probably in several of those instances a smaller difference would have been noticed. It is this fluctuation in the power of discrimination, due partly to nervous changes in the observer, that has caused a series of experiments to be regarded as indispensable in the determination of the least noticeable difference.

The method of just noticeable difference may be applied in two somewhat different ways. Either two stimuli with a certain difference between them may be given the experimentee, and the difference increased or decreased until the observer considers it just noticeable —or a single stimulus may be given, and the experimentee required to fix upon another just noticeably greater or less. The just noticeable difference is here assumed to be the average obtained by combining the results of a number of experiments. In all the experiments given below as made by this method, the latter course was adopted. In this form, it will be seen that the method is analogous to that of average error; and as the numbers of right and of wrong cases were recorded, the three psychophysical methods have been combined.

With the simple apparatus first described, 800 experiments were made by the method under discussion. Half of them were attempts to mark off on the scale a distance just greater, and half a distance just less than 500 mm. As details concerning the methods have already been given, it is only necessary to say that the recorder placed the movable upright at the 500 mm. mark on the scale, the experimentee moved his finger between the two uprights in the manner described, and then attempted, the movable upright having been taken away, to measure off a distance just greater or just less, as the case might be. The results of the experiments appear in the accompanying table.

TABLE II.—EXTENT OF MOVEMENT—METHOD OF JUST NOTICEABLE DIFFERENCE— *F* EXPERIMENTEE—800 EXPERIMENTS—VII. VIII. 1890

	Just greater than 500 mm.				Just less than 500 mm.			
	Ext.	V.E.	*V*	% W.	Ext.	V.E.	*V*	% W.
Av..............	+36.6	11.4	5.7	3	−24.7	10.	5.4	6
Var..............	*16.6*	*1.6*	*1.1*		*13.1*	*1.8*	*1.2*	
Av..............	+60.1	9.8	5.0	0	− 4.8	9.1	5.1	33
Var..............	*8.2*	*2.7*	*1.2*		*8.4*	*2.3*	*1.1*	
Av..............	+39.4	7.8	4.7	0	−24.2	9.	5.3	4
Var..............	*5.6*	*1.6*	*1.1*		*7.2*	*1.8*	*1.1*	
Av..............	+21.5	8.9	4.7	5	−37.7	8.6	5.1	0
Var..............	*6.3*	*2.*	*1.1*		*11.1*	*1.2*	*1.3*	
Av. Av..........	**+39.4**	**9.5**	**5.**	**2**	**−22.8**	**9.2**	**5.2**	**10.7**
Av. V..........	*9.2*	*2.*	*1.1*		*9.9*	*1.8*	*1.2*	

Ext. The extent of the second movement as compared with 500 mm.
V.E. The average variable error made.
V. The mean variation of the variable error.
%W. The percentage of wrong cases; *i.e.*, attempts at greater which resulted in less, and *vice versa*.
Av. The average extent, variable error, and variation of the variable error for 100 experiments.
Var. The mean variation of the results of the ten sets of ten experiments each from their average as given above opposite *Av.*
Av. Av. The average of the four sets of figures opposite *Av.* above, giving the averages for 400 experiments.
Av. V. The average of the four sets of figures opposite *Var.* above.

As has been said, ten experiments of each of the eleven kinds made with the first apparatus were made at one sitting. The results of each such set of ten experiments have been calculated, and then these results combined in sets of ten to get the averages which appear in the four tables embodying the results of this investigation. The averages given in the tables consequently represent in each case 100 experiments. As 400 experiments of each kind were made, there are four such sets of averages for each kind of experiment, and these are combined at the foot of the tables in figures which represent averages for the whole 400 experiments. The averages are given in their chronological order, those at the top of each table representing the first hundred experiments made of the class indicated, those below them the second hundred, etc. The experiments made later with the second piece of apparatus were also made in sets of ten, and the results have been computed in the same way.

To enter more into detail, let the first set of averages in the table just given and under just greater than 500 mm. be taken. The figures to the right of *Av.* and under the headings *Ext.*, *V.E.*, *V* and *% W* indicate that, in a hundred experiments, the average distance measured off as just greater than 500 mm. was 536.6 mm.; the average variable error or mean variation of the individual distances from the average of each series of 10 experiments was 11.4 mm.; the mean variation of the variable error, or the average of the deviations of the variable error from its average, was 5.7 mm.; while three per cent of the attempts to mark off a distance just greater than 500 mm. resulted in marking off a distance actually less.

The figures in italics below these averages have reference to the results of the separate sets of ten experiments each. For each set of ten experiments the average extent of the distance measured off, the variable error or mean variation of the single distances from this average, and the mean variation of this variable error, were computed. The averages described in the preceding paragraph were, of course, obtained by taking the average of ten sets of results thus obtained. The mean variation from their average of these results representing in each case ten series appears in the second row opposite *Var.* Thus, the mean variation of the average distance measured off, in the first ten sets of ten experiments, from the 536.6, the figures obtained by averaging these averages, was 16.6 mm. Similarly the mean variation of the variable error for the ten sets was 1.6, and the mean variation of the variation of this variable error for the ten sets 1.1.

These explanations will apply, with a few obvious changes, to all the sets of figures on the table. Of course, where the endeavor was to measure off a distance just less than 500 mm., and the minus sign is used under the heading *Ext.*, it is meant that the distance measured off was as much less than 500 mm. as is indicated by the figures. For example, in the first block of averages under "just less than 500 mm.," the −24.7 means that the average distance measured off in 100 experiments was 475.3 mm. The significance of the averages at the bottom of the table is too plain to need comment.

It appears, as a result of 400 experiments, that a movement, to be just noticeably greater than a previous movement of 500 mm. must be 539.4 mm. long; and from the same number of experiments, it appears that to be just noticeably shorter a movement must be 477.2 mm. long. The difference between the attempt at just less and the standard movement (5 per cent of the former) is thus considerably less than the difference between the standard movement and the attempt at just greater (8 per cent of the standard). A glance at the table will show, however, that these results are modified by a marked tendency to overrate the standard in the second group of 100 experiments of both kinds. In these experiments the attempts at just greater gave an average of 560.1 mm., and the attempts at just less one of 495.2 mm., while 33 per cent of the attempts at just less resulted in a movement actually greater than 500 mm. Still, in three out of the four groups of experiments of both kinds there appears to be a tendency to overrate the standard movement.

What has been said of the highly variable character of the just noticeable difference may be well illustrated from the table. Even for groups of 100 experiments it varies, for the attempt at just greater, between 60.1 mm. and 21.5 mm., and for the attempt at just less between 37.7 mm. and 4.8 mm. For the smaller groups of ten experiments the variation was still more marked. In the attempts at just greater it varied between 76 mm. and 9 mm., and in the attempts at just less between 49 mm. and 1 mm.

In striking contrast with these figures stands the very slight degree of fluctuation in the variable error and its mean variation. These would seem to be a much better measure of discriminative power than the least noticeable difference itself, for they do not appear to be subject to the disturbing influence of constants. For example, the average increment necessary to produce the consciousness of just greater in the second group of 100 experiments was 60.1 mm., and in the fourth group only 21.5 mm.; but the mean variations corresponding to these were respectively 9.8 and 8.9, and their variations in turn 5.0 and 4.7. Or, to take the second group of 100 experiments alone, as the tendency to overrate the stimulus was there most marked, while the increment under "just greater" was 60.1 mm., and the decrease under "just less" only 4.8 mm., their variable error was respectively 9.8 and 9.1, and the mean variation of this 5.0 and 5.1.

It is sufficiently evident that the just noticeable difference is of little value in psychophysical experiments. It varies within wide limits even for sets of 100 experiments, and the only objective criterion of its significance—the percentage of right and wrong cases obtained—varies correspondingly. If the average of a large number of experiments be taken, the difference will be found to be too large, and the percentage of wrong cases too small to be satisfactory in experiments by the method of right and wrong cases. Where the proportion of right cases is so large, the results may easily be modified by accidental variations. Moreover, as the percentage of right cases does not increase uniformly as the difference increases, the average percentage of errors given in the table does not really correspond to the average just noticeable difference, but is somewhat too low. One may, it is true, apply the probability integral to the separate averages for 100 experiments, and compute the percentage of errors corresponding to the average just noticeable difference, but even in this case the results would not be wholly trustworthy, as the difference was highly variable even within the sets of 100 experiments. The variable error of the just noticeable difference furnishes a more satisfactory measure of discrimination, but there is no special advantage in taking the average variable error of this difference, as it is more regular when the method of average error is used.

SEC. 15. *Experiments by the Method of Estimated Amount of Difference.*—The method of mean gradation favored by Wundt[1] concerns itself only with the attempt to find a mean between two given stimuli (sensations?). There appears, however, no good reason for not using other relations as a measure of accuracy in discrimination. If one observer can fix more accurately than another upon a stimulus half as great, or twice as great, as a given one, his sense of the quantitative relations between stimuli must be finer. The method of estimated amount of difference would include all such estimates of the quantitative relations of differing stimuli.

Twelve hundred experiments were made by the method of estimated amount of difference. Of these 400 were attempts to mark off on the scale the half of 500 mm., 400 were attempts to double 300 mm., and 400 were attempts to find the mean between 300 and 700 mm. The details of the experiments were similar to those of the experiments by the method of just noticeable difference. In the attempt to halve 500 mm., the movable upright was placed by the recorder at the 500 mark on the scale, the experimentee moved his finger between the uprights, and then tried to make a movement half as long. In the same way a stimulus of 300 mm. was given, and then an attempt was made to double the distance; and, in the third case, two stimuli of 300 and 700 mm. were given one second apart, and the attempt made to give their mean in a third movement.

The results have been calculated and tabulated in precisely the same way as those of the experiments by the method of just noticeable difference, so that it is scarcely necessary to give a detailed description of the table. The four sets of averages for each kind of experiment represent in each case 100 experiments. *Var.* gives the

[1] Phys. Psy., Bd. I. 8, § 1.

mean variation from their average of the results obtained from the separate sets of ten experiments in each group of 100. Thus, to take the first 100 attempts to halve 500 mm., the figures on the first line in the table indicate that the average distance marked off was 305.8 mm., or 55.8 mm. too great; that the mean variation of the single distances from the average of each series of ten was 13.3, and the mean variation of the variations 7.5. The −41.2 to the right of these in the same line indicates that the average distance measured off in the attempt to double 300 mm. was 558.8 mm., or 41.2 mm. too short. The corresponding figures for experiments of the third kind show that the average of 100 attempts to find the mean between 300 mm. and 700 mm. resulted in a distance of 517.4 mm., or 17.4 mm. too great. The three sets of averages at the bottom of the table represent in each case 400 experiments.

TABLE III.—EXTENT OF MOVEMENT—METHOD OF ESTIMATED DIFFERENCE—
F EXPERIMENTEE—1200 EXPERIMENTS—VII. VIII. 1890

	Halve 500 mm.			Double 300 mm.			Mean 300 and 700 mm.		
	Ext.	V.E.	*V*	Ext.	V.E.	*V*	Ext.	V.E.	*V*
Av........	+55.8	13.3	7.5	−41.2	16.6	9.1	+17.4	15.2	8.2
Var........	*13.4*	*2.5*	*1.1*	*23.4*	*4.6*	*2.3*	*15.5*	*3.8*	*2.4*
Av........	+71.9	12.3	6.7	−18.1	14.4	7.7	+36.3	16.4	9.2
Var........	*9.9*	*2.3*	*2.1*	*12.7*	*3.1*	*1.9*	*8.7*	*4.4*	*2.8*
Av........	+51.9	11.	6.6	−42.3	11.5	7.1	+ 3.3	14.	8.9
Var........	*10.8*	*3.2*	*2.*	*16.1*	*2.3*	*1.7*	*13.9*	*3.2*	*2.3*
Av........	+41.3	11.3	5.9	−58.2	13.1	6.6	− 7.4	14.1	8.6
Var........	*6.9*	*2.7*	*1.7*	*17.6*	*2.1*	*1.6*	*11.6*	*4.7*	*2.*
Av. Av....	**+55.2**	**12.**	**6.7**	**−39.9**	**13.9**	**7.6**	**+12.4**	**14.9**	**8.7**
Av. V......	**10.2**	**2.7**	**1.7**	**17.4**	**3.**	**1.9**	**12.4**	**4.**	**2.4**

As a result of 400 experiments of each kind, we find that the attempt to halve 500 mm. gave an average distance 55.2 mm. too long; the attempt to double 300 mm. a distance 39.9 mm. too short; and the attempt to find a mean between 300 and 700 mm. a distance 12.4 mm. too long. From the figures above these averages it is evident that the tendency toward the error they exhibit was fairly constant. In the attempts to halve 500 mm., not one of the forty sets of ten experiments gave an average that was not too great. In the attempts to double 300 mm., on the contrary, all but one set (1 mm.

too great) gave an average that was too small. The experiments of the third kind were less constant. In three of the four groups of 100, the mean fixed upon was too great, but in only one of these groups did each of the ten sets of ten experiments give an average too great. The final averages are considerably modified by the marked tendency to overrate the standard observable in the second 100 experiments of each kind. This tendency has been pointed out in discussing the corresponding groups of the experiments made by the method of just noticeable difference.

It is not easy to compare with each other the results obtained in the three kinds of experiments under discussion, for the experiments are quite different. It is, however, worthy of note that, whether we take the relation of the constant error made to the distance aimed at or to the stimulus given (in the experiments of the third class, to either of the stimuli), we find that the attempt to strike a mean between two stimuli results in a smaller error than the attempt to halve or to double a single stimulus. This is in harmony with the statement Wundt makes[1] in speaking of the measurement of mental intensities—namely, that the mean between two stimuli can be more accurately determined than can a stimulus bearing some given relation to a single stimulus. The difference does not, however, appear to be so great as his words would lead one to expect. Moreover, it should be kept in mind that the mean between 300 and 700 mm. is 500 mm., that this was one of the stimuli most constantly used, and that the objective quantitative relations of the stimuli were known to the experimentee. Before the first ten experiments of the kind in question were made, a stimulus of 500 mm. had been given the experimentee twenty times, and a but slightly different stimulus of 510 mm. had been given ten times. As a result of the experiments discussed in this monograph, the writers have been led to believe that the memory for absolute stimuli is better than has been commonly thought. Some experiments to show the memory of the experimentee for the stimuli employed in these experiments on the extent of movement will be given in a later section.

Furthermore, if we take, not the constant error, but the variable error or its variation, as a measure of the fineness of discrimination, what has been said of the accuracy with which a mean between two stimuli may be found does not hold. The 400 attempts to halve 500 mm. gave a variable error of 12; the attempts to double 300 mm. a variable error of 13.9; while the attempts at the mean between 300 and 700 mm. gave a variable error greater than either, 14.9. The average variation of the variable error for the forty sets of ten experi-

[1] Phys. Psy., Bd. I. 8, § 1.

ments in each case (in the table, under the figures just quoted) was, too, least for the experiments of the first kind, and greatest for those of the third, being respectively 2.7, 3.0 and 4.0.

The results of these experiments are all contrary to Fechner's law. If we assume that in such experiments we base our judgment on the quantitative relations of two sensations, and if, as Fechner maintained, the sensation increase as the logarithm of the stimulus, the attempt to halve 500 mm. should result in a distance less than 250, whereas it has given one of 305.2; the attempt to double 300 mm. ought to give a distance greater than 600, whereas it has given only 560.1; and the attempt to find the mean between 300 and 700 mm. should give a distance under 500, whereas the mean found is 512.4. That these results are not due simply to a constant tendency to over or underestimate the given stimuli, is evident from the fact that they are all contrary to Fechner's law, while any constant tendency to an over or underestimation of the stimuli would have the effect of making all the results greater or less together, and would not diminish the results of the experiments of the second kind, while increasing those of the first and third.

It will be noticed that in these experiments by the method of estimated amount of difference, the variable error is, in proportion to the whole extent of the movement made, greater than in the case of the experiments by the method of just noticeable difference. The attempts at just greater than 500 mm. resulted in a distance of 539.4, with a variable error of 9.5, or .018, and the attempts at just less in a distance of 477.2, with a variable error of 8.7, or .018 of that movement. In the three kinds of experiments now under discussion the movements were respectively 305.2, 560.1 and 512.4 mm., and the variable errors corresponding to them .039, .025 and .029. The attempt to double 300 mm. resulted in a variable error smaller in relation to the whole extent of the movement made than was the variable error in the experiments of the first and third kinds.

SEC. 16. *Experiments by the Method of Average Error.*—By the method of average error 1600 experiments were made with the apparatus first described, and 800 more were made later upon two different experimentees with the second piece of apparatus. Only the 1600 first made will be discussed in this section. They were of four different kinds, and consisted in attempts to measure off on the scale 100, 300, 500 and 700 mm. Thus, the recorder placed the movable upright at the 100 mm. mark on the scale, the experimentee moved his finger as described between the uprights, and then, the movable upright having been taken off the scale, attempted to mark off a distance equal to the standard. The same thing was done for 300, 500 and 700 mm.

Four hundred experiments of each kind were made, and they were made, as were those described in the preceding sections, in sets of ten. The results have been counted out and tabulated in the same way as those already given. The four sets of averages for each kind of experiment represent in each case 100 experiments. The general averages at the bottom of the table give the results of the whole 400 experiments of each kind. The figures in italics refer to the results obtained for the separate sets of ten experiments. To take again as representative a single block of figures: the +8.9, in the first line under 100 mm., and opposite Av., signifies that the first hundred attempts to repeat a movement of 100 mm. resulted in an average movement of 108.9 mm., or one 8.9 mm. too long; the 5.7 in the same line gives the mean variation of the single distances from the average of each series of ten; and the 3.5 gives the mean variation from its average of this variation. In the second line, the 5.1, .6 and .6 give the mean variations of the results obtained for the ten separate sets of ten experiments from their respective averages as indicated in the line above.

TABLE IV.—EXTENT OF MOVEMENT—METHOD OF AVERAGE ERROR—
F EXPERIMENTEE—1600 EXPERIMENTS—VII. VIII. 1890

	100 mm.			300 mm.			500 mm.			700 mm.		
	Ext.	V.E.	V	Ext.	V.E.	V	Ext.	V.E.	V	Ext.	V.E.	V
Av............	+ 8.9	5.7	3.5	+ 3.7	8.8	4.6	+ .8	10.8	6.2	+ 2.8	10.4	6.1
Var..........	*5.1*	*.6*	*.6*	*9.6*	*1.6*	*1.0*	*7.4*	*1.8*	*1.2*	*10.8*	*2.8*	*1.7*
Av............	+18.4	5.3	3.3	+21.4	9.5	5.5	+27.6	10.8	6.3	+13.1	7.7	4.9
Var..........	*3.1*	*1.1*	*.5*	*9.0*	*1.9*	*1.7*	*5.6*	*2.8*	*1.3*	*4.7*	*2.1*	*1.3*
Av............	+14.7	5.3	2.9	+ 2.4	7.3	4.6	+ 3.0	8.3	4.3	− 6.4	9.4	5.7
Var..........	*2.9*	*1.7*	*.7*	*8.6*	*2.4*	*1.6*	*6.2*	*2.2*	*1.1*	*7.8*	*2.0*	*1.2*
Av............	+ 5.4	4.8	2.8	−16.4	9.5	5.2	−14.0	8.2	5.4	−28.9	8.	4.9
Var..........	*3.6*	*.8*	*.6*	*9.6*	*2.1*	*.8*	*8.6*	*2.0*	*1.4*	*9.3*	*2.0*	*1.7*
Av. Av........	+11.8	5.3	3.1	+ 2.8	8.8	5.0	+ 4.3	9.5	5.5	− 4.8	8.9	5.4
Av. Var........	*3.7*	*1.*	*.6*	*9.2*	*2.*	*1.3*	*6.9*	*2.2*	*1.2*	*8.1*	*.22*	*1.5*

From the table it appears, in each case as a result of 400 experiments, that the attempts to mark off 100, 300, 500 and 700 mm. gave an average of, respectively, 111.8, 302.8, 504.3 and 695.2 mm. The tendency to overestimate the shortest distance, 100 mm., was very marked. The greatest distance, 700 mm., was underestimated. There is a general agreement between these results and those of the experiments made with the second piece of apparatus, as will be pointed out in the next section; and it will be seen, when the experiments made on the force of movement are described, that a similar tendency is apparent. Evidently the constant error, as it stands here, cannot be taken alone as a measure of the fineness of discrimination in judging of the extent of movements. It is much the greatest in the case of the smallest movement.

The variable error increases as the distance increases, until we come to the 700 mm. movement, when it falls somewhat. For the four movements it is respectively 5.3, 8.8, 9.5 and 8.9; or

	For 100 mm.	300	500	700
Compared with the standard movement.........	.053	.029	0.19	0.13
Compared with the movement actually made....	.047	.029	0.91	0.13

Thus the variable error does not accord with Weber's law, but increases much more slowly than the stimulus. Its relation to the square root of the stimulus is for the four movements:

For 100 mm.	300	500	700
.530	.513	.424	.336

It increases, therefore, somewhat more slowly than the square root of the stimulus, for the first three movements, and falls considerably with the last.

If this variable error be taken as a measure of discriminative power, it would seem that a distance of 500 mm. is not as accurately discriminated as one of 700. It should be taken into consideration that, in making such movements as those employed in these experiments, very different muscles are brought into play at different times, and the tension upon the skin and joints is much greater in the more extended movements. Placed as the experimentee was, before the 100 mm. mark on the scale, there was a distinct feeling of strain in reaching to the 700 mm. point, although the finger could readily be extended some distance beyond it. It is not inconceivable that the peculiar factors entering into the consciousness of a movement of 700 mm. should make discrimination finer for such a movement than for one of 500 mm. A similar fall of the error with the last movement will be seen in the results of the later experiments to be described below.

The amount of the variable error, of its variation, and of the constant error, for each of the four stimuli selected may be seen at a glance from the accompanying curves.

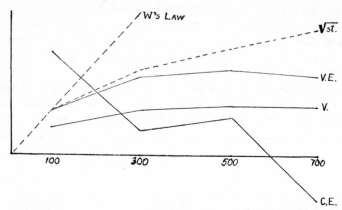

FIG. 3.

V.E.   Curve representing the amount of the variable error for 100, 300, 500 and 700 mm. as determined for each point by 400 experiments by the method of average error. F. experimentee.

V.   Similar curve representing the mean variation of the above variable error.

C.E.   Similar curve representing the amount of the constant error.

W's Law.   A line representing the increase of the variable error according to Weber's law, the smallest magnitude being taken as norm.

$\sqrt{st}$.   Curve representing the increase of the variable error as proportional to the square root of the stimulus.

It is interesting to compare the variable error obtained in these experiments with that obtained in the experiments by the methods of just noticeable difference and estimated amount of difference, when the movement was approximately the same. In the experiments by the method of just noticeable difference, with movements of 477.2 and 539.4 mm., the error was .018; in those by the method of estimated amount of difference, with the movement of 512.4, the error was .029; in these experiments, with a movement of 504.3, the error was .019. Again, in the experiments by the method of estimated amount of difference, with a movement of 305.2, the error was .039; in these experiments, with a movement of 302.8, the error was .029.

We find, therefore, that the variable error is greatest in experiments by the method of estimated amount of difference—a result one would naturally expect, in view of the difficulty of holding such relations in mind during the experiments.

It may be well to insert here the record of a few attempts made to mark off from memory, and without previous stimulus being given, the distances used as stimuli in the experiments on the extent of movement. After twenty complete series of experiments had been made, that is, after one-half of the whole number, the experimentee tried to measure off ten times in succession a distance of 100, then one of 300, of 500 and of 700 mm. After forty series—the whole number of experiments—this was done again, but then done three times, making thirty attempts at each of the distances. The results of the forty trials at each of the four stimuli are as follows:

TABLE V

	100 mm.		300 mm.		500 mm.		700 mm.	
	Ext.	V.E.	Ext.	V.E.	Ext.	V.E.	Ext.	V.E.
After 20.....	+34	14	+48	21	+37	25	+11	10
After 40.....	+22	10	− 7	31	− 5	17	−10	14
	+20	12	+ 1	13	−20	13	+ 8	15
	+19	8	− 9	14	−29	21	−16	16
Av..........	+24	11	+ 8	20	− 4	19	− 7	14

Thus forty attempts to measure off without previous stimulus 100 mm. resulted in a distance 24 mm. too great; as many to measure off 300 gave a distance 8 mm. too great; the same number for 500 and 700 gave distances too short by, respectively, 4 and 7 mm. There is evidence of the tendency before remarked to overrate the shorter distance. The variable error is in every case greater than in the corresponding division of the experiments by the method of average error, where previous stimulus was given. The error falls, as it does, with the last movement, indicating a greater accuracy of discrimination.

These experiments show that our memory for absolute distances is fairly accurate, and they are of some significance in connection with the experiments by the method of estimated amount of difference. The attempt to find a mean between 300 and 700 mm. resulted in a constant error of +12.4; this mean was known by the experimentee to be 500; the attempt to mark off 500 mm. from memory gave a constant error of −4 only. It follows that the smallness of the constant error in the attempts to find the mean between 300 and 700 mm. proves little in regard to the accuracy with which a mean can, in general, be found between two stimuli. On the other hand, the fact that the variable error in these attempts to find a mean was .029 of the movement made, while the variable error in the memory-experiments was .038 of the movement made, indicates that the presence of the stimulus had the effect of heightening the accuracy of the judgments.

The amount of the variable error, in the experiments by the

method of average error, when previous stimulus was given, was, as has been said,

	For 100 mm.	300	500	700
Compared with the standard movement.........	.053	.029	.019	.013
Compared with the movement actually made....	.047	.029	.019	.013

In these experiments it is

	For 100 mm.	300	500	700
Compared with the movement aimed at.........	.110	.067	.038	.020
Compared with the movement actually made....	.089	.065	.038	.022

It is thus about double the error obtained with previous stimulus given. Its excess over this would seem to indicate the variable error of memory.

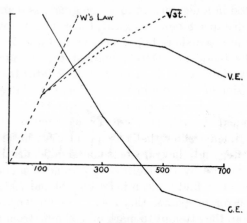

Fig. 4.

The amount of this error, and of the constant error for each of the four distances, is represented in the accompanying curves. They represent the amount of the error as compared with the distance aimed at, and not as compared with the movement actually made. As they are drawn on the same scale as the former curves, their divergence from these may be readily seen.

Sec. 17. *Later Experiments by the Method of Average Error.*—The 800 experiments by the method of average error with the second piece of apparatus were made upon two subjects—400 upon each.

The distances taken as stimuli were, as before, 100, 300, 500 and 700 mm. The details of the experiments were similar in the two cases, except that in the later experiments the stimulus was not determined by the two uprights, but was set by the experimentee himself. Before each set of ten experiments with the one stimulus, the experimentee was told to measure off the distance chosen as stimulus. He was then informed whether the distance he had measured off was too great or too small. Four more trials were allowed him, after each of which he was informed of the nature and amount of his error, and he was then required, in making the experiments, to determine the extent of the first movement by the standard thus held in memory. The second movement was an attempt to repeat the first. It will be seen that the conditions of the first and second movements were, in this case, similar, neither of them being terminated by a fixed limit.

These experiments were, unfortunately, not made on *F*, the subject in the earlier experiments, and one cannot be sure that the difference in the constant error is due to the difference in the conditions under which the experiments were made. Still, it is interesting to note that in these experiments there is a tendency to diminish the relative extent of the second movement, and it is not improbable that the absence of the upright, which, in the earlier experiments, limited the first movement, has something to do with this.

The tendency to underestimate the standard movement, as the distance increases, is here, as before, sufficiently marked. For the first three movements the constant error varies nearly as the movement. With the last movement it diminishes.

Neither the average error nor the variable error increases directly as the extent of the movement, and hence they do not agree with Weber's law. For both subjects they increase more nearly as the square root of the distance for the first three movements, though the approximation is not very close. For both subjects these errors fall decidedly with the last movement.

Whether, therefore, we consider the constant error, the variable error or the average error, we find that discrimination is finer for a movement of 700 mm. than for one of 500. This accords with the results of the earlier experiments, as far as the variable error is constant. In those experiments, however, the constant error does not follow the course it does here. It falls, then rises, then falls again to a negative error rather greater than the positive error at 500 mm.

It will be seen that, though the results obtained with the two subjects are of the same general nature, all three errors are much greater in the case of the second subject. This would indicate a greater fineness of discrimination in the first, who is a woman. Whether women gen-

TABLE VI.—EXTENT OF MOVEMENT—METHOD OF AVERAGE ERROR—K AND D EXPERIMENTEES—800 EXPERIMENTS—1890

		100 mm.				300 mm.				500 mm.				700 mm.			
		Ext. I	Ext. II	Av. E.	V.E.	Ext. I	Ext. II	Av. E.	V.E.	Ext. I	Ext. II	Av. E.	V.E.	Ext. I	Ext. II	Av. E.	V.E.
K	Av..........	105.9	+3.8	11.9	11.4	307.8	+0.2	21.8	21.1	506.3	− 3.2	25.8	22.6	692.9	− 0.7	21.0	16.9
	Var..........	8.8	5.6	2.1	2.0	21.2	10.0	4.6	5.1	15.6	11.0	7.4	6.5	13.0	13.8	5.9	8.7
D	Av..........	101.0	−2.9	17.3	16.2	301.1	−14.3	32.4	26.1	473.9	−24.1	41.3	31.3	697.7	−19.7	33.5	25.7
	Var..........	5.6	4.3	2.8	3.7	14.7	10.0	5.1	7.1	14.9	10.1	6.3	5.5	15.6	13.9	10.2	7.5
	Av. Av..........	103.4	+0.4	14.6	13.8	304.4	− 7.0	27.1	23-6	490.1	−13.6	33.5	26.9	695.3	−10.2	27.2	21.3
	Av. Var..........	7.2	4.9	2.4	2.8	17.9	10.0	4.8	6.1	15.2	10.5	6.8	6.0	14.3	13.8	8.0	5.6

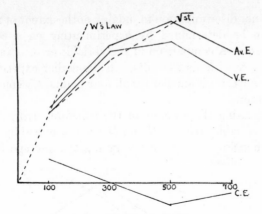

FIG. 5.—Curves for K.

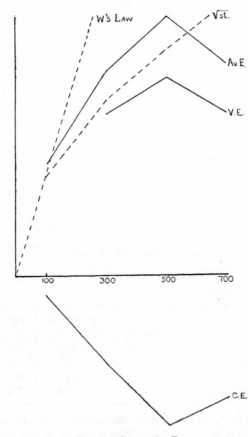

FIG. 6.—Curves for D.

erally have a finer discrimination in judging of the extent of movements would have to be determined by experimenting on a considerable number of persons. A comparison of the variable error obtained in the experiments on *K* with that obtained in the earlier experiments on *F* will show that *F*'s error is smaller for all four points. *F*'s constant error, however, is larger.

Curves indicating the amount of the constant error, the average error, and the variable error for *K* and *D*, as determined by 100 experiments for each point, as also curves giving the average for the two subjects, are subjoined.

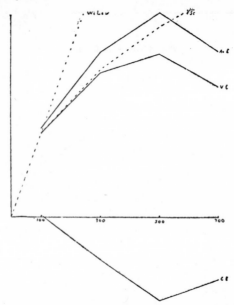

FIG. 7.—Average for K. and D.

The amount of the average and variable errors is thus, in relation to the distance aimed at:

	For 100 mm.	300	500	700
Average error for *K*	.119	.073	.051	.030
Average error for *D*	.173	.108	.083	.048
Variable error for *K*	.114	.070	.045	.024
Variable error for *D*	.162	.087	.063	.037

If the error be compared with the distance actually measured off, the figures are but little changed. The *abscissæ* in the curves indicate the distance aimed at. The relative amount of the constant error in figures might be misleading, as it passes from + to −.

Sec. 18. *Experiments by the Method of Right and Wrong Cases.*—
By the method of right and wrong cases 800 experiments were made,
the stimuli used being 500 and 510 mm. The method has been described
and criticised in the introduction, and it is not necessary to dwell upon
it here. Most of the needful details concerning the experiments have

TABLE VII.—EXTENT OF MOVEMENT—METHOD OF RIGHT AND WRONG CASES—
500:510 mm.—*F* EXPERIMENTEE—800 EXPERIMENTS—VII. VIII. 1890

	2d the greater			2d the less			Average		
	R	W	D	R	W	D	R	W	D
1st group.........	76	21	3	75	22	3	75.5	21.5	3
2d group.........	67	32	1	71	28	1	69	30	1
3d group.........	81	19	0	67	33	0	74	26	0
4th group........	76	24	0	74	26	0	75	25	0
Average..........	75	24	1	71.8	27.2	1	73.4	25.6	1

% of whole number of right cases when the 2d was greater............	51.1
% of whole number of wrong cases when the 2d was greater..........	46.9

Degree of confidence	a	b	c	d
% of times used..................................	.5	12.5	86.	1.
% of times used when right.......................	.7	15.1	84.2	
% of times used when wrong......................	.0	5.1	94.9	
% of times right in the case of each degree..........	100	97.	71.7	

R, Right.
W, Wrong.
D, Doubtful.
First group representing 100 experiments of each sort, as does each of the other groups.
Average, The average of 400 experiments.
a, Quite confident.
b, Fairly confident.
c, Less confident.

already been given. Briefly stated, the experiments were made as
follows: The movable upright was placed by the recorder at the 500
or the 510 mm. mark on the scale, as the case might be. The experimentee then moved his finger between the uprights, and thus obtained
the standard movement. As he recovered position for a second movement, the movable standard was shifted to the 510 or the 500 mm.
mark. He again made a movement between the two uprights, and then
gave a decision as to whether the second movement was longer or
shorter than the first. In giving his decision he used the letters *a*, *b* or
c to express his degree of confidence in the correctness of this judgment,

a indicating that he was quite confident, *b* that he was fairly confident, and *c* that he was less confident.

Twenty experiments by this method were made at a sitting; in ten of them the second stimulus was the greater, and in ten the less. Of course, the second stimulus was made greater or less at random, and care was taken to avoid following any order which could be surmised by the experimentee. The twenty experiments were all made, as were the sets of ten in the other kinds of experiments, before taking up another kind. The results of the experiments are given in Table VII.

The 400 experiments in which the second movement was greater, and the 400 in which it was less, are each divided into four groups of 100 experiments, and the percentages, which are also the numbers of right, wrong and doubtful judgments, are given for each group, under *R*, *W*, and *D*. The groups are arranged in chronological order. Thus, in the first 100 experiments made with the second movement greater, it was judged greater seventy-six times, less twenty-one times, and the experimentee was unable to come to a decision three times. In the first 100 with the second movement less, it was judged less seventy-five times, greater twenty-two times, and three times no decision was arrived at. Combining these two sets of figures in an average we get (in the table, to the right of the figures just given) 75.5 per cent of right judgments, 21.5 per cent of wrong ones, and three per cent of cases in which the experimentee was in doubt. Below the averages for the groups of 100 are the averages for the four groups of each kind. To the right of these is their average, which, consequently, represents 800 experiments.

The percentage of the whole number of right cases when the second movement was greater (51.1) is obtained, of course, by adding the two averages 75 and 71.8 and dividing 75 by their sum. The percentage of the whole number of wrong cases when the second movement was greater (46.9) is similarly obtained from the averages 24 and 27.2.

As regards the degree of confidence expressed, the figures in the table are sufficiently clear. They have reference to the whole 800 experiments. Thus, the experimentee was quite confident he was right only 0.5 per cent of the time; he was fairly confident 12.5 per cent less confident still 86.0 per cent, and wholly undecided 1.0 per cent. To pass to the second line, he was quite confident he was right 0.7 per cent of the whole number of times in which he was right; he was fairly confident 15.1 per cent and less confident 84.2 per cent. The third line of figures so resembles the second as to need no comment. The fourth shows to what degree the subjective feeling of confidence corresponded with objective correctness in the judgment. It indicates that when the experimentee was quite confident he was right, he was always right; when he was fairly confident, he was right 97 per cent of the time; and when he was less confident, he was right 71.7 per cent of the time.

Thus it appears that with the two stimuli 500 and 510 mm., 75 per cent of the judgments were right when the second stimulus was the greater, and 71.8 per cent were right when the second was the less. This would indicate that the first movement was slightly underrated on the whole. In the earlier experiments by the method of average error a standard movement of 500 mm. was slightly overrated. In the later experiments it was underrated. The second group of the experiments by the method of right and wrong cases differs from the other three in showing an inclination to overestimate the standard. It will be remembered that the corresponding groups in the experiments by each of the other three methods showed a similar tendency. The ten series of experiments represented by these groups were made within a period of seven days. During this time the standard movement seems to have been pretty constantly overrated.

As in the criticism of the just noticeable difference as a standard of measurement it was objected that the significance of the words "just noticeable" is not easily determined, so with regard to the degrees of confidence a, b, and c, it may be objected that the terms "quite confident," "fairly confident" and "less confident" are extremely vague. In a series of experiments with the one observer each of these terms may be assumed, perhaps, to have approximately the same meaning in different parts of the series; but the quantitative relations of the subjective feeling of confidence in the three cases remain very obscure, nor can it be assumed that they may be measured by the percentage of right cases corresponding to each degree of confidence. The fact that an observer is always right when he feels quite confident, and right ninety-seven per cent of the times when he feels fairly confident, does not prove that the amount or intensity of his confidence in the two instances is as 100 to 97. We see, however, from the figures in the table that the observer was sure to be right when he felt confident enough to say a, nearly sure to be right when he was willing to say b, and much less likely to be right when moved to say c.

The average variable error obtained with a stimulus of 500 mm. in the experiments by the method of average error was 9.5. Now, if we eliminate in these experiments the constant error (.7), and calculate the average error (that corresponding to 78 per cent of right cases) by applying the probability integral to the figures in the above table, we obtain an error of 12.1. The average variable error in the experiments by the method of just noticeable difference was, for just greater than 500 mm., 9.5, and for just less 8.7. If, by the use of the probability integral, we calculate from the just noticeable difference (Table II), the difference with which the observer should be right in his judgment seventy-eight per cent of the time, we obtain a difference of 12.9, which agrees very well with the results obtained by the method of right and wrong cases. But it is evident that the several series vary more, and that the probable error of the result is greater.

PART II

On the Force of Movement

SEC. 19. *Introductory.*—The experiments hitherto made on the so-called "muscular sense," or "sense of innervation," have been carried out with weights. We also began with such experiments (which are described in Part IV), but the great advantage of using a dynamometer soon occurred to us. With a dynamometer the several psychophysical methods may be used and compared, and the factors concerned in the perception of movement may be distinguished and studied separately. If lifted weights be used as stimuli, the only method which can be applied conveniently is that of right and wrong cases. It is not possible to make one weight equal to another, just heavier or twice as heavy, without repeated trials, and if regularity be observed the method of right and wrong cases must be introduced as a secondary help. The method of right and wrong cases is indeed admirably suited to the discrimination of lifted weights, as the magnitude of the stimulus can be measured without appreciable error. But this method, as we have seen, requires numerous experiments before conclusive results can be reached.[1]

Further, it is not easy to analyze the factors concerned in the perception of lifted weights. We might expect the lighter weight to be lifted higher and faster than the heavier, and the judgment of the observer might depend on the perception of the force, of the extent or of the time. Müller and Schumann[2] conclude that the observer's judgment is due chiefly to the time, and explain Weber's law by the principle of mechanics, according to which a proportional increase in force is required to cause an equal increase in velocity. Our experiments prove the incorrectness of this ingenious theory, as they show that the force of a movement can be judged better than its time, and that the

[1] Fechner heroically made 67072 trials with lifted weights, and yet considered these too few. Galton (Inquiries into Human Faculty, London, 1883, Appendix D) suggests that the influence of chance may be lessened by allowing the observer to arrange three weights in order. But the observer might distinguish the heaviest weight from the lightest and place the third between.

[2] G. E. Müller und Fr. Schumann. Ueber die psychologischen Grundlagen der Vergleichung gehobener Gewichte. Pflüger's Archiv, XLV, 1889.

judgment of time follows Weber's law more nearly than the judgment of force.

Sec. 20. *Apparatus and Methods.*—The clinical dynamometers in use are too inaccurate for scientific experiment.[1] We therefore constructed a special dynamometer for our work. This is shown in Fig. 8.

A heavy spiral spring is enclosed in the brass cylinder (*RP*) to which the handle (*H*) is attached by a bar. The bar runs on double

Fig. 8.—Apparatus for measuring the force of movement.

wheels almost without friction. When the handle is pulled out the amount of force applied is shown on the scale (*P*), as in an ordinary spring balance. The pointer, however, not being attached to the bar, is only pushed forward, and stays at the point of the maximum pull. The recorder can thus take the exact reading before replacing the pointer. The scale registers up to 10 kg., and in addition a second scale (*R*) is attached, registering 15 kg. further. By means of the bar, pivot and screw (at *N*) the spring can be set at any point up to 15 kg. In such a case, the observer must pull the set amount before the handle moves, while the force of his pull beyond this amount is registered on the front scale. The advantage of a double scale is twofold. The maximum force of movement may be kept the same, while the extent and rate are altered, and the total extent of the movement may be made as small as desired.[2] The instrument was tested carefully, and

[1] We tested an oval (Collin) dynamometer and found the absolute readings to be worthless, while the average error of adjustment was very large. A reputable instrument-maker informed us that he did not know whether the reading on his dynamometers gave lbs. or kg. He made the springs, and, without testing them, copied the scale from a French dynamometer The scientific value and practical usefulness of clinical observations would be much increased by more accurate methods and instruments.

[2] In some clinical dynamometers the amount of movement is so great that the grasp with which the observer begins must be altered while the movement is being made; if, on the other hand, the amount of the movement be less, it is too small to be accurately registered. In our dynamometer there is an attachment which may be fastened to the extension (below *H*), if it be desired to use the grasp of the hand, or the pressure of the thumb and forefinger. The range (25 kg.) of this dyna-

the errors of adjustment and of reading were small as compared with the quantity measured. The force of pull was varied from 2 to 16 kg., and the reading was taken to .01 kg.[1]

The movement used in our experiments was a free pull with the arm. The observer sat on a high chair with his right shoulder opposite the instrument, which was fastened to an ordinary table. The handle was conveniently grasped, always in the same manner. A natural pull was made, the muscular mechanism being different for pulls of different force, but kept as nearly as possible the same for the same pull. A screen (attached in *S*) hid the scale and record-book from the observer. We had intended to give the observer the first or normal force of pull by an adjustable stop which can be attached to the extension (below *H*), and removed before the second or judgment pull be made. We saw, however, that some part of the force of the first pull would be spent in striking the stop, which led us to adopt the method described in Part I, which we believe to be a great advantage in all psychological experiments in which it can be used.

The observer was told to give a pull of (say) 2 kg. As might have been expected, his error in estimating a standard magnitude was usually very great. He was then told the direction and approximate amount of his error and allowed to try again. This was repeated until he had made five trials, by which time he could usually give the standard without great variation. A series of ten judgments was then made, the observer giving in each trial first the standard pull from memory, and then a pull as nearly as possible (say) equal to it. A series of five trials preceded each series of ten judgments, and if in the course of the series the first pulls varied greatly from the standard, the observer was told to make his pulls less or greater as the case might be. The observer was told not to attend particularly to the amount of the standard, but to concentrate his attention on the comparison; and the error of his observation, as discovered in the difference of the stimuli, was made the basis of the averages. With this method the observer produces and perceives both stimuli under like conditions, and the comparison can be made to great advantage.

The time conditions were made as constant as possible. A pendulum,

---

mometer is suitable for the latter movement, which we recommend for clinical observation, as it is less liable to accidental alterations of position than the grasp of hand.

[1] The error of reading would not increase as the magnitude of the stimulus is taken greater, and would form a larger part of the (apparent) error of observation when small than when great. It is, however, so small a part of the total error in these experiments that it may be disregarded. The error of the instrument and possible errors of calculation are more serious complications, but we should not know how to allow for these.

giving seconds, swung in front of the observer, and after a little practice its movement could be followed automatically. The first or standard pull was made at the beginning of a second and lasted about one second, a second was allowed for recovery, and the judgment pull was made during the third second. The stronger pulls lasted, approximately, one second, while the weaker pulls were made in a little less time, the observer being allowed to make them in the manner which he found most convenient. He was expected to make his decision during the fourth second. If we had been able to continue our work, we should have measured these times by means of a chronoscope, so as to discover more exactly the relations between force, extent and rate. We believe that interesting results would be disclosed by such a research.

When 2, 4 and 8 kg. were used as stimuli, the extent of the pull was proportional to the force. When a stimulus of 16 kg. was used, the spring was set at 10, and the handle began to move when the force was 10, and the distance it moved was proportional to the force beyond 10. The handle moved 6.4 mm. for each kg. If time had permitted, we should have used dynamometers in which the extent would have been kept constant, and also those in which it would have varied otherwise than in direct proportion to the force. We believe the relations between these magnitudes to be an interesting subject for research. The present experiments on the force of movement are complicated by the variation in extent. The observer's attention was concentrated on the force, and casual introspection indicated that the difference in force only was regarded. More careful introspection (taken in connection with the accuracy with which the extent of movements can be judged, as shown in Part I) seemed, however, to indicate that the observer was helped more by the variation in extent than he had at first supposed. As the extent varied directly with the force for 2, 4 and 8 kg., any general relation (such as Weber's law) between the error of observation and the magnitude of the stimulus would not be affected. With 16 kg., however, the extent was to the force as 6:16. If the observer therefore judged partly by the extent, the error for 16 kg. would be relatively smaller than if he judged only by the force.

Most of the experiments (4000 judgments) on the force of movement were made by J and C who acted alternately as observer and recorder. They did not know any results of their own experiments until the whole series had been completed, and but little concerning the results of the other observer, as these were not calculated while the work was in progress. A series of experiments with the several magnitudes and by the different methods was made together, the order being altered in each series, so as to eliminate, as far as possible, the effects of fatigue and contrast. By the method of average error,

400 experiments each were made on F, D and K, C or F acting as recorder.

SEC. 21. *Experiments by the Method of the Just Noticeable Difference.*—In these experiments a standard pull, 2, 4, 8 or 16 kg., was fixed in mind by a series of five trials, and then a series of ten judgments was made. The observer gave the standard, and then a pull which appeared just greater (or less). We have already considered the difficulties in the way of making experiments by the method of the just noticeable difference. In these experiments the observer did not attempt to make the difference in the pulls so great that he was sure that he was right in the objective relation of the magnitudes, but so great that he felt tolerably confident in the correctness of his judgment. He would have guessed himself to have been right in his judgment about nine times out of ten, the confidence corresponding to that marked "b" in the method of right and wrong cases. If the observer made the difference greater than he had intended, or for some other reason felt sure that his judgment was correct, this experiment was marked "a"; if, on the other hand, he felt uncertain as to the correctness of his judgment, the experiment was marked "c." It would have been more accurate to have treated these different classes of judgment separately, but as "a" and "c" seldom occurred, we did not undertake the additional calculation which this would have involved.

The results of the experiments by this method are given in Table VIII, which is arranged in a manner analogous to those in Part I.

We think the table will be readily understood. The unit used in the tables and text is .01 kg. The results for the two observers, J and C, and for "just greater" and "just less" are given separately. The basis of the figures opposite J and C is ten series, each containing ten judgments, while the average is the result of the 400 experiments with each magnitude. The figures in italics opposite *Var.* give the average variations of the ten series. This variation is very nearly proportional to the probable error of the average, which is about $\dfrac{.845}{\sqrt{n-1}}$ or $\frac{1}{4}$ (more nearly .282), the variation given in the tables. Under I is given the average force of the first or standard pull, and under II the average amount of difference between the two pulls, together with its direction—that is, the "just noticeable difference." Under V and V^1, respectively, are given the average variations of the pulls from the series to which they belong. These variations are dependent on memory for the standard, and the observer was directed not to pay special attention to this. They are, therefore, more complex than the other errors, and less suitable for studying the relation between the magnitude of the stimulus and the error of observation. Under V.E., the

TABLE VIII.—FORCE OF MOVEMENT—METHOD OF THE JUST NOTICEABLE DIFFERENCE—*J* AND *C*—1600 EXPERIMENTS—IX. 1890—I. 1891

	2 kg. = 200						4 kg. = 400						8 kg. = 800						16 kg. = 1600					
	I	V	II	V¹	V.E.	%W	I	V	II	V¹	V.E.	%W	I	V	II	V¹	V.E.	%W	I	V	II	V¹	V.E.	%W
Attempt at just greater																								
J	205	15	+34	17	13.1	3	389	20	+49	26	20.	7	781	43	+55	48	35.8	12	1608	51	+56	47	53.5	27
Var	*8*	*6*	*7*	*6*	*4.1*		*29*	*8*	*13*	*8*	*5.2*		*31*	*14*	*17*	*15*	*15.6*		*56*	*15*	*35*	*16*	*13.1*	
C	209	21	+65	20	17.3	1	389	30	+84	34	33.5	3	789	52	+91	48	37.5	5	1609	40	+79	45	37.3	5
Var	*7*	*7*	*10*	*7*	*4.3*		*15*	*8*	*15*	*8*	*8.7*		*31*	*10*	*23*	*11*	*8.3*		*32*	*10*	*20*	*9*	*5.1*	
Attempt at just less																								
J	210	14	−20	13	10.8	10	400	24	−31	26	19.7	17	778	34	−72	36	29.2	8	1617	40	−89	49	39.6	9
Var	*10*	*4*	*8*	*3*	*2.8*		*32*	*8*	*21*	*5*	*7.1*		*43*	*8*	*28*	*7*	*7.8*		*56*	*10*	*24*	*10*	*10.*	
C	215	18	−36	18	20.	7	383	31	−54	25	26.8	11	812	45	−142	42	38.9	5	1644	49	−133	34	34.9	2
Var	*18*	*4*	*11*	*7*	*3.8*		*18*	*6*	*17*	*9*	*7.*		*39*	*10*	*36*	*11*	*10.9*		*41*	*19*	*28*	*16*	*4.7*	
Av	210	14	±39	17	15.3	5.2	390	26	±54	28	25.	9.5	790	43	±90	43	35.3	7.5	1620	45	±89	44	41.3	10.7

variable error, is given the average variation of the difference between the pulls. Thus, if in a series of ten experiments, the observer make the second pull on the average .5 kg. greater than the first, sometimes the difference will be greater than .5 kg., sometimes less, sometimes even negative; the average variation or error of these differences is the variable error, V.E., in the tables. Under $\%W$ is given the percentage (as there are 100 experiments, it is also the number) of wrong cases; that is, those cases in which the real relation of the stimuli was the reverse of that intended by the observer. Thus, in the first quarter of the first line of figures in the table, we see that the observer, J, in giving the standard pull 2 kg. = 200 from memory, made it on the average 205, or $\frac{1}{40}$ too great, with an average variation in each series of 15. In attempting to make the second pull just greater than the first, the observer made it on the average 34 greater, with an average variation in each series of 17. The just noticeable difference would, therefore, be 34, or $\frac{1}{6}$ of the stimulus. This is the only figure usually recorded in experiments by this method. We, however, believe that the just noticeable difference only has an exact meaning when taken in connection with the number of errors, or the variable error. By regarding these quantities we are able to combine the several methods, and regard this as one of the chief results of our work. In the case under consideration J's variable error was 13.1, and in the course of the 100 judgments the second pull was made less than the first three times.

SEC. 22. *Discussion of the Method and Results.*—The relation of the just noticeable difference to the magnitude of the stimulus and its variation with the two observers, and according as just greater or just less was attempted, may be conveniently seen in the accompanying curves. From the just noticeable differences shown in the table and curves, we should be compelled to conclude that J's fineness of discrimination is nearly twice as great as C's, whereas the variable error and ratio of right to wrong cases in the same experiments give nearly the same fineness of discrimination for the two observers. In fact, J was right 88 %, of the time, while C was right 95 %, which shows that the just noticeable difference meant something quite different to each of the observers. With unskilled observers we might expect still greater variation in choosing a just noticeable difference.

The just noticeable difference seems, further, to have been given a different value, according as just less or just greater was attempted. It is evident that the corresponding curves for J and C have much the same shape, whereas the "just less" curves differ entirely in their shape from the "just greater" curves. For the two smaller magnitudes "just less" was taken smaller than "just greater," whereas the reverse holds with the two larger magnitudes. This seems to show a marked tendency to underestimate the second pull as compared with the first in the case of the smaller magnitudes, and to overestimate it in the case of the greater magnitudes. Such a tendency is also apparent in the experiments by the method of average error (see Table X), but is not there so marked.

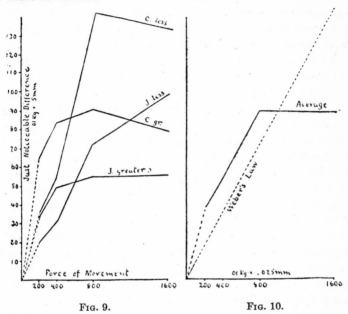

FIG. 9.   FIG. 10.

If Weber's law obtained, all the curves representing the just noticeable difference in the figures would be straight lines beginning at the origin, and the average would follow the broken line. The just noticeable difference is, on the average, about one-eighth of the stimulus, but it grows rapidly smaller as the stimulus is taken greater. It is approximately

Magnitude	2	4	8	16 kg.
Just noticeable difference	⅕	¼	⅑	¹⁄₁₈

consequently, according to the method of just noticeable difference, Weber's law does not obtain, even within narrow limits, for the force of movement.

We have given our reasons for holding that the just noticeable difference is an arbitrary point without objective criterion. We think it cannot be used as a test for comparing different observers. We see that it failed with *J* and *C*. In Parts IV and V we shall find that some observers rarely think their judgment correct, unless it be in fact correct, while others are continually sure that they notice a difference which is not present. If observers be arranged according to the difference they think they can perceive, an order exactly the reverse of their real fineness of discrimination will often be obtained. An observer may, indeed, keep the just noticeable difference fairly constant under the same circumstances, but this, we think, is because he has in mind a certain apparent amount of difference or degree of confidence. When the circumstances are altered, it is very difficult for the observer to give the same value to the just noticeable difference. Thus "just greater" for J was 34 with 200, and 56 with 1600. We find, therefore, that the just noticeable difference was less than doubled when the stimuli were taken eight times as great. On regarding the variable error, however, we see that for 200 it is less than half the just noticeable difference, and we conclude that the observer could usually notice this difference, and on regarding the percentage of wrong cases, we see that it was, in fact, misjudged only three times out of 100 trials. With 1600, on the other hand, the variable error is nearly as great as the just noticeable difference, and we must conclude that the observer would often fail to notice this difference; and on regarding the percentage of wrong cases, we see that it was, in fact, misjudged twenty-seven times out of 100. The just noticeable differences in the two cases do not mean the same thing, and cannot be used to measure the accuracy of discrimination; still less can they be regarded as equal mental magnitudes. The fact that the just noticeable difference tends to increase more slowly than the variable error shows an inclination on the part of the observer to make the just noticeable difference, not an equally noticeable difference, but an equal objective difference. As in our other experiments with estimated amounts of difference, therefore, the observer tends to judge such magnitudes (doubtless through association) according to their real relations, and not according to the logarithms of these.

SEC. 23. *Reduction of the Method to That of Right and Wrong Cases.*— In making a difference so great as to be just noticeable, the observer did not aim to make it so great as to be absolutely sure of the correctness of his judgment, but so great as to feel fairly confident of its correctness, expecting in a general way to be right about nine times out of ten. If an observer could, in fact, employ such a criterion, the just noticeable difference would measure his fineness of discrimination. We should in this case, however, have substituted the method of right and wrong cases for the method of just noticeable difference. In our experiments the observer did not know the result of his judgments, and could not tell how nearly he was coming to such a standard.

The table shows that, in fact, the percentages of right cases varied from 73 to 99. Still, if the probability integral may be applied to these series, we can reduce them to a common standard. From the just noticeable difference and the percentage of right cases actually obtained, we can calculate how large the just noticeable difference should have been made in order to give a certain constant percentage of right cases. We thus replace the method of the just noticeable difference by the method of right and wrong cases. The probable errors (the differences with which the observer might expect to be right 75% of the time) are given in Table IX, and the relations are shown in Figs. 11 and 12.

TABLE IX.—PROBABLE ERRORS FROM THE JUST NOTICEABLE DIFFERENCE

	200	400	800	1600
Just Greater				
J	12.2	22.4	30.2	61.5
C	18.3	30.1	37.3	32.4
Just Less				
J	10.5	22.	34.6	44.7
C	16.4	29.7	58.	43.6
Av	14.3	26.	40.	45.5

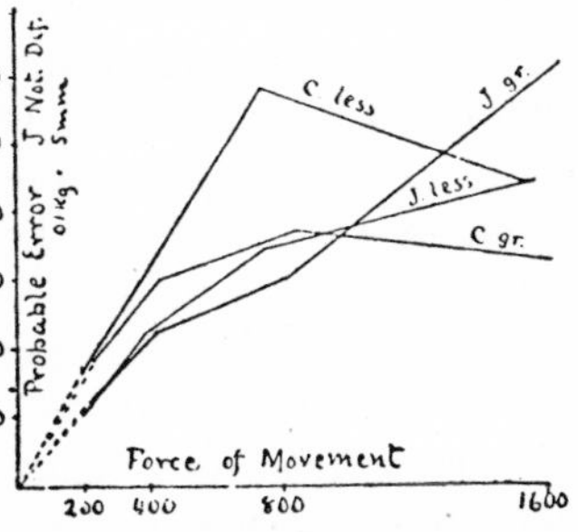

FIG. 11. 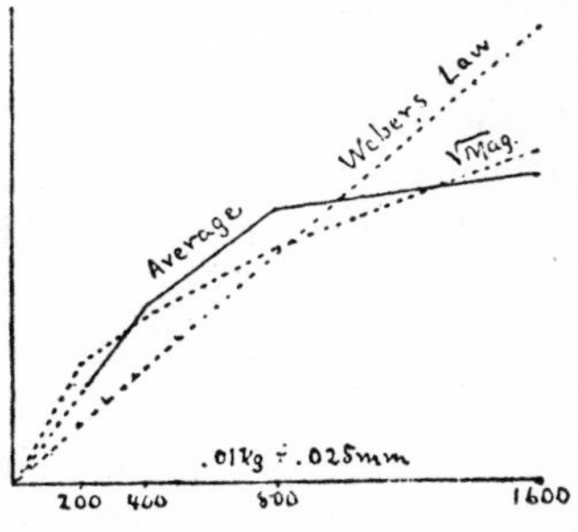   FIG. 12.

The errors given in the table and shown in the curves are evidently more regular and accordant than those for the method of just noticeable difference. They also agree with the results obtained by other methods. They show that the fineness of discrimination of the two observers is nearly the same, but that J is more accurate with the three smaller, C with the largest magnitude. This result seems natural, as C's arm is much stronger than J's, but it is contrary to Weber's law.

As the curves for J and C, and it may be for "just greater" and "just less," follow different equations, an average is fictitious, but the average curve given in the figure is evidently quite regular. It shows no inclination to follow Weber's law. The error of observation increases as the stimulus is taken greater, but much more slowly than in direct proportion to the stimulus. A curve drawn according to the square root of the magnitude is also shown in the figure. It follows fairly well the curve obtained by experiment.

The just noticeable difference converted into the method of right and wrong cases in this manner is a satisfactory test of the accuracy of discrimination. It suffers, however, from the practical drawback that a very large number of experiments must be made before a reliable result can be reached. Although one hundred judgments of each sort were made in the case before us, the value of at least one ordinate (C just less 8 kg.) seems to be considerably influenced by chance. As has been explained, the method of right and wrong cases can be used most advantageously when the difference is such as to give about 84% of right cases. But this difference is smaller than most observers would call just noticeable. When the observer is always right in his decision, our theory fails us entirely, for it requires us to say that the fineness of discrimination of such an observer is infinitely greater than that of one who is right 999 times out of 1000. The theory is, indeed, saved by the assumption, that if the series were continued long enough, there would be a mistake, but we think the theory of probability cannot assign a probable time for such a mistake to occur. If several observers, even with varying differences between the stimuli, are always right in their judgments, we must regard their fineness of discrimination as alike and indefinitely great. The method of the just noticeable difference, in its original form, is thus reduced to an absurdity.

SEC. 24. *The Variable Error of the Just Noticeable Difference.*—We have seen that the method of right and wrong cases, at its best, requires many trials, whereas the variable error gives us a reliable result more quickly. In these experiments we have calculated the variable error of the just noticeable difference, and believe this to be a far better test than the just noticeable difference itself. The value of the variable error is given in the table and shown in the accompanying curves (Figs. 13 and 14).

It is evident that the curves agree with those obtained independently by the method of right and wrong cases, and this proves conclusively the reliability, both of the methods and of the experiments. The average curves for the probable error and for the variable error are shown together in Fig. 16, below. The variable errors are smaller than the probable errors because they are calculated from series of 10 experiments, while the probable errors are from series of 100 experiments. The fact that the probable error of the final average is smaller for the variable error, and more especially that the variation of the separate series of the same sort is much less, shows that the variable error gives the more reliable result. We see that the accuracy of discrimination of the two observers is about the same, J being the better for the three smallest magnitudes, and C for the largest. The variable error for just less tends to be smaller than for just greater, which is natural, as the magnitude aimed at is smaller. The average curve gives no indication of following Weber's law, but does tend to follow

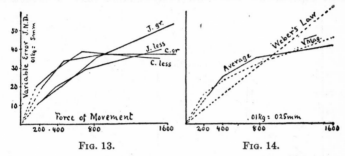

FIG. 13. FIG. 14.

the law of the square root of the magnitude. We conclude that the variable error of the just noticeable difference is a satisfactory test of the accuracy of discrimination, but as the variable error, when just equal is attempted, is still smaller and more constant (Table X), we see no advantage in using the just noticeable difference.

SEC. 25. *Further Results.*—We have still to call attention to the average variation of the pulls from the average of the series to which they belong, as also the absolute value of the first pull. These have turned out far more constant than we had expected. They depend on memory for the stimulus, and show that during a series of ten trials a magnitude can be held in mind very well. The average variation of the pulls is slightly larger than the variable error of the just noticeable difference, and almost exactly proportional to it, so that the curves could scarcely be distinguished. This confirms independently the results obtained by the other methods, and shows that a greater dependence on memory did not alter the relation between the error of observation and the magnitude of the stimulus.

The average variations of the several series, given in italics in the table, should be noticed, as these show what reliance may be placed on the results, they being about four times the probable error. It is, however, a somewhat complex quantity, depending not only on the normal variation of perception for the different magnitudes and methods, but also on the condition of the observer from day to day, on practice, etc.

Before leaving the comparison of methods, it may prove interesting to give curves indicating the confidence which may be placed on a few experiments. They show the results of the first ten experiments on J "just greater," the general character of curves for J's "just less" and for C being the same, with great variation in the separate curves. In Fig. 16 the final results obtained by the three methods are shown together.

A comparison of the curves in Fig. 15 with the average of one hundred experiments will show what reliance may be placed on ten

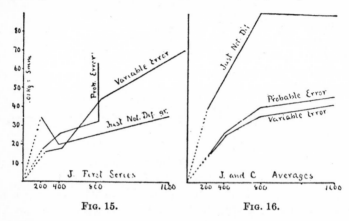

FIG. 15.   FIG. 16.

trials. Weber and others have based their laws on fewer experiments than this. From the curve for the just noticeable difference (Weber's method) the conclusion would follow that the just noticeable difference is nearly a constant magnitude whatever the stimulus may be. But the just noticeable difference here does not agree at all with the final result. It is about half the variable error and was mistaken about one-fourth of the time. That is, the observer called a difference noticeably greater that was half the time smaller than the probable error of observation. When the just noticeable difference is corrected by the proportion of right cases, an entirely different curve is obtained. It agrees very well with the final result for the first three magnitudes, but fails with 16 kg. In this case there were five errors, and the probable error must be regarded as indefinitely great. In about half the series there were no errors, and the probable error must be regarded as indefinitely small; that is, in a series of ten experiments, the method of right and wrong cases is apt to fail. The variable error gives a curve agreeing fairly well with the final result; but as it is nearly a straight line, it would follow from it that Weber's law obtains.

We finally conclude that the just noticeable difference cannot be used in comparing different observers, and cannot even be kept constant for the same observer under changed conditions. The method of right and wrong cases, including the application of the probability integral, gives correct results, but requires a large number of experiments (at least 100), and should be used with a difference smaller than "just noticeable." The method of average error gives the best results with a limited number of experiments (say 100), and a few (say 10) will serve for clinical and anthropometric purposes. But the average error of "just equal" is a better test than the average error of the just noticeable difference.

SEC. 26. *Experiments by the Method of Average Error.*—Experiments by this method were made by *J* and *C* on the same days as the experiments treated in the preceding sections. After the standard had been set by five pulls, a series of ten judgments was made, in each of which the observer first gave the standard, and then a second pull as nearly as possible equal to the first. The standard was then again set, and a second series made, in order to obtain as many experiments as by the method of the just noticeable difference. After each pair of pulls had been made, the observer was required to decide or guess which of the two had been the greater, and give the confidence of his decision. This was, naturally, nearly always *c*, little or no confidence.[1] It will be noticed that we have thus combined the two fundamental psychophysical methods.

The table of results (Table X) will be readily understood, as it is much like the foregoing.

In this table, two series of the same sort, each containing 100 experiments, are given for *J* and *C*, the final average being thus the result of 400 experiments. In so far as Pull II is much different from I, we must regard this as due to a constant error. After the two pulls and their variations, we give the average error (A.E.) of the observer. If there were no constant error present, this is the only quantity we should have to consider. But, as has been explained, when there is a constant error, the average error is made up of two factors—this constant error and a variable error. Both of these factors are interesting, and deserve separate study. In a series of ten experiments, indeed, the apparent constant error is complex, being partly a true constant error, due to overestimating or underestimating the force of the second pull as compared with the first, and partly due to the variable error. In calculating the variable error of the separate series, however, we have treated the apparent constant error as a true constant error,

[1] *b* only occurred twice for *J* and once for *C*. In later experiments we have subdivided *c*, so as to distinguish small confidence from none whatever.

TABLE X.—FORCE OF MOVEMENT—METHOD OF AVERAGE ERROR—J AND C—1600 EXPERIMENTS—IX. 1890—II. 1891

	2 kg. = 200							4 kg. = 4							8 kg. = 800							8 kg. = 1600						
	I	V	II	V¹	A.E.	V²	V.E.	I	V	II	V¹	A.E.	V²	V.E.	I	V	II	V¹	A.E.	V²	V.E.	I	V	II	V¹	A.E.	V²	V.E.
J I	212	16	+4	17	15	9	12.4	428	29	-13	31	31	14	21.9	808	52	-25	47	48	28	41.9	1630	38	-17	52	55	29	48.9
Var.	*7*	*3*	*8*	*4*	*4*	*3*	*4.2*	*36*	*13*	*17*	*14*	*17*	*5*	*7.5*	*32*	*10*	*15*	*9*	*14*	*5*	*7.5*	*32*	*12*	*19*	*19*	*16*	*8*	*14.9*
J II	204	11	+10	13	14	7	9.5	385	17	+17	18	21	12	14.4	805	39	+2	37	39	22	35.6	1597	37	-19	44	47	24	37.6
Var.	*11*	*3*	*7*	*4*	*5*	*3*	*2.9*	*19*	*3*	*7*	*3*	*6*	*2*	*1.8*	*34*	*5*	*16*	*11*	*9*	*3*	*9.2*	*38*	*12*	*20*	*12*	*8*	*3*	*7.4*
Av.	208	13	+7	15	14	8	10.9	406	23	+2	24	26	13	18.1	806	45	-11	42	43	25	38.7	1613	37	-18	48	51	26	43.2
C I	218	15	+2	15	15	9	14.4	404	27	-6	23	27	17	24.5	822	41	-46	38	59	29	37.	1626	40	-60	38	68	35	41.8
Var.	*19*	*5*	*6*	*2*	*3*	*3*	*2.4*	*20*	*9*	*13*	*4*	*7*	*7*	*7.7*	*29*	*13*	*29*	*7*	*21*	*8*	*8.2*	*31*	*8*	*11*	*11*	*9*	*7*	*6.*
C II	191	18	+10	17	17	9	13.1	385	30	+12	27	24	15	21.4	839	46	-47	38	58	27	34.1	1625	39	-56	33	61	27	32.6
Var.	*10*	*5*	*8*	*3*	*6*	*3*	*4.3*	*12*	*8*	*11*	*8*	*6*	*5*	*5.*	*19*	*10*	*18*	*9*	*12*	*7*	*6.1*	*34*	*7*	*15*	*8*	*13*	*11*	*7.2*
Av.	204	16	+6	16	16	9	13.7	394	28	+3	25	25	16	22.9	830	43	-46	38	58	28	35.5	1625	39	-58	35	64	31	37.2
Av. Av.	206	15	+6	15	15	8	12.3	400	26	+2	25	26	14	20.5	818	44	-29	40	51	26	37.1	1619	38	-38	42	58	29	40.2

and subtracted it algebraically from each average error to obtain an apparent variable error, V.E., in the table. This was necessary, as the constant error might have been either increased or decreased by the normal variation of the variable error.

The limited number of experiments in the series makes the variable error too small, but as the series throughout contained the same number of experiments the relative value is not affected. The variation of the average error (V^2) gives an additional measure of the accuracy of discrimination.

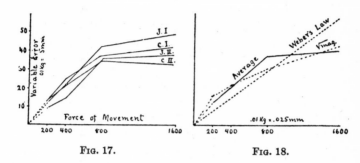

FIG. 17.   FIG. 18.

From the table and the curves (Figs. 17 and 18) showing the relations of the variable error, we see that these are much the same as for the variable error of the just noticeable difference. The two series of the same sort on each observer correspond almost exactly, the second series showing the improvement with practice, but not altering the shape of the curves. This improvement was greater for J, which is doubtless explained by the fact that, though neither observer had previously made experiments of this sort, C had had the more practice in psychological experiments. This calls attention to a difficulty in all anthropometric experiments. The results depend as much on adaptation to the conditions of experiment as on differences in the senses and faculties. C's error of observation was the less with the greater, and J's with the smaller magnitudes, probably due to the greater strength of C's arm. Yet this is contrary to Weber's law. It is worth notice that the experiments on J throughout depart less from Weber's law than those on C. In the present case J's curves follow Weber's law fairly well for the three smaller magnitudes.

Curves for the constant errors of the first series are given below (Fig. 21). The constant errors show a tendency to slightly overestimate the second pull with the smaller magnitudes, and to considerably underestimate it with the greater. At first sight, one is tempted to account for the underestimation of the second pull with the large magnitudes by means of fatigue. If the observer were tired by the

TABLE XI.—FORCE OF MOVEMENT—METHOD OF AVERAGE ERROR—5 OBSERVERS AND 2000 EXPERIMENTS—IX. 1890—III. 1891

	2 kg. = 200				4 kg. = 400				8 kg. = 800				16 kg. = 1600			
	I	II	A.E.	V.E.	I	II	A.E.	V.E.	I	II	A.E.	V.E.	I	II	A.E.	V.E.
K	204	+16	32	25.2	396	+ 6	37	32.6	792	+17	61	55.	1580	+ 6	59	54.3
Var	*31*	*13*	*8*	*3.2*	*37*	*18*	*8*	*8.2*	*34*	*23*	*9*	*7.8*	*62*	*23*	*11*	*11.9*
D	189	+17	26	22.8	411	+17	45	41.2	765	+21	54	43.5	1625	+ 8	49	42.7
Var	*20*	*4*	*6*	*6*	*29*	*12*	*9*	*9.8*	*29*	*19*	*8*	*10.7*	*35*	*22*	*6*	*5.7*
F	228	+18	25	18.3	408	+11	30	28.	794	+ 8	38	37.3	1642	− 8	44	43.4
Var	*30*	*8*	*7*	*5.9*	*47*	*8*	*4*	*5.8*	*38*	*10*	*9*	*7.9*	*60*	*14*	*10*	*11.*
J I	212	+ 4	15	12.4	428	−13	31	21.9	808	−25	48	4.19	1630	−17	55	48.9
Var	*7*	*8*	*4*	*4.2*	*36*	*17*	*17*	*7.5*	*32*	*15*	*14*	*11.1*	*32*	*19*	*16*	*14.9*
C I	218	+ 2	15	14.4	404	− 6	27	24.2	822	−46	59	37.	1626	−60	68	41.8
Var	*19*	*6*	*3*	*2.4*	*20*	*13*	*7*	*7.7*	*29*	*29*	*21*	*8.2*	*31*	*11*	*9*	*6.*
Av	210	+11	23	18.6	409	+ 3	34	29.6	796	− 5	52	42.9	1621	−14	55	46.2

first pull, a second pull might seem as great when, in fact, less. But this theory would require J (whose arm is the weaker) to have a larger constant error than C, whereas the contrary holds, and, besides, a series of ten pairs of pulls was made continuously, and fatigue should tell if anywhere in the pairs becoming smaller, whereas the standards are overestimated.

The average or crude error, being the resultant of the constant and variable errors, is, of course, larger than the variable error, but it is no less regular. It has usually been neglected, the variable error alone being used, but it seems to us that it measures a real error of discrimination. Thus C's variable error for the larger magnitudes is smaller than J's, whereas his constant error and his average error are larger. This indicates for C perhaps greater practice in such experiments, more constant attention, etc., but it is a fact that J could distinguish the smaller difference. It remains a question, therefore, which of the two quantities should be regarded as the measure of fineness of discrimination.

As regards the other figures in the table, it is worth noticing that the variation of the average error is about one-half this error, while the variation of the pulls from the series to which they belong is about equal to the average error for the smaller magnitudes, but is less for the larger magnitudes, where there is a considerable constant error. Either of these quantities could thus be used to measure the error of observation, and we have in all six different quantities, any of which could be used for this purpose.

In all cases the error becomes too small for Weber's law, as the magnitude is increased, which, we believe, is the conclusion of most careful experiments on the discrimination of small differences. The values follow fairly well the law of the square root of the magnitude, but the departure is greater than can be attributed to chance variations.

Sec. 27. *Further Experiments by the Method of Average Error.*— Experiments by this method were also made with three additional observers. The results are given in the accompanying table, together with the first series made with J and C. The variations of the series, and the variations of the average error have not been calculated, as these have been sufficiently illustrated.

The relations of the variable error to the magnitude of the stimulus for K, D and F are shown in Fig. 19, and the averages for K, D, F, J I and C I (together with curves for Weber's law and the square root of the magnitude) are shown in Fig. 20.

The curves for F and C (C's curves are given in Fig. 17) correspond closely, and this was usually the case when the two observers made the same experiments. A similarity in pursuits and interests thus seems to lead to uniformity in the processes of perception and comparison. When results correspond so well as those of F, C and J, and the probable error for each observer is so small, we may regard the results as established, and it would not be profitable to further increase the number of experiments, unless it were in order to study the effects of practice. The curves for K and D bear witness to a larger error and greater irregularity, but tend toward the same shape as the others. J and K are women, and their curves do not permit us to draw any inference as to greater fineness of discrimination in one of the sexes.

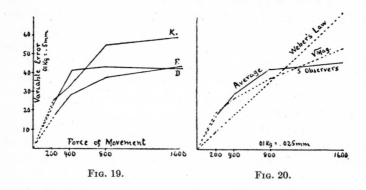

FIG. 19.   FIG. 20.

In Fig. 20 the average curve for the several observers is given, together with a curve for Weber's law and for the square root of the magnitude. There is no doubt but that the average curve is regular and bends away from the vertical axis. Weber's law, consequently, does not obtain. The error of observation becomes greater as the stimulus is taken greater, but more slowly. Unfortunately, we cannot compare 16 kg. with the other magnitudes, as the extent of the movement was even less than for 8 kg. But in the experiments on extent of movement (Part I) we saw that the error was actually smaller for 700 than for 500 mm., and a similar inclination of the curve toward the horizontal axis might have occurred if movements of greater force than 16 kg. had been used.

The curve drawn according to the square root of the magnitude is evidently more like the experimental curve than is that drawn according to Weber's law, and it would correspond better if the error for 16 kg. were corrected for the smaller extent of this movement. The curves for F and C follow closely the theoretical curve, but the difference in the curves cannot be attributed to chance, and we may assume the presence of factors in addition to the summation of errors, for which alone the law of the square root of the magnitude accounts. Hypotheses to account for these secondary variations might easily be made, but it may be better to wait for further experiments, more particularly on magnitudes smaller than 2 and larger than 16 kg.

The combined curve for the average error would follow almost exactly the same course as that for the variable error. The average error for the individual observers, however, differs considerably from their variable error. Thus *C* has large constant errors with 8 and 16 kg., and his average error is, consequently, much larger than his variable error; with *F*, on the other hand, the constant error is small, and the average error is not much reduced by its elimination. *K* and *D* had a positive constant error with all the magnitudes, but with a comparatively large probable error. All the observers had a positive constant error with the smallest magnitude. The relation of the constant errors to the magnitude of the stimulus can be studied most conveniently in the accompanying figures.

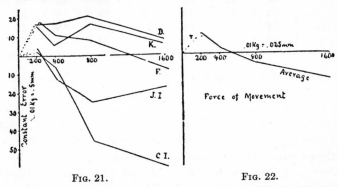

FIG. 21.   FIG. 22.

SEC. 28. *Analysis of the Error into an Error of Perception and an Error of Movement.*—In all our experiments on the perception of movement the observer first adjusted the two movements in the manner required, and afterward estimated the correctness with which this had been done. Thus, after the observer had made the force of his second movement as nearly as possible equal to that of his first, we did not consider the experiment complete, as has hitherto been the case, but required the observer to decide or guess which of the two movements had been the greater, in spite of his attempt to make them exactly alike, and to assign a degree of confidence to his decision. The degree of confidence was nearly always *c*, *a* and *b* occurring rarely except in the first few series with *K* and *D*.

The percentages of right cases for the several observers and magnitudes are given in the accompanying table.

This table shows that the observers could often correctly distinguish a difference, even when they had attempted to make the two movements exactly alike. We are thus led to believe that the error which we have hitherto been considering is complex, being partly due to an error of perception and partly to an error of movement.[1] If the entire error, in the attempt to make the two movements alike, were due to an error of perception, they would seem, when completed,

TABLE XII.—PERCENTAGES OF RIGHT CASES IN JUDGING THE FORCE OF TWO MOVEMENTS MADE AS NEARLY AS POSSIBLE ALIKE

	Second less				Second greater			
	2 kg.	4	8	16	2	4	8	16
K...........	82	70	70	70	57	67	67	82
D...........	81	92	82	91	60	55	55	57
F...........	71	77	47	54	69	65	69	55
J I..........	67	49	51	55	56	46	62	60
J II.........	52	60	52	62	59	59	58	51
C I.........	64	64	61	55	58	46	56	77
C II........	69	71	56	51	59	55	33	58

exactly alike, and the observer's judgment would have been a mere guess, as likely to be wrong as right. If, on the other hand, the observer did not make the two movements apparently alike, he should perceive his error of movement as a difference, and this difference would give a percentage of right cases corresponding to its size. Further, the average variable error of perception, when used as the amount of difference in the method of right and wrong cases, should theoretically give about 78 per cent of right cases.[2] If the error of movement gave this same percentage, we should conclude that the error of movement and the error of perception were equal. The table shows that the percentage of right cases (apart from constant errors, which are eliminated as explained in Part IV) was always less than 78 per cent; we, therefore, know that in these experiments the error of movement was less than the error of perception, and by comparing the value of

[1] This was suggested by Müller (*op. cit.* 71 *sq.*). He says, "Es ist aber ganz unmöglich, näher anzugeben, in welcher Weise diese beiden Factoren, die Trüglichkeit unseres Urtheils und die Unsicherheit der Hand, das Wahrscheinlichkeitsgesetz der Einstellungsfehler bei Anwendung verschiedener Normaldistanzen beeinflüsen." Our experiments, however, accomplish this.

[2] So Fechner (Revision, 115), who gives the percentage as 78.4, and we used the nearest whole percentage in calculating the table. Fechner, however, seems to have made a slight mistake in his interpolation, the correct percentage being 78.7. The variable error, calculated from series of ten experiments, is, further, relatively smaller than the probable error, calculated from series of varying size. It should also be remembered that the difference varied in each experiment. But the number of experiments is too small to require great accuracy in calculation.

$\dfrac{\Delta}{\text{P.E.}}$ (Table I), which would give 78 per cent of right cases, with those

values of $\dfrac{\Delta}{\text{P.E.}}$ corresponding to the percentages of right cases in the

table, we determine the size of the error of perception as compared with the error of movement. We already know the size of the complex variable error, and can thus readily calculate the actual values of the error of perception and the error of movement, the complex variable error being equal to the square root of the sum of the squares of the separate errors.

The analysis of the variable error in judging the force of movement (Tables X and XI) gives the results contained in the accompanying table.

TABLE XIII.—ANALYSIS OF THE ERROR INTO AN ERROR OF PERCEPTION AND AN ERROR OF MOVEMENT

	Error of perception				Error of movement			
	2 kg.	4	8	16	2	4	8	16
K...........	21	28	47	40	15	17	29	37
D...........	18	29	40	30	13	29	24	30
F...........	15	23	36	43	10	16	10	6
J I..........	11	22	40	48	4	0	9	12
J II.........	9	14	35	36	2	5	6	8
C I..........	14	24	36	37	5	4	10	20
C II........	12	20	34	32	6	9	0	5
Av..........	14	23	38	38	8	11	13	17

The averages show that the error in adjusting the movement was about half as large as the error in perceiving it, and that the variable error obtained by the method of average error is reduced by about one-eighth when the error of adjustment is eliminated. The error of perception increases more rapidly than the error of movement for the three smallest magnitudes, but is the same for 8 and 16 kg. Curves for the averages are given below (Fig. 49).

It is to be noted that the observers who had the larger complex errors had the larger errors both of perception and of movement, but that in their case the error of movement is relatively larger, being nearly equal to the error of perception. Hence we may, perhaps, conclude that exactness in movement, as needed in manual work and games, can, by training, be improved more than accuracy of discrimination. The traits latest acquired by the race and individual are the most easily altered. So far as a conclusion can be drawn from five observers, it would seem that woman as compared with man is relatively more accurate in movement than in perception.

SEC. 29. *The Distribution of Errors.*—An average cannot give as exact information as the separate quantities from which it is taken. It is like a common noun, which, for convenience, neglects individual differences. The arithmetical average together with its probable error gives, indeed, for ordinary purposes, all the information needed; but as we have in this paper under consideration the nature of the method of average error, some study of the distribution of the errors making up the average seems desirable. In so far as this distribution follows the exponential equation (curve of error, § 3), we can discover it from the averages. But it may be useful to compare the mathematical theory with actual experiment. We have, consequently, divided the errors made by the five observers (Tables X and XI) into fourteen classes in accordance with their size and direction. All the errors of 20 (.2 kg.) or smaller are placed together in two classes, one for positive, the other for negative errors; all the errors between 21 and 40 are placed in classes together, and so on up to 120, and in the seventh pair of classes all errors larger than 120 are placed. The few cases (in all 34) in which there was no error (*i.e.*, the error was smaller than the reading of the instrument) are divided equally between + and −. In place of a table, which would be somewhat cumbersome, we give curves, by means of which the distribution of errors for the several observers and magnitudes may be conveniently seen. There are 100 errors in each set, and the area of the curve may be regarded as unity. Owing to the limited number of errors, however, it is necessary to place them in classes, and a continuous curve is not, of course, obtained. The abscissæ are proportional to the size of the mean error (or mid-error) of each class, and the ordinates to the number of errors in each class. Two sets were made on *J* and *C*, the curve representing the second set being drawn in heavier lines.

These curves show distinctly how far the distribution of 100 errors follows the bell-shaped curve required by the theory of probability. All the curves do, in fact tend to approach the theoretical curve, and the agreement is best for the best observers (*F, J* and *C*), and for the stimulus (4 kg.) in which the relation of the ordinates to the abscissæ is the most favorable for drawing the curve. If the number of errors were greater than 100, the curves would of course become more regular. For various reasons we are not prepared to introduce into this paper more mathematical discussion than necessary. But these curves might be treated in a manner which would compare the average and variable error, and the relation and relative accuracy of these compared with the probable error, the error of mean square and the modulus. The departure from the theoretical curve could further be used to discuss and possibly to amend the assumptions made by Laplace and Gauss in their mathematical deductions.

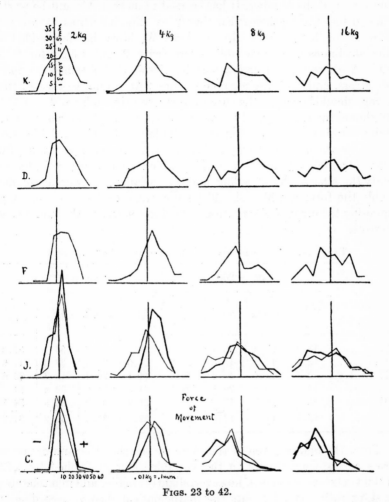

FIGS. 23 to 42.

Many of the facts already discussed may be observed with advantage in these curves. Thus the taller and narrower curves show distinctly which of the observers were the more accurate, and which of the stimuli were the more exactly perceived. The position of the curve to the right or left of the perpendicular axis shows the amount and direction of constant errors. The two curves given for *J* and *C* show the accuracy with which the same series can be repeated and the improvement with practice.

SEC. 30. *The Summation of Errors.*—Our theory to account for the increase of the error of observation with the size of the magnitude assumes that the algebraic sum of a number of errors increases as the square root of the number. It has seemed to us that it might be worth while to test the mathematical theory by experiment, as we are not aware of this having been directly done. We have therefore added in pairs algebraically the variable errors (with 2 and 4 kg.) for *F*, *J* and *C*. As there were ten errors in each series we thus obtained five complex errors, and took the average of these. According to theory, this average should be nearly the variable error, multiplied by $\sqrt{2} = 1.414$, and should further be equal to the variable error made with a stimulus double the size. In the accompanying table we give the variable error (V.E.), its value when multiplied by the $\sqrt{2}$, the result of adding the errors algebraically in pairs (S.E.), which should theoretically be nearly the same as the preceding, and the variable error with a stimulus double the former, which should be the same as the two preceding, supposing the error of observation to be due entirely to the summation of errors.

TABLE XIV.—SUMMATION OF ERRORS—1000 EXPERIMENTS

	2 kg. = 200				4 kg. = 400			
	V.E.	$\times \sqrt{2}$	S.E.	V.E. 4 kg.	V.E.	$\times \sqrt{2}$	S.E.	V.E. 8 kg.
F...........	18.3	25.9	23.4	28.	28.	39.6	34.1	37.3
J I.........	12.4	17.5	15.8	21.9	21.9	31.0	33.3	41.9
J II........	9.5	13.4	12.6	14.4	14.4	20.4	18.7	35.6
C I.........	14.4	20.4	20.1	24.5	24.5	34.6	34.4	37.
C II........	13.1	18.5	17.	21.4	21.4	30.3	35.5	34.1
Av..........	**13.5**	**19.1**	**17.8**	**22.**	**22.**	**31.2**	**31.2**	**37.2**

From the figures given in the table we see that the summation of errors corresponds closely to the variable error multiplied by $\sqrt{2}$. In eight sets out of ten it is, however, slightly smaller and in a tolerably constant ratio. At all events the mathematical theory, according to which combined errors increase as the square root of the number of observations, and the probable error of an average decreases as the square root of the number, is confirmed fairly well by these experiments.

The error of observation when the stimulus was doubled was greater than either mathematical theory or actual summation of the errors admits. We consequently assume that the error of observation was increased by the summation of errors in the manner required by theory, but also by other factors entering into the execution of the movement. It would not be likely that the error made (say) in giving 2 kg. would be the same as in going on from 2 to 4 kg. Many factors— the magnitudes most commonly compared in daily life, the muscular mechanism used, the strength of the observer, fatigue, etc.—would alter the error of observation with different magnitudes, and these must be empirically determined by experiment. But while these would sometimes increase and sometimes decrease the error of observation, the general tendency of the error to increase as the magnitude is taken larger is accounted for in a satisfactory manner by the summation of errors.

Sec. 31. *Experiments by the Method of Estimated Amount of Difference.*—This method was used by *J* and *C* in conjunction with the experiments just described. The attempt was made to double 3 kg., to halve 12 kg., and to find a mean between 2 and 4 kg., and 4 and 8 kg. respectively. The standards were set in the manner already described. When the method of mean gradation was used, two standards had to be determined and held in mind; after this had been done in five trials the observer gave one pull (the greater or less in alternate series), then the second, and thirdly a pull which seemed midway

TABLE XV.—FORCE OF MOVEMENT—METHOD OF ESTIMATED AMOUNT OF DIFFERENCE—*J* AND *C*—800 EXPERIMENTS—IX. 1890—I. 1891

	Double 3 kg. = 300							Halve 12 kg. = 1200						
	I	V	II	V¹	A.E.	V²	V.E.	I	V	II	V¹	A.E.	V²	V.E.
J....	326	26	− 10	48	72	37	56	1238	43	+266	41	266	41	43
	14	*6*	*92*	*14*	*17*	*6*	*8*	*33*	*10*	*50*	*9*	*50*	*11*	*14*
C....	312	24	−131	37	132	44	46	1232	53	+239	37	239	34	34
	24	*6*	*39*	*8*	*39*	*12*	*10*	*38*	*17*	*49*	*11*	*49*	*6*	*4*
Av..	**319**	**25**	**− 70**	**42**	**102**	**40**	**51**	**1235**	**48**	**+252**	**39**	**252**	**37**	**38**

	Mean between 2 and 4 kg.									Mean between 4 and 8 kg.								
	I	V	II	V¹	III	V²	A.E.	V³	V.E.	I	V	II	V¹	III	V²	A.E.	V³	V.E.
J....	231	20	428	28	−7	27	36	18	28	424	31	849	44	−44	39	69	32	44
	11	*6*	*28*	*7*	*21*	*7*	*13*	*6*	*10*	*34*	*9*	*33*	*14*	*40*	*9*	*21*	*12*	*16*
C....	236	19	417	31	−3	26	41	18	24	450	38	858	51	−54	48	63	33	42
	24	*7*	*32*	*4*	*38*	*6*	*11*	*6*	*9*	*36*	*10*	*18*	*13*	*17*	*16*	*16*	*12*	*8*
Av..	**233**	**19**	**422**	**29**	**−5**	**26**	**38**	**18**	**26**	**437**	**34**	**853**	**47**	**+49**	**43**	**66**	**32**	**43**

between the two. The error of each experiment was separately calculated. In halving 12 kg. the dynamometer was set at 4 kg., the extent of this pull being consequently proportional to the force of 8 kg., when the stop was set at zero. The magnitudes to be estimated were chosen so as not to be the same as any of the standards. The results of these experiments are given in the accompanying table.

In attempting to double a given pull J did so very nearly, whereas C gave a pull scarcely more than half again as great as his first pull. We cannot explain this difference in the two observers, whose variable error here as elsewhere agrees very well, but consider it of interest as showing how difficult it is to make quantitative estimates of sensations. We, ourselves, think that such estimates depend on association with known quantitative relations of the stimuli, and it seems quite likely that these should vary greatly with different observers. This experiment of doubling a stimulus (sensation?) would seem to reduce Fechner's law to an absurdity. If we measure the intensity of a sensation by estimating the number of just noticeable differences which it contains, and if the just noticeable difference be proportional to the magnitude of the stimulus, the difference between no sensation and the force of 3 kg. ought to seem immensely greater than the difference between 3 and 6 kg., and in attempting to double 3 kg. the observer ought to give a pull beyond the strength of any arm. But, in fact, both observers less than doubled the first magnitude.

In attempting to halve 12 kg., the two observers agree tolerably well in their estimates, greatly overestimating the true half. This, too, is exactly contrary to the result required by Fechner's law. The experiment was complicated by the fact that the dynamometer was set at 4 kg., so that both observers more nearly halved the extent than the force of the movement. This indicates that throughout these experiments the observer may have based his judgment largely on the extent (and possibly the time) of the movement.

The results of the two observers in using the method of mean gradation agree very well. The arithmetical mean is underestimated, and so far this is the result required by Fechner's law. But the estimates do not give the geometric mean.

The results of experiments by this method are considerably influenced by contrast, as has been found to be the case with lights.[1] Thus when the order was 200—400—estimated mean, J's constant error was -28, and C's -50; whereas, when the order was 400—200—esti-

---

[1] Alfr. Lehmann, Ueber die Anwendung der Methode der mittleren Abstufungen auf den Lichtsinn, Philos. Stud., III. 497, 1886. .

     Hjahmar Neiglick, Zur Psychophysik des Lichtsinns, Philos. Stud., IV. 28, 1887.

mated mean, J's constant error was $+14$, and C's $+34$. With 4 and 8 kg., a similar but less marked result was obtained for both observers. These, like many other effects of contrast, seem somewhat difficult to explain. We may, if we like, assume that the latter standard was somewhat better in mind than the former, and a greater objective difference between it and the judgment-pull seemed equal to a less difference between this judgment-pull and the more vaguely remembered first standard.

The variable error in these experiments is more nearly alike for the two observers, and has a smaller probable error than the constant error of estimation, and is better suited for measuring the fineness of discrimination. But for ordinary purposes it cannot be recommended, as the variable error, when "equal" is attempted, is less complex and more regular.

It will be remembered that experiments on extent of movement by this method also gave an irregular constant error, but that the half of a movement was also overestimated and the double underestimated. In that case, the mean tended to be overestimated. All our experiments, therefore, are contrary to the assumption that sensations are estimated as proportional to the logarithm of the stimulus. We believe that differences (they may be qualitative) in sensation, being associated with quantitative differences in the stimuli, are used to estimate the relations of these magnitudes, and our experiments show that such estimations are subject to large constant errors, but tend to discover the true objective relations of the extent and force of movements.

PART III

On the Time of Movement

SEC. 32. *Introductory.*—Experiments on the time of movement have not, we think, hitherto been published. Numerous experiments have, indeed, been made on the estimation of intervals of time and on the accuracy with which a rhythm can be kept.[1] These researches contradict each other concerning the validity of Weber's law, and in most other respects. Galton has recently recommended the rate of movement as an anthropometric test, and devised an instrument for its measurement.[2]

Our chief object was to determine the accuracy with which the

---

[1] The most recent, by Herbert Nichols, "The Psychology of Time," Am. Jour. of Psy., Vol. III. 4, IV. 1, 1891, who gives an excellent summary and criticism of preceding researches, twenty-one in number.

[2] Francis Galton, A New Instrument for Measuring the Rate of Movement of the Various Limbs, Journal of the Anthropological Institute, 1890.

time of movements can be discriminated, and to study the part played by rate as compared with extent and force in the perception of movement. We also give some experiments on the maximum rate of movement, which subject deserves study, if only on account of its possible pedagogical and clinical applications.

SEC. 33. *Apparatus and Methods.*—A detailed description of the apparatus needed to measure short intervals of time with exactness need not be given here. The arrangement which we consider the most convenient has been described elsewhere by one of us.[1] It consists of an electric chronoscope, with the pieces necessary to control and regulate it. The great accuracy of this apparatus is sufficiently shown

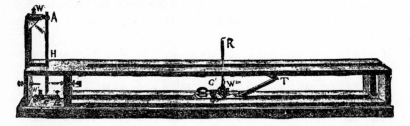

FIG. 43.

by the fact that the average variation in the time of fifty blows (in five series) in one case was 1.6 thousandth of a second, which very small variation includes the error of all the apparatus as well as the irregularity of the blow. In addition to the apparatus for measuring the time, we needed an instrument which would close an electric current when the movement was begun, and break it when the movement was ended. This is shown in Fig. 43.

An electric current passes through the contacts at C and C'. The observer sat in a convenient position in front of the instrument, and placed his right hand on H and against the bar AHC. When the hand was moved the spring drew up the bar and closed the contact. We give a special figure of this contact. We should like to call attention to it, as we think it might be useful in physical instruments. Contacts are usually closed by means of mercury, but owing to combustion and spilling it is difficult to keep the mercury at a constant level. Besides,

[1] Mind, XI. 1886; Phil. Stud., III., 1886. We have, however, introduced several improvements. The chronoscope, as made by Peyer and Favarger, often fails to give the proper time. We have obviated this fault by replacing the string with which the instrument is started by a bar and key, by which means it can be started constantly and regularly, and by placing a clamp on the carriage of the tuning-fork, which prevents it from becoming loosened with the vibrations. A wooden house, with padding placed over the clock-work, deadens the noise and keeps out dust. We also constructed a new regulator, made by C. Krille, Leipzig.

mercury is always troublesome in a laboratory. This contact is closed at an exact point by the platinum bar touching the platinum sunk into the inclined plane at C. The pressure can be regulated by the spring and screw at S, and the contact is kept clean by the rubbing. The contact is never broken after it has once been made. There is no rebound, as the movement is stopped gradually by the increasing friction of the inclined plane. When the hand has moved from H to R and touches the bar, the lever breaks the contact at C'. This bar is very light, and the most violent blow will not injure hand or apparatus.

The electric current is thus closed while the hand moves, and the time of the movement in thousandths of a second is directly read from the chronoscope. The duration of either a quick blow or a slow movement can thus be measured conveniently and exactly.

In our experiments on the discrimination of the time of movement, the extent was always 50 cm. The force of the blow therefore varied, being greater for the quicker movements. The observer could, consequently, use the perception of a difference in force to judge the time. We regret that we have not been able to carry out experiments which we had planned to discover how the judgment of the time of movement

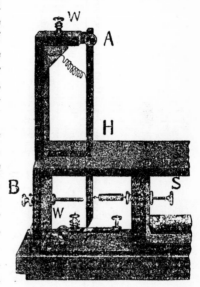

Fig. 44.

is affected by alterations in the extent and force. The time between the two movements was made as nearly as possible one second, but owing to the nature of the experiments this interval could not be given to the observer.

We used as normal times 1, ½ and ¼ sec., and the time of a blow made as quickly as possible. This blow required about ⅛ sec., so we had a geometric series of four magnitudes, as with the force of movement. The normal time was given to the observer in the same manner as in the experiments already described. He made a movement in what he supposed to be about (say) 1 sec., and was told the direction and amount of his error. After he had learned the approximate size of the standard by five such trials, a series of ten judgments was made. The observer made the normal movement, and then a second movement, as nearly as possible, in the same time. The four magnitudes

TABLE XVI.—TIME OF MOVEMENT—METHOD OF AVERAGE ERROR—4 OBSERVERS—1600 EXPERIMENTS—XI. 1890—III. 1891

	Maximum				¼ sec. = 250σ				½ sec. = 500σ				1 sec. = 1000σ			
	I	II	A.E.	V.E.	I	II	A.E.	V.E.	I	II	A.E.	V.E.	I	II	A.E.	V.E.
K	188	−13	26	23.7	283	+8	37	31.3	496	+11	61	53.9	878	+45	145	133
Var	35	13	15	12.9	10	16	6	5.7	38	43	21	19.3	115	65	24	27.6
D	136	−16	21	14.2	215	−4	38	36.7	544	+16	96	85.	1020	+41	168	139.
Var	9	10	9	3.8	21	10	10	11.7	71	34	28	26.3	99	86	43	32.7
C	87	−5	12	10.	286	+3	28	24.7	480	+27	47	35.1	1055	+36	78	66.7
Var	6	6	4	2.4	13	9	5	5.1	31	19	8	7.9	109	22	15	12.9
F	110	−7	13	9.7	273	−14	24	18.8	492	+2	35	34.1	959	+69	88	60.6
Var	6	6	5	4.3	14	6	6	6	34	24	7	8.7	87	31	30	15.6
Av	130	−10	18	14.4	264	−2	32	27.9	503	+14	60	52.0	978	+48	120	99.8

were used at one sitting, the order being varied, so as to eliminate the effects of contrast and fatigue.

SEC. 34. *Results of Experiments.*—By the method of average error 400 experiments each were made on *K*, *D*, *F* and *C*. The method of calculating and tabulating the results was the same as in the corresponding experiments on extent and force. The table will, therefore, be readily understood.

We have in the table the time of the first movement (I), the time of the second movement (II) compared to the first (the constant error),

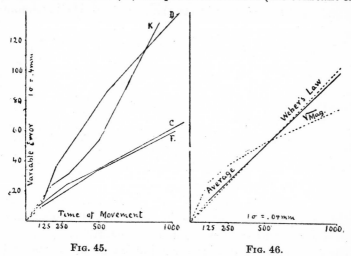

FIG. 45.   FIG. 46.

the average error (A.E.) in attempting to make the two movements alike, and the variable error (V.E.) obtained by eliminating as far as possible the constant error from the average error. One-thousandth of a second (σ) is used as the unit of time.

The variable error has usually been made the measure of discrimination in experiments by the method of average error. We give in Figs. 45 and 46 curves showing the relation of the variable error to the magnitude of the stimulus. The relations given in the table and shown in the figures prove that the error in judging the time of movement tended to vary as the time, although, as is usually the case, the error becomes too small as the magnitude is increased. The apparent close agreement of the average with Weber's law is, indeed, due to the irregularity of *K*'s curve. The curves for the other observers depart about equally from Weber's law and from the square root of the magnitude.[1]

[1] One of the writers (J. McK. C.) thinks that the comparatively large errors with the slower movements were due to the fact that the force of the blow was used in judging the quicker movements—force being judged more accurately than time.

Sec. 35. *The Constant Error.*—The average error is, of course, larger than the variable error, but would give nearly the same curves. It is the constant error which has received most attention in experiments on rhythm and the sense of time, but different investigations differ greatly in their results. We give curves showing the constant errors in our experiments (Figs. 47 and 48). The curves for the several observers agree better than is usually the case with constant errors. The average curve is nearly a straight line crossing the horizontal axis just beyond one-fourth second. With one-half and one second, the second movement was made more slowly than the first. With the maximum blow

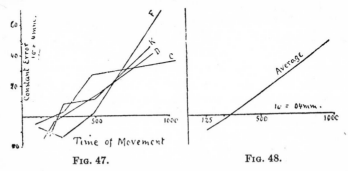

FIG. 47.　　　　　　　　　　　　FIG. 48.

the second movement was made more quickly than the first and also seemed easier and quicker. The accomplishment of one blow thus makes one following it quicker and more powerful.

The error made by an observer in judging a standard magnitude is usually very great. Before making these experiments the observers were required to estimate one, one-half and one-fourth second. The averages of ten such estimations are given in the accompanying table.

TABLE XVII.—ESTIMATION OF A STANDARD INTERVAL OF TIME—4 OBSERVERS—
100 EXPERIMENTS

	¼ sec. = 250σ		½ sec. = 500σ		1 sec. = 1000σ	
	Time	V	Time	V	Time	V
K..............	...	...	...	...	201	10
D..............	171	15	143	6	274	20
C..............	390	63	616	115	901	226
F..............	191	19	273	27	437	55
Av.............	276	32	344	49	453	78

The table shows that one second was much underestimated, although all the observers had been using one second (given by a pendulum) as the time of movement in other experiments. The attempt to estimate longer intervals of time and other standard magnitudes gave very great errors, which shows how little reliance should be placed on such estimates—for example, in a court of justice.

As we did not make other experiments on the time of movement by the method of estimated amount of difference, it is worth noting that in the present case when the observer attempted to give an interval half as great as another (the order of the series was one, one-half, and one-quarter second), the half was greatly overestimated. All through the experiments the same constant error was present: one-half second seemed to F and C less than the half of one second, and more than the double of one-fourth second. That is, the estimation of intervals of time gives a result contrary to Fechner's law. This increase in subjective estimation of equal objective increments may be related to the fact that the error of observation increases faster than the objective increment warrants, according to the summation of errors. Both facts are perhaps due to the greater part played by force in the quicker movements, and may be related to the commonly observed phenomenon that time passes more quickly when we are active than when we are passive.

SEC. 36. *Analysis of the Error into an Error of Perception and an Error of Movement.*—As in the corresponding experiments on extent and force, the observer, after he had made the time of the two movements as nearly as possible alike, was required to judge the success with which this had been done. The percentages of right cases for the several observers and magnitudes are given in the table.

TABLE XVIII.—PERCENTAGES OF RIGHT CASES IN JUDGING THE TIME OF TWO MOVEMENTS MADE AS NEARLY AS POSSIBLE ALIKE

	Second less				Second greater			
	Max.	250	500	1000	Max.	250	500	1000
K...........	100	88	83	69	5	40	51	69
D...........	82	76	67	47	63	64	79	82
F...........	82	68	86	83	32	75	51	61
C...........	67	58	57	73	20	76	62	58

The table shows that the movements could be judged much better than they could be made. The great excess of right cases with the maximum blow, when the second movement was the quicker, shows that the second blow seemed far quicker and more powerful than the first. It was, in fact, quicker, but less so than it seemed.

When the complex variable error given in Table XVI is analyzed into an error of perception and an error of movement in the manner described (Sec. 28), we obtain the results given in Table XIX, and the accompanying curves (Fig. 50).

TABLE XIX.—ANALYSIS OF THE ERROR INTO AN ERROR OF PERCEPTION AND AN ERROR OF MOVEMENT

	Error of perception				Error of movement			
	Max.	250	500	1000	Max.	250	500	1000
K..........	22	26	46	112	10	16	29	72
D..........	11	30	66	122	9	21	53	66
F..........	9	15	28	47	3	11	20	38
C..........	10	21	33	58	0	12	10	31
Av..........	13	23	43	85	5	15	28	52

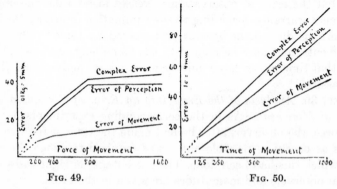

FIG. 49.   FIG. 50.

We thus see that both the error of perception and the error of movement increase nearly in direct proportion to the magnitude of the stimulus, but somewhat more slowly. The error of perception is somewhat less than double the error of movement, and about four-fifths of the complex variable error.

In Fig. 49 the corresponding curves for the force of movement are shown. In comparing the curves it must be noticed that the ordinates representing the error in force are twenty times the abscissæ, whereas those representing the error in time are only ten times the abscissæ. It is evident that force was judged relatively much better than time, especially for the larger magnitudes.

SEC. 37. *The Distribution of Error.*—The errors in adjusting the time of movements were classified in the same manner as those on the force of movement (Sec. 29). The accompanying curves show clearly the distribution of small and large errors, and the variation for the several observers and magnitudes. The classes are 0–25σ, 26–50σ, etc.

The curves are tolerably regular and approach the bell-shape required by the theory of probability. Small errors are evidently more frequent than large ones. The taller and narrower curves of F and C bear witness to greater fineness of discrimination, and their more regular shape to smaller variation. Regularity cannot be expected with the larger magnitudes, as there were comparatively few small errors.

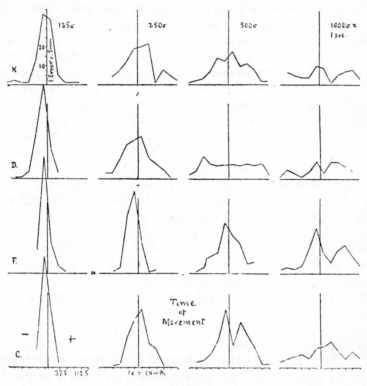

FIGS. 51–66.

SEC. 38. *The Summation of Errors.*—In exactly the same manner as in the experiments on the force of movement (Sec. 30), we added algebraically in pairs the variable errors of F and C with ¼ and ½ second. The results are given in the table.

TABLE XX.—SUMMATION OF ERRORS—400 EXPERIMENTS

	¼ sec. = 250σ				½ sec. = 500σ			
	V.E.	× √2	S.E.	V.E. ½	V.E.	× √2	S.E.	V.E. 1
F..........	18.8	26.6	29.2	34.1	34.1	48.2	50.3	60.6
C..........	24.7	34.9	35.4	35.1	35.1	49.6	49.2	66.7
Av..........	21.7	30.7	32.3	34.6	34.6	48.9	49.7	63.6

It is evident that the results obtained by the summation of the errors correspond very closely with the variable error multiplied by the square root of two. The variation is not larger than the probable error would lead us to expect, and the mathematical theory is thus confirmed by the experiments. The variable error in these experiments on the time of movement increases, as we have seen, more rapidly than the mere summation of errors would warrant.

SEC. 39. *The Maximum Rate of Movement.*—We believe that the time of the quickest blow which can be made is a useful test for clinical and anthropometric purposes. Under constant conditions it is very regular, but differs considerably with different observers and under changed conditions. In ten series of ten experiments made on C the average variation of a blow fifty cm. in extent was only 5σ. The average time of the separate series, however, varied from 96 to 138σ, and this variation tells of some change in the condition of the observer. In certain diseases of the nervous system the rate of movement might be most useful as a test of progression or recovery, perhaps fully as valuable as the dynamometer test now used universally. The difference in the rate of movement with right and left hand (or foot) may also prove useful in the diagnosis of unilateral disease. The rate of movement for C as the result of 120 experiments was exactly the same (119σ) for the two hands. C's reaction time with right and left hand is also the same, and this test may also be recommended for clinical experiment. For C, a blow with the right hand from right to left was a little slower (7σ as the result of 120 experiments) than from left to right.

In the experiments which we have described (Table XVI) the maximum rate of movement for the four observers was respectively 87, 110, 136 and 188σ, and the results obtained from other observers fell within these limits. The time for women is decidedly longer than for men, which measures a well-known difference in the sexes, due doubtless to selection and heredity.

In these experiments only the time of the entire movement was measured, its extent being always 50 cm. We also made a few experiments in which the extent was varied, in order to study the rate of a movement during its course. As the result of 200 experiments on C we obtained the following times:

Extent	10	30	50	70 cm.
Time	13	63	104	141σ

The motion was therefore nearly uniform at the rate of 5 M. per second. But at the beginning of the movement there was apparently a greater followed by a lesser rate.

Part IV
On Lifted Weights

Sec. 40. *Introductory.*—Weber's generalization concerning the relation of the least observable difference in sensation to the magnitude of the stimulus was chiefly based on experiments with lifted weights.[1] These experiments are of considerable historical interest, but they were too few and too inexact to contribute to our present knowledge. Fechner's research with lifted weights is well known, and has, perhaps, never been surpassed in extent and thoroughness by any investigation in any science. The experiments were made 1856–1859, and Fechner always intended to publish the details, but left this unaccomplished. Summaries are, however, contained in the *Elemente* and in the *Revision.* Fechner made 67,072 experiments on himself by the method of right and wrong cases. The normal weight was varied between 300 and 3000 grammes, and the "comparison weight" was from 1.5 to 8 per cent heavier. The experiments show that the percentage of right cases ($+\frac{1}{2}$ the doubtful cases) remained tolerably constant, when the difference between the two weights was proportional to the normal weight. The experiments thus tend to support Weber's law. The percentage of right cases, however, generally becomes less, as the normal weight is taken smaller, and this Fechner explains by supposing that the weight of the arm should be added to both of the weights. The most serious criticism to which Fechner's experiments are open would seem to be that it is difficult, when the relations of the weights are known, to compare the sensations without taking the known differences of the stimuli into account. Fechner defends[2] this method, naïvely arguing that its objectivity is proved by the close correspondence of his experiments with the law in defence of which they were undertaken. We had intended to compare the results of experiments, when the subject knew the objective relations of the stimuli, with those in which he was ignorant of these. We have, however, only found that it is more difficult for us to come to a decision when we know the objective relations. The large number of doubtful cases recorded by Fechner (they are nearly one-seventh of the whole number) seems, indeed, to bear witness to a similar difficulty.

Hering[3] gives an account of some experiments on lifted weights made by Biedermann and Loewit at his suggestion. These seem to show that the least noticeable difference becomes greater as the stimulus is

[1] See references, Sec. 2.
[2] Revision, p. 58.
[3] Ueber Fechner's psychophysisches Gesetz, Sitzungsb. d. Wiener Akad. d. Wiss., III. Abth., 1875, p. 33.

taken greater, but much more slowly than in direct proportion. The variation from Weber's law is thus in the same direction as in Fechner's experiments, but far greater.

Merkel,[1] in his extended psychophysical study, found Weber's law to hold for pressure made by the moving finger with great exactness, the least perceptible difference being $\frac{1}{9}$ of the stimulus. These experiments were made by Merkel on himself, and we judge them to be in need of independent confirmation. Pierce and Jastrow (*op. cit.*) found the probable error for pressure, from which the muscular sense was not entirely excluded, to be about $\frac{1}{20}$ of the stimulus (250 gm.), and to be further diminished by practice.

Several observers have studied the perception of lifted weights in order to determine what part is due to the skin sensations, and what part to the muscular sensations. These experiments have been made on paralytic patients, and by stimulating the muscle electrically.[2] They seem to show that the discrimination of lifted weights is not interfered with, though the skin be ataxic, or though the movement be caused by electric stimulation. But, as is so common in clinical experiments, cases are cited from which exactly opposite conclusions are drawn.

The only research remaining for us to mention is the recent interesting paper by Müller and Schumann, already noted. In view of the effects of contrast, etc., they study the nature of the motor impulse, and conclude that the velocity with which a weight is lifted is the chief factor in the discrimination of the force of movement.

Our experiments with lifted weights were made with a view to studying methods for determining the fineness of discrimination and the factors entering into the perception of movement. They are not concerned with the relation between the magnitude of the stimulus and the error of observation, and were mostly made earlier than the experiments in the foregoing Parts of this paper.

SEC. 41. *Apparatus and Methods.*—When lifted weights are used as stimuli they can be easily arranged and accurately measured. We loaded wooden boxes so that they weighed (to $\frac{1}{100000}$) 100, 104, 108, 112 and 116 gm. Care was taken to place the load in the centre of the box and to make the packing firm. The boxes were cylinders about 6 cm. in diameter and 3 cm. high. The weights looked alike, and several sets were used, so that the observer might not by any chance learn them. In the later experiments paper caps were made, and shifted from weight to weight. But these precautions were scarcely necessary, as the observer did not look at the weights. The observer sat on an ordi-

[1] *Op. cit.*

[2] References will be found in Wundt, James and Müller.

nary chair facing a low table. The boxes were placed, two at a time, in a line parallel to the edge of the table, but a little back and opposite the left shoulder. A seconds pendulum swung in front of the observer.

The recorder placed the 100 gm. weight and one of the heavier weights for the observer. One was about 1 cm. to the right of the other, and this was always lifted first. The weight was lightly grasped on the side with the thumb and fingers, the observer being allowed to choose the position which seemed to him the most convenient. The weights were not raised perpendicularly, but carried along from left to right. We chose this movement because we thought it could be kept the most constant. The movements were made in time with the pendulum, and in the direction in which it swung. The first weight was lifted, as nearly as possible, for one second, during the next second the position was recovered, and, lastly, the second weight was lifted for one second. The time was easily kept, as the motion of the pendulum was followed almost automatically. It was our intention to have the extent of movement 30 cm., but all the observers showed a tendency to make it greater, and we did not check this. A swing of the arm of about 40 cm. would thus seem to be most natural, as there is a most natural swing of the leg in walking, due to its acting as a pendulum.

After the observer had lifted the two weights he was required to say whether the second weight seemed lighter or heavier than the first. He was also required to estimate what confidence he felt in his decision. *a, b* and *c* were used in the manner already described, *a* meaning sure of the correctness of the decision, *b* less certain, and *c* uncertain. If the observer could discern no difference whatever, he was allowed to say "doubtful" (*d*), but was asked to use this as seldom as possible, and in our later experiments he was required to guess even when quite doubtful. Forty experiments were made in a series, each of the four differences being used ten times, and the second weight being, in half the cases, the heavier, in half the lighter. The order was irregular, and could not have been guessed by the observer. Ten series were made with each observer, so that 100 trials were made with each difference. The observer was always ignorant of the real relations of the weights, and only the writers knew the results of previous experiments.

SEC. 42. *Results of Experiments.*—The results of 4000 experiments made on nine observers are contained in the accompanying table. The number of right, of wrong and of doubtful cases is given, for each amount of difference, and according to whether the second weight was the lighter or the heavier.

As we have seen, the figures given in the table do not directly measure in the fineness of discrimination. In the manner described in the Introduction we have calculated the probable errors of the several

TABLE XXI.—THE DISCRIMINATION OF LIFTED WEIGHTS WEIGHING ABOUT 100 GM.—METHOD OF RIGHT AND WRONG CASES—9 OBSERVERS—4000 EXPERIMENTS—II. 1890—I. 1891

100	Second weight the lighter												Second weight the heavier											
	104			108			112			116			104			108			112			116		
	R	W	D	R	W	D	R	W	D	R	W	D	R	W	D	R	W	D	R	W	D	R	W	D
R	36	14	0	35	15	0	45	5	0	45	5	0	28	22	0	36	14	0	41	9	0	45	5	0
K	25	25	0	30	20	0	40	10	0	36	13	1	40	10	0	43	7	0	46	4	0	49	1	0
G	17	27	6	29	15	6	32	13	5	37	11	2	43	7	0	47	1	2	48	1	1	50	0	0
L	33	17	0	36	14	0	45	5	0	47	3	0	37	13	0	39	11	0	49	1	0	48	2	0
S	33	17	0	37	11	2	41	9	0	45	3	2	33	17	0	36	14	0	47	2	1	46	4	0
N	27	13	10	33	12	5	43	5	2	45	4	1	34	14	2	44	2	4	38	3	9	49	0	1
D I	30	16	4	36	10	4	47	2	1	50	0	0	39	9	2	39	10	1	49	1	0	50	0	0
D II	43	7	0	34	14	2	46	4	0	47	3	0	36	13	1	42	8	0	50	0	0	50	0	0
F	33	16	1	41	6	3	46	3	1	47	3	0	36	10	4	45	2	3	44	5	1	48	1	1
C	38	11	1	42	6	2	45	4	1	50	0	0	35	13	2	41	6	3	42	7	1	50	0	0

observers for the four amounts of difference and give the results in Table XXII.[1]

TABLE XXII.—PROBABLE ERROR WITH LIFTED WEIGHTS

100	104	108	112	116	Av.	*V*
R.............	7.4	9.8	7.3	8.3	**8.2**	*.8*
K.............	6.4	8.1	7.2	8.2	**7.5**	*.7*
G.............	6.5	5.1	6.8	7.	**6.3**	*.6*
L.............	5.1	8.	4.8	6.6	**6.1**	*1.2*
S.............	6.8	8.4	6.3	7.7	**7.3**	*.7*
N.............	6.1	5.5	7.3	5.9	**6.2**	*.5*
D I...........	4.5	7.1	4.3	4.6	**5.1**	*1.0*
D II..........	3.2	7.1	4.3	5.6	**5.**	*1.3*
F.............	4.7	4.3	6.	6.2	**5.3**	*.8*
C.............	4.1	5.1	6.8	4.6	**5.1**	*.8*
Av...........	**5.5**	**6.8**	**6.1**	**6.5**	**6.2**	*.8*
V.............	*1.2*	*1.5*	*1.*	*1.1*	*.9*	

This table shows clearly the probable error of the several observers —that is, the difference in grammes which each of them could expect to distinguish 75 times out of 100. On the average, weights can thus be discriminated when they are about as 100:106 (or 110:116) gm.[2] or when the difference is (say) $6/108 = 1/18$ of the stimulus. If we wish to know what difference can be distinguished 99 times out of 100 the figures in the table are to be multiplied by 3.45, or about $3\frac{1}{2}$. Thus, on the average, the difference between 100 and 121 gm. can be distinguished 99 times out of 100.

The table shows that the fineness of discrimination of the observers did not differ greatly, the probable error varying from 8.2 to 5 gm., or from about $1/13$ to $1/22$ of the stimulus. If the observers be classified we find that the average probable error for two women was 7.8, for two

---

[1] In this calculation the doubtful cases have been divided equally between "right and wrong." Much discussion has arisen concerning the disposition of doubtful cases, but we think the correct solution has not been suggested. We believe it is found in the proper application of the probability integral. However, when there are but few doubtful cases, this would not give a result appreciably different from an equal division. As has been said, we think it best to let the observer divide his doubtful cases by guessing, and this has been done in our later experiments. When the observer is always right in his judgment his fineness of discrimination has not been measured. We must assume that errors would occur if the series were continued long enough, and have somewhat arbitrarily set 99 as the most probable percentage of right cases.

[2] It will be noticed that in these calculations the error of observation is assumed to be the same for the several weights. This assumption is not strictly correct, but cannot be avoided until the relation between the error of observation and the magnitude of the stimulus is known.

advanced students of biology 6.2, for three advanced students of psychology 6.2, and for the two writers 5.2. As 400 experiments were made with each observer the results must be considered accurate, but it should be remembered that in all anthropometric experiments the size of the error may be due to accommodation to the conditions of experiment, as well as to real differences in the senses or faculties. The smaller probable error of the writers (nearly the same for the two) is thus probably not so much due to finer senses as to more practice in careful observation.

From this point of view as well as for other reasons it is interesting to note the improvement with practice. We have therefore divided the experiments into five sets, each containing eighty judgments, and give in the accompanying table the percentages of right cases for the observers with increasing practice.

TABLE XXIII.—RIGHT CASES IN PERCENTAGES WITH INCREASING PRACTICE

	I	II	III	IV	V
R.	78	75	70	81	85
K.	78	79	74	80	74
G.	82	82	83	68	78
L.	70	80	85	90	83
S.	83	78	80	78	83
N.	84	75	84	84	83
D I.	84	88	81	88	92
D II.	86	90	83	88	89
F.	86	85	89	81	93
C.	90	87	86	86	88
Av.	82	83	81	82	85

The averages in this table show a slight improvement in accuracy of discrimination as the series were continued, but it is so little that it might be due to chance variations. Two sets were made on *D*, and the second was slightly the better. The different series on the same observer vary considerably, and eighty judgments by the method of right and wrong cases would, therefore, scracely be sufficient as a test. Ten experiments by this method would be worthless.

SEC. 43. *The Amount of Difference and the Degree of Confidence.*—In these experiments we used four amounts of difference, our object being to combine the method of the just noticeable difference with the method of right and wrong cases, and to study the application of the probability integral. As regards this latter, our experiments agree very well with the mathematical theory. The probable error is nearly the same, whether it be calculated from a small difference and a relatively small percentage of right cases, or from a larger difference and a larger percentage of right cases. With the smallest difference the probable error is the least, but this is most likely due to chance variations. If the probable error became gradually smaller as the differences were made smaller, it would indicate either a larger probable error with the greater weights (which is doubtless the case but to a small degree) or, if considerable, the presence of factors other than the amount of difference, such as unconscious recognition of the weights by touch, or an inference from the order of presentation. Below (in Sec. 49) we give a curve showing the percentages of right cases for the several differences required by the probability integral, and those obtained by actual experiment.

By varying the amount of difference and making it in some cases so large that it was usually perceived correctly, we have combined the method of right and wrong cases with the method of the just noticeable difference. This shows clearly that the method of the just noticeable difference in its scientific form is simply a case of the method of right and wrong cases. We also see that it is not the most favorable amount of difference to choose for experiment; if the observer be always right, we have no satisfactory basis for comparison; and, further, a chance error, due, say, to complete distraction of the attention, affects the probable error more when the percentage of right cases is above 90 than when it is between 80 and 90.

TABLE XXIV.—THE DEGREE OF CONFIDENCE OF THE OBSERVERS WITH VARYING AMOUNTS OF DIFFERENCE

	100		104		108		112		116		Av.	
	A	*B*	*A*	*B*	*A*	*B*	*A*	*B*	*A*	*B*	*A*	*B*
R	10	45	19	46	25	46	33	46			22	46
K	41	0	51	0	62	1	64	0			54	0
G	47	37	64	22	71	15	72	21			63	24
L	13	72	22	69	32	58	39	53			26	63
S	60	36	51	45	83	15	81	16			69	28
N	34	29	40	28	47	21	62	26			46	26
D I	14	61	11	68	28	64	39	56			23	62
D II	5	50	8	54	24	59	30	57			17	55
F	3	31	17	29	23	34	37	34			20	32
C	1	16	2	28	9	31	12	58			6	33
Av	23	38	28	39	40	34	47	37			35	37

The method of the just noticeable difference, in its less scientific form, has also been combined with the method of right and wrong cases by recording the degree of confidence of the observer. If the just noticeable difference be the difference the observer is sure that he can notice; it is that difference with which a was given; if it be the difference he feels some confidence that he can notice, it was that with which b was given. The number (which is also the percentage) of times a and b were given by the several observers is shown in the accompanying table.[1]

We see from the figures in the table that the number of times the observer felt confidence in the correctness of his decision usually increased as the amount of difference was taken greater.

Compared with the percentages of right cases, the fictitious averages are:

100	104	108	112	116
Percentage of times right...............	69	77	89	94
Percentage of times a and b..............	61	67	74	84

The confidence thus varies nearly as the percentage of right cases, and some reliance may, therefore, be placed on such introspection. We see, however, from the table, that different individuals place very different meanings on the degree of confidence. Some observers are nearly always quite or fairly confident, while others are seldom quite confident. If this table be compared with the preceding, it will, indeed, appear that those observers who felt the greatest degree of confidence in their judgment had the largest probable error, while those who were most seldom quite confident had the smallest probable error. It is, therefore, absurd to measure the fineness of discrimination of an observer by the difference which he thinks he can notice, as is done when the method of the just noticeable difference is used in its usual form.

We give in Table XXV the percentage of times the observer was right in his judgment when he used a, b and c respectively.

TABLE XXV.—PERCENTAGE OF TIMES THE OBSERVERS WÉRE RIGHT WITH EACH DEGREE OF CONFIDENCE

	R	K	G	L	S	N	$D\,I$	$D\,II$	F	C	Av.
a..................	95	89	90	97	86	91	96	100	100	100	94
b..................	79	..	58	81	66	78	89	91	97	98	82
c..................	65	63	68	65	75	72	68	74	77	81	71

We see from the table that an observer is more apt to be right than wrong, even when he feels very little confidence in the correct-

[1] c was given in the remaining cases of the 100, unless the observer were doubtful. The number of times this occurred is shown in Table XXI.

ness of his decision. We also obtain a rough measure of what reliance may be placed on the judgment of the observer.

SEC. 44. *The Constant Error.*—Table XXI shows that most of the observers were the more often right in their judgment when the second weight was the heavier. The second weight seemed relatively heavier than the first, which increased the apparent difference when it was in fact the heavier, and decreased it when it was in fact the lighter. This constant error becomes eliminated in calculating the probable error, for we have in the one series $\dfrac{\Delta + C}{\text{P.E.}}$ and in the other $\dfrac{\Delta - C}{\text{P.E.}}$, so that C disappears in the average value of $\dfrac{\Delta}{\text{P.E.}}$ from which the probable error is calculated. If, however, we subtract the one equation from the other, we can find the relation of C to P.E., and, consequently, the value of the constant error. These values for the several observers and differences are given in the accompanying table.[1]

TABLE XXVI.—CONSTANT ERROR IN DISTINGUISHING WEIGHTS WEIGHING ABOUT 100 GM.—METHOD OF RIGHT AND WRONG CASES—9 OBSERVERS—4000 EXPERIMENTS

	100	104	108	112	116	Ab. ±
R.............		−2.4	.4	−2.	0.	1.2
K.............		4.	5.	3.	8.6	5.1
G.............		6.5	5.3	7.	8.6	6.8
L.............		.9	1.1	2.8	3.8	2.1
S.............		.1	− .8	3.4	0.	1.3
N.............		.7	3.5	− .8	4.3	2.3
D I.............		1.6	.5	1.3	0.	.8
D II.............		−1.1	2.5	3.	3.2	2.4
F.............		.9	1.4	−1.1	1.5	1.2
C.............		− .5	− .2	−1.5	0.	.5
Av. ±.........		**1.9**	**2.1**	**2.6**	**3.**	**2.4**

The table shows that the constant error varied more than the probable or variable error. For two of the observers the constant error is about as large as their probable error. The constant error for F and C is small (within the limits of chance variations), and this may possibly be owing to the observers having unconsciously made allowance for a constant error, as they knew the tendency of other observers to overestimate the second weight. The constant error of the average increases regularly as the difference is taken greater. As is usually the case with constant errors, the overestimation of the

---

[1] Owing to the limited number of experiments, some part of the errors given in this table is due to the variable error.

second weight in these experiments is difficult to explain. At first sight it might be attributed to fatigue; but as many pairs of trials were made in succession, fatigue could scarcely tell in a single pair. The overestimation of the second weight may possibly be due to the fact that it was the more recently perceived. But the various effects of contrast have not yet been explained.

SEC. 45. *Conditions Affecting the Perception of Lifted Weights.*—In the experiments which we have been discussing the weights were lifted as described, and the movement was always made in the same manner. It would evidently be an advantage to alter the nature of the movement, and from the variation in the probable error attempt to learn the factors concerned in the perception of lifted weights. With this object in view we made the movements in various ways, and give the results in the accompanying table. Only 200 experiments of each sort were made, and the probable and constant errors can only be regarded as approximate. The weights used were 100 and 108 gm., the probable and constant errors being calculated as described. The nature of the movement is given in the table, and will be described more exactly below. The series were made in the order in which they are given in the table, but the groups collected under *Av. Av.* were made simultaneously, and half of the experiments on lifting the weights up and down with one and with two hands were made at the close.

TABLE XXVII.—PROBABLE AND CONSTANT ERRORS IN LIFTING WEIGHTS
100:108 GM.—*J* AND *C*—3000 EXPERIMENTS—I. 1891—I. 1892

Nature of the movement	Probable error				Constant error			
	J	*C*	Av.	Av. Av.	*J*	*C*	Av.	Av. Av.
Right to left ca. 40 cm............	5.7	5.1	5.4	5.4	− .4	− .2	− .3	− .3
Up and down, right weight first....	8.8	7.6	8.2		− .4	−1.5	− .9	
Up and down, left weight first......	6.3	4.8	5.5	6.9	+1.3	+3.0	+2.1	+ .6
Two hands, right first.............	7.3	9.8	8.5		−3.7	− .4	−2.0	
Two hands, left first..............	11.1	6.4	8.7	8.6	+4.7	+3.1	+3.9	+ .9
Up only, 16 cm...................	8.6	9.8	9.2		+2.8	−1.3	+ .7	
Down only, 16 cm......	5.1	13.1	9.1	9.1	− .7	+1.0	+ .1	+ .4
From wrist only..................	7.5	8.2	7.8		+2.2	+2.2	+2.2	
From forearm only................	6.2	6.6	6.4		+2.	−1.7	+ .1	
From shoulder only...............	10.3	8.2	9.2	7.8	+1.8	−6.2	−2.2	+ .1
First 4 cm., second 16 cm.........	4.8	6.4	5.6		− .3	+ .7	+ .2	
First 16 cm., second 4 cm.........	7.8	5.4	6.6		+5.6	−3.3	+1.1	
First 12 sec., second 2 sec........	5.6	5.3	5.4		−1.7	−3.0	−2.3	
First 2 sec., second 12 sec........	5.4	4.6	5.0	5.7	−1.3	.0	− .6	− .4
Pressing the weights..............	10.9	10.3	10.6	10.6	−1.4	−1.8	−1.6	−1.6
Averages......................	7.4	7.4	7.4	7.4	+ .6	− .6	0	0

The average probable error for J and C is exactly the same—7.4 gm., or about $\frac{1}{14}$ of the stimulus. Throughout our experiments the results for F J and C agree closely. The average constant error is small for both J and C—less than $\frac{1}{10}$ of the probable error. It is negative for C—that is, the second weight seemed relatively slightly the lighter, as was the case before. It is positive for J, as was the case with eight of the ten observers given in Table XXVI.

In considering the probable errors for the different kinds of movements, it must be remembered that they (being the result of only 100 experiments with each observer) would vary considerably even were the movement always the same. However, some reliance may be placed on the figures given under *Av. Av.* The probable error was smaller, and was subject to smaller constant errors when the weights were lifted across 40 cm., than when they were lifted up 8 cm., and set down again. The time of the movement in each case was one second. As before noted, a movement of about 40 cm. seems the most natural. J was not told how long to make the movement, but made it on the average 42.6 cm. When the weights were lifted up and down the height was determined by loose horizontal silk threads, which marked the distance without offering resistance. The distance the weights were lifted by J in series two and three was noted without the observer's knowledge. When the judgment was right the heavier weight was lifted on the average 7.9, the lighter 7.8 cm.; when wrong the heavier weight was lifted 7.9, the lighter 7.9 cm. The distance which the weights were lifted was, consequently, not proportional to the weight, and the observer cannot judge of the difference by the distance (or rate) as maintained by Müller and Schumann (*op. cit.*). The probable error was increased by about $\frac{1}{4}$ when the weights were lifted with different hands. It was considerably increased when the weight was lifted up only (16 cm.) or down only. It became larger when the movement was made from the shoulder only, the wrist and forearm not being bent. It seems, therefore, that the perception depends on sensations accompanying the movements of the wrist and forearm, but when either of these is present the error is not appreciably greater than when the three joints are used. When the rate of movement was altered so that the one weight was lifted four times as rapidly as the other, either by being lifted higher in the same time or the same distance more quickly, the probable error was not increased. This result was unexpected, and proves conclusively that we do not judge of difference in weights by the rate at which they are lifted. When the weights were pressed by the fingers with force sufficient to lift 2 kg., the probable error was considerably increased. The observer is, consequently, helped by the lightness of touch, which normally is made just sufficient to hold the weights. The sensation may be partly touch and partly a muscular sensation from the fingers. When two hands were used the weight lifted with the right hand seemed relatively the heavier. But the constant errors are throughout within the limits of probable chance variations.

In all these experiments the observer's confidence in his decision was recorded. The confidence seemed to correspond exactly with the apparent amount of difference. Thus the observer said a if the difference seemed quite evident, b if the difference was apparent but not so great that he felt sure of the correctness of his judgment, c if he noticed but little difference and felt doubtful as to his correctness, and d if he could discern no difference, and felt that his judgment was a mere guess. The percentages of the times the several degrees of confidence were given were as follows:

	a	b	c	d
J	10	25	46	19
C	0	13	60	27

a or b is the just noticeable difference, and d is the threshold of German psychologists. The just noticeable difference (and also the threshold) would make J a much better observer than C. No weight, consequently, can be laid on such determinations.

The percentages of times the observer was right in his judgment were as follows:

	a	b	c	d
J	93	86	74	65
C	x	97	81	60

It is interesting to note that when the decision of the observer seemed a mere guess, he was considerably more likely to be right than wrong. This bears witness to the part played by subconscious mental processes in our daily life. C's judgment was more accurate than J's, as he was right a larger percentage of times when he felt some confidence, and wrong a larger percentage of times when he felt none. C could notice no difference when the apparent difference (assuming the theory of the distribution of errors to obtain in this case) was less than ½ the probable error, and could notice the difference with some confidence when the apparent difference was more than double the probable error. C should by theory have been right in about 57 per cent of the cases when he gave *d*, and in 97 per cent of the cases when he gave *b*. These are nearly the percentages of right cases actually obtained, whence it follows that an observer can judge apparent differences in sensation with considerable accuracy.

PART V

On Lights

SEC. 46. *Introductory.*—Numerous experiments have been made with a view to testing Weber's law for the sense of sight. We need not give an abstract of these, as our own experiments do not bear directly on the subject. The early experiments by Bouguer, Lambert, Steinthal, Masson, Fechner and Volkmann seemed to show that the just noticeable difference is a proportional part of the stimulus. The conclusion of later experiments,[1] however, is that Weber's law holds only approximately and for lights of medium intensity.

In these experiments the figures obtained as expressing the accuracy of discrimination proper to the sense of sight place it very high. Sight has, accordingly, been described as the most accurate of the senses. But it is evident that in the experiments with shadows and with disks, as they have been carried out, the conditions are very different from those of experiments with lifted weights. In comparing a shadow with its background, the observer receives both impressions simultaneously, and attention passes from one to the other and back again, thus receiving a complex series of impressions. So it is also with variegated disks. In lifting weights, on the contrary, the impressions are successive. This must also be the case in experimenting on hearing and other senses. In our own experiments with lights we have tried to make the conditions similar to those of our experiments on weights. Our results, in connection with which the size of the illuminated area on

----

[1] Volkmann, Physiol. Untersuch., etc., Leipzig, 1863.
Aubert, *op. cit.*
Helmholtz, *op. cit.*
Delbœuf, *op. cit.*
Camerer, Mon. Bl. f. Augenheil., 1877.
Kraepelin, Phil. Stud., II. 1885.
Neiglick, Phil. Stud., IV. 1887.
Merkel, *op. cit.*
Koenig und Brodhun, Sitz. d. Acad. zu Berlin, 1888.
Müller-Lyer, Archiv. f. [Anat. u.] Physiol., Sup. Bd., 1889.
The two papers last mentioned are of special importance. The German physiological archives and proceedings are, unfortunately, not included in the libraries of the University of Pennsylvania or Columbia College, and were not accessible to us while this paper was being written. Since going to press we have examined some papers in the Astor Library, and added references, but it is too late to give abstracts.

the retina must, of course, be taken into account, do not give preeminence in discriminative power to the sense of sight as compared with the muscular sense.

SEC. 47. *Apparatus and Methods.*—The apparatus used in these experiments was planned by the writers. It is represented in the accompanying cut.

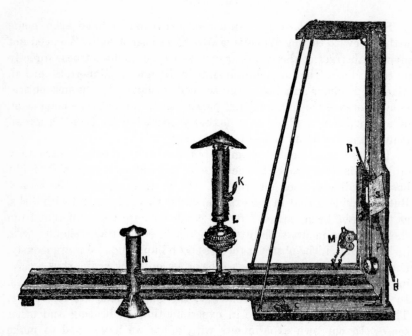

FIG. 67.

A lamp (*L*), provided with a metal hood, runs on a wooden slide. At one end of the slide is an upright plank pierced by a hole. This aperture can be enlarged or diminished in size by pulling out or pushing in two brass rods (*RR*[1]) which are attached to overlapping plates of metal so cut as to leave between their edges a square hole. A seconds pendulum (*P*) swings in front of this hole, and a sheet-iron screen (*S*), attached to the bar of the pendulum, covers the hole, when the pendulum is held up by the electro-magnet (*M*). There is in the hood of the lamp, opposite the flame, a small hole (15 mm.) with a hinged cap (*K*). As the pendulum swings freely, the light of the lamp shines for one second through the aperture in the upright plank, and then is for one second cut off by the screen on the pendulum. The pendulum, weighted by a heavy iron ball, can at any time be held up by the electro-magnet (*M*), the recorder manipulating the key (at *C*). The hooded lamp (N) gives the recorder light to keep his record and to measure the movement of the lamp.

In the following cut may be seen the positions of the observer, of the recorder, and of the several parts of the apparatus.

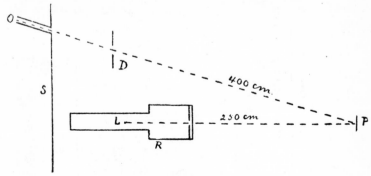

Fɪɢ. 68.

The observer (O), behind a wooden partition (S), looked with one eye through a tube fixed in the partition at a piece of white paper (P) on the opposite wall and distant 4 M. A diaphragm (D) permitted him to see on this paper a circle 10 cm. in diameter. The lamp (L) illuminated this paper through the aperture in the upright plank, when the aperture was not covered by the screen on the pendulum. The lamp was 250 cm. distant from the paper when at its farthest point. The recorder (R) moved the lamp to or from the paper, and regulated the swinging of the pendulum by means of the key. During the experiments the room was darkened by the use of double blinds at the windows, and every effort was made to prevent scattered light escaping into the room from the two lamps.

The experiments were made as follows:—The observer having placed himself in position, the recorder gave him a signal to secure attention, and then, turning the key, allowed the pendulum to swing away from the magnet. The lamp[1] being, say, at what we may call the normal distance (250 cm. from the paper,) the observer was thus given the standard sensation of light. With the return swing of the pendulum, and while the light was cut off by the screen, the lamp was moved nearer to the paper by a certain distance marked on the slide, so that the second light seen by the observer should be more intense than the first in the ratio of 100:110, 120, 130 or 140. At its next return the pendulum was caught up by the magnet. Between the next

[1] The lamp at the usual height was ten-candle power. To prevent the observer from gaining a familiarity with the absolute intensity of the normal light, the lamp was frequently turned up or down a little. These variations in intensity were not great.

TABLE XXVIII.—THE DISCRIMINATION OF LIGHTS—METHOD OF RIGHT AND WRONG CASES—9 OBSERVERS—4000 EXPERIMENTS

100	Second light the fainter												Second light the brighter											
	110			120			130			140			110			120			130			140		
	R	W	D	R	W	D	R	W	D	R	W	D	R	W	D	R	W	D	R	W	D	R	W	D
R	37	13	0	42	8	0	49	1	0	50	0	0	28	22	0	29	21	0	31	19	0	37	13	0
K	38	12	0	39	11	0	44	6	0	46	4	0	36	14	0	38	12	0	41	9	0	46	4	0
G	37	9	4	46	2	2	48	2	0	50	0	0	18	27	5	31	18	1	40	7	3	40	8	2
L	44	6	0	46	4	0	48	2	0	50	0	0	28	22	0	39	11	0	48	2	0	50	0	0
S	48	2	0	50	0	0	49	1	0	50	0	0	14	35	1	29	20	1	33	16	1	46	4	0
N	37	8	5	42	1	7	47	1	2	49	0	1	29	12	9	41	2	7	39	1	10	48	0	2
D I	42	2	6	45	1	4	48	1	1	50	0	0	21	19	10	32	9	9	36	11	3	40	7	3
D II	45	5	0	50	0	0	50	0	0	50	0	0	25	15	10	42	3	5	45	4	1	49	1	0
F	43	6	1	48	1	1	47	0	3	50	0	0	22	18	10	33	8	9	42	2	6	49	0	1
C	37	10	3	43	4	3	48	2	0	50	0	0	24	12	14	35	7	8	43	0	7	45	0	5

two lights the movement might be from the 140 point to the 100 point, etc. Each light lasted one second, and there was an interval of one second between the two lights. The observer was required to state whether the second light in each pair seemed brighter or fainter than the first, and to express his degree of confidence by *a*, *b* or *c*. A record was made after each experiment.

Forty experiments were made in each series, in twenty of which the second light was fainter, and in twenty brighter than the first. Five experiments of each of these kinds were made in the one series for each of the four differences chosen. The results have been computed and tabulated as in the experiments on lifted weights. Of course the different experiments in each series were made in an irregular order, and the observer had no clue to guide him except the objective difference in the lights. Only the writers knew the results of previous experiments.

SEC. 48. *Results of Experiments.*—The results of 4000 experiments made on nine observers are contained in the accompanying table. The number of right, wrong and doubtful cases is given for each amount of difference and according to whether the second light was the fainter or the brighter.

As the figures given in the table do not directly measure the fineness of discrimination of the observer, we have calculated, as in the experiments with lifted weights, the probable errors of the several observers for the four amounts of difference. The results are contained in Table XXIX.[1]

TABLE XXIX.—PROBABLE ERROR WITH LIGHTS

	100	110	120	130	140	Av.	V
R.............	17.0	22.5	17.2	18.0	18.7	1.9
K.............	10.4	18.3	19.3	19.	16.8	3.2
G.............	24.6	14.3	15.0	16.6	17.8	3.5
L.............	10.0	12.4	11.5	11.6	11.4	0.7
S.............	11.2	10.6	16.2	14.5	13.1	2.2
N.............	10.8	14.5	13.8	11.6	12.7	1.5
D I............	10.1	12.5	15.8	16.4	13.7	2.4
D II...........	8.8	7.6	11.0	12.3	9.9	1.7
F.............	11.0	10.6	12.8	11.6	11.5	0.7
C.............	12.9	13.5	13.7	13.6	13.4	0.3
Av.............	12.7	13.7	14.6	14.5	13.9	1.8
V.............	3.3	3.0	2.1	2.4	2.3	.8

[1] As before, the doubtful cases have been divided equally between the right and wrong cases.

We have here the difference, given in hundredths, of the intensity of the light chosen as a standard, which each observer may expect to distinguish 75 times out of 100. On the average, lights can thus be distinguished when they are about as 100:114, or when the difference is about one-seventh of the stimulus. Reckoning upon this basis, we find that a difference, to be distinguished 99 times out of 100, would have to be about 48, or nearly one-half the stimulus. It will be noticed that the difference is here much greater than that obtained in the experiments with lifted weights, and our results would seem to contradict the commonly accepted doctrine of the greater fineness of discrimination of the sense of sight. It should, however, be borne in mind that in these experiments the retina was illuminated over a comparatively small area, and but one eye was used. Had the area illuminated been greater, and had the light been seen with both eyes, a lesser difference could probably have been perceived. The lights used, moreover, were comparatively faint. We have as yet made no experiments to determine the influence upon our results of such changes in the conditions of experiment. In one perhaps very important respect, the experiments on lights and those on lifted weights were alike. The two lights were seen, as the two weights were lifted, successively, and the time allowed each stimulus, as well as the time between each pair of stimuli, was accurately determined and kept constant. Any experiments designed to determine the relative degree of fineness of discrimination proper to sight and the other senses must observe such conditions if trustworthy results are to be obtained.

The variation of the averages for the several observers from their average (2.3) shows that the difference in discriminative power was not great, though there is a greater disparity between the best and the worst series (9.9 and 18.7) than in the case of lifted weights. Classifying the observers as before, we find the average probable error for two women was 17.7; for two advanced students of biology, 14.5; for three advanced students of psychology (the first series on *D* only being used), 13.2; and for the two writers, 12.4.

To show the effects of practice on accuracy of discrimination, the experiments have been divided into five sets, each containing eighty judgments, and we give in the accompanying table the percentages of right cases for each set in the case of each observer. The second series of experiments made on *D* was, of course, made after the first series was completed. In this table, however, it is treated like the other series. It will be noticed that it is considerably better than the first series on *D*.

The table shows a slight improvement in accuracy of discrimination in the successive sets of eighty judgments, but it is very slight, and much stress cannot be put upon it. It might be due to accidental variations.

TABLE XXX.—RIGHT CASES IN PERCENTAGES WITH INCREASING PRACTICE

	I	II	III	IV	V
R.	82	74	72	82	69
K.	82	81	74	91	81
G.	59	81	80	85	82
L.	86	87	84	86	90
S.	77	82	79	81	79
N.	84	85	80	86	80
D I.	72	79	74	77	85
D II.	87	85	87	91	92
F.	72	84	69	91	97
C.	81	76	74	87	87
Av.	78	81	77	86	84

SEC. 49. *The Amount of Difference and the Degree of Confidence.*— In these experiments, as in those with lifted weights, four amounts of difference were used. The probable error is, as the table shows, nearly the same whether calculated from the number of right cases with a lesser difference or the number of right cases with a greater. This verifies experimentally the mathematical theory of the relation of the number of right cases to the difference used. The probable error is, however, as before, somewhat smaller with the smaller differences, and this indicates the presence of some small disturbing factor. We give curves showing the results of our experiments on weights and lights, as compared with curves showing the relations required by the probability integral. The agreement is close, and the probable error,

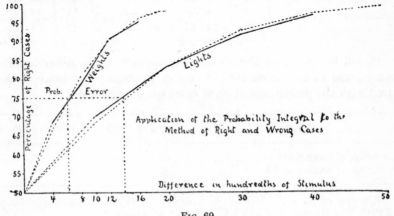

FIG. 69.

whatever the difference and corresponding percentage of right cases, may, consequently, be used as a measure of accuracy of discrimination. The curves show clearly that under the condition employed by us weights can be distinguished much better than lights.

By making the difference in some cases so large that the observer was nearly always right (100 : 140), we have combined with the method of right and wrong cases that of the just noticeable difference. It is scarcely necessary to point out again that this last-mentioned method, when used in any satisfactory way, is simply a form of the method of right and wrong cases, and that the difference employed is not the best difference to use in experiments by the method of right and wrong cases.

The observer was required in these experiments to use *a*, *b* and *c*, in the manner already described, to indicate the degree of his confidence in the judgment made. The accompanying table shows how many times *a* and *b* were given by the several observers.[1]

TABLE XXXI.—THE DEGREE OF CONFIDENCE OF THE OBSERVERS WITH VARYING AMOUNTS OF DIFFERENCE. IN PER CENT

	100	110		120		130		140		Av.	
		a	*b*	*a*	*b*	*a*	*b*	*a*	*b*	*a*	*b*
R.		0	38	5	42	15	48	14	58	8	46
K.		1	6	2	6	8	13	12	18	6	11
G.		50	24	63	28	71	15	87	8	68	19
L.		6	44	16	52	35	55	70	26 .	32	44
S.		68	28	65	30	77	17	79	19	72	23
N.		16	23	28	34	54	26	69	20	42	26
D I.		11	33	20	34	33	48	56	34	30	37
D II.		3	26	1	65	15	65	47	48	16	51
F.		5	17	9	36	20	47	50	35	21	34
C.		1	13	4	23	17	32	28	35	12	26
Av.		16	25	12	35	34	37	51	30	31	32

It will be seen that the *a*'s and *b*'s increase as the difference increases, and as the percentage of correct judgments increases. Compared with the percentage of right cases the averages are:

	100	110	120	130	140
Percentage of times right		69	83	89	95
Percentage of times *a* and *b*		40	56	71	81

[1] The rest of the time the observer gave *c* or *d*. The *d*'s are recorded in Table XXVIII. The figures in Table XXXI are also percentages.

The confidence of the observer is, hence, a fair measure of the correctness of his judgment, but it is evident that a and b have a widely different meaning in the case of the several observers. G and S used a much more freely than did the others, and yet their probable error is not correspondingly small. That they used these letters in a looser sense than did the others is clear from the following table, which gives the percentage of times the several observers were right with each degree of confidence. S was willing to say b when he was right only 62 per cent of the time. He seems, indeed, to have made no real distinction between b and c. It is worth noting that when the discrimina-

TABLE XXXII.—PERCENTAGE OF TIMES THE SEVERAL OBSERVERS WERE RIGHT
WITH EACH DEGREE OF CONFIDENCE

	R	K	G	L	S	N	D I	D II	F	C	Av.
a...........	94.1	100	80.8	99.2	87.2	100	95.8	100	100	100	**95.7**
b...........	81.2	95.0	70.7	88.7	61.7	96.1	86.3	95.7	94.1	95.1	**86.5**
c...........	66.7	79.0	48.6	72.9	64.3	75.9	74.5	79.8	82.6	85.5	**73.0**

tion was equally good the confidence was less with lights than with weights.

SEC. 50. *The Constant Error.*—All the observers showed a tendency to underestimate the second light, though the tendency was much more marked with some than with others. The amount of this error for each observer and for each degree of difference is shown in Table XXXII.[1]

TABLE XXXIII.—CONSTANT ERROR IN DISTINGUISHING LIGHTS—METHOD OF
RIGHT AND WRONG CASES—9 OBSERVERS—4000 EXPERIMENTS

100	110	120	130	140	Av.
R.............	6.2	13.2	22.2	22.7	**16.1**
K.............	0.9	0.9	3.7	0.0	**1.4**
G.............	18.1	12.9	8.8	17.4	**14.3**
L.............	7.7	5.8	0.0	0.0	**3.4**
S.............	19.2	16.4	19.4	9.9	**16.2**
N.............	2.9	0.9	5.9	0.2	**2.5**
D I...........	9.2	8.7	14.2	16.7	**12.2**
D II..........	6.7	6.2	8.1	2.5	**5.9**
F.............	8.4	9.4	5.7	0.0	**5.9**
C.............	4.1	4.5	2.6	6.9	**4.5**
Av............	8.3	7.9	9.1	7.6	**8.2**
V.............	*4.3*	*4.2*	*5.7*	*7.2*	*5.2*

[1] The constant error was obtained here as in the experiments on lifted weights.

It will be observed that the error varies considerably with different observers, and, indeed, with the same observer as the difference is greater or less. The averages do not increase with the difference, as is the case in the experiments with lifted weights. It is interesting to note that in no case was the first light underestimated, and in this respect the error is more constant than it is in the experiments with weights.

As we have seen, when two weights are successively lifted, there is a sufficiently marked tendency to overestimate the second. When two lights are successively looked at, there is a still more marked tendency to underestimate the second. The cause of this underestimation is not clear. Fatigue would not seem to account for it in an entirely satisfactory manner, for the second light in each pair was the one which seemed fainter, and the successive pairs of lights did not grow proportionally fainter as the series was continued. To test this more fully we made two series of ten experiments each upon C and two upon F. The pendulum was allowed to swing freely eleven times, while the observer compared the eleven resulting sensations, and described them to the recorder. The intensity of the objective stimulus was kept the same. The results of these experiments were as follows:

	1	2	3	4	5	6	7	8	9	10
C I............	*f*	e	f	f	f	e	f	e	f	f
C II............	*e*	f	f	e	f	e	*f*	e	f	f
F I............	*f*	f	e	e	e	e	e	f	f	e
F II............	*f*	e	f	e	f	f	e	e	e	f

Here f indicates that the light it represents appeared fainter than the one preceding, e that the light it stands for appeared the same as the one preceding. The letters in italics indicate that the difference was distinct. The writers have little confidence in the judgments not marked by letters in italics. The judgments had to be made rapidly, and the differences were felt to be slight. They are, however, confident that they were never inclined to regard a light as brighter than the one before it.

Sec. 51. *Memory for Weights and Lights.*—In making experiments on the perception of small differences, the time elapsing between the sensations to be compared should not be neglected. In the experiments hitherto described the interval was always one second. It is possible that two seconds or longer might be a more favorable interval for comparison, but were the interval further lengthened the first sensation might be expected to fade from memory, while the rate of forgetting would be measured in terms of the error of observation. The study of memory for sensation is thus an attractive subject for psychological research, one quantity being studied as the function of another. Indeed, the earliest workers[1] in the field of psychophysics made a few experiments on the subject, but they did not continue them long enough to obtain definite results. Wolfe[2] carried out extended experiments on memory for the pitch of tones. He found about two seconds the most favorable interval; after this the percentage of right cases decreased, at first rapidly and then more slowly, until with an interval of sixty seconds the probable error is about ffve times as great as with one second. Lehmann[3] made a few experiments with shades of gray produced by revolving wheels, and obtained results agreeing with Wolfe's. On the other hand, Paneth[4] recently found that intervals of time could be reproduced nearly as well after longer (up to five minutes) as after shorter intervals; and Exner, who communicates these results, says that another experimenter obtained similar results with lights. The important monograph on Memory by Ebbinghaus,[5] in which more complex impressions were used, is well known.

Our own experiments on memory were the first we made. They were postponed in order that we might study the method, and were not afterward completed. We used seven intervals varying from one second to about one minute, the experiments otherwise being conducted in a manner similar to those already described. The time of stimulation was one second. The normal weight was about 100 gm., and the difference usually 8 gm. The light was that described, the difference being one-fifth of the whole amount. The weights and lights were usually varied within narrow limits in order that the observer might not learn them, and thus be helped in his decision. On the weights 100 experiments were made with each interval, and on the lights 180, except with the 31 and 61 second intervals, with which only 80 were made. Ten different observers took part in the experiments. Owing to the large number of experiments required by the method of right and wrong cases, the probable errors given in the table are only approximate. The variable and constant errors have not been distinguished. In taking the average the probable errors with the lights have been halved in order to reduce them approximately to the standard of the weights.

[1] Weber, Hagelmayer and Fechner.

[2] H. K. Wolfe, Philos. Stud., III. 1886. Wolfe finds that the ratio of right to wrong cases is inversely proportional to the logarithm of the time. But accuracy of discrimination is not directly measured by the percentage of right cases.

[3] Alfred Lehmann, Philos. Stud., V. 1888.

[4] J. Paneth, Centr. f. Physiol., IV. 1890.

[5] Herm. Ebbinghaus, Ueber das Gedächtniss, Leipzig, 1885.

TABLE XXXIV.—MEMORY FOR WEIGHTS AND LIGHTS—PROBABLE ERRORS FOR INTERVALS FROM 1 TO 61 SECS.—10 OBSERVERS AND 1760 EXPERIMENTS— V TO XII. 1888—140 EXPERIMENTS—XII. 1891

Interval in sec.	1	3	5	9	15	31	61	Av.
Weights 100 gm. P.E.....	9.8	5.8	8.1	7.6	15.2	12.4	8.3	9.6
Lights 100 ½ P.E........	8	11.4	10.2	7.7	9.3	[11.8]	[10.2]	9.8
Average................	8.9	8.6	9.1	7.8	12.2	12.1	9.2	9.7

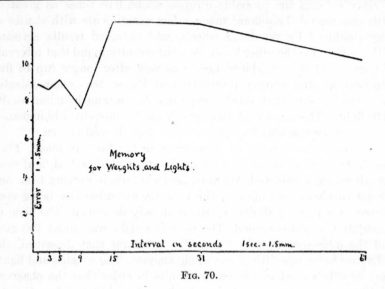

FIG. 70.

The accompanying curve shows the relation between the probable error and the interval between the stimuli.

The experiments were not sufficient to determine exactly the probable errors with the different intervals, but these evidently do not become much larger as the interval is taken longer. The error of observation seems to be nearly the same so long as the interval is not over 9 sec., after which it is increased by about one-third. The smaller probable error with 61 sec. is most likely accidental. We had supposed that the increase in the error of observation with the larger interval would be more decided; the comparison becomes much more difficult to the observer, especially for the three longest intervals. The memory-image seems to last up to 9 sec., after which the observer does not so much compare the sensations as decide on the approximate intensity of each sensation separately, and compare the decisions. For example, the first sensation seems weaker than was expected, and this decision is remembered during the interval rather than the intensity itself.

Conclusion

Sec. 52. *Psychophysical Methods.*—The method of the just noticeable difference—in which an observer finds a difference which he can just perceive—is not satisfactory. If the observer simply choose a difference which he thinks he can always or usually perceive, the result is without objective criterion. Indeed our experiments show that those who think they can perceive the smallest difference are apt to be the worst observers. If the percentage of mistakes made by the observer be recorded, this method becomes a case of the following. But "the just noticeable difference" is not a convenient difference to use in the method of right and wrong cases. If the percentage of right cases be very large, a single chance variation greatly affects the average. If there be no mistake we have indeed found a difference which can be perceived, but not the difference which can just be perceived, nor any other quantity which can be used as a measure of discrimination. If the just noticeable difference be interpreted by the observer as a difference apparently equal to some other difference, the method is reduced to that of estimated amount of difference.

The method of right and wrong cases—in which two stimuli nearly alike are presented to an observer, and he is required to say which seems the greater—is the most accurate of the methods. It requires a considerable number of experiments—at least 100—and the number must be the greater, the less practised the observer. The method is consequently not well suited for provisional, anthropometric or clinical purposes. The percentages of right cases obtained do not directly measure the fineness of discrimination. The probable error, that is the difference with which the observer should be right 75 per cent of the time, is the most convenient measure of discrimination. The probability integral may be used to calculate the probable error, when the amount of difference is known, and the percentage of right cases is greater or less than 75. It is better not to allow the observer to give doubtful as his decision, but the confidence felt by him in its correctness may be recorded with advantage. The observer is more apt to be right than wrong even when he feels little or no confidence in his decision. Some observers are not confident unless they are, in fact, right, while others are often confident when they are wrong. By recording the degree of confidence and using comparatively large differences the method of the just noticeable difference may be combined with that of right and wrong cases. The probable error and the constant error may be determined separately. The latter is more irregular than the former. It is worth noting that this most accurate method of observation has not been used in the physical sciences. Psychology has hitherto been much indebted to physics for its methods, but the obligation will soon be mutual.

The method of average error—in which an observer makes one stimulus as nearly as possible like another—is in many cases the most convenient of the methods. It is closely related to the preceding, as the probable error can be found either from the average error or from the percentage of right cases. The probable error of the just noticeable difference or of an estimated amount of difference may also be determined, and the several methods thus combined. The error obtained by the method of average error is complex, being partly an error of adjustment and partly an error of perception. These errors may be separately determined by requiring the observer to judge the stimuli by the method of right and wrong cases after they have been adjusted. The average error may be analyzed into a constant and a variable error. The distribution of the errors tends to follow the probability curve. This method can be used to special advantage when only a few experiments are made, as a result is reached more quickly than by the method of right and wrong cases.

The method of estimated amount of differences—in which an observer judges the definite quantitative relations of stimuli, as in making one difference equal to or double another—gives variable results. The observer probably does not estimate quantitative relations in sensation, but quantitative differences in the stimuli learned by association. It is, consequently, an open question whether the differences in sensation are qualitative or quantitative.

Great care should be taken in psychological experiments to keep all the conditions constant except the variable to be investigated. The observer should not know the results of preceding experiments nor the objective relations of the stimuli. Experiments should not be rejected because they make the averages less accordant. The results of experiment depend on accommodation to the conditions of experiment as well as on differences in senses or faculties, and these factors should be separately studied.

SEC. 53. *The Error of Observation and the Magnitude of the Stimulus.*—Weber's law, according to which the least noticeable difference is proportional to the magnitude of the stimulus, does not hold for movement, as the least noticeable difference (or the error of observation) increases more slowly than the stimulus. Fechner's law, according to which the sensation increases as the logarithm of the stimulus, does not hold, as it rests on Weber's law and on assumptions which are probably incorrect. As there is no logarithmic relation between mental and physical processes, the psychophysical, physiological and psychological theories put forward to account for it are superfluous.

When amounts of difference in movements are estimated, the stimuli tend to be judged in their objective relations, and not as the logarithm of these. The results obtained by the method of right and wrong cases, and, by the method of average error, determine the error of observation. This is a physical quantity. Its correlation with other physical quantities (for example, the magnitude of the stimulus) depends on psychophysical conditions, and offers an important subject for psychological research. A mental quantity is not, however, directly measured. The error of observation usually increases as the stimulus is taken greater, but more slowly than in direct proportion to the magnitude. If the errors made in observing two stimuli of the same sort be combined, they will not be twice as large as the average error, but will equal the average error multiplied by the square root of two. This results both from theory and from our experiments; consequently, if two magnitudes, say two seconds, be observed continuously, the combined error in observing the two seconds would tend to equal the error in observing one second multiplied by square root of two, and generally the error in observing a magnitude, extensive or intensive, would increase as the square root of the magnitude. The summation of errors in this manner seems to account perfectly for the usual increase of the error of observation ("just noticeable difference") with larger magnitudes. The error would increase as the square root of the magnitude if each fraction of the magnitude, physically equal, were, in fact, subject to the same error of observation. In actual perception this would seldom or never be the case, but most of our experiments give an error of observation more nearly proportional to the square root of the magnitude than directly proportional to the magnitude. We, therefore, substitute for Weber's law the following: *The error of observation tends to increase as the square root of the magnitude, the increase being subject to variations whose amount and cause must be determined for each special case.*[1]

SEC. 54. *The Extent of Movement.*—Experiments on the extent of movement were made by moving the finger along a scale fastened to the edge of the table. The four distances chosen were 100, 300, 500 and 700 mm. Time was kept by a seconds pendulum, one second being allowed for each movement, and one second for the interval between the two movements to be compared. Experiments were made by the four psychophysical methods on one observer, and by the method of average error upon two others.

The attempts to mark off a distance just greater and one just less than 500 mm. resulted in, respectively, 539.4 and 477.2 mm. The dis-

---

[1] One of the writers (*G.S.F.*) does not give unqualified assent to the subject-matter of this section. See the note to Sec. 8.

tance marked off in separate experiments was highly variable. Even for groups of 100 experiments the average just noticeable difference varied, for the attempt at just greater, between 60.1 and 21.5 mm., and for the attempt at just less, between 37.7 and 4.8 mm. In striking contrast with these figures was the slight degree of variation in the variable error and its variation. For instance, where in two groups of 100 experiments each, the just noticeable difference was 60.1 and 21.5 mm., the corresponding variable error was 9.8 and 8.9. The highly variable character of the just noticeable difference makes it of small value in psychophysical experiment.

By the method of estimated amount of difference three kinds of experiments were made. It was attempted to halve 500 mm., to double 300 mm., and to find the mean between 300 and 700 mm. The results of these experiments were all contrary to Fechner's law, the attempt to halve 500 mm. resulting in a distance of 305.2, the attempt to double 300 giving one of 560.1, and that to find the mean between 300 and 700 giving one of 512.4. In these experiments the variable error was, in relation to the whole extent of the movement made, greater than in the experiments by the method of just noticeable difference.

The experiments by the method of average error consisted in attempts to measure off on the scale 100, 300, 500 and 700 mm. The variable errors for these magnitudes (with three observers) were 10.0, 18.7, 21.1 and 17.2. The best of the observers was about three times as accurate as the worst. The variable error does not accord with Weber's law, but increases much more slowly than the stimulus. For all the observers it was actually smaller for 700 than for 500 mm., this probably because the distance was nearly the limit which could be reached, and the observer was helped by the strain.

In the experiments by the method of right and wrong cases the stimuli used were 500 and 510 mm. When the second stimulus was the greater, 75 per cent of the judgments were right, and when the second was the less, 71.8 per cent. The probable error (the difference which could be distinguished 75 per cent of the time) is 11 mm. The first movement was slightly underrated, the constant error being .7 mm. The degree of confidence expressed by the observer was a fair index of the objective correctness of his judgment.

Sec. 55. *The Force of Movement.*—A dynamometer may be used to advantage in studying the discrimination of the force of movements, but the clinical dynamometers are too inaccurate for scientific experiment. In making experiments on movement the observer can himself give the first or normal movement as well as the second or judgment movement, and the two movements will thus be made and perceived under like conditions.

"The just noticeable difference" in the force of movement varied greatly, not being proportional to the error of observation, but more accordant results are obtained if the probable error be found by taking into account the number of mistakes made by the observer. The average error of the just noticeable difference may also be used as a measure of discrimination. The just noticeable differences (for two observers) for about 2, 4, 8 and 16 kg. were, respectively, about $\frac{1}{5}$, $\frac{1}{7}$, $\frac{1}{9}$ and $\frac{1}{18}$ of the stimulus. The variable errors of observation were, respectively, .12, .20, .37 and .41 kg., and the probable errors obtained by taking the percentage of the errors into account were, respectively, .14, .26, .40 and .45 kg.

Experiments by the method of average error gave (for five observers) variable errors .19, .29, .43 and .46 kg.; for the magnitudes 2, 4, 8 and 16 kg., respectively. The worst of the five observers had an error about one-third larger than the best. Some observers are relatively better with the weaker, some with the stronger movements. There were considerable constant errors varying with different observers. The second pull was too great with the smallest magnitude, and usually two small with the largest. Neither the just noticeable difference nor the error of observation is a proportional part of the stimulus. Weber's law, consequently, does not hold for the force of movement. The error of observation is nearly proportional to the square root of the magnitude.

The error, when two movements are made as nearly alike as possible, is partly an error of perception and partly an error of adjustment, and these two factors may be separated. The error of perception was, on the average, about twice as great as the error of adjustment, but the error of adjustment was relatively the smallest for the best observers. The errors in making two movements as nearly alike as possible tend to be distributed as required by the probability curve. The combined error obtained by adding algebraically the errors in pairs is nearly equal to the average error multiplied by the square root of two.

Experiments by the method of estimated amount of difference showed that the force of movements tends to be estimated in their objective relations, and not as the logarithm of these. The results are variable and subject to large constant errors.

SEC. 56. *The Time of Movement.*—Apparatus can be constructed which will measure accurately and conveniently the time either of a slow movement or of a quick blow. When movements are discriminated it is an advantage to let the observer adjust the time of the first as well as of the second movement.

The average errors in judging the time of movements (50 cm. in extent) with the arm, lasting about $\frac{1}{8}$, $\frac{1}{4}$, $\frac{1}{2}$ and 1 sec., were (as the average of four observers) .014, .028, .052 and .100 sec., respectively.

The error of the worst of the observers was about twice that with the best.

With ½ and 1 sec., when the time of the two movements seemed equal, the second was the slower; when two blows in succession are made as quickly as possible, the second is the quicker and seems the quicker. ½ sec. seemed less than half of 1 sec., and more than double ¼ sec.

The results obtained by analyzing the error into an error of perception and an error of adjustment, and from the distribution of errors and summation of errors, were nearly the same as with the force of movement.

The time of the quickest possible blow (50 cm. in extent) varied (with four observers) from .085 to .181 sec. While the rate of movement varies considerably with different observers, its average variation under like conditions is small—for a good observer .005 sec. The time was about the same for the right and left hand, and the rate was nearly uniform. The rate of movement should be used in the study of diseases of the nervous system.

Within the limits investigated the extent of movements can be judged better than the force, and the force better than the time.

SEC. 57. *Lifted Weights.*—The probable error in discriminating lifted weights weighing about 100 gm. varied (for nine observers) from 5 to 8.2 gm., the average being 6.2 gm. This is the difference which could be correctly distinguished three-fourths of the time. The difference which could be correctly given 99 times out of 100 would be about 21 gm. The probable error is nearly the same, whether calculated from a large difference and large percentage of right cases, or from a small difference and smaller percentage of right cases. The confidence felt by different observers in the correctness of their judgment varies greatly, and is not proportional to their fineness of discrimination. The constant error can be calculated. In these experiments it varied from .5 to 6.8 grammes. The second of the two weights seemed relatively the heavier to nearly all the observers. In judging the accuracy of discrimination of an observer, both variable and constant errors should be considered.

The probable error is not greatly altered when the manner of lifting the weights is altered. It becomes larger when the weights are lifted with different hands, or up or down only, or are pressed with the fingers. It is scarcely altered when one weight is lifted four times as high or four times as fast as the other.

SEC. 58. *Lights.*—In our experiments on lights, apparatus was devised to give the observer two sensations of light in succession, each lasting one second and one second apart. The conditions were thus similar to those in the experiments with lifted weights. The lights compared were as 100 to 110, 120, 130 and 140. The probable error (given in hundredths of the intensity of the stimulus) varied, for nine observers, from 9.9 to 18.7, with an average of 13.9. Reckoning upon this basis, a difference, to be correctly given 99 times out of 100, would have to be about 48, or nearly half the stimulus. This large figure may be due partly to the fact that the illuminated area on the retina was small and the lights comparatively faint, but it was probably chiefly due to the sensations being successive. We consider it an advantage to have the sensations successive, as the conditions can thus be kept constant, and sight can be compared with the other senses, muscular sense, hearing, etc. Different observers differed much in their degree of confidence in the correctness of their judgment, and their degree of confidence was no indication of the relative fineness of their power of discrimination. For the same observer, however, the degree of confidence corresponded fairly well to the degree of objective accuracy. All the observers showed a tendency to underestimate the second light, the constant error varying from 1.4 to 16.2. Under the conditions employed the muscular sense is about again as accurate as the sense of sight.

Memory for sensations may be studied by increasing the interval between the two stimuli to be compared, the probable error of an observer measuring his rate of forgetting. Observers remembered lifted weights and lights so well up to 9 sec. that their error of observation was not increased. When the time was from 15 to 61 sec., the error was increased by about one-third. This is contrary to the common view, according to which we are supposed to forget most rapidly at first.

10

ATTENTION AND REACTION

An experiment performed at Columbia College and described under the title, "Aufmerksamkeit und Reaction" in *Philosophische Studien*, **8**: 403–406, 1893. Translated by R. S. Woodworth for inclusion in this volume.

The difference between reactions with attention directed toward the movement to be executed, and reactions with attention directed toward the sense impression received from the stimulus, deserves careful investigation because of the important position that has been assigned to it in the third edition of Wundt's *Physiologische Psychologie*. Wundt assumes that almost all reactions that are shorter than the average are of the muscular type while all that are longer are of the sensorial type. The greater length of sensorial reactions was first noticed by Lange,[1] later by Martius[2] and by Titchener,[3] and recently the distinction has been extended by Münsterberg[4] to more complex mental processes.

I agree with Wundt that a muscular reaction is a brain reflex resulting from practice, but I am not convinced that an apperception process is added when attention is directed toward the sense impression or the sense organ. It is of course theoretically possible to attach an apperception time to the reaction, if the subject holds back his movement until the impression is apperceived. This form of reaction has been attempted in Wundt's laboratory by Friedrich, Trautscholdt, Tischer, Kraepelin, and Merkel; but although these experiments are not without interest, the great variation of the single time measurements bears witness to the lack of an objective criterion. I myself was unable to obtain any satisfactory results by this method, and its difficulties have been recognized by Wundt in the revision of the second edition of his *Psychologie*. Still Wundt insists that the same result is obtained with a sufficiently objective criterion, if the subject directs his attention to the sense impression. On theoretical grounds I would not expect this result. In the practiced automatic movements of daily life attention is directed to the sense impression and not to the movement. So, in piano playing, the beginner may attend to his fingers

[1] *Phil. Stud.*, **4**, 479–510.
[2] *Phil. Stud.*, **6**, 167–216.
[3] *Phil. Stud.*, **8**, 138–145.
[4] Beiträge zur experim. Psychol. Heft I, 64–188.

but the practiced player attends only to the notes or to the melody. In speaking, writing and reading aloud, and in games and manual work, attention is always directed to the goal, never to the movement. In fact, as soon as attention is directed to the movement, this becomes less automatic and less dependable. For this reason I was surprised at the results of the experiments which seemed to show that the reaction time becomes almost twice as long when attention is directed to the sense impression; for whatever makes the reaction less like a reflex will make it slower and more irregular. I have shown, for example, that when the stimulus follows the ready signal at intervals varying from 1 to 15 sec. the reaction time is approximately 25σ longer than when the interval amounts to only 1 sec. approximately. But in all such cases it would seem that the motor time is lengthened rather than that a process of apperception is added to the reaction. When the reaction time is lengthened by the subject's attention to the sense impression, the explanation would seem to be that the motor impulse is not held in readiness for discharge but has to be made ready after the arrival of the impression. In my experiments[1] with Berger, which were done before those of Lange, I did not find that the length or regularity of the reaction time was greatly influenced by the direction of attention, and at present, too, on repetition of such experiments, it seems to me to make little difference whether attention is directed to the movement, to the sense impression, or away from both of them.

Recently (in July, 1892) I have made reactions to sound and to electrical stimuli, taking the greatest possible care to follow the instructions given by Lange and Wundt. Each average is based on 100 reactions which were made in series of 10 each. By *mv* is denoted the mean variation of the single reactions, and by *MV* that of the series averages. I have excluded no measures, and accordingly the series always contain the same number of reactions. No premature reaction occurred in either the sensorial or the muscular series.

	Muscular reactions			Sensorial reactions		
	M	*mv*	*MV*	*M*	*mv*	*MV*
Sound stimulus..........	105.9	6.9	3.9	105.4	5.9	3.0
Electrical stimulus......	142.7	10.1	4.6	142.8	8.4	4.6

My own reaction time is thus the same whether attention is directed to the movement or to the sense impression, but the regularity both of the single reactions and of the different series was greater in the sensorial reactions.

[1] *Phil. Stud.*, **3**, 305–335.

This result could be attributed to my extensive practice in making these reactions, or even to theoretical preconception. For this reason I performed the experiment with two other subjects. In May, 1890 subject *J* (my wife) made 100 reactions to sound, 50 being muscular and 50 sensorial. The subject had never served in a reaction time experiment, apart from 20 practice trials, and knew nothing of Lange's experiments. The results were as follows:

	Muscular reactions			Sensorial reactions		
	M	*mv*	*MV*	*M*	*mv*	*MV*
Sound stimulus.......	105.6	15.4	11.9	108.8	11.2	6.6

This year (July, 1892) the same subject, now acquainted with the results of the earlier experiments, made 100 muscular and 100 sensorial reactions to sound, and the same to an electrical stimulus, with the following results:

	Muscular reactions			Sensorial reactions		
	M	*mv*	*MV*	*M*	*mv*	*MV*
Sound stimulus........	105.5	12.2	3.7	104.97	7.7	2.9
Electrical stimulus.....	119.0	9.4	3.8	121.5	10.1	3.4

J's reaction times agree with those of *C* in that they are short and regular and show no difference dependent on the direction of attention.

I was able to repeat the experiment with a third person, *D* (Dr. C. S. Dolley, Professor of Biology at the University of Pennsylvania), who had previously made some 2000 reactions to electrical stimuli but who had not heard of the distinction between muscular and sensorial reactions. The result of his 100 muscular and 100 sensorial reactions was the following:

	Muscular reactions			Sensorial reactions		
	M	*mv*	*MV*	*M*	*mv*	*MV*
Electric stimulus....	281.4	58.3	17.1	201.6	31.2	11.3

These data show that subject *D*'s sensorial reactions are about ¾ as long as his muscular reactions, while their mean variation is scarcely more than half as great. Introspectively, also, he found the sensorial

reactions quicker and easier. His reaction time, in comparison with
C's and J's, is long and irregular, from which we can conclude that his
reactions are not wholly reflex in character, but they have less of the
reflex character when attention is directed to the movement than when
it is directed to the sense impression.

It is clear, then, that the results published by Lange do not have
universal validity. With subjects whose reactions are quick and regular
the direction of attention seems to make no difference. With subjects
whose reactions are slower and less regular the reaction time may be
lengthened either when they attend exclusively to the movement, as
in D's case, or when they attend exclusively to the sense impression,
as in Lange's case.

11

ON ERRORS OF OBSERVATION

A paper read before the American Psychological Association at its annual meeting in Philadelphia, 1892. Printed in the *American Journal of Psychology*, **5**: 285–293, 1893. An abstract under the title "Errors of Observation in Physics and Psychology" was printed in the Proceedings of the American Psychological Association, 1892, pp. 3–4.

Currents of thought often arise at different sources, and flow on for a long way before they mingle. This has been the case with the investigation of errors of observation in physics and in psychology. On the one hand methods for securing the nearest approximation to the true value from discordant observations have been studied by many of the most eminent mathematicians and physicists since the revival of learning. On the other hand the accuracy with which the external world is perceived has always been a central subject in psychology, and in the development of experimental psychology no portion has received more attention than the perception and comparison of differences in intensity. It has, however, to a considerable extent been overlooked that physics and psychology are concerned with the same phenomena. This is not surprising, as the points of view of the two sciences are different. Physics seeks to eliminate errors of observation; psychology seeks to study their nature. But the time has now come when each science should profit from the progress of the other. Physical science can better eliminate errors of observation by learning what is known of their cause and nature. Psychology will gain greatly in clearness and accuracy by using the methods of physics and mathematics.

The errors of observation with which physics and mathematics have dealt are variable errors, such errors as would occur were each error composed of a very large number of comparatively small and independent errors, equally likely to be positive or negative. In this case the average of the observations is the most likely value, and its approximation to the true value is measured by the dispersion of the errors, and increases as the square root of the number of observations. In two important respects the mathematical theory needs to be supplemented by psychological experiment. In the first place, constant errors are entirely beyond the range of the method of least squares, and yet these are evidently more dangerous in physical observations than variable errors. Thus, for example, in the case of the personal equation of the astronomers, the variable error of an observer can be reduced to any desired extent by increasing the number of observations. But it was found on comparing the observations of different observers that they had constant errors far more serious than their variable errors. It was (and apparently is still) thought that the constant error of an observer becomes a variable error when the observations of several observers are combined. It is very unlikely that this is the case. The uniformity of the processes of perception and movement is greater than their variability. We may feel confident that the combined personal equations of all the astronomers would be subject to a constant error which cannot be eliminated by physical or mathematical science. But such constant errors depend on fixed psycho-physical conditions, and can be measured by the psychologist.

In the second place it may be urged that the theory of probability can only give a rough and ready account of the distribution even of variable errors. In measuring an inch an error of a mile will not occur, and a negative error of a mile is inconceivable. The probability assigned to such errors by theory is, indeed, extremely small, but the same probability is assigned to positive and negative errors, and they are not equally likely. It would seem that as a rule positive errors are more likely than negative errors. In measuring an actual inch, a positive error of two inches might occur, a negative error of the same size cannot occur. In ordinary errors of observation a corresponding preponderance of positive errors may be expected, and a correction for such excess must be empirically determined. The same holds for the averages which are so widely used in statistics. Thus, if the average weight of men be 150 pounds, men weighing 300 pounds occur, men weighing 0 do not occur. The average is not identical with the median, as required by the theory of probability. The assumption made by the mathematicians, that an error is composed of a very large number of comparatively small and independent errors, cannot be admitted by the psychologist. If the fiction of indefinitely small errors be accepted at all, the elemental errors cannot be regarded as independent, but are interdependent and occur in groups. The distribution of errors will not follow simple and universal formulæ, but the greater our knowledge the more complicated will the formulæ become, and they will be as numerous as there are observers and observations. The deductions of Laplace and Gauss are of the greatest importance, but it should not be forgotten that the laws of nature cannot be invented, they must be discovered. It is within the province of psychology to supply physics with the formulæ it requires for eliminating errors of observation in special cases.

Turning now to what psychology can learn from physics, we find that the variable error of the method of average error and the probable error (or h as used in Germany) of the method of right and wrong cases are the error of observation of physical science. We may ask, why should there be an error of observation? Why should not the same stimulus be accompanied by the same sensation? The natural answer is that the conditions do not remain the same. In the first place the stimulus itself cannot be kept exactly constant. Lights are always variable, and sounds and touches cannot be exactly reproduced. Temperatures and smells are especially inconstant. Weights may remain nearly the same, but the manner of lifting them is always different. We have, therefore, a variable stimulus which in part accounts for the variation in sensation. In the second place the nervous mechanism is constantly changing. The sense organ is rhythmically exhausted and restored, and is subject to various irregular alterations. The nerves and paths of conduction in the brain would transmit more or less of the energy of the stimulus according to their ever changing condition. Lastly, the brain centres immediately concerned with perception alter greatly in metabolism. These latter changes are best known to us on the side of consciousness; there is a more or less regular rhythm in attention, and very numerous irregularities due to fatigue, interest, inhibition, etc. These sources of variation will sufficiently account for the fact that the same sensation does not recur. They are, indeed, so numerous and to a certain extent so independent, that they justify roughly the assumption of the mathematician, and the results of experiments show that the errors are in a general way distributed as required by the theory of probability.

In psycho-physical experiment two magnitudes are perceived and compared. The combined error of perception would be larger than a single error of perception, being the square root of the sum of the squares of the separate errors, or nearly the error in a single case multiplied by the square root of two. We have further the errors of memory and comparison. The analysis of these factors at the present time would be very difficult, but I believe they would simply increase the variable error of observation, and introduce additional constant errors. This is not the view taken by Fechner, Müller, Wundt and others, to whom we chiefly owe the development of psycho-physical research and theory. They maintain that there is a threshold of difference, and when sensations differ by less than this amount there is no difference in consciousness. Fechner does not question the application of the probability integral to the comparison of magnitudes,[1] on the

---

[1] As implied by Peirce and Jastrow in their important paper (*On Small Differences in Sensation;* National Academy of Sciences, III [1884]), which for the first time denied the supposed fact of the threshold.

contrary it was he who first applied it to the method of right and wrong cases. He argues that a difference in the stimuli smaller than the threshold might be made apparent in consciousness by the error of observation, and would give the preponderance of right cases required by theory. But in about one-seventh of his trials he was doubtful as to which of the weights used by him was the heavier, and holds that in these cases the difference in the weights and the error of observation combined fell within the threshold, and that there was no difference in consciousness.

Prof. Fullerton and the writer[1] made experiments with lifted weights similar to Fechner's. In one series of 3000 experiments in which the probable error was much the same as Fechner's, the observers were doubtful 23 % of the time, but on guessing which of the weights was the heavier they were right 62½ % of the time. This is the percentage of right cases required by the theory of probability, on the supposition that the differences in consciousness follow Gauss' formula, and we may conclude that the difference in consciousness always exists and affects the course of mental life, even when it is so small that it cannot be detected.

Another case in which German psychologists have run counter to the theory of probability is in the assumption of a just noticeable difference. According to the theory of probability the apparent difference in sensation and the probability of correct judgment tend to increase continuously as the difference between the stimuli is made greater, but it is entirely arbitrary to choose one difference and call it just noticeable. A difference in the stimuli can be found which will be obscured by the error of observation 1 time in 10, or 1 time in 1000, but no difference can be called just noticeable, meaning that it and larger differences will be correctly distinguished, while smaller differences will be indistinguishable. In actual experiments Prof. Fullerton and the writer found that the difference fixed on by the same observer under changed conditions as just noticeable was not at all proportional to the error of observation, and with different observers the difference which they considered just noticeable in no way measured their accuracy of discrimination. In the many researches in which the method of just noticeable difference has been used, the just noticeable difference fixed on by the observer has probably been determined partly by his general knowledge of his error of observation (the difference he would seldom mistake) and partly by association, he choosing an apparently equal difference.

The last application of the theory of probability which I wish to

---

[1] *On the Perception of Small Differences;* Univ. of Penn. Press, 1892. The present paper is largely based on this monograph.

make concerns the relation of the error of observation to the magnitude of the stimulus. The algebraic sum of a number of variable errors tends to increase as the square root of the number. In measuring the base line of a survey the variable error of observation increases as the square root of the length of the line. It seems to me the same relation might be expected to hold in a general way when the length of a line is estimated by the eye or compared with another line. Or to take another example, if we estimate one second of time and repeat the trial four times, the algebraic sum of the four variable errors, or the combined error in estimating the four seconds, will tend to be twice as great as the error in estimating a single second. If we estimate or compare the four seconds continuously, the same elements would to a considerable extent be present, and we might expect an error twice as great as in estimating a single second—not four times as great as required by Weber's law.[1] The error in estimating each of the several seconds might and doubtless would be different, and in the case of intensive magnitudes equal objective increments would seldom or never be accompanied by equal changes in consciousness, nor be subject to equal and independent errors. The theory of probability only considers the simplest and most general case. We must use all the knowledge we have as well as our theory, and the general formula must be adjusted to each special case.

In attempting to pull a dynamometer twice with the same force we do not compare the movements as we proceed, but the final result, and if the force were near the limit of our strength, the error might be less than for a smaller magnitude. We should expect a post-office clerk to judge very light weights better than a blacksmith, a blacksmith to judge heavy weights the better. We should expect to discriminate lights best within the range of ordinary daylight, and sounds best within the range of the human voice. Such results would be contrary to Weber's law, but are simply factors additional to the summation of errors required by the theory of probability. The relation between the error of observation and the magnitude of the stimulus will differ for each stimulus and for each observer, and will not remain constant even for the same stimulus and the same observer. But the usual increase of the error of observation with the magnitude of the stimulus is accounted for in a satisfactory manner by the summation of errors, and I should substitute for Weber's law the following: *The error of observation tends to increase as the square root of the magnitude, the in-*

---

[1] Constant errors increase in direct ratio to the magnitude, and would tend to follow Weber's law. But, curiously enough, constant errors have not been supposed by the psychologists to follow Weber's law. As a matter of fact "constant errors" are very inconstant and difficult to investigate.

*crease being subject to variation whose amount and cause must be deter-
mined for each special case.*[1]

It may be asked if this view be correct, why do the results of
researches confirm Weber's law? As a matter of fact Weber's law has not
yet been confirmed exactly by any careful research, the error of observation usually becoming larger as the magnitude of the stimulus is taken
larger, but almost always more slowly than in direct proportion to the
magnitude. The attempt has been made by Fechner, Wundt, Helmholtz
and others to explain away the variations by additional hypotheses,
but it is universally admitted that the validity of a law or hypothesis
decreases as the number of subsidiary hypotheses increase.

I venture to think that it is an open question whether in the researches hitherto made the error of observation increases more nearly
as the magnitude or as the square root of the magnitude. Researches
in which the method of just noticeable difference has been used do not
of necessity measure the error of observation at all. The variation in
adjusting the just noticeable difference would roughly measure the error
of observation, but this has been neglected. All the researches on lights
with which I am acquainted[2] (excepting that by Prof. Fullerton and the
writer) used the method of just noticeable (or more than noticeable)
difference. Now it is natural enough (considering its elasticity) to
make the just noticeable difference within the range of ordinary daylight proportional to the intensity of the light. We see the same objects
more or less brightly illuminated, and should tend to regard the differences in shade and color as equal differences, whatever the intensity.
It may also be remarked that the mechanism of the eye (accommodation of the pupil and sensitiveness of the retina) tends to obliterate
objective differences in brightness. Further in all these researches on
lights (excepting Merkel's) the lights were side by side, and the time
of exposure was not limited. In such a case the error of observation
becomes much obscured, and almost any result can be obtained.

I venture to maintain this conclusion even against the very careful
research by König and Brodhun, which supports Weber's law for a
considerable range of intensity. It is especially difficult to adjust a just
noticeable difference when the areas of light are very small, and for
colors not usually seen. König and Brodhun found the just noticeable

---

[1] Prof. Fullerton pointed out at the meeting of the association that the conditions which made the first fractional or elemental error positive or negative might
make the following error tend in the same direction. So far as such a tendency is
present the error of observation would increase more rapidly than the square root
of the stimulus, and more nearly in direct proportion to it (Weber's law).

[2] Bouguer, Lambert, Arago, Masson, Fechner, Volkmann, Aubert, Helmholtz,
Plateau, Delbœuf, Kraepelin, Dobrowolsky, Lamensky, Breton, Ebbinghaus,
Merkel, Lehmann, Neiglick, Schrimer, Müller-Lyer, König and Brodhun.

difference for different colors of apparently the same intensity to be the same (ca. $\frac{1}{75}$ of the light). Previously with much the same methods Lamansky found the just noticeable difference for red $\frac{1}{70}$, for yellow and green $\frac{1}{286}$, for violet $\frac{1}{106}$, whereas Dobrowolsky found for red $\frac{1}{14}$, yellow $\frac{1}{46}$, green $\frac{1}{59}$, violet $\frac{1}{268}$-$\frac{1}{67}$. The three researches were carried out in Helmholz' laboratory, and we may well be at a loss to draw any conclusions from such discordant results.[1] Perhaps the two best researches with lights have been carried out by Aubert and by Müller-Lyer. Both of these writers think their results do not support Weber's law.

It is not necessary in this place further to review and compare results of researches on lights and other stimuli. If it be admitted that the just noticeable difference be not proportional to the error of observation, the amount of work to be considered would be greatly reduced. Further, many researches by the method of average error and right and wrong cases have only a tolerable validity (e.g., Fechner's and Merkel's) because the observer knew the relation of the stimuli before comparing them. In other cases (e.g., with tastes, temperatures, touches and sounds), the stimuli have not been measured in a satisfactory manner. I believe the various researches are so disparate, having been made by so many observers (often young men working for a degree) and by such varying (and in many cases inadequate) methods, that the only general conclusion which can be drawn is that the error of observation tends to increase as the stimulus is made larger and usually more slowly than in direct proportion to the stimulus.

Before concluding I wish to notice the relation between the error of observation and the estimation of mental intensity. It has commonly been assumed that the variable error and the probable error (or h in Germany) are proportional to the just noticeable difference. The just noticeable difference has further been used to measure the intensity of sensation. The just noticeable difference is thus used ambiguously, on the one hand as a difference equally likely to be correctly perceived, on the other hand as a difference accompanied by an apparently equal increment in sensation. I entirely question the application of the error of observation to the measurement of the intensity of sensation. Supposing the intensity of sensation to be measurable, it may increase as the stimulus or (conceivably) as the logarithm of the stimulus, while the error of observation may be any other function of the stimulus.[2] When it is evident that the error of observation may be

---

[1] More especially as Helmholtz, in the revision of his *Physiologische Optik*, does not even mention Lamensky and Dobrowolsky. Nor does he refer to work not done in Berlin.

[2] This was noticed by G. E. Müller in 1879 (Zur Grundlegung der Psychophysic, p. 79-80).

increased or decreased in many ways without greatly altering the apparent intensity of sensation, I cannot understand how it has come to be used as a unit suitable for measuring the intensity of sensation. The error of observation is a physical quantity, a function of the intensity, area, duration, etc., of the stimulus, of the condition of the nervous system, and of the faculties, training, attention, etc., of the observer. That it should increase with the magnitude of the stimulus, and tend to increase as the square root of the magnitude, seems to me a natural consequence of the summation of errors. But I see no necessary connection between the supposed fact that the error of observation increases in direct proportion to the stimulus and the consequence which has been drawn from it that the intensity of sensation increases as the logarithm of the stimulus.

The measurement of the intensity of sensation is not out of the question because the error of observation cannot be used as a unit. The attempt is made to accomplish this when for different intensities sensations are adjusted midway between two others, when they are made apparently half or double others, or, lastly, when they are made just greater or less than others in the sense that the difference in sensation is apparently equal. The question here is whether we do in fact judge differences in the intensity of sensations, or whether we merely judge differences in the stimuli determined by association with their known objective relations. I am inclined to think that the latter is the case. I find it comparatively easy to adjust one time, length of line or weight midway between two others, much more difficult to judge when one light or sound is midway between two others, and almost impossible to judge one temperature or pain midway between two others. The difficulty of making a decision increases as the objective relations are less familiar, and I believe that my adjustment is always determined by association with the known quantitative relations of the physical world. With lights and sounds, association might lead us to consider relative differences as equal differences, and the data would be obtained from which the logarithmic relation between stimulus and sensation has been deduced. With the force, extent and time of movement, Prof. Fullerton and the writer have shown that our estimates tend to follow the objective relations. But, in any case, if we merely judge the relations of objective magnitudes by association, we have no basis whatever for determining a relation between physical energy and mental intensity.

I conclude, consequently, that we cannot measure the intensity of sensation and its relation to the energy of the stimulus either by determining the error of observation or by estimating amounts of difference. The most natural assumption would seem to be that the intensity of sensation increases directly as the energy of the brain changes correlated with it. The relation between the energy of the brain changes and the physical stimulus is a physiological question. This conclusion does not mean, however, that psycho-physical research is valueless. On the contrary it is an important contribution to the science of psychology, whence its application will be extended to physical science, to art, to medicine, to pedagogy and in other directions.

12

ON REACTION-TIMES AND THE VELOCITY OF THE NERVOUS IMPULSE

The research reported here was done with the collaboration of Professor Charles S. Dolley, Philadelphia. It was presented before a meeting of the National Academy of Sciences, held in Albany in 1893. This full account of it was subsequently published in the Memoirs of the National Academy of Sciences as Second Memoir, Volume VII, 1896. A shortened version without tables and figures was also published in *The Psychological Review*, 1: 159–168, 1894.

The object of this research is to determine the conditions which affect the length of the reaction-time on dermal stimuli, and to study the application of the reaction-time to the measurement of the velocity of the nervous impulse in motor and sensory nerves and in motor and sensory tracts of the spinal cord.

Since von Helmholtz first measured the velocity of the nervous impulse in 1850 much work has been directed to the subject, but the results are not accordant. The experiments on the nerve-muscle preparation of the frog are the most easily carried out, and these are usually regarded as valid for the motor and sensory nerves of man. It does not, however, follow that the effects of electrical stimulation on the excised and dying nerve of the frog are the same as the effects of cerebral discharge in the living animal, nor that these effects (could they be determined) would hold for man.

Determinations made by electrically stimulating the living nerve of the lower mammals and of man are of more value for human physiology than those on the excised nerve of a frog. They are, however, less accordant. We are ignorant of the relations between electrical stimulation and nervous discharge, and do not know what happens in the motor nerve and muscle when the skin is stimulated by electricity. It seems evident that the velocity of the normal nervous impulse can not be determined in this way, owing to the great variation in results, which must be due to the method of stimulation and not to the velocity of the normal impulse. Thus von Helmholtz obtained times twice as long in winter as in summer, and supposes this to be due to differences in the conductivity of the nerve. This is not, however, the case, as we find that the reaction-time, in which the time of transition along the nerves is a large factor, is the same in winter as in summer. It is further evident that such experiments apply only to the motor nerve. The time of transmission may be the same as in the sensory nerve, but to assume this would be arbitrary.

So long as we can not record the progress of the nervous impulse along the nerve nor the instant at which it reaches or leaves the brain, the rate of transmission of the normal sensory or motor impulse can only be determined indirectly. In the case of motor nerves it is necessary to make movements with muscles at varying distances from the brain following as quickly as possible on the same stimulus. In the case of sensory nerves the stimulation must be given at varying distances from the brain, and the arrival must be followed by a movement or directly judged by consciousness.

In these experiments the results are obtained by measuring the time of a complex process—the reaction. The reaction-time is the interval elapsing before a predetermined movement follows on a predetermined stimulus. During this interval a series of physiological processes takes place. (1) The stimulus is converted into a nervous impulse; (2) the nervous impulse travels along the sensory nerve and, it may be, the spinal cord to the brain; (3) through sensory tracts of the brain to a sensory center; (4) changes occur in this center; (5) these changes are followed by a discharge from a motor center; (6) the motor impulse travels along motor tracts in the brain; (7) along the motor nerve and, it may be, spinal cord, and, finally, (8) the muscle is innervated. The process is probably an acquired cerebral reflex, not accompanied by consciousness. The stimulus is indeed perceived, but probably not before the motor impulse has been discharged. The stimulus causes two sorts of cerebral changes, the discharge of the motor impulse, and changes in the cortex, which are accompanied by consciousness. But, contrary to the views of most physiologists, we think the movement does not follow on changes in consciousness, but is simultaneous with or actually prior to them. What volition is concerned in the process precedes the reaction and consists in preparing the motor impulse, which is reflexly discharged.[1]

The conditions on which the duration of the reaction depends are partly such as relate to the object reacting and partly such as relate to the stimulus. Some subjects react more quickly than others, and this difference in time must represent real differences in the nervous

[1] It is not necessary to repeat in this place references to the somewhat extended literature on reaction-time and the velocity of the nervous impulse; cf. for these Hermann, in his Handbuch der Physiologie, Vol. II, and Exner, in the same work, Vol. III, Leipzig, 1879; Wundt, Grundzüge der physiologischen Psychologie, 4th edition, Leipzig, 1893; Cattell, Philosophische Studien, Vol. III, and Mind, Vol. XI, 1886; Dumreicher, Zur Messung der Reactionszeit, Dissertation, Strassburg, 1889; Jastrow, The Time Relations of Mental Phenomena, New York, 1890, and the Catalogue of the Surgeon-General's Library.

system. The personal difference in reacting has not yet been adequ_
investigated.[1] Observations which we have made indicate that _
reaction-time is shorter for women than for men, and for Americans
than for Germans. The reaction-time is said to be longer in childhood
and in old age. We have, however, found a normally short reaction in
a child of 3 and an unusually short and regular reaction in a man of
65. We have found the reaction-time to be lengthened in certain diseases of the nervous system, and the test (especially in unilateral diseases in which the reacting hand or foot and the point of application
may be varied) might prove useful in diagnosis, more especially in
indicating progression or recovery. We have found the times of mental
processes such as perception, volition, memory, association, etc., to
vary more in different individuals than the times of the simple reaction, and these may prove useful not only in diagnosis of disease, but
in scientific pedagogy and in directing the ordinary conduct of life.
Our experiments on personal differences are not completed, and will
not be treated in this paper.

In the same individual the duration of the reaction-time and of
mental processes differs at different times. Owing, however, to the
reflex nature of the reaction its length is not greatly affected by the
condition of the observer, the time of day, the number of reactions already made, nor the amount of practice. These factors, and especially
the effects of attention, we shall consider in view of our own results.
It may here be stated that in our experiments the mean variation of a
reaction from the series to which it belongs was usually less than
0.01 second, and the mean variation of series made on different days
was also usually less than 0.01 second.

The length of the reaction-time is clearly influenced by the nature
of the stimulus and the point of its application. The reaction-time is
about 0.025 second longer for light than for sound and touch. This
may be due to the greater time required for converting the physical
motion into a nervous impulse in the retina, where a chemical process

---

[1] It is, indeed, the case that the whole question of reaction-time has had its
origin in the personal equation of the astronomer. But the problems, though often
confused, are quite distinct. The astronomer watches the star as it crosses the field
of his telescope and records as nearly as he can the instant at which it passes the
central thread. In such a case a reaction may perhaps be said to take place, but the
personal equation of the astronomer depends not on the duration of the reaction
but on the time at which the process is initiated, and may be as great as one second.
It seems likely that the astronomer could greatly reduce his personal equation by
adopting the methods of the psychologist. If the star passed behind a screen and
emerged as it passed the meridian, the observer could not have a negative personal
equation, and the probable error of a single observation might be reduced to
0.01 second.

is supposed to take place. It may also be due to the cerebral reflex being less perfect, reflex and automatic movements being made more readily in answer to sounds and touches than to lights. We have found the reaction on touch shorter than on electric stimulation. The reaction-time becomes shorter as the intensity of the stimulus is increased, though the difference is not great except in the case of very weak stimuli. The area of the stimulus probably only affects the length of reaction in so far as it alters the intensity. The quality of stimuli of the same intensity (*e.g.*, different colors or noises) does not appreciably affect the length of the reaction.

The point of application of the stimulus on the body affects the length of the reaction, and this is the problem which we have more especially attempted to study. If the cerebral reflex and motor processes remain the same, the difference in the time of reaction may be used to measure the velocity of the sensory impulse in the nerve and spinal cord. The chief difficulty we have met is not the variable error in the cerebral reflex, but the fact that the same physical stimulus applied at different parts of the body produces physiological effects varying in intensity and cerebral reflexes varying in facility.

The length of the reaction is also affected by the muscles used, and by using organs at varying distances from the brain (*e.g.*, hand or foot) the velocity of the motor impulse may be studied. *The duration of the reaction is the same for the right and left hands, but is shorter when the stimulus is applied to the reacting hand than when applied to the other.* In this case, the cerebral reflex is shorter, because it is natural to draw away the hand from a stimulus which may be hurtful (*e.g.*, a hot surface). The reaction is shorter and more regular when the hand releases a key than when it presses a key—this doubtless because the innervation can not be prepared so thoroughly in advance in the latter case, lest it be discharged prematurely. This is a point which has not been duly regarded by experimenters and has increased the irregularity of some investigations.

The factors which we have been considering chiefly concern the nature of the cerebral reflex. We, ourselves, believe that the time of transmission of the impulse in the nerve must be far more constant than might be supposed from the discordant results of former investigations. We shall show that the mean variation (and probable error) of a reaction-time may be as small as one-thirtieth of the time, and this small variation is doubtless due to changes in the nature of the cerebral processes rather than to alteration in the rate of transmission in the motor and sensory nerves.

In conclusion, it may be noted that the experiments here described were begun (in 1889) in the psychological laboratory of the University of Pennsylvania and completed (in 1893) at Columbia College. The observations were made and the records taken by *C* and *D* (the writers), and *J* (Mrs. J. McKeen Cattell). The larger part of the new apparatus was secured through an appropriation from the Bache fund of the National Academy of Sciences and is preserved by the Academy.

PART I.—APPARATUS AND METHODS

In order to measure a reaction-time at least three instruments are required—one to give the stimulus and record the instant at which it is given, one to record the instant at which a movement is made, and one to measure the intervening time. For measuring time we used the Hipp modification of the Wheatstone electric chronoscope and a new instrument, which we may call a gravity chronometer.[1]

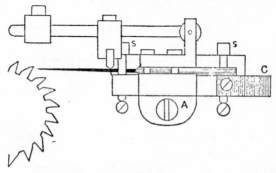

FIG. 1.

The electric chronoscope has been described in various places. It is much more convenient than any chronographic method in which a tuning fork writes on a moving surface, and when properly regulated it is fully as accurate. The chronoscope is a clockwork moved by a weight and regulated by a vibrating rod. The rod vibrates (say) five hundred times in a second, and at each vibration the tooth of a wheel is allowed to pass, as in the escapement of a clock. The details of the clockwork and method of regulation are not essential, and can be improved. The rod and wheel are shown in fig. 1. The rod is adjusted by the screws *ss*, the carriage of the rod moving on the axle *A*. When the rod vibrates, however, the screws *ss* become loosened and the rod retreats from the wheel. We have corrected this fault to a large extent by placing a clamp, *C*, on the carriage. In the chronoscope the clockwork is started by pulling a string, and unless the string be pulled with a given force and to a given extent the clockwork is apt not to

---

[1] The electric chronoscope is made by Peyer & Favarger, Neuchatel. The gravity chronometer was made by D. G. Brown, Camden, N. J., who also made alterations for us in the electric chronoscope.

start properly. We have replaced the string with a bar attached to a telegraphic key, and when the key is tapped the clockwork is properly started. We have replaced the glass bell supplied by the makers with a wooden house. This keeps out dust, deadens the noise, and need not be removed on winding. Lastly, we have rewound the electro-magnets with coarser wire, which greatly reduces the latent time of magnetization and demagnetization. The chronoscope runs one minute only, and must consequently be stopped after each experiment. A clockwork running a longer time, say one hour, would be much more convenient, and could be regulated more exactly. It would also be convenient if the hands could be sprung back to zero as in an ordinary stop watch.

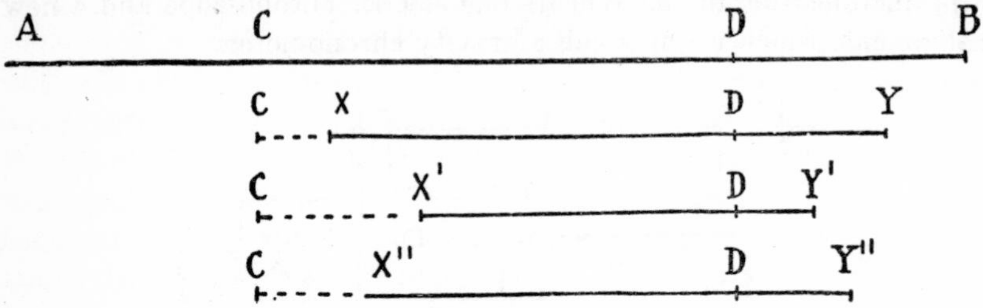

Fig. 2.

The value of the chronoscope consists in the application of an electro-magnet. The hands recording the time are not in connection with the clockwork, and do not move when it is set in motion; but when an electric current is sent through the coil of the electro-magnet the armature is attracted, a system of levers throws the hands into connection with the clockwork, and they are set in motion. Then when the current is broken a spring draws back the armature and the hands stand still.[1] The distance the hands have moved is read from the two disks, time being recorded to one-thousandth of a second, and the hands returning to their original position every ten seconds.

It is evident that short times can thus be measured with great convenience. It is easy to close or break an electric current when events occur, and the time is found by subtracting the position of the hands before their motion began from that after it ended. This method of measuring the time of an event is, however, subject to a considerable error, which was first corrected by one of us. If the strength of the current in relation to that of the spring be too great the recorded times are too long and conversely. This may be conveniently illustrated by a diagram (fig. 2). Let the time be represented by the line *AB*, and the interval the current is closed (which is the duration of the

---

[1] A second electro-magnet makes it possible to reverse this process and measure the time a current has been broken.

process) by the line CD. After the current is closed there is a latent period before the armature is attracted and the hands are started, and after the current is broken there is a second latent period before the magnetization disappears sufficiently for the spring to draw away the armature. Supposing the tension of the spring to remain constant, when a strong current is used the magnetization occurs quickly, say in the time CX, and the demagnetization slowly and the time recorded by the hands XY is longer than the real time of the event CD. On the other hand, when a weak current is used the magnetism requires a comparatively long time, say CX', whereas the demagnetization occurs more quickly, say in DY', and the recorded time is shorter than the real time. This is not a mere matter of theory. With the chronoscope used by us, the real time being 100σ (one-tenth second, $\sigma = 0.001$ second), the recorded time may have an error greater than 50σ. The discordant results obtained by different observers and the large variation in the time of reaction is probably in many cases due to neglect of this factor. With a variable battery (such as Grenet, which is or was formerly supplied by the makers of the chronoscope) the recorded times would scarcely ever be correct, and would become much shortened in the course of an hour's work.[1]

For each degree of tension of the spring there is one strength of current with which the time of magnetization and demagnetization will be equal, CX'' being in this case the same as DY'', and the recorded time $X''Y''$ is equal to the real time CD. This strength of current may be found empirically by letting the chronoscope measure a known interval and adjusting the current until it gives the correct time. The times given by the chronoscope will then be constant so long as the current remains constant.

In order to secure such a standard time (and for other chronometric purposes) we have constructed an instrument which is, to a certain extent, the inversion of the principle of the Atwood gravity machine. This is a falling screen, which is shown in outline in the accompanying figure (fig. 3). On a heavy triangular base, BB, a perpendicular iron column 2 m. in height is fastened. This column may be made exactly perpendicular by means of the heavy set screws SS in the base. On this iron column two brass bars, 3 cm. square, are bolted 5 cm. apart and exactly parallel (having been planed in position). On the inside

---

[1] In the Hipp chronoscope the latent time of magnetization is much larger than necessary. The electro-magnet has a very high resistance and self-induction, and the levers carried by the armature are needlessly complicated and heavy. We have, as stated, greatly reduced the latent time by rewinding the magnets with coarser wire. We are sure that a chronoscope could be constructed in every way better than that by Hipp, and it is only the expense which has prevented us from making one.

of these brass bars or columns are triangular grooves, in which a screen, SS, runs up and down. The screen is 30 cm. long, 5 cm. wide, and 2 cm. thick, and weighs 2 kg. On each side of the screen two wheels are inserted, which barely touch the grooves and allow the screen to run up and down almost without friction. This screen is held at the top of the columns by the electro-magnet MM, or may be held at any height by means of a second adjustable magnet not shown in the figure. When the current supplying the electro-magnet is broken the screen falls, and at the rate required by the laws of gravity, excepting in so far as it may be retarded by resistance of the air and friction. Owing to the shape and weight of the screen the resistance of the air is slight, and as the column is exactly perpendicular the wheels of the screen scarcely touch the grooves, and what slight friction there would be is nearly obviated by the revolution of the wheels. We did not, however, depend on the theoretical time of fall, but measured the time with a tuning fork, as described below. The force with which the screen strikes the base is broken by rubber cushions on the bottom and sides. The cushions on the sides are especially useful. The screen is slightly cut away, as shown in the figure, and is gradually stopped by the projecting rubber bars on both sides; these obviate most of the jar and prevent the screen from rebounding. The screen is lifted by means of the pulley shown in the cut. The cord aa is pulled by the handle b and lifts a carriage behind the screen, which in turn lifts the screen. The carriage moves in separate grooves back of the screen and falls into its place when the screen touches the electro-magnet.

On the front of the brass columns are also grooves in which pins are inserted which can be placed in any position. By means of these pins electrical contacts CC can be securely adjusted to the columns at any height. The electrical contacts were made especially for us. They consist of wheels (WW', fig. 4) which turn on points. The circumference of each wheel is half platinum (PP), the rest being rubber or being cut away. From the wheel a pin (not visible in the figure) projects, and this is struck by the screen when it falls, causing the wheel to turn. A platinum contact presses gently on the wheel, and as the wheel revolves the contact is brought against the platinum circumference, thus closing one circuit and simultaneously breaking a second circuit. A current is thus closed or broken (or two circuits may be simultaneously closed or broken, or one circuit closed at the instant another is broken) at a given point in the fall of the screen. We especially recommend this contact for closing a circuit; a circuit may be readily broken, but in order to close a circuit a mercury contact is nearly always used, which involves various inconveniences and sources of error. By means of this wheel-contact a current can be closed at a given instant and

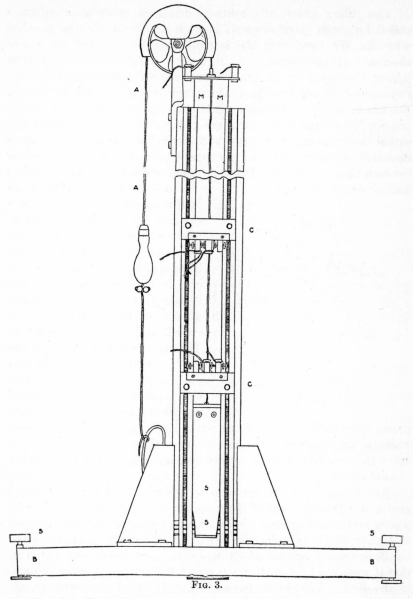

FIG. 3.

remains closed, or the circuit could be closed for any given fraction of a hundredth of a second, which might be useful for many experiments. The rubbing keeps the contacts clean.

The current in these wheels does not pass through the points of the axis (which might cause variation in the resistance), but through a platinum spring, *S*, which touches the side of the wheel.

The falling screen and contacts described make a chronoscope useful for many psychological, physiological, and perhaps physical purposes. We have used the instrument chiefly to simultaneously close and break currents, and to give a standard interval of 100σ (one-tenth second) for the regulation of the chronoscope. In two other directions, however, experiments have been begun with the instrument. Electric shocks are produced separated by (say) 10σ. These shocks are applied to the nerve at varying distances from the brain, the earlier shock having farther to travel. When the shocks are felt simultaneously we have measured the time it takes to travel the distance between the two contacts. This method involves several psychological difficulties, but we hope to secure results supplementary to those given

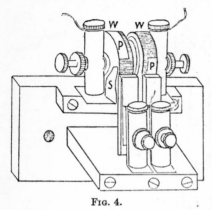

in this paper. In the second place the instrument has been used to uncover any object and register the instant at which this occurs. Thus a printed word may be covered by the screen and the screen be allowed to fall. The instant the word becomes visible a current is closed and the time recorded. Thus the time required to see the word, for the association of ideas, etc., may be measured. The special experiments now in progress consist of uncovering two surfaces

FIG. 4.

nearly alike in intensity and measuring the time required to perceive which is the brighter. The time becomes longer as the difference is taken less, and one mental quantity is thus determined as the function of another.

We may here confine ourselves to describing the method used to give a standard interval of time. A key which closes a contact was placed so that it was struck by the falling screen, and the contact closed at a given point, say when the screen had fallen 44.1 mm., or three-tenths second. A contact which broke the same circuit was placed so that it would be broken when the screen had fallen 78.4 mm., or four-tenths second. The circuit was consequently closed one-tenth second. The distances were calculated theoretically and controlled by means of a recording tuning fork.

When the chronoscope was being regulated and when the experiments were being made, the apparatus was arranged as shown in the figure. The current which controlled the chronoscope was from twenty-four large gravity cells in pairs, which were placed in a separate room.

After the electro-magnet had been rewound with coarser wire fewer cells sufficed. The wires were led from a battery, B', to a commutator, C, and thence the current passes through a rheostat, R, and could, when required, be sent by a switch, S, through a galvanometer, G. From the rheostat the current was led to a room in another part of the building in which the subject was placed. In this room the current passed through one or two sensitive telegraphic keys. From these keys the current was conducted to the chronoscope and thence to the

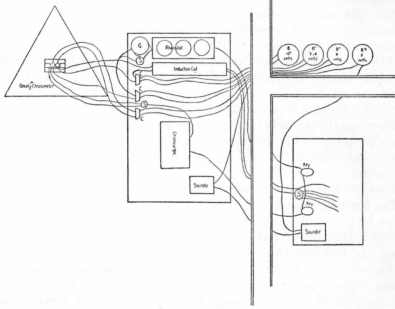

FIG. 5.

contacts of the gravity chronometer and back to the commutator and battery.

When the chronoscope was being regulated the circuit was closed, excepting the upper circuit of the gravity chronoscope. The electric chronoscope was set in motion and the screen allowed to fall by breaking the separate current (from four gravity cells) B'', which supplied the electro-magnet. When the screen fell to the contact (C on fig. 3) it closed the circuit, and the hands of the electric chronoscope were set in motion. After the screen had fallen 100σ farther it struck the lower contact (C on fig. 3) and broke the circuit, and the hands were stopped. The time recorded by the hands would not usually be 100σ, but a time perhaps 10σ or even 50σ longer or shorter. The strength of the current (or the tension of the spring in the chronoscope) was then adjusted until the chronoscope gave the correct time. The current from the battery being very constant, the variation from day to day was small, usually not more than 2σ, but it might be considerable if a change in temperature occurred. Under the conditions present a change in time of 1σ was caused by a change in resistance of about 5 ohms. The time was adjusted so that the chronoscope had a constant error of less than 1σ. The average variable error of the chronoscope as controlled by the falling screen was usually less than 1σ. Thus, in one trial (June 18, 1892) the average variable errors in seven series each containing ten measurements were 0.96, 0.8, 0.42, 0.4, 0.64, 0.64, and 0.56σ. Occasionally, however (about once in ten trials), the time was about 7σ too short. We were unable to discover the origin of this error, but it was probably due to an irregularity in the teeth of the wheel which caught up the hands of the chronoscope. This error would make all times given in this paper about 1σ too short, and would increase the mean error of the series. As we are, however, concerned with a difference in times, the result would not be affected except by increasing the probable error to the amount shown in the tables.

The errors of the chronoscope are thus small. The variable error is practically eliminated in a series of one hundred experiments. The constant error of adjustment would not affect a difference in time when the processes were measured alternately and on the same day. The constant error in the rate at which the chronoscope runs would also be practically eliminated when a difference is taken. As a matter of fact, this error is very small. In a series of seven determinations it was one two-thousandth of the time. There is a theoretical error in the fact that the chronoscope is regulated for 100σ, and in measuring longer times the current would magnetize the magnet more and the times given would be too long. The magnetism would, however, be nearly complete within 100σ, and the times actually measured were always in the neighborhood of 100σ. We had proposed measuring this error, if appreciable, but in the meanwhile this has been attempted in Germany[1] with entirely negative results. A very serious inconvenience in the chronoscope, as supplied by the makers, is found in the fact that the bar regulating the rate sometimes allows two vibrations between each tooth of the escapement, and the times recorded are only half of the true times. This error we have, however, nearly corrected, as described above; in any case it does not cause other than inconvenience, as the false rate is betrayed by the tone of the instrument.

As shown in fig. 5, the subject was placed in a quiet room, where the sounds of the apparatus could not be heard. In the case of experiments with touch, this was not done, as no disturbance in the length or variation of the reaction could be noticed when the subject was in

---

[1] Külpe und Kirschmann, Philos. Stud., vii, 1892.

the same room, and this was more convenient. When the subject was in a separate room signals were made by Morse sounders, as shown in fig. 5.

In measuring reactions the circuit was closed, excepting in the instrument giving the stimulus. The instruments used for various kinds of stimuli will be described below. In all cases, the circuit was closed (either directly or by means of a secondary circuit) when the stimulus was given. The circuit was then broken by the subject lifting the hand (or foot) which held a telegraphic key closed. The difference in readings of the chronoscope would then give the time of the reaction.

In making a reaction the subject placed two fingers of his hand on the telegraphic key and awaited the stimulus, of whose intensity, point of application, etc., he was aware. The recorder gave an auditory signal about two seconds in advance of the stimulus. The recorder obtained this time by watching a seconds pendulum which swung before him. This interval allowed the subject to prepare for the stimulus, but was not so exactly constant that he was likely to react prematurely before its occurrence. When the stimulus occurred the subject lifted his hand as quickly as possible. He did not, however, use great efforts to be quick, as we have found that this makes the reactions more irregular without appreciably shortening the time. As stated above, the reaction is apparently reflex, the movement following the stimulus automatically. Greater attention can only place the centers in a state of more unstable equilibrium, and this is done before, not after, the occurrence of the stimulus. Owing to the reflex character of the reaction, its time is not greatly altered by the condition of the observer, the time of day, the number of reactions already made, or the amount of practice. These factors we shall consider in describing our results.

Usually ten reactions of the same sort were made in succession, the interval between the separate reactions being about twenty seconds. The kind of reaction was then altered, the series to be immediately compared being made alternately, and the order being reversed on different days. In some cases (which are noted in the tables) ten reactions were made in succession at intervals of about two seconds, and only the resultant time of the ten reactions recorded. This can in many cases be recommended as an improvement in method, as in a given time about five times as many reactions can be measured and calculated as when they are recorded singly.

We have in all cases made ten series of each sort of reactions, and this result of one hundred reactions is given in the tables. Our tables are consequently more condensed than is usual in this kind of work (the times of each separate reaction being often published), but all necessary information is given by the mean variation (or average variable error) of the separate experiments and of the separate series. The mean variation of a single measurement from the average of ten measurements made under the same conditions was (approximately) 8σ for J and C and 12σ for D. To find the probable error of each series by the method of mean squares would involve a needless amount of calculation. When, as in this case, sufficient measurements have been made, we may regard the probable error of a single measurement as proportional to the variable error of a single measurement (0.845;1), and the probable error of the average of one hundred measurements would be about one-tenth of this—that is, about $.68\sigma$ for J and C and 1.01σ for D. In cases where we are concerned with the difference in the times of two series the probable error would be increased by $\sqrt{2}$.

It is worthy of note, however, that in measuring reactions, and in many other kinds of measurements and statistics, the ordinary assumptions of the theory of probabilities do not hold. Thus, in the case of reactions, there is a certain minimum reaction whose negative departure from the average is not considerable, whereas the positive lengthening of the reaction may be much greater. The median reaction is consequently smaller than the average reaction. We hope on some future occasion to consider these relations in view of our experimental results.

The methods of adjusting observations developed in the physical sciences have not always been followed in psychological and physiological measurements. Thus in the case of reactions the more irregular times have usually been omitted, and in some cases this has been carried so far as to invalidate the results. We have omitted no times whatever which measured reactions. We thus always have ten reactions in a series and ten series in a set. We did, indeed, consider, in addition to the ordinary criteria which have been proposed for rejecting observations with large residuals, two methods adjusted to the present work. One of these was for the subject, after he had made a reaction, to judge whether or not it was normal, and to assign its weight. We found, however, that directing the attention to the reaction interfered with its reflex character, and that it was difficult to assign a weight. We did not, therefore, continue this plan. We also applied a method for rejecting the more discordant observations. In each series we made thirteen reactions, and rejected the time which departed most from the mean, then the time which departed most from the mean of the remaining twelve reactions, and finally the third most discordant time. We thus had the mean of the ten most accordant reactions, which would represent a compromise between the median and the mean. We did not, however, continue this method, owing to the considerable calculation involved and to the fact that the corrected mean departed very little from the mean of all the observations. It is evident, however, that a result would be reached more quickly if some objective method were adopted which would exclude observations which are not normal, and we hope at some future time to consider the result of applying various criteria to our actual experiments. In this paper and others previously published we have made over twenty-five thousand separate measurements of the times of physiological and mental processes, and have consequently ample material for studying methods for adjusting errors of observation.

PART II.—REACTIONS ON ELECTRICAL STIMULI

An electric shock can be applied conveniently to different parts of the body. We used a Du Bois-Reymond induction coil (cf. fig. 5) and the shock following breaking of the primary circuit. By means of a double key (fig. 4) on the gravity chronometer (which was at first closed by the falling screen and later by hand) the primary circuit was broken and the current controlling the chronoscope simultaneously closed. We had supposed, from theoretical considerations, that the induced current might occur at a not inconsiderable interval after the breaking of the primary circuit, and that this would explain the fact that the times were longer for electrical stimuli than touches. By the kindness of Dr. Scripture we tested this on a chronograph, but could discover no appreciable interval between the breaking of the primary circuit and the spark from the induced current.

Various electrodes were used to apply the shock to the skin. We used electrodes 5 cm. apart and electrodes (platinum surfaces 10 mm. in diameter) which could be adjusted on opposite sides of the limb. The method we found best was to apply one electrode (usually 10 mm. in diameter) to the skin at the point we wished to stimulate while the other was conducted to a pail of saturated salt water in which the left foot and leg were placed. Electrodes were applied to several parts of the body, and the current could be switched to any electrode (fig. 5). The stimulus was given ten times in succession at the same point and then switched to another point immediately and without shifting the electrodes. The shock was usually given on the left-hand side of the body, the reaction being made with the right hand or foot.

The sensory effects of electrical stimulation of the skin have not been properly investigated. While works on physiology and psychology (e.g. Hermann, Foster, Wundt) discuss in detail the effects of electrical stimulation on the organs of sight, hearing, taste, and smell, they are curiously silent as to the sensory effects of electrically stimulating the skin. These effects are varied and interesting, and deserve a more careful investigation than we were able to make. In the case of a galvanic current from twenty-eight gravity cells in pairs the sensory effects on C were as follows: When the current passed through the body to the foot in saline solution no sensation was felt in the foot. When the *positive* pole was applied to the dry skin of the arm no sensation occurred on making, breaking, or with continuous current. When the skin was moistened with saline solution a slight prickling was felt on closing, not perceptible afterwards nor on breaking. When the *negative* pole was applied to the moistened skin of the arm there was a slight sensation on closing, then after a brief latent period a sensation as of piercing and boring followed, which became very painful. The stimulation caused tetanus of the muscle and left blisters on the skin. When the *positive* pole of the same current was applied to the dry skin of the outside of the upper lip there was on closing a slight prickling sensation, a slight flash of light, and a slight metallic taste. When the lip was moistened these were all stronger, the prickling and taste continued while the current was closed, and there was a flash of light on breaking. When the *negative* pole was applied to the dry lip there was a very slight shock and flash of light and no perceptible taste, but sensations of piercing quickly followed, which were unendurably painful. When the electrodes were taken 5 mm. apart and applied on the arm or lip, there was a slight shock on closing, followed by prickling sensations, not very painful and without tetanus The pain was at the negative pole. We wish especially to call attention to the fact that the current from the negative pole was more intense and from the positive pole more diffused (extending with considerable energy from the lip to the visual apparatus), which indicates that the current passes through the body from negative to positive pole, confirming certain physical observations.

We are not here further concerned with the galvanic current, having used a momentary induced current in our experiments. The breaking of the primary circuit causes a steeper wave and greater physiological shock than the making. Unless we are mistaken in the direction of the winding of the coils (we had proposed determining the direction of the induced current directly, but failed to do so), the breaking shock was strongest from the positive pole, and we used this pole to give the stimulus, the negative pole being conducted to the foot, where little or no sensation occurred. When, however, the shock was weak there was but little difference between the poles, and the negative pole might even give the stronger shock.[1]

[1] We are not in this place especially concerned with the muscular contraction directly following on electrical stimulation of the skin. Motor points have been mapped out on the skin, the stimulation of which is followed by the contraction of

The intensity and nature of the sensation varies according to the size of the electrode and the part of the body stimulated. The sensation is more piercing from a pointed or small electrode or when applied close to the nerve; it is more massive (as from a blow) when applied by a larger electrode or when there is muscle intervening. The sensation of a shock from eight cells on the upper arm might be equal to that from twenty-eight cells on the wrist. The shock from the same current also varied with the pressure of the electrode and especially with the moisture of the skin. Further, as the experiments proceeded, the part of the skin to which the shock was applied became continually more sensitive. These were the most perplexing factors in our experiments, as the difference in the time of the reaction might be due to

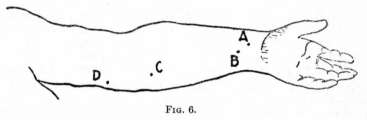

Fig. 6.

differences in the cerebral reflex rather than to the distance traveled by the impulse. We tried to eliminate these complications by adjusting the intensity and area and by choosing points on the skin where the sensations were alike, and shall subjoin the results of our experiments. It was, however, this difficulty which led us to substitute a touch or blow for an electric shock, and we believe our experiments on touch are the more satisfactory, as we could measure the force of the blow, whereas we could not measure the physiological effect of an electric shock.

In our first experiments we chose four points on the skin for the application of the stimulus. These were permanently fixed by pricking the skin and introducing nitrate of silver. Two of the points were on the arm over the median nerve and two on the leg over the posterior tibial nerve. The points on the arm *B* and *D* are shown in the cut; they were 30 cm. apart, and the length of the intervening nerve would be nearly the same. The corresponding points on the leg *M* and *N* were 50 cm. apart. The same objective current did not call up the same sensation on the several points. The shock was more massive and stronger at the upper points, and was followed by contractions of the muscles. It was rather stronger on the arm than on the leg.

---

special muscles. These are considered in work on the application of electricity to medicine. We have made some observations on this matter, especially on the effects of successive stimuli, but they are not sufficiently systematic for publication.

TABLE I.—REACTION-TIMES ON ELECTRICAL STIMULATION ON FOUR POINTS OF THE BODY. MOVEMENT WITH HAND AND WITH FOOT D AND C OBSERVERS. 6,360 REACTIONS

	Movement with hand				With foot	
	Upper arm	Lower arm	Upper leg	Lower leg	Lower arm	Lower leg
	131.3 *13.7*	132 *10.9*	140.8 *13.2*	143.1 *12.1*	157.3 *14.2*	170.1 *16.3*
	166 *9*	189 *11.2*	197 *14.4*	215.7 *21.2*	226.2 *32.5*	248.1 *18.3*
D	153.4 *5.2*	167.8 *7.1*	179.3 *7.6*	201.3 *10.1*	208.5 *4.9*	221.6 *10.4*
	148.4 *5.6*	160.3 *5.9*	176.8 *5*	197.6 *5.8*	206.3 *6.6*	230.3 *5.6*
	149.1 *4.9*	170 *4.6*	179.3 *3.8*	196 *6.8*	209.2 *4.7*	232 *7*
Av......	**149.6** *7.7*	**163.8** *7.9*	**174.6** *8.8*	**190.7** *11.2*	**201.5** *12.6*	**220.4** *11.*
	110.4 *5.8*	115.5 *8.5*	127.5 *6.2*	125.6 *8.2*	161.4 *7.5*	166.2 *8.1*
	108.7 *2.4*	116.4 *1.9*	139.7 *3.7*	150.4 *4.7*	162.9 *5.9*	163.6 *12.2*
C	109.6 *1.5*	115.8 *4.8*	139.2 *5.7*	149.6 *5.4*	173.7 *8.4*	212.9 *8.2*
	120 *2.5*	128.4 *5.2*	143.2 *4.6*	154.5 *6.5*	190.3 *7*	215 *9.8*
	116.7 *3.2*	120.1 *4.7*	148.7 *3.5*	156.6 *8.2*	179.7 *4.2*	203.8 *5.3*
Av......	**113.1** *3.1*	**119.2** *5*	**139.7** *4.7*	**147.3** *6.6*	**173.6** *6.6*	**192.3** *8.7*

		I	II	III	IV	V	Av.	Av. Av.
D	Lower arm less upper arm.	0.7	23	14.4	11.9	20.9	**14.2**	} 15.1
	Lower leg less upper leg..	2.3	18.7	22	20.8	16.7	**16.1**	
	Upper leg less upper arm.	9.5	31	25.9	28.4	30.2	**25**	
	Lower leg less lower arm.	11.1	26.7	33.5	37.3	26	**26.9**	} 23.6
	Lower leg (foot) less lower arm (foot)............	12.8	21.9	13.1	24	22.8	**18.9**	
	Lower arm (foot) less lower leg................	25.3	37.2	40.7	46	39.2	**37.7**	} 33.7
	Lower leg (foot) less lower leg................	27	32.4	20.3	32.7	36	**29.7**	
C	Lower arm less upper arm.	5.1	7.7	6.2	8.4	3.4	**6.1**	} 6.9
	Lower leg less upper leg..	−1.9	10.7	10.4	11.3	7.9	**7.7**	
	Upper leg less upper arm.	17.1	31	29.6	23.2	32	**26.6**	
	Lower leg less lower arm.	10.1	34	33.8	26.1	36.5	**28.1**	} 24.5
	Lower leg (foot) less lower arm (foot)............	4.8	.7	39.2	24.7	24.1	**18.7**	
	Lower arm (foot) less lower arm................	45.9	46.5	57.9	61.9	59.6	**54.4**	} 49.7
	Lower leg (foot) less lower leg................	40.6	13.2	63.3	60.5	47.2	**45**	

The first set of 1,560 experiments was made in the winter of 1890. The experiments were then interrupted, owing to change of residence, until the summer of 1892.

In the first set 13 reactions were made in a series, and each time in the table is the average of 130 reactions. In the remaining sets and in the following table each time is the average of 100 reactions. In the first set on C and in all the sets on D the reactions were measured singly. In the last four sets on C, 10 reactions were made in succession, and only the resultant time recorded. In several cases, owing to inadvertence or the occurrence of times which could not be reaction-times, there was one reaction too few in a series. Premature reactions scarcely ever occurred, not once in 100 reactions. In the first set the electrodes were 5 mm. apart. In the remaining sets the electrodes were on opposite sides of the limb for D. In the case of C, one pole was conducted through salt water to the left foot.

The time is given in thousandths of a second. After the time of reaction the mean variation of the separate series from the average time of the 10 series is given in *italics*. This multiplied by 0.845 and divided by $\sqrt{10}$ would give approximately the probable error of the average of 100 experiments.

Five hundred reactions with the hand to stimulation of each of these points and five hundred reactions with the right foot to A and M were made by two observers, D and C. The reactions were made in series of ten, the order of the series being altered each day. The results of the sets of one hundred reactions, together with the mean variations of the ten series which made up the set, are given in the first part of the accompanying table. In the second part of the table are given the differences obtained by comparing the times for the several points of application of the stimulus and the two movements. Following the table are some further explanations, which to a certain extent apply to all the tables.

This table contains the result of more reactions than have been published in the many researches hitherto made on the subject. The probable error of a single experiment is also much smaller. When the probable error of each measurement is five times as great as in these experiments, as has often been the case, it is evidently necessary to make twenty-five times as many measurements in order to secure a result equally valid. We consequently believe that these experiments supersede those hitherto made.

We find that the reaction-time for an electric stimulus applied to the upper arm was 149.6σ for D and 113.1σ for C, about one-seventh and one-ninth second, respectively. The cause of this personal difference remains obscure. It must either be due to differences in the nature of the process or to differences in the sensitiveness of the parts of the nervous system concerned. The maximum and minimum times in the sets differed by 34.7σ for D, and by 11.3σ for C. The differences are not due to the variable error, but to real differences in the condition of the nervous system. These are obscure, but the longer times in the case of D were obtained at a time when the nervous system was in a less efficient condition.

When the stimulus was applied on the lower arm or on the leg the reaction-time was longer. The excess of time when it was applied on the lower arm was 14.2σ for D and 6.1σ for C. The maximum and minimum times differed by 22.3σ for D and 5σ for C. These considerable differences are not due to the variable error, but to real differences in the process. The lower point was 30 cm. farther from the brain than the upper point, and if we can assume the difference in time to be due to the difference in the length of the nerve traveled, we shall have a velocity of the impulse in the median nerve of 21.1 meters per second for D and 49.5 meters per second for C. The velocities in the sensory fibers of the posterior tibial nerve would be for D 31.1 meters per second and for C 64.9 meters per second. These times would come within the limits of those obtained by others, but we are not prepared to accept them as valid. The differences in the times of reaction are undoubtedly correct, and with a very small probable error. The variable error of reactions has been eliminated, and the times give the reaction-times on objectively equal stimuli applied to the four points. But in the first place it does not seem likely that the velocity of the nervous impulse in the plain nerve should differ so greatly in the two observers. We can understand that the entire complex process of reaction might be 25 per cent longer in one case, as this may be due to less complete coordination in the brain centers, but there seems to be no reason why the velocity in the plain nerve should be 140 per cent slower. This would require us to conclude that the central reflex was actually shorter in the case of D. In the second place the probable error in the case of the velocity of the impulse is far greater than it should be from the variations in the reactions.

We are consequently compelled to conclude that the differences in the reaction-times are due to differences in the cerebral processes, and not merely to the length of the nerve traveled. The times for the points nearer the brain may be shorter because the physiological effects of the shock were greater (as was in fact the case) or because the fibers from the upper points lead to a more rapid transference in the brain. The difference in the two observers and in the same observer at different times are not due to variation in the velocity of the nervous impulse, but to differences in the nature of the cerebral reflex. For example, C's reaction-time being shorter and more regular than D's, we may conclude that it is more automatic and less influenced by changing conditions. The greater intensity and massiveness of the shock on the upper points would consequently shorten the reaction-time less for C than for D, and the results in the table are thus explained. This would also explain the larger variation in the sets in the case of D. This variation may be partly attributed to differences in the relative effect of the shock on the two points at different times, and may be partly due to cerebral changes. These considerations led to further experiments by which they were fully confirmed.

When the shock was applied to the leg in one case and to the arm in the other the impulse in the former case had in addition to travel through the spinal cord from the lumbar to the brachial plexus and the times are considerably longer. The difference in reaction-time with the hand when the shock was applied to the upper leg and upper arm, respectively, was for D 25σ for C 26.6σ. When the shock was applied to the lower leg and arm, respectively, the differences were for D 26.9σ, and for C 28.1σ. These times agree very well, better, perhaps, than the probable error would warrant; but in this case the probable error is a comparatively small part of the whole time, and the difference is undoubtedly due to the different point of application. It remains an open question whether the cerebral reflex might not be shorter when the stimulus is applied to the arm, in which case the times would not measure the velocity in the sensory tracts of the spinal cord. Indeed, this seems to be proved by the fifth line in the table, which gives the difference in time when the movement was made with the foot and the stimulus applied to the lower leg and lower arm, respectively. In this case the difference in time (with a rather large probable error for C) was for D 18.9σ, for C 18.7σ. The excess of distance in the spinal cord was the same as before, but the times are about 8σ shorter. We are enabled, consequently, to draw the interesting conclusion that when the stimulus is applied to the left arm the cerebral reflex is 8σ shorter when the movement is made with the arm than when made with the leg and conversely. The sensory fibers from one part of the body are most closely connected with the motor fibers to the same part.

We conclude, with some confidence, that when a stimulus is applied so that the impulse must traverse the spinal cord and from the lumbar to the brachial plexus the time of reaction is about 26σ longer when the movement is made with the hand and about 18σ longer when the movement is made with the foot. The difference in the two cases is due to greater rapidity of the central reflex owing to closer connection in the brain between sensory and motor fibers from the same part of the body. If the whole excess of time in the case compared be due to transmission in the cord we should have a velocity of about 15 meters per second in the sensory tracts of the spinal cord. The velocity is at least not less than this.

There remains for consideration the difference in the time of reaction when the movement is made with the hand and foot, respectively. When the stimulus was applied to the lower arm the difference was for D 37.7σ and for C 54.4σ; when the stimulus was applied to the lower leg the difference was for D 29.7σ and for C 45σ. The difference was less (D 8σ and C 9.4σ) when the stimulus was applied to the leg, and by almost exactly the same amount as before. We have evidently measured the difference in time of the cerebral reflex when the motor impulse proceeds to the part of the body from which the sensory impulse arrives, and when it proceeds to a different part. The differences in the times when the reaction is made with hand and foot are partly due to the time required to traverse the motor tracts of the spinal cord, but they may also be due to differences in the cerebral processes. The cerebral reflex is undoubtedly less perfect for the foot than for the hand. The difference in the case of the two observers (16.3σ greater for C) is almost certainly a difference in the cerebral process. C's reaction with the hand is very automatic; with the foot it is more nearly like D's. How much of the delay is due to traversing the motor tracts between the brachial and lumbar plexus can not be decided. If the whole time in the case of D were so consumed (ignoring the difference in the plain nerve) the velocity of transmission would be about 10 meters per second, and this is at least a minimum velocity. In so far as we can accept these results the velocity in the sensory tracts of the cord would be greater than in the motor tracts. This difference in velocity might be explained by the partial coordination of the movement in the cord. The difference, however, may be equally well attributed to the delay of coordination in the brain centers.

In view of the fact that the velocity in the sensory nerve had not been determined in a satisfactory manner, owing partly to the varying physiological effects of the shock on the points stimulated, we sought for a point on the lower arm for which the sensation should be as nearly as possible the same as on the point D of the upper arm. The best place we could find was a point 3 cm. below B and a little on the side of the line of the median nerve, as shown in fig. 6, the point being marked A. The stimulation of this point was followed by a strong contraction of the thumb and a massive sensation similar to that following the stimulation of the point D. We also chose a point, C (fig. 6), on the line of the median nerve, the stimulation of which was followed by a sensation similar in quality to that from the point B. This point was 20 cm. above B and 10 cm. below D. In Table II are given the reaction-times when the points A and B were alternately stimulated; also reactions in which the current was from electrodes 5 mm. apart, when on opposite sides of the limb, and when it passed through the body to the foot.

The experiments do not discover any marked difference in the time of reaction when the shock was applied to the skin by electrodes 5 mm. apart, when the electrodes were on opposite sides of the limb, and when the current was conducted through the body to the foot. In the two sets in which the differences were directly compared the times were 1.6σ and 4.3σ shorter when the current passed through the limb than when it was applied simply to the skin. The sensation is more *intense* when the shock is applied through electrodes close together, and more *massive* when they are farther apart. This is a psychological distinction of some importance. One sensation would be

TABLE II.—REACTION-TIMES ON ELECTRICAL STIMULATION. *D* AND *J* OBSERVERS. 2,800 REACTIONS

C...	Current through arm	On *A* 142.3 *4.9*	On *B*.............. 143.2 *4.8*
	Current through arm	On *A* 120.2 *5.2*	On *B*.............. 127.5 *3*
Av..	....	**131.3** *5*	**135.4** *3.9*
J...	Current through arm	On *A* 119 *3.8*	On *B* 121 *3.4*
C...	Electrodes 5 millimeters apart	On *A* 120.7 *4.2*	On *B* 125.7 *4.7*
	Electrodes 5 millimeters apart	On *A* 121.6 *4*	On *B* 132.9 *4.1*
	Electrodes 5 millimeters apart	On *A* 117.7 *4*	On *B* 130.3 *4.7*
Av..	....	**120** *4.1*	**129.6** *4.5*
J...	Electrodes 5 millimeters apart	On *A* 137.8 *6.8*	On *B* 141.5 *8*
C...	Electrodes 5 millimeters apart	On *A* 121.6 *5*	Through arm (at *A*) 120 *4.1*
	Electrodes 5 millimeters apart	On *B* 122.4 *3.3*	Through arm (at *B*) 118.1 *2.6*
	Electrodes 5 millimeters apart	On *A* 116.7 ...	On *D* 117
C...	Electrodes 5 millimeters apart	On *A* 122.7 *3.1*	On *D* (5 ohms resistance) 125 *2.9*

The total time of ten reactions was measured, excepting in the first, second, third, and eighth sets, in which the reactions were measured singly. In these sets the mean variation of the single reactions from the series to which they belong was for *J*, 9.7σ; *C*, 8.7σ.

greater than another either because it is more intense, the same nervous elements being more actively stimulated, or more massive, more nervous elements being stimulated. When the points *A* and *B* were stimulated—*A* being slightly the more distant from the brain—the reaction-time on *A* was the shorter, the differences being, for *C*, 0.9, 7.3, 5, 11.3, 12.6, 0.8, and −1.9σ; for *J*, 2 and 3.7σ; on the average, 4.6σ. The shorter time for the point *D* is due to the greater massiveness of the shock or the different nerve supply and cerebral connections. It is, consequently, evident that the reaction-time from the same physical stimulus applied to different points on the skin does not of necessity measure the velocity of the impulse in the plain nerve. When the shock was applied on A and D, at which points the quality of the shock was nearly the same, the times were nearly alike—116.7σ and 117σ—and when 5 ohms resistance was placed in the current giving the shock on D (in order to make the intensities the same) the times were A 122.7σ, and D 125σ.

The experiments given in Table II were preliminary to a more thorough investigation of the variation in the reaction-time according to the point to which the stimulus was applied and its intensity. We took the four points in the arm marked (in fig. 7) A, B, C, and D, and made a large number of reactions on each of these points, the physical stimulus being always the same. As already stated, the sensation was not the same either in intensity or quality. The quality of sensation was much alike for A and D, massive as from a blow, and for C and B more piercing. This difference is accounted for by the intervening muscle in the case of A and D and the muscular contractions which followed stimulation of these points. The intensity of sensation was not, however, alike for A and D and for B and C, respectively. A further and unexpected complication occurred, the relative intensities not being the same for the two observers who took part in the experiments. In the case of C the order of intensity was D, A, C, B, the differences between D and A and between C and B being large. A and C were nearly alike in intensity, but the difference in quality made it difficult to compare the intensities. The shock from eight cells in pairs on D was nearly the same as from twenty-eight cells on A; that from fourteen cells on A or C was nearly the same as from twenty-eight cells on B. In the case of J the order of intensity was A, D, B, C, but the differences were not large and seemed to vary from time to time. The results of these experiments are given on Table III.

TABLE III.—ELECTRIC STIMULATION; POINTS A, B, C, AND D. J AND C OBSERVERS.
2,400 REACTIONS

	A	B	C	D	Av.
J ⎧	115.7 7.7	123.5 6.4	131　4.6	123.8 9.3	**123.5** 7
⎨	124.3 3.4	122.8 5.3	137.3 5.1	128.5 6.6	**128.2** 5.1
⎩	124.8 6.2	127.1 7.1	137.8 6	132.2 6.1	**130.5** 6.3
Av.	**121.6** 5.8	**124.5** 6.3	**135.4** 5.2	**128.2** 7.3	**127.4** 6.1
C ⎧	123.8 2.9	134.3 5.2	128.9 5.1	116.6 4.2	**125.9** 4.3
⎨	127.2 3.2	138.5 5	131.6 2.9	123.3 1.7	**130.1** 3.2
⎩	124.7 4.2	138.1 6.6	131.8 3.8	121.1 3.5	**128.9** 4.5
Av.	**125.2** 3.4	**137**　5.6	**130.8** 3.9	**120.3** 3.1	**128.3** 4
Av., Av.	**123.4** 4.6	**130.7** 5.9	**133.1** 4.6	**124.2** 5.2	**127.8** 5.1

The averages of all the times for the two observers were almost exactly the same—127.4σ for J and 128.3σ for C. The departures from the average for the different points consequently represent real differences in the nature of the process. These are for J on A −5.8σ B, −2.9σ; D +0.8σ and C +8σ; for C on D, −8σ A −3.1σ; C +2.5σ and B +8.7σ. The reaction-times are without exception inversely proportional to the intensity of the sensation. It is consequently impossible to draw any conclusion from the experiments concerning the velocity of the nervous impulse in the sensory nerve.

In order to accomplish this it would at all events be necessary to make the sensations subjectively alike in intensity, or to make a correction for intensity. In order to study the relation between reaction time and intensity we made reactions on the four points on the arm with three intensities of shock. The strongest was nearly the same as in the preceding experiments, but a little stronger so as to be somewhat painful for J. The weakest was barely perceptible for C on the point B. The same physical stimulus produced much greater physiological effects on J than on C. The middle intensity was intended to be midway between the strongest and weakest, but after the experiments had been made it was thought to have been too weak. In Table IV the results are given of one hundred reactions on each of the four points and with each of the three intensities.

TABLE IV.—ELECTRIC STIMULATION; STRONG, MEDIUM, AND WEAK SHOCKS. POINTS A, B, C, AND D. J AND C OBSERVERS. 2,400 REACTIONS

		A	B	C	D	Av.
J	Strong......	108.8 *5*	111.2 *4.1*	116.9 *5.6*	108.6 *5*	**111.4** *4.9*
	Medium....	122.6 *4.9*	125.4 *6.1*	131.3 *4.4*	118.5 *7.3*	**124.4** *5.7*
	Weak......	126.8 *8.1*	130.9 *9.1*	143.5 *4.7*	126.1 *5.6*	**131.8** *6.9*
	Av..........	**119.4** *6*	**122.5** *6.4*	**130.6** *4.9*	**117.7** *6*	**122.5** *5.8*
C	Strong......	125.3 *5*	132 *5.9*	127.5 *4*	121 *4.4*	**126.4** *4.8*
	Medium....	144.4 *11.6*	171.2 *8.6*	149.2 *6.8*	145.8 *6.6*	**152.6** *8.4*
	Weak......	151.4 *9.3*	186.2 *5.8*	166.9 *4.9*	156.7 *8.5*	**165.3** *7.1*
	Av..........	**140.4** *8.6*	**163.1** *6.8*	**147.9** *5.2*	**141.2** *6.5*	**148.1** *6.8*
	Av., Av......	**129.9** *7.3*	**142.8** *6.6*	**139.2** *5.1*	**129.4** *6.2*	**135.3** *6.3*

The table shows that the reaction-time was shorter when the shock was stronger. The decrease in time, when the intensity was increased from weak to medium, was for J 7.4σ, for C 12.7σ; from medium to strong, for J 13σ and for C 26.2σ. The difference in the case of the two observers is due to the fact that the subjective differences were greater for C, in whose case the weakest shock was barely perceptible on B.

The difference in the time of reaction for C, when the shock was barely perceptible (on B) and when it was very strong (on D), was 65.2σ. The average times were nearly the same on A and D, for J 1.7σ shorter on D, for C 0.8σ longer. The shock seemed stronger on D. We must consequently conclude that the time of transmission in the nerve from A to D is counterbalanced by a shorter central time in the case of A, and that this shorter central time is not due to difference in intensity, but to difference in the distribution of fibers in the brain. As in the case of impulses from the arm and leg, we may here conclude that impulses from near the left hand lead more readily to a movement of the right hand than do impulses from the upper arm. This fact is itself interesting, but makes the determination of the velocity in the plain nerve by this method difficult or impossible.

In addition to these experiments on intensity we made reactions, in which the area of stimulation was altered. The sensation from a larger area is more massive, from a smaller area more piercing. It is consequently possible to make sensations from different parts of the body qualitatively more equal by using a smaller electrode on a point where the sensation is more massive, owing to anatomical structure. The small electrode was 1 mm., the large electrode 10 mm. in diameter, the area being consequently one hundred times as great in the case of the larger area. The electrodes were applied on the points A and D.

TABLE V.—ELECTRIC STIMULATION; LARGE AND SMALL AREAS. J AND C OBSERVERS. 800 REACTIONS

	Large		Small	
	A	D	A	D
J...............	117.6 *4.8*	120 *5.9*	114.3 *6.4*	123.6 *6.2*
C...............	121.3 *4.4*	121.4 *3*	130.8 *5.4*	123.4 *2.4*

For J the time was 0.1σ shorter with the large area, for C 5.7σ shorter. The difference in the case of the two observers is due to the fact that for J the small area on A was the strongest and most painful of the four shocks, whereas for C it was the weakest. Owing to the same fact, for J the time was 5.8σ shorter on A, for C it was 3.5σ longer.

It is evident that if the velocity of the impulse is to be measured by the difference in the reaction-times, points on the skin should be chosen in which the sensations are as nearly as possible alike, and the intensity and area of the shocks should be adjusted to make the sensations, so far as possible, exactly alike. We did not proceed with such experiments, however, partly because it did not seem possible to allow for the difference in time of the cerebral reflex due to the place of stimulation and partly because we found that better results could be obtained from mechanical touches or blows. Before going on, however, to describe our experiments on touch, we shall notice some experiments, chiefly on electrical stimulation, which we made with a view to studying the effects of attention directed to the point stimulated and the effects of the nature of the movement.

Experiments have recently been published in Germany[1] which gave a much longer reaction time when the attention was directed to the stimulus than when it was directed to the movement, and Wundt holds that in the former case the time is longer because the stimulus must be perceived before the movement is made. This might prove a complication in our experiments, as when the shock was shifted from place to place the attention would be naturally directed to it, more especially as it was somewhat painful. We made, consequently, reactions in which the attention was directed alternately to the stimulus and the movement, and used sounds as well as electrical shocks. The sound was a tolerably loud noise made by the single click of a Morse sounder, a strong current being used.

TABLE VI.—MOTOR AND SENSORY REACTIONS ON ELECTRICAL STIMULATION AND SOUND. C, J, AND D OBSERVERS. 1,000 REACTIONS

		Motor reactions	Sensory reactions
C.......	Electrical stimulation	142.7 10.1 (4.6)	142.8 8.4 (4.6)
J.......	Electrical stimulation	119 9.4 (3.8)	121.5 10.1 (3.4)
D.......	Electrical stimulation	281.4 58.3 (17.1)	201.6 31.2 (11.3)
C.......	Sound	105.9 6.9 (3.9)	105.4 5.9 (3)
J.......	Sound	105.5 12.2 (3.7)	105 7.7 (2.9)

It follows that the length and variability of the reaction-time is the same for J and C, whether the attention be directed to the stimulus or to the movement. In the case of D the time was considerably lengthened when the attention was directed to the movement, he being in the habit of directing his attention to the stimulus. The shorter and more regular reactions of J and C are due to the process being more completely reflex, and in this case, as we might expect, the direction of the attention does not alter the times. But it seems that when the reaction is not completely reflex it may be lengthened by an unusual direction of the attention. Thus D is used to attending to biological details, whereas the observers in Germany may have their mental processes more exclusively accompanied by motor impulses.[2]

[1] By Lange, Münsterberg, Martius, Külpe, and Titchener.
[2] Results similar to ours have been simultaneously obtained by Dessoir, Flournoy, and Baldwin.

We next give some experiments in which the nature of the movement was varied. In one set the stimulus was applied alternately to the left and right hands, the reaction being made with the right hand.[1] The electrodes were introduced into the knob of the key and the shock applied to the first and second fingers. In this case only one battery was used, the current being divided and passing partly through the induction coil and partly through the chronoscope. Owing to the high resistance in the chronoscope nearly all the current passed through the induction coil. When the current passing through the coil was broken the shock was given, and all the current was simultaneously sent to the electro-magnet of the chronoscope and the hands started. This method is convenient, as only one battery is required and the current is sent through the chronoscope at exactly the instant in which the primary circuit of the induction coil is broken. In one set the reactions were made at intervals of about twenty seconds, and measured singly; in the other set they were made in series of ten seconds, the reactions being made at intervals of two seconds, and only the resultant time of ten reactions measured.

TABLE VII.—ELECTRICAL STIMULUS ON LEFT AND ON REACTING HAND. *C* AND *J* OBSERVERS. 800 REACTIONS

		Shock on left hand	Shock on right (reacting) hand
C	Readings singly.................	112.8 *6.5 (3.5)*	97 *5.3 (2.7)*
	Readings in tens................	121.4 ... *(2.4)*	118.3 ... *(5.8)*
J	Readings singly.................	128.9 *6.2 (4.4)*	106.6 *5.2 (3.2)*
	Readings in tens................	118.5 ... *(3)*	98.5 ... *(3.3)*

The reaction-time was shorter (for *J* 21.1σ, for *C* 9.4σ) when the movement was made with the hand to which the shock was applied. This might be expected, as the movement is a natural reflex—a person will without reflection withdraw the hand when it touches a hot surface. The fact is of interest in connection with the results noticed above, which show that the cerebral reflex is in general quicker when the sensory fibers stimulated are from the same part of the body as that with which the movement is made. The table further shows that *J* made the reactions more quickly when ten were made in succession, whereas *C* made them more quickly when they were made singly. This would have a bearing on the relative times of the two observers in the other tables, but the experiments were not sufficient in number to determine the exact difference.

[1] Cf. Exner, Dumreicher and Reigart.

We give, lastly, reactions on sound in which the key was released by a movement made, respectively, with the finger, the wrist, the forearm, and the shoulder.

TABLE VIII.—REACTIONS ON SOUND; MOVEMENT WITH FINGER, WRIST, FOREARM, AND SHOULDER. J AND C OBSERVERS. 800 REACTIONS

	Finger	Wrist	Forearm	Shoulder
$J.$	121 14.6 (5.7)	117.1 11.9 (7)	130 12.7 (6)	138.7 15.4 (5.8)
$C.$	114.4 9.9 (4.3)	118.6 9.3 (3.2)	117.2 7.9 (1.8)	134.2 10.5 (4.2)

The times show that the reactions were slower when the movement was made from the shoulder, although the muscles concerned are nearer the brain. In the case of J it was also slower with the forearm. The movement with the finger and wrist seems to require about the same time. This shows that when the reaction is made with the foot the delay may be partly due to a more difficult coordination in the higher centers. In earlier experiments made by one of us it was also found that a time about 30σ longer was required to make a movement with the organs of speech than with the hand. The reaction-time seems, however, to be the same for the right and left hands. Thus, for C the reaction-time on light was 146σ with the right hand, and 147σ with the left hand.

PART III.—REACTIONS ON TOUCH

In the case of reaction experiments with dermal stimuli the electric shock has mostly been used, as it is easy to apply the shock to different parts of the body. We have, however, seen that the physiological effects of the shock vary greatly on different parts of the body, and even at the same point they can not be kept constant. The reaction-time following a touch or blow can be measured without difficulty beyond the inconvenience of applying the blow to different parts of the body. We have found that the same objective force of blow is followed by the same subjective sensation more nearly than in the case of electric stimulation. On different parts of the body the same blow, indeed, calls forth different sensations, the sensations being more intense when the part is harder, as over a bone. But the difference is not so great as in the case of the electric shock, and at the same point the same sensation can be given time after time and day after day. The probable error is consequently smaller than in the case of electric shock; indeed, the variable error in our experiments on touch is much smaller than in any reaction-time experiments hitherto published. We have, for example, measured ten successive reaction-times, as follows: 102, 102, 100, 100, 100, 100, 100, 100, 101, 100σ. We have in this series a mean variation or variable error of 0.7σ, which of course includes the error of the apparatus, with which readings are only made to thousandths of a second. Such experiments certainly demonstrate great constancy in complex physiological processes, the variable error comparing favorably with that of many physical measurements.

We used three methods for applying the blow, the last of which was much the best. We shall, however, describe briefly our earlier experiments, as the methods might prove useful in clinical work when the greatest accuracy is not necessary. In our first experiments we tied telegraphic keys to the limb. These were adjusted so that a surface about 10 mm. across touched the spot. When the arm of the key was hit with a hammer the circuit was broken, and at the same time the knob was forced against the skin. In this case a contact was broken, not closed, and the chronoscope was started by means of a secondary circuit. The current could pass either through the contact of the key or the coils of the electro-magnet of the chronoscope. As the resistance in the chronoscope is great, the current would pass almost exclusively through the key, but when the contact at the key was broken the current would go to the chronoscope and start the hands. In this case a secondary current must also be used in regulating the chronoscope by means of the gravity chronometer.

The keys were applied on the lower and upper arm at the points A and D, and three intensities were used—a gentle pressure, a medium blow, and a hard blow. The gentle pressure was barely perceptible, as the surface was always in contact with the skin. The results of 2,400 reactions, ten being made in succession at intervals of two seconds, are given in Table IX.

TABLE IX.—PRESSURE STRONG, MEDIUM, AND WEAK. POINTS A AND D. J AND C
OBSERVERS. 2,400 REACTIONS

		First set		Second set		Av.
		A	D	A	D	
	Strong.....	114.9 *5.4*	106.2 *4.8*	120.5 *7*	109.9 *5.9*	**112.9** *5.8*
J	Medium...	121.2 *3.6*	116.3 *6.7*	121.7 *7.2*	119.8 *4.1*	**119.7** *5.4*
	Weak......	152.5 *8.6*	139.6 *11.7*	161.9 *7*	148.7 *7.7*	**150.7** *8.7*
	Av........	**129.5** *5.9*	**120.7** *7.7*	**134.7** *7.1*	**126.1** *5.9*	**127.8** *6.6*
	Strong.....	110.6 *4.9*	105.7 *3.4*	118.3 *4.6*	112.5 *7.4*	**111.8** *5.1*
C	Medium...	109.9 *4.8*	114.9 *7.3*	117.8 *8.9*	116.6 *4*	**114.8** *6.2*
	Weak......	145.8 *7.4*	142.7 *4.7*	153.1 *6.5*	141.4 *6.3*	**145.7** *6.2*
	Av........	**122.1** *5.7*	**121.1** *5.1*	**129.7** *6.7*	**123.4** *5.9*	**124.1** *5.8*
	Av., Av....	**125.8** *5.8*	**120.9** *6.4*	**132.2** *6.9*	**124.7** *5.9*	**125.9** *6.2*

It is evident that the reactions on the weakest pressures are long, the sensation being near the threshold. In this case the reaction is always long, as the brain centers can not be held in a state of unstable equilibrium, lest the motor impulses be [1σ] prematurely discharged. The time was for J 6.8σ, and for C 3σ, shorter for a strong blow than for a medium blow. The strong blow was just less than painful, but the intensities could not be measured, nor were the blows exactly constant. The differences in time for D and A were fairly constant, being shorter for the point nearer the brain. In the two sets the differences were for J 8.8σ and 8.6σ, and for C 1σ and 6.3σ; but in view of our other experiments, and for reasons already given, we can not regard these differences as the time of transmission in the median nerve.

In order to keep the force of the blow constant and to avoid a continual pressure on the point of application we devised a second method, which can be recommended for anthropmetric and clinical work. We placed thin tin foil over the part of the limb to be stimulated, and this was connected with one wire of the circuit. Then we allowed a hammer to fall on the tin foil. The surface of the hammer which struck the foil was 10 mm. across, and was connected with the other wire of the circuit. Consequently when the hammer struck the foil the blow was given and the circuit closed. The hammer swung in points and fell from a height of 15 cm., the blow thus being constant. The arm was held in position by being placed in a wooden case, and the blow applied to the back or outside of the arm on points E and F, nearly opposite the points B and D. The back of the arm was used because it could be struck by the hammer when placed in an unstrained position.

TABLE X.—REACTION-TIMES ON BLOWS. J AND C OBSERVERS. 800 REACTIONS

	E	F		E	F
J............	120.1 *6.9*	126.5 *5.9*	C..........	104.9 *4*	121.3 *6.8*
	112.5 *4.5*	119.3 *4.7*		113.6 *4.8*	128 *4.9*
Av..........	**116.3** *5.7*	**122.9** *5.3*	Av..........	**109.2** *4.4*	**124.6** *5.8*

In these experiments the reaction-time was shorter (for J 6.6σ, for C 15.4σ) when the blow was applied nearer the wrist than when it was applied to the upper arm, exactly the opposite of what was found on the opposite side of the arm. The shorter reaction-time with the lower point was due to the fact that the blow was given over the bone, and was much stronger than when the same blow was given in the muscle of the upper arm.

In order to avoid the tin foil over the skin and the rebound (which would break the circuit) we devised a hammer which worked in a very satisfactory manner. In its final form the instrument is shown in fig. 7.

The hammer swings in points, and is held up by the electro-magnet M. This magnet can be placed at any height, and the velocity of the blow can thus be altered. In our experiments the hammer fell a perpendicular distance of 20 cm. The area of the surface giving the blow can also be altered, but in our experiments it was always circular, 10 mm. across, the edge being slightly rounded. The arm of the hammer (25 cm. in length from the points to the center of the area with which the blow was given) is a very light aluminium tube, and the weight is almost exclusively in the hammer at the point where the blow is given. The weight of the hammer can be adjusted by means of weights which are screwed on the tip. In our experiments the weights (the hammer being in its points) were 15, 30, and 60 grams, and the force of blow was proportional to these weights. Sixty grams falling 20 cm. gave a sensation which was just short of painful when the blow was on a part of the body in which the skin is close to the bone.[1]

The current was closed when the blow was given by means of the contact shown in the figure. A small platinum spring makes the contact at almost exactly the instant the blow is given, and the current remains closed until the larger spring is released.

With this hammer we gave stimuli on various parts of the body and measured the time of reaction. It was necessary to place the part of the body in a horizontal position, and this was done and the part supported by simple devices. Thus the arm was placed comfortably in a padded wooden box and the base of the hammer could be swung around so that the blows could be given successively on the lower and upper arm without moving the arm. The points used were the back of the lower and upper arm (E and F, opposite the points B and D, fig. 7), at a distance of 30 cm., the lower and upper parts of the thigh (G and H, the front of the leg, but anatomically corresponding to the back of the arm) at a distance of 25 cm., the back of the second joint of the left forefinger (I) and of the left great toe (J), the cheek (K) below the zygoma about 2 cm. from the base of the concha of the ear, and the back of the neck (L) over the second spinal process. Reactions were also made with the hand and foot, the stimulus being applied on the forefinger. The experiments were made in

---

[1] With this instrument experiments are now in progress in the psychological laboratory of Columbia College which should yield interesting results. The accuracy of discrimination is measured with blows of varying force (Weber's law) and the correlation of velocity, mass and area determined (e.g., is the sensation the same when the velocity is 1 and the mass 2 as when the mass is 1 and the velocity 2).

sets, *E* and *F*, *G* and *H*, *I* and *J*, *K* and *L*, and the movement with foot and hand, respectively, being made simultaneously. Experiments made simultaneously and under the same conditions can be best compared, but our times were found to vary but little from day to day. In these experiments the objective force of the blow was always the same (a weight of 30 grams falling 20 cm.). The reactions were measured singly, the variations of the separate times from the average time of the series and of the separate series from the average time of the set both being given.

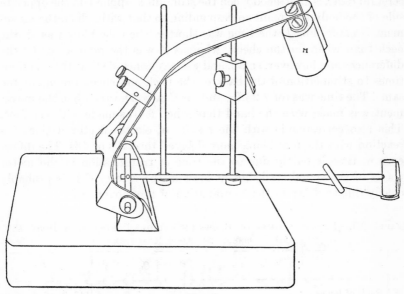

Fᴵɢ. 7.

The reaction-times were shorter than when the same points on the skin were electrically stimulated, and the mean variations of the separate reactions and of the series are less. An exact comparison can not be made, as the experiments on touch and electrical stimulation were not made simultaneously; but we may conclude that the reaction-time on touch is about 10σ shorter than on electrical stimulation. The mean variations are smaller than any hitherto published, although we have omitted no measurements in calculating the averages. As in the case of electrical stimulation, the reaction-times of *J* and *C* are nearly the same, those of *D* being about 30 per cent longer.

In the case of *C* the shortest reactions followed stimulation of the forefinger or cheek. The two sets on the forefinger made at different times agree closely (105.5σ and 106.1σ). The times for the upper and lower arm and for the upper and lower thigh, respectively, are practically the same in all cases. The differences on the arm are: J 1.4σ, and C 0.8σ, the times being shorter on the lower point. On the thigh the time for the upper point was 0.6σ shorter for D, and 0.8σ longer for C. As in the case of electrical stimulation, we are unable to determine the velocity in the sensory nerve. The time of transmission is in this case exactly counterbalanced by a shorter cerebral reflex for the lower point. In the case of C the time is about 10σ shorter when the forefinger is stimulated than when the arm is stimulated, and about 1σ shorter for the toe than for the thigh. As before, we find that the cerebral reflex is shortened when the stimulus is applied on the opposite side of the body to a point corresponding to that with which the movement is made. For D the time was shorter when the blow was on the neck than when on the cheek, whereas it was the reverse for C; the differences are, however, small, and we may conclude that the reaction-times to stimulation of the back of the neck and cheek are about the same. The time was for J 26.7σ, and for C 62.8σ shorter when the movement was made with the hand than when it was made with the foot. This also corresponds with the results of electrical stimulation, C's reaction with the foot being more delayed than J's or D's. The difference in time is partly due to the time of transmission in the motor tracts of the spinal cord, but at least in the case of C it is probably chiefly due to delay in the coordination of the movement.

TABLE XI.—REACTION-TIMES ON BLOWS ON VARIOUS PARTS OF THE BODY. D, C AND J OBSERVERS. 2,000 REACTIONS

		D			C			J		
E	Back of lower arm..	....			115	6.9	(7.4)	113.3	9.5	(6.3)
F	Back of upper arm..	....			115.8	8	(5.4)	114.7	9.8	(4.3)
G	Front of lower thigh	147.1	11.6	(4.6)	121.4	7.8	(4.3)			
H	Front of upper thigh	146.5	11.1	(5.2)	122.2	7.5	(3.7)			
I	Back of second joint of forefinger.......	137.3	10.5	(5.3)	105.5	6.6	(3.5)			
J	Back of second joint of big toe.........	160.7	13.9	(6.6)	120.8	7.3	(2.7)			
K	Cheek............	130.2	10.8	(4.9)	103.1	5.9	(2.7)			
L	Back of neck......	122.1	9.7	(7.4)	110.3	7.5	(3.1)			
I	Second joint of fore-finger R with hand.	....			106.1	5.7	(2.5)	110.6	7.2	(3)
I	Second joint of fore-finger R with foot..	....			168.9	10.6	(5.8)	147.3	11	(3.7)

With the falling hammer we also made reactions in which the force of the blow was varied. In the experiments described above on electrical stimulation and on touch and in researches hitherto published[1] on the relation between the intensity of the stimulus and the length of the reaction-time, the intensity has not been measured. In this case we were able to measure exactly the force of the blow. The hammer always fell 20 cm., and the weight was 60, 30, or 15 grams. The blow from the heaviest weight was just less than painful; from the lightest it was still quite strong. The points E and F on the arm and G and H on the thigh were used. The sets, with 30 grams stimulus, are the same as those given in the preceding table.

The reaction-time thus becomes shorter as the intensity of the stimulus is increased, but the difference in time is small so long as the stimuli are moderately strong. The difference is, indeed, so small that it is obscured by the error of observation, but in the final average of the two thousand four hundred reactions the time was decreased 1.3 when the intensity was increased from 15 to 30 grams, and decreased 1.7 when the intensity was increased from 30 to 60 grams. If, as Fechner's law assumes, the intensity of sensation increases as the logarithm of the stimulus, the reaction time would tend to decrease inversely as the intensity of sensation.

In the table we have a large number of experiments in which the points E and F, and G and H were stimulated by blows objectively alike. The differences with reference to the upper points are, on the arm for J, -1.2, $+1.4$, -0.7σ; for C, -0.6, $+0.8$, $+1.6\sigma$; on the leg for D, -5.2, -0.6, $+1.1\sigma$; for C, -0.1, $+0.8$, and -1.0σ. Considering the small unit of time in which the differences are given, the variations are strikingly small, and show how completely the variable error of reaction-times may be eliminated. There is no doubt but that we have to a thousandth of a second the reaction-time under the conditions employed, and that the reaction-time is the same when the stimulus is applied to the upper and lower arm or the upper and lower thigh. Unless it is very short the time of transmission in the nerve is not counterbalanced by greater intensity of stimulus on the lower points, for doubling the stimulus shortens the reaction by only 1.5σ, and the differences in sensation were not so great on the different points as on the same point when the stimulus was doubled. The time of transmission in the nerve seems to be counterbalanced by a shorter cerebral time when the stimulus is applied to a point farther from the brain, the sensory fibers from a point nearer the extremities discharging more quickly into the motor fibers to the extremities.

---

[1] Excepting that on light by Berger and Cattell. Bryan also reported experiments at the meeting of the American Psychological Association (1892) in which the intensity of sounds was measured, and obtained results corresponding to those here given.

TABLE XII.—REACTION-TIMES ON BLOWS OF VARYING INTENSITY. LOWER AND UPPER ARM AND LOWER AND UPPER THIGH. D, C AND J OBSERVERS. 2,400 REACTIONS

		E	F	G	H	Av.
D	Intensity 15	......	......	151.6 12 (7.1)	146.4 10.7 (6.8)	148.9 11.3 (6.9)
	Intensity 30	......	......	147.1 11.6 (4.6)	146.5 11.1 (5.2)	146.9 11.3 (4.9)
	Intensity 60	......	......	147.9 11.8 (7)	149 11.2 (7.4)	148.4 11.5 (7.2)
	Av.	......	......	148.9 11.8 (6.2)	147.3 11 (6.5)	148 11.4 (6.3)
C	Intensity 15	115 6.6 (8.2)	114.4 7.5 (17.2)	122.2 6.1 (4.6)	122.1 6.3 (3.8)	118.4 6.6 (5.9)
	Intensity 30	115 6.9 (7.4)	115.8 8 (5.4)	121.4 7.8 (4.3)	122.2 7.5 (3.7)	118.6 7.6 (5.2)
	Intensity 60	110.8 6.6 (7.1)	112.4 6.6 (6.2)	121.3 6.3 (5.3)	120.3 6.3 (4)	116.2 6.5 (5.6)
	Av.	113.6 6.7 (7.6)	114.2 7.4 (6.3)	121.6 6.7 (4.7)	121.5 6.7 (3.8)	117.7 6.9 (5.6)
J	Intensity 15	119.3 10.1 (6.1)	118.1 11.7 (5.1)			118.7 10.9 (5.6)
	Intensity 30	113.3 9.5 (6.3)	114.7 9.8 (4.3)			114 9.6 (5.3)
	Intensity 60	111.8 8.8 (4.6)	111.1 9.6 (3.9)			111.4 9.2 (4.2)
	Av.	114.8 9.5 (5.7)	114.6 10.4 (4.4)			114.7 9.9 (5)
	Av., Av.	114.2 8.1 (6.6)	114.4 9 (5.3)	135.2 9.2 (5.4)	134.4 8.8 (5.1)	124.5 8.8 (5.6)

While we do not think that the velocity in the plain nerve can be measured by the difference in reaction-time, we believe that a general survey of our experiments indicate that the velocity is greater than that commonly accepted—30 meters per second. When the reaction is from hand to hand the whole time may be 100σ, and the distance traveled in sensory and motor nerves must be in the neighborhood of 2 meters. It is not likely that two-thirds of the time is taken up in transmission and only one-third in the cerebral reflex. If so, the time from cheek to mouth would scarcely be longer than from hand to hand. Again, our experiments show that the cerebral reflex is almost certainly slower when the leg is stimulated than when the arm is stimulated, the movement being made with the hand, but the difference in time of the entire reaction is much too small to allow for a rate of 30 meters per second in the nerve. We do not think the difficulties in the way of determining the velocity in the nerve are obviated by electrically stimulating the motor nerve, as here the difference in time may depend on the point stimulated rather than on the rate of transmission. Indeed, our experiments show conclusively that the differences which von Helmholtz found—velocities twice as great in summer as in winter—are out of the question. And we do not in the least know the relation between movements due to electrical stimulation and such as are due to normal cerebral discharge. It would seem that the velocity of the nervous impulse in the plain nerve can not be measured until we are able to record its progress, as by electrical or chemical changes;[1] but more light may be thrown on the process by studying the variation of the cerebral processes with the part of the body stimulated.

In the table we have six cases on C in which the arm and leg, respectively, were stimulated, but the experiments were not made simultaneously. The times were always shorter for the arm 7.2, 6.4, 10.5, 7.8, 6.4, and 7.9—an average of 7.7σ. We do not know why this time should be so much shorter than in the case of electrical stimulation. We have every reason to suppose that the cerebral reflex is slower when the leg is stimulated, and 7.7σ should be the maximum time of transmission between the lumbar and brachial parts of the spinal cord. This would give a velocity of about 40 meters per second in the sensory tracts of the cord.

[1] We do not even know whether or not the velocity is uniform.

13

CHRONOSCOPE AND CHRONOGRAPH

Printed in *Philosophische Studien*, **9**: 307–310, 1894, as "Chronoskop und Chronograph." It was translated into English by R. S. Woodworth for inclusion in this volume.

In my review (*American Journal of Psychology*, 1891–1892 4, 596–597) of an article of Külpe and Kirschmann (*Philosophische Studien*, 1893 8, 145–172) I noted that the fall hammer described by these authors, when tested by aid of the Wundt chronograph, showed a variable error of 1.04σ, and that the Hipp chronoscope showed essentially the same variable error when tested by aid of the fall hammer. I drew the conclusion that the variable error was the same for the chronograph and for the chronoscope. In Wundt's reply to this review of mine ("Chronograph und Chronoscop, Notiz zu einer Bemerkung J. M. Cattell's," *Philosophische Studien*, 1893 8, 653–654) he has objected that I have confused the testing of the control hammer with that of the chronograph. I do not think this is the case. When the hammer is tested by aid of the chronograph, the resulting variable error is to be charged partly to the account of the hammer and partly to that of the chronograph; it is indeed the square root of the sums of the squares of the two single variations. If therefore the variable error of the chronograph is denoted by g, and that of the hammer by h, the obtained result is that

$$\sqrt{g^2 + h^2} = 1.04\sigma$$

If, further, the variable error of the chronoscope is denoted by s, the result obtained on testing it by aid of the hammer is, similarly,

$$\sqrt{s^2 + h^2} = 1.05\sigma$$

Since the probable errors of the measures 1.04σ and 1.05σ are greater than their difference of 0.01σ, it is proper to place

$$\sqrt{g^2 + h^2} = \sqrt{s^2 + h^2},$$

and since h is the same in both cases, it follows that

$$g = s$$

That is, the variable error (and the probable error) is equal for the chronoscope and for the chronograph.

In the preceding case the chronograph and chronoscope were tested for the same 10 intervals, ranging from 616 down to 56.6σ, and these are the times which occur most frequently in psychological experiments. We do not know the variable error of either the chronoscope or the chronograph; we only know that it is approximately the same for both and probably less than 1σ. The variable error of the chronograph would naturally be smaller in measuring a time of 10σ than in measuring longer times, but it cannot be used for the purpose of comparing the accuracy of the two instruments in cases where both can be used. As a matter of fact Lange's tests (*Philosophische Studien*, 1888 4, 457–470) did not really reveal the probable error of the chronograph in measuring a time of 10σ; what they did reveal was the probable error of the constant error in registering the time by use of the two magnets.

I take this opportunity of examining the question, which form of chronoscope regulator is the more advantageous: a falling screen such as I first used (*Philosophische Studien*, 1886 3, 305–335); or a fall hammer, as used by Berger and me (Berger, *Philosophische Studien*, 1886 3, 38–82) and later by Lange (*Philosophische Studien*, 1888 4, 479–510) and as recommended, in an enlarged model, by Külpe and Kirschmann (l.c.) and by Wundt (*Philosophische Studien*, 1893 8, 653–654). The fall screen used by me in Leipzig, together with the chronoscope, had a variable error of < 2σ and were found to be more exact and convenient than the hammer which had already been employed in the Psychological Institute for other purposes. When Lange later, after making certain modifications in the hammer, recommended it highly, I had Krille construct one for me, but I found it quite unsatisfactory—its error was comparatively large, it was always getting out of order, and the absolute falling time could not be precisely determined. Other users in this country had similar experiences, and Martius (*Philosophische Studien*, 1891 6, 167–216) employed the hammer for control of the chronoscope without knowing the times for hammer and chronoscope. I then ordered an improved fall screen from Krille. Külpe and Kirschmann (l.c.) report that they have tested this instrument and found for it a variable error of 2.2σ. This in itself is not a very large error but it must have arisen from either the screen or the chronograph not being quite in order. I found for this screen and the chronoscope combined a variable error slightly under 1σ. So, in 8 successive series of 5 trials each, the variable errors in measuring a normal time of 110σ were as follows:

$$0.8 \quad 0.8 \quad 1.0 \quad 1.2 \quad 0.4 \quad 0.8 \quad 0.8 \quad 0.8\sigma$$

Witmer, the present director of the laboratory of the University of Pennsylvania, which has possession of the instrument in question, reported at the last meeting of the American Psychological Association that the fall screen combined with the chronoscope gave an error under 1σ.

I am now using a new fall chronometer constructed by Clay & Torbensen, Camden, N. J. The side pillars are 2 m. tall and make it possible to measure times up to 600σ. The screen weighs 2 kg. and friction is almost completely removed by wheel bearings. In the use of this regulator both the constant error and the variable error are $<1\sigma$. So, in 3 successive series of 10 trials each (dated June 18, 1892), with a normal time of 100σ, the variable errors were 0.54, 0.64 and 0.56σ. Even this very small variation is to be charged almost wholly to the chronoscope, which can only indicate the single times to the nearest unit of one-thousandth of a second.

I have no doubt that the fall hammer described by Külpe and Kirschmann can serve very well for the regulation of the chronoscope,[1] but I believe that a fall screen is better. Its absolute falling time can be determined without use of a chronograph, it does not easily get out of order, and the same instrument can be used for manifold psychological purposes.

[1] The same can be said for several other chronoscope regulators: for the pendulum described by Witmer at the meeting of the American Psychological Association, for the method employed by Jastrow (*American Journal of Psychology,* 1891–1892 4, 198–223) and by Dessoir (*Archiv für Anatomie und Physiologie,* 1892, 175–339), and also for the fall apparatus furnished by Peyer & Favarger if the positions of the break and make contacts are interchanged.

14

PHYSICAL AND MENTAL MEASUREMENTS OF THE STUDENTS OF COLUMBIA UNIVERSITY

An investigation carried out with the collaboration of Dr. Livingston Farrand and published in *The Psychological Review*, **3**: 618–648, 1896.

Extended measurements have been published of certain traits of soldiers, of school children and of the defective classes, more especially of their height, weight, eyesight and defects of body. Single tests of a psychological character have been made on school children and on groups of adults, and we have the many researches from our psychological laboratories giving the results of experiments on a few individuals. As it is not our object to give a detailed historical sketch[1] of the statistics and experiments hitherto published it will suffice to refer especially to the two undertakings most similar to our own. Mr. Francis Galton recommended in 1882[2] the establishment of anthropometric laboratories, and subsequently carried his plan into effect by placing a laboratory in the South Kensington Museum, London, which was continued until last year, when the apparatus was removed to

[1] There have been at least four series of mental tests proposed in which methods have been discussed without the communication of results: "Mental Tests and Measurements": J. McK. Cattell, with an appendix by Francis Galton, *Mind*, 1890; "Zur Individual Psychologie": Hugo Münsterberg, *Centralblatt f. Nervenheilkunde und Psychiatrie*, 1891; "Der Psychologische Versuch in der Psychiatrie": Emil Kraepelin, *Psychologische Arbeiten*, 1895; and "La Psychologie Individuelle": A. Binet et V. Henri, *L'Année psychologique*, 1896. One of the present writers was perhaps the first (1885 and subsequently) to publish experiments on individual psychology made in the laboratory, its introduction having, probably, been delayed because Professor Wundt was not favorable to it. Recently the individual ariation in some special psycho-physical or mental trait has been frequently ᵛnvestigated. This has been encouraged by Galton in England (to whom we owe ᵗthe method of the *questionnaire*), by Kraepelin in Germany, and by Binet in France, but by far the most numerous contributions to the subject have come from American Laboratories—Harvard, Yale, Clark, Columbia, Princeton, Pennsylvania, Chicago, Cornell, Wisconsin and others. Two papers which describe several tests made on a number of individuals deserve special mention in connection with this paper: "Experimentelle Studien zur Individual Psychologie." A. Oehrn; Dissertation (under Kraepelin), Dorpat, 1889, reprinted with slight alterations, *Psychologische Arbeiten*, 1895; and "Researches on the Mental and Physical Development of School Children": J. A. Gilbert, *Studies from the Yale Laboratory*, 1895, reported also by E. W. Scripture, *Zeitschrift f. Psychologie*, etc., X, 1896, and THE PSYCHOLOGICAL REVIEW, III, 1896.

[2] *Fortnightly Review; cf.* also *Inquiries into Human Faculty*, London, 1883.

the Clarenden Museum, at Oxford. Visitors could there have certain tests made on payment of a small fee. The tests included, in addition to several purely physical measurements, keenness of eyesight and hearing, color-sense and highest audible note, dynamometer pressure, reaction-time and errors in dividing a line and angles. At the World's Columbian Exposition, Chicago, 1893, Professor Joseph Jastrow arranged a psychological laboratory in which a considerable number of tests strictly psychological in character were undertaken.

The early publication of the results obtained by Mr. Galton[1] and by Prof. Jastrow may be expected, but without awaiting these we shall proceed with the description of our work. We are led to do this at the present time more especially because at the Philadelphia meeting of the American Psychological Association (December, 1895), a committee, consisting of Professors Cattell, Baldwin, Jastrow, Sanford and Witmer, was appointed to consider the feasibility of coöperation among the various psychological laboratories in the collection of mental and physical statistics. As a report from this committee is to be expected at the next meeting of the Association, it is desirable that the members have before them such tests as have already been made. It may also be mentioned that at the meeting of the American Association for the Advancement of Science (Buffalo, August, 1896), a standing committee, consisting of Messrs. Brinton, Cattell, McGee, Newell and Boas, was appointed to organize an ethnographic survey of the white race in the United States. It is important that psychological tests be included in this survey, and that the work be coördinated with that proposed by the Psychological Association.

One of the present writers began the collection of physical and mental measurements of students of Cambridge University, the University of Pennsylvania and Bryn Mawr College in 1887-8, and some description of the tests was published in 1890 (op. cit.). The methods have been gradually revised and we shall confine our present account to experiments made on students of Columbia University in 1894-5 and 1895-6. These have been described by Prof. Cattell before the New York Academy of Sciences, May, 1895, and the American Association for the Advancement of Science, August, 1896, and by Dr. Farrand before the American Psychological Association, December, 1895.

Our chief object in the present paper is the description and discussion of methods rather than the communication of results, but we

---

[1] Since the above was written, Mr. Galton has informed one of the writers that the people who came to his laboratory were so mixed that no homogeneous group can be extracted out of them that is both large and interesting. Still it is to be hoped that the large mass of data collected under Mr. Galton's direction will be published.

give the averages secured from 100 students. This is a comparatively small number, but it suffices for our present purposes. For the study of the distribution of variations extended statistics are needed, but in that case it would not be necessary to make a large number of different tests. The average of a group of 100 homogeneous individuals has a relatively small probable error, and suffices to determine the place of the individual in the group and for the comparison of this group with other groups. Differences that can be established as the result of 100 measurements should be investigated before we undertake the study of minor or inconstant deviations. The 100 measurements at our disposal cannot, however, be subdivided, and about 1,000 measurements will be needed in order to arrive at the end we have more especially in view, namely, the study of the development and correlation of mental and physical traits. We want to know how a man who has, for example, a large head, a short reaction-time or a good memory, is likely to vary from the average in other directions, and how likely he is to vary to a certain extent. As in other scientific work these tests have two chief ends, the one genetic, the other quantitative. We wish to study growth as dependent on environment and heredity, and the correlation of traits from the point of view of exact science.

Before proceeding with this difficult undertaking it is necessary to learn what tests are the most typical and useful, and what methods are the best and most feasible. It is important that coöperation be secured in deciding what tests shall be used, and in studying and eliminating the numerous drawbacks and sources of error. We do not regard it as necessary or desirable that each laboratory should undertake the same tests. It would, however, be useful to select a few tests made in exactly the same manner, and for different investigators to undertake to extend the measurements in the direction in which they are most interested.

We give on the following page a reduced (the original sheet apart from the margin is about 23 × 18 cm.) facsimile of the blank used in recording our tests from which their general character may be seen. The tests can only be made individually, one recorder having charge of one student, and, unless the apparatus is duplicated, only three or four records can be made simultaneously. It is consequently essential that the tests should be such that the records can be taken quickly. Our series contains 10 records and 26 measurements (several consisting of from two to five separate determinations), which can be completed in from 40 min. to one hour, varying within these limits according to the skill of the recorder, the intelligence of the student and the degree in which the apparatus is in order.

In selecting the tests, the time required to make them must be especially considered, and some attention should also be paid to the time taken in collating the results. The student would, in nearly all cases, be willing to submit to a longer examination, but this requires a considerable expenditure of time on the part of a skilled observer. Our object has been to form a series that can be made within one hour, and but little can be added to this series without omitting something to make place for it. We suggest below several additional tests of psychological interest, for which time might be found when the series is made under favorable conditions. It might be desirable to place at the end several tests (we have done this in the case of *mental imagery*), which could be made or omitted as time might require. We give below additional observations which can be made by the recorder without

LABORATORY OF PSYCHOLOGY OF COLUMBIA COLLEGE, PHYSICAL AND MENTAL
TESTS

Name_____Date of Birth_____

Birthplace_____of father_____of mother_____

Class_____Profession of father_____

Color of eyes_____of hair_____

Perception of size_____Memory for size_____

Height_____Weight_____

Breathing capacity { 1_____
                    2_____   Size of head_____Right handed?_____

Strength of hand, right { 1_____   Left { 1_____
                          2_____   2_____

Keeness of sight, right eye_____Left_____

Keeness of hearing, right ear_____Left_____

Reaction-time {   1   2   3   4   5   Av.
                 _____
                 _____

After-images_____

Color vision_____Perception of pitch_____

Perception of weight 1____2____3____Sensation areas 1____2____3____4____5____

Sensitiveness to pain { right hand_____
                        left hand_____   Preference for color_____

                        1   2   3

Perception of time_____

Accuracy of movement_____Rate of perception and movement_____

Memory_____

Imagery_____

Are you willing to repeat these tests at the end of the Sophomore and Senior years?_____Do you wish to have a copy of these tests sent you?_____

Date of measurement_____Recorded by_____

much expenditure of time, and a series of questions which can be answered by the student at home.

We fully appreciate the force of the arguments urged by Professor Münsterberg and by MM. Binet and Henri in favor of making tests of a strictly psychological character. For the psychologist these are, of course, the most interesting and important. But we are at present concerned with anthropometric work, and measurements of the body and of the senses come as completely within our scope as the higher mental processes. We can determine in thirty seconds whether or not a man is color-blind, and thus secure a fact of great personal interest to him, and a typical and sharp variation which can be studied in relation to other traits. If we undertake to study attention or suggestibility we find it difficult to measure definitely a definite thing. We have a complex problem still requiring much research in the laboratory and careful analyses before the results can be interpreted, and, indeed, before suitable tests can be devised.

In addition to the writers several graduate students acted as recorders. A large number of records were taken by Mr. Franz, fellow in psychology, and by Mr. Houston, scholar in psychology, and some records were taken by Mr. McWhood, now fellow in psychology, by Mr. Lay, lately fellow in philosophy, by Mr. Schneider, lately fellow in botany, and by Mr. Kingham. All the recorders had had training in making the tests, but it must be remembered that the results depend somewhat on the methods used by the recorder, and it would be desirable to collate the results for the different recorders and to have the same students tested by different recorders, in order to learn what variations may be due to this source. The methods should be, as far as possible, automatic, and it would perhaps be best to let the recorder read written instructions to the student. Still a certain amount of latitude is inevitable, as students vary greatly in the quickness with which they understand what is to be done.

The attempt was made to follow the order given on the blank (except that memory for size was tested at the end), but this could not be done exactly when 2 or 3 students were tested simultaneously. It would, however, be desirable to test all observers in exactly the same order, as some skill is acquired in the course of the experiments. The five rooms of the laboratory were used, and we tried to leave the student alone with the recorder in cases where the test depended on the attention.

We requested the Freshmen of the School of Arts and of the School of Mines to come by appointment. About one-half of them came, and all were interested in the tests and agreed without hesitation to repeat them at the end of the Sophomore and Senior years. The repetition of the tests will be one of the best criteria of their validity, and we hope the results will be of interest in showing the development of the student during his college course, more especially when taken in connection with the nature of his course, his standing in his studies, etc.

The 100 records used were taken alphabetically, none being omitted. They include 60 Freshmen from the School of Arts, 20 Freshmen from the School of Mines and 20 more advanced students. The records were arranged for these groups alphabetically in sets of ten, and the individual variation from the average of each set calculated. Then the average variation of the sets of 10 from the average of the 100 records was taken. We give these two variations in addition to the average, denoting them by v and V, respectively. We have not omitted any record unless it seemed to contain an error on the part of the recorder. In a few cases tests were omitted by accident, and certain of the tests were added the second year, it being found that more could be made within the hour than we had expected. Some of the sets thus contain less than ten records, the total number made in the group being given.

We shall not at present undertake to discuss in detail the distribution of the deviations, or whether the average, or the median, or the limits within which a certain percentage of the records fall, is the best standard. When the records are arranged in small groups the average is most convenient. If an individual varies from the group by an amount not more than the average variation he may be regarded as normal. This would include about one-half of the students. Those coming above may be regarded as hyper-normal and those coming below as sub-normal. The best method of adjusting the observations must be worked out with a larger mass of material than we have as yet at our disposal.

We shall now proceed to the discussion of the separate tests.

Preliminary Data

The student was required to write his own name, the date of his birth, his birthplace and the birthplaces of his parents, the profession of his father, his class and course in college.

Handwriting.—It is desirable to let the student write in ink his own name and the other data. "Graphology" has fallen into disrepute because too much has been asked of it. The handwriting, however, is certainly characteristic of the individual and may prove interesting when collated with the other tests. But we are not prepared to communicate any results based upon our present data.

Age.—The average age of the Freshmen, School of Arts (59 cases), in their first term was 18. The age of our college students has often been discussed and our records are of value only in connection with subsequent tests. It may be worth while to call the attention of those who compare statistics of the age of students to the fact that while there are no students whose age is considerably below the average there are sometimes a few older men in the class. For most purposes it would consequently be better to use the median than the average. There were no men over 23 among the Columbia Freshmen, and it appears that the average age is younger than at Harvard or Yale.

Birthplace.—The nationality was, in percentages (which are also the actual numbers), as follows:

	Student	Father	Mother
North America..............................	**94**	**64**	**81**
New York City..............................	(29)	(10)	(17)
Foreign.......................................	**5**	**34**	**17**
German.....................................	(2)	(20)	(7)
Irish..	(0)	(5)	(2)
English.....................................	(1)	(5)	(2)
Not given....................................	1	2	2

As we have already stated all our data have their chief interest in their correlations with the others, and we shall not be able to work out these relations for some years. It will, for example, be of interest to compare the physical and mental traits of students of American parentage with those of German or of English parentage and to study the effects of heredity and environment. For this purpose it would undoubtedly be desirable to record the nationality of at least the grandparents (see the supplementary set of questions given below). We may, however, call attention to the large percentage of foreign parents, especially of fathers. It is a characteristic sexual difference that twice as many men as women should have emigrated.

The profession of the fathers was as follows:

Business... **56**
Profession... **26**
   Lawyers   (6)
   Physicians   (6)
   Clergymen,   (4)
Farmers.. **3**
No calling.. **1**
Not given.. **14**

A majority of the students of Columbia University come from the business classes, and the father in most cases did not have a college education.

Supplementary Data.—Further details regarding the heredity, interests, habits and condition of the student, such as he himself could give or such as could be secured from the impressions of the recorder would undoubtedly add greatly to the value of these tests. The limitations are due to the need of completing the series within one hour and additional records should not lengthen this time.

We suggest the two following series of records, the first of which should be filled up by the recorder and not seen by the student, while the second blank should be given to the student to be filled up at his convenience at home and returned in an addressed envelope. These series are only provisional, and have not as yet been used by us. We shall, however, use them this year, and should be glad to have suggestions regarding them.

SUPPLEMENTARY OBSERVATIONS BY THE RECORDER
[To be filled in while the student is writing his name]

What is his apparent age? (   ), 17 (   ), 18 (   ), 19 (   ), 20 (   ), (   ).
Is his apparent state of health good (   ), medium (   ), poor (   )?
Is he tall (   ), medium (   ), short (   )?
Is his head large (   ), medium (   ), small (   )?
Do you think his physical development good (   ), medium (   ), poor (   )?
Do you think him likely to be as a student good (   ), medium (   ), poor (   )?
In these mental tests do you think him likely to be good (   ), medium (   ), poor (   )?

[To be filled in during or after the tests]

Hair: dark (   ), medium (   ), light (   )?
Complexion: dark (   ), medium (   ), light (   )?
Complexion: clear (   ), medium (   ), blotched (   )?
Eyes: dark (   ), medium (   ), light (   )?
Hair: straight (   ), wavy (   ), curly (   )?
Nose: convex (   ), straight (   ), concave (   )?
Elevation of nose: high (   ), medium (   ), low (   )?
Ears: large (   ), medium (   ), small (   )?
Ears: projecting (   ), medium (   ), close (   )?
Mouth: large (   ), medium (   ), small (   )?
Lips: thick (   ), medium (   ), thin (   ).
Hands: (in relation to size of body,) large (   ), medium (   ), small (   )?
Fingers: (in relation to width of hand), long (   ), medium (   ), short (   )?
Face and Head: note symmetry or asymmetry, also any abnormality as malformation of ears, squint, etc.

[To be filled in after the tests have been completed. The recorder is expected to use any suggestions that he may obtain from having made the records, but not to examine these with a view to using the information.]

Do you think his state of health good (   ), medium (   ), poor (   )?
Do you think his physical development good (   ), medium (   ), poor (   )?
Do you think him likely to be as a student good (   ), medium (   ), poor (   )?
Do you think that in the mental tests he has done well (   ), fairly (   ), poorly (   )?
In understanding what was wanted, was he quick (   ), medium (   ), slow (   )?

Was he talkative ( ), medium ( ), quiet ( )?
Do you judge him to be accurate ( ), medium ( ) not accurate ( )?
Do you judge him to be straightforward ( ), medium ( ), not straightforward ( )?
Do you judge him to be intellectual ( ), medium ( ), not intellectual ( )?
Do you judge his will to be strong ( ), medium ( ), weak ( )?
Do you judge his emotions to be strong ( ), medium ( ), weak ( )?
Would you call him well-balanced ( ), medium ( ), not well-balanced ( )?
Would you call his temperament choleric ( ), sanguine ( ), melancholic ( ), phlegmatic ( )?
Name_____
Recorded by_____
Date_____

SUPPLEMENTARY DATA TO BE FILLED IN BY THE STUDENT
[Place a check (✓) in the proper parenthesis; use a question mark (?) when you are unable to answer a question or would prefer not to do so. If you can only answer a question approximately do so and add *ca.*]

	Father	Mother	Paternal grand-father	Paternal grand-mother	Maternal grand-father	Maternal grand-mother
Living? (if so, give age), Deceased? (if so, give year of death and age at time of death)....						
Cause of death, if deceased..............						
Most serious diseases from which they have suffered.............						

	1	2	3	4	5	6	Etc.
Your mother's children. born...............							
deceased............							

[Write B for brother and S for sister in the order of age and in the proper column. Include yourself designated by X. After B, S or X write date of birth thus, B. Feb. 10, '84. In case any brothers or sisters have died, write date of death after 'deceased.']

How many brothers did your father have? ( ), how many sisters? ( ), was your father his mother's 1st ( ), 2d ( ), 3d ( ), 4th ( ), 5th ( ), 6th ( ) or what ( ) child?

How many brothers did your mother have? ( ), how many sisters? ( ), was your mother her mother's 1st ( ), 2d ( ), 3d ( ), 4th ( ), 5th ( ), 6th ( ), or what ( ) child?

[In answering questions such as this one, think of the people you know as in three classes equal in number and decide to which class you belong.]

Do you regard your general health as good ( ), medium ( ), not good ( )?

Do you regard your present health as better than usual ( ), same as usual ( ), not as good as usual ( )?

Indicate such of the following diseases as you have had by writing in the parenthesis the approximate age at which you had them: convulsions in childhood ( ), measles ( ), diphtheria ( ), scarlet fever ( ), pneumonia ( ), brain fever (meningitis) ( ), malaria ( ), nervous prostration (neurasthenia) ( ).

Do you have headaches often ( ), seldom ( ), never ( )?

Do you have colds often ( ), seldom ( ), never ( )?

Are your teeth good ( ), medium ( ), poor ( )?

Have you consulted an oculist? ( ), If so, at what age for the first time? ( ), Do you wear glasses? ( ), Give the nature of the defect if you know it. ( ).

How many hours do you usually sleep ( )?

Do you dream much ( ), little ( ), never ( )?

Are your dreams as a rule pleasant ( ), commonplace ( ), fearful ( )?

As a child were you subject to bad dreams which you have since outgrown? ( ).

Is your appetite good ( ), medium ( ), poor ( )?

At what time of day do you feel in the best spirits? ( ).

At what time of day can you study best? ( ).

Do you drink coffee ( ), tea ( )? If so, how many cups daily, coffee ( ), tea ( )? At what age did you begin? ( ).

Do you smoke? ( ). If so, how many pipes ( ), cigars ( ), cigarettes daily ( )? At what age did you begin? ( ).

Do you use alcoholic drinks? ( ). If so, occasionally ( ), daily ( )? If daily, how many glasses of beer ( ), wine ( ), spirits ( )?

About how many hours or minutes daily on the average during the month of October do you spend in study ( ), in reading books other than text and reference books ( ), in playing sedentary games ( ), in playing athletic games ( ), in other physical exercise, as walking, riding a bicycle, etc. ( )?

Do you play a musical instrument? ( ), if so, what one or ones? ( ), how long daily? ( ), what musical instrument do you prefer to hear played? ( ), which opera that you have heard do you prefer? ( ).

What novelist do you prefer? ( ), what poet? ( ), what painter? ( ), what play that you have seen acted? ( ).

Supposing the following ten ways of spending an hour give to you pleasure, write numbers after them in the order of amount of pleasure they give. Eating dinner ( ), playing your favorite athletic game ( ), playing your favorite sedentary game ( ), working with tools as in a garden ( ), reading a novel ( ), hearing music ( ), talking to a friend ( ), day dreaming ( ), learning something ( ), writing something ( )?

What profession or business do you propose to follow? ( ), in what calling would you prefer to succeed if you had your choice? ( ).

Send with this, if possible, your most recent photograph (with date at which it was taken,) and if you have them, or can have them taken, send photographs both in full face and in profile.

Name, (in full)_____

Date of Birth_____Place of Birth_____

Class and Course in College_____

PHYSICAL CHARACTERS

The colors of the hair and of the eyes were recorded with the results given below. The figures are both percentages and actual numbers.

Hair		Eyes	
Black	8	Gray	33
Dark brown	56	Blue	30
Light brown	34	Brown	31
Flaxen	1	Green	1
Red	0	Not given	5
Not given	1		

In making these records it would be well to confine the designations to those given above, and it would be an advantage to have standards by which the recorder could make the comparison.[1] A lock of the hair might be preserved with the record. Unless the recorder has been carefully trained such descriptions do not have great value. The same eyes may be called gray, blue and brown, respectively, by different recorders. In a population so mixed as that of New York City, it is questionable how far these records are of use. If taken at all the description should be made more complete by giving the traits enumerated in the supplementary blank printed above. The finger prints could be taken for purposes of identification.

Height and weight can be measured with comparative ease. We had a Fairbanks' scale with an upright adjustable measuring rod graduated for the metric system. The averages give:

	Av.	v	V
Height in cm	175.1	4.9	1.7
Weight in kg	66.2	6.0	1.7

Both height and weight are above the average of the population and above the averages for the freshmen entering Yale University.

It so happens that the subdivisions of the metric system are not well suited for these measurements. It is not quite accurate enough to measure to kilograms and centimeters, whereas to measure to tenths of these, especially in the case of weight, is needlessly exact. In these measurements the weight was taken in ordinary indoor clothing, and the height of the heel was subtracted. The record should be written, *e.g.*, 162.7 cm. −1.4 cm = 161.3 cm. In some cases the height of the heel was not subtracted, and the average given above is slightly too large.

[1] Such standards are sold by the Cambridge Scientific Instrument Co., but at a very high price.

The size of the head was measured with the *conformateur* used by hatters. This was placed horizontally above the temples, giving approximately the largest horizontal area of the head. The diameters are given below together with the ratio of length to breadth.

	Av.	*v*	*V*
Length in cm........................	19.3	0.5	0.2
Breadth.............................	14.9	0.4	0.1

The measurements are not sufficiently accurate to study growth, but would serve for comparison with the other data. The method has the advantage of being easily carried out and leaving a permanent record. It also measures irregularities in the shape of the head that would not be shown by the perimeter. There is a slight inaccuracy owing to the hair being included in the measurement, and a more serious one in the difficulty of placing the instrument in the proper position. This latter difficulty indeed holds for all measurements of the head which can only be made with exactness by a skillful observer.

On the whole we think the conformateur in its present form is less accurate and (in the subsequent calculations) more troublesome than the perimeter and expect hereafter to use the latter instrument.

The breathing capacity was measured with a fluid spirometer, two tests being taken, the averages in liters (98 cases):

	Av.	*v*	*V*
Capacity in liters..................	3.73	0.45	0.19

In a determination such as this it is desirable to take two records, as one, especially the first, is sometimes faulty. We think it best to record both measurements, but to use not the average, but the maximum. The averages of the maxima are:

	Av.	*v*	*V*
Capacity in liters..................	3.83	0.41	0.19

The maximum of the two trials is thus 0.1 liter greater than the average. If time permit it would be desirable to continue a test such as this until the maximum has been reached. If on a sufficient number of observers a larger series of trials were made we could determine how likely it is that the maximum be reached in the first trial, the first two trials, etc.

In addition to these measurements Mr. Galton proposes taking the span of the arms, the height sitting, the height to the top of the knee, the length from elbow to finger-tip and the length of the middle finger of the left hand. These measurements would probably prove useful for purposes of identification, but do not seem otherwise advisable unless a more thorough physical examination is undertaken than that proposed by Mr. Galton.

It would indeed be highly desirable to make a thorough physical examination, but for this purpose the recorder would need some special training. The most important tests would be of heart (including pulse tracing), lungs (including rate and tracing of breathing), temperature and urine which could be made in a few minutes by a practiced physician. There are many other physical data, such as deformities, peculiarities, stigmata, tendon reflexes, etc., which it would be desirable to have, and we may hope that coöperation between physicians, students of criminology and of the defective classes and those interested in anthropometry may be obtained to select the most important determinations and devise the best means for carrying them out.

VISION

Color blindness was tested by letting the observer select the four green shades from the woolen skeins supplied by the Cambridge Scientific Instrument Company in accordance with Mr. Galton's instructions. Three per cent of those tested (71 cases) were color blind and three per cent appeared to have defective color vision.

The method of selecting colors suffices to show whether or not color vision is normal, if the recorder have sufficient skill to note hesitation on the part of the student. In the case of those color blind or having defective color vision it would of course be desirable to investigate more carefully the nature of the defect.

The Galton instrument is needlessly expensive, as the yarns could be matched for a few cents. If the instrument is used the four pointers should be removed, as the observer should not know that he is expected to find just four shades of green.

Keenness of sight was tested with Mr. Galton's instrument. This gives the distance in cm. at which diamond numerals can be read by each eye singly. We made the test in a room lit only by an electric lamp of 100 candles at a distance of 1 m. from the type. We determined the distance at which at least 8 letters out of 10 could be correctly read, making sure that all letters could be read on the card one step nearer. The percentages (94 cases) for the different distances and for each eye are:

Distance in cm.	Right eye	Left eye
72	1.06%	2.02%
61	29.9	16.00
52	26.6	29.80
44	18.09	31.99
37	10.64	7.49
31	6.38	7.49
26	3.19	3.19
22	1.06	0.
19	1.06	0.
16	2.02	2.02

The right eye is thus better than the left, the "normal" for the right eye being a distance of about 52–61 cm., and for the left eye of 44–52 cm., or a little more.

It is perhaps a needless precaution to use a dark room and standard illumination, but we have found great variations when test-types are illuminated by ordinary daylight. Test-types of varying size at a distance of 5 or 6 m. will do as well as small type at varying distances, but it is easier to have a selection of lines in small type than in large and to expose them for a fairly constant time while the observer is in ignorance of their nature. The tests used by oculists are as a rule defective from a scientific standpoint. The near as well as the far limit ought perhaps to be taken and astigmatism tested.

The test in any case is not very exact, but perhaps as good as any that can be made quickly. It would however, be desirable to compare various methods, such as counting dots placed at a distance, or drawing a series of figures, and determine which gives the most accurate results in the least time. The test requires atropin to be accurate and an objective examination of the eye such as can only be carried out by a skilled oculist. It is, however, a great advantage for the student to know whether his eyesight is normal, sub-normal or abnormal, and, if desired, a more careful determination of the nature and amount of the defect can be made either in the laboratory or in the office of an oculist.

The least light visible cannot be readily measured owing to the variations accompanying adaptation; and the least noticeable difference in intensity cannot be measured quickly. A series of shades of gray nearly alike can, however, be sorted by the observer on the plan recommended by Mr. Galton for weights. We must, however, admit that the least noticeable difference in intensity cannot be determined in two or three minutes, and that vision is one of the most difficult senses to test.

Preference for color was tested by showing rectangles (about 5 × 3 cm., the "golden mean") of the following colors in irregular order on a black field and asking the student which he liked best. The preferences (66 cases) were as follows:

Blue, 34.9%; red, 22.7; violet, 12.1; yellow, 7.5; green, 6.1; white, 6.1; no preference, 10.6.

The student was asked to define his degree of preference, in four grades, but our data are not sufficient to warrant a discussion of the results.

HEARING

Hearing was tested by determining the distance at which the ticking of the laboratory stop-watch could be heard with each ear singly. The results (86 cases) were in percentages:

	Normal	Subnormal	Abnormal
Right ear..........................	86	13	1
Left ear............................	84	13	3

We did not undertake to measure sharpness of hearing exactly as the laboratory was too noisy. There is unfortunately no good method for measuring the intensity of a faint sound, and one cannot do much more than determine whether the hearing is normal, sub-normal or abnormal.

The accuracy of the perception of pitch was determined by giving twice on a monochord the *f* below the middle *c*, the observer being required to find the sound by adjusting the bridge which had been in the meanwhile shifted (which should have been done to about *c'*). The average variation (48 cases) was 7.5 cm. (*v*, 5.9; *V*, 1.9) or nearly one whole tone. Of those tested 10% could adjust the monochord within about ⅒ tone, 61% came between ⅒ and one tone, and 29% had a greater error.

The observer was not allowed to hum the tone. Perhaps a simpler method would be to strike a key on the piano and let the observer find it. In this case three notes could be struck—high, middle and low. The highest audible note is probably a good test and one not difficult to make.

DERMAL AND MUSCULAR SENSATIONS

Sensation areas were determined by using an aesthesiometer in which the points were 2 cm. apart, the instrument being applied longitudinally on the back of the left hand between the tendons of the fingers. Five tests were made, the subject being touched with one or two points in the order, "two, two, one, one, two" and being required to decide in each case whether he were touched with one or with two points. The percentages of the men (49) who were correct a given number of times is as follows:

Correct	5 times	16 per cent
Correct	4 times	38 per cent
Correct	3 times	20 per cent
Correct	2 times	22 per cent
Correct	1 time	2 per cent
Correct	0 times	2 per cent

The answers were correct in 67% of all the trials, and were correct in 60% of the cases with two points, and in 75% of the cases with one point. It is difficult to determine sensation areas exactly, as there are many sources of error, both in the decision of the student and the way in which the points are applied by the recorder. Perhaps a method of equivalents in which, say, the observer were touched by points 5 cm. apart, and were then required to indicate the distance on the skin, or were touched and required to touch as nearly as possible the same point, would give more satisfactory results. The data given above determine the sensitiveness of the group, but not of the individual.

The perception of the force of movement was measured by letting the observer make with a dynamometer two pulls in succession as nearly as possible alike, and measuring his error. He was instructed how to make a pull about 4 kg. in strength, and then required to make three pairs of pulls. The average error, from the average of the differences in the three pairs of pulls, was (48 cases):

	Av.	v	V
Error in kg....................	0.63	0.45	0.12

The method of average error always gives results more quickly than the method of right and wrong cases, and it is consequently an advantage to use a dynamometer rather than weights for this test. It is not possible to determine the least perceptible difference in weight by lifting two weights without a large number of experiments. A series of, say, five weights differing by small increments can be arranged in order as suggested by Mr. Galton. In this case, however, it is difficult to find the series that can be just arranged correctly, or to calculate the probable error from the mistakes.

Sensitiveness to pain was determined for the ball of the thumb of the right and left hands. An algometer was used in which the surface applied was of rubber 1 cm. in diameter and rounded at the corners. The instrument was applied with gradually increasing pressure by the student himself or by the recorder (it should be done always by the recorder to secure exactly comparable results), and the student was told to say as soon as the pressure became disagreeable. If he showed signs of discomfort the pressure was stopped. Two tests were made on each hand in alternation, beginning with the right hand. The averages (95 cases) are as follows:

PRESSURE IN KG.

	Av.	v	V
Right Hand...................	6.90	2.90	0.96
Left Hand....................	6.70	2.64	0.94

The strength of the right and left hands was measured with the ordinary oval dynamometer. Two tests were made with each hand in alternation, beginning with the right hand. The averages (99 cases) of the two trials with each hand are as follows:

STRENGTH IN KG.

	Av.	v	V
Right Hand...................	38.8	5.7	2.4
Left Hand....................	34.6	5.3	2.6

In this test it would save time to make two trials and use the maximum. The dynamometers ordinarily sold are not very accurate, and the amount of pressure measured depends largely on how the instrument is held. We believe the maximum pressure of the thumb and forefinger would be a better test if it could be generally introduced.

Accuracy of movement and tremor were measured by allowing the observer to join two points distant 10 cm., the line being drawn as straight as possible with the free and unsupported hand. The observer was shown at about what rate the movement should be made, the line being drawn in about two seconds. A calculation of the results quantitatively would require much labor, but they could be readily classed for comparison with the other data. Three or five classes could be used, say: straight, medium or crooked; and tremor, much, medium or little.

We think it desirable to add at least one further test of movement and fatigue, and expect this year to try the following: Let the observer make with a spring dynamometer maximum contractions of the thumb and forefinger as rapidly as possible for fifteen seconds. The rate and force of the movements must be recorded on a kymograph. A dynamogenetic test might be added by giving, say, at the end a loud sound and determining its effects on the curve. This experiment would require expensive and complicated apparatus, but there is no special objection to using such apparatus so long as the test itself can be easily and quickly made. The trial should be made with both right and left hands, and perhaps twice, the second record only being used. This determination would make the ordinary dynamometer test unnecessary, except for purposes of comparison.

Professor Jastrow includes a number of other tests on movement. The number of movements that can be made in 15 seconds is a good test, though we think that the one recommended above is better. It can be carried out by tapping a telegraph key and recording the taps on a kymograph. The counting instrument which records the number of pressures made could be used. It is cheap and does get out of order, but the amount of pressure is a variable factor.

The maximum rate of movement is also a valuable test and one easily made after the apparatus is in order. The accuracy with which a movement of given extent can be repeated may be measured, as also the accuracy with which movements can be made in different directions and with the right and left hands. Tremor and involuntary movement can be recorded with the planchette, and the whole field of dynamogenesis offers opportunity for interesting tests if time permit.

Time Measurements

The reaction-time for sound was measured 5 times in succession with the Hipp chronoscope giving the following results (97 cases):

Time in σ

	Av.	v	V
Reaction-time	174 ($v = 29^1$)	30	13

1 This variation is the average of the variations of the five reactions made by each observer. In several cases five valid reactions were not recorded.

It is possible that more regular and typical results might be secured if, in place of a sound for stimulus, an electric shock were applied to the fingers with which the reaction is made. Sound is, however, better than light. We do not regard it as desirable to use several senses when time is limited. We believe that the Hipp chronoscope is the most convenient instrument for measuring reaction-times. When once in order it can be used by anyone, and the times are written immediately on the record blank. But the method is immaterial, as it would suffice to measure the times to 0.01 sec. For the well fitted laboratory nothing more suitable than the Hipp chronoscope (in the form in which we use it) can be wanted, but there is urgent need of a simple and portable instrument that will measure times to 0.01 sec. In measuring the reaction-times of an unskilled subject it is not desirable to place him in a separate room, as he must be watched and instructed by the recorder, but a screen should be used to hide the apparatus.

The observer was told to lift (not press, which is a slower and more complex movement) his fingers as quickly as possible after the occurrence of the noise, and was allowed to direct his attention as he found most convenient. It might be desirable to ask the observer after the experiments have been completed as to the direction of attention, but it would scarcely be possible to investigate "sensory" and "motor" reactions.

As stated above, we let each observer make five reactions. When all the first reactions, all the second reactions, etc., are averaged together the following results are obtained:

TIMES IN σ

	Av.	v	V
I.	196	55	16
II.	178	46	19
III.	170	43	16
IV.	169	40	19
V.	166	35	19
Av.	176	44	18

The first reaction is thus likely to be about 25σ and the second about 10σ longer than the subsequent ones, which show only a slight decrease.[1] To get an observer's reaction-time, therefore, it might be well to make five reactions and use the averages of the last three. The variations, however, show that the first two reactions, though longer, are not more irregular than the subsequent ones, and for purposes of comparison the five first reactions can be used.

The reaction-time is one of the tests naturally thought of first in a series such as this, but we do not regard it as one of the most satisfactory. To make reactions quickly and regularly is something of a "trick" and the variations in time which occur with unpracticed observers depend on complex causes.

Both Prof. Jastrow and Prof. Münsterberg recommend a number

[1] The average of the first reactions is lengthened by two of over 500σ which were not true reactions and have been excluded from the averages given at the beginning of the section.

of psychometric tests for a limited series such as this. Those used by Prof. Jastrow, which consist of discrimination and choice are even more difficult to carry out and interpret than reaction-times. The results vary greatly with the apparatus used, with the instructions of the recorder and with the attitude of the subject.

The plan first used by one of the present writers of giving lists of colors, words, etc., and measuring the total time required to name them, to form associations, etc., is recommended by Münsterberg and indeed makes up about one-half of his tests. We have used one test of this character, and doubtless others would be useful if time permitted. We gave the observer a blank containing 500 11-point capital letters, of which 100 were A's. Each of the other letters occurred 16 times, and the whole series was arranged in an order drawn by lot. The observer was required to mark as quickly as possible all the A's. We thus have the time (93 cases) required to recognize and mark 100 letters and to discriminate cursorily 400 more.

	Time in secs.		
	Av.	v	V
Marking 100 letters..................	95.0	12.8	6.4

The average number of A's omitted was 2.6. It was but seldom that a wrong letter was marked. It would be desirable to correlate the rapidity with the number of mistakes. A rough correction could perhaps be made to the rate by adding to the total time the time that would be required to discriminate and mark the letters omitted or wrongly marked. This would increase the average time to about 97.5 seconds, which is very nearly one second per letter. The order of the individuals would be somewhat changed by such a correction, as there are a few who make a great many mistakes. This itself is typical; some will do a task quickly and well, some quickly and ill, some slowly and well, and some slowly and ill.

If time permit the making of other psychometric tests we should recommend reading as rapidly as possible a list of 100 words, and 100 similar words making sentences;[1] naming 100 (or 20) colors (say red, yellow, green, blue, violet, gray and black, 1 cm. sq. arranged in a chance order on a white ground), which is useful in determining color-blindness as well as quickness of perception and speech, and lastly giving 100 (or fewer) words and requiring the student to write as rapidly as possible the suggested ideas.

This last test would of course be useful in the study of associa-

[1] The rate at which a foreign language can be read is a good test of familiarity with the language.

tion of ideas, which has not been included in our series. We regret this has been the case and may try to take up some study of associa-tion in our subsequent work. The difficulty is that this subject (like imagery and memory, which we have included), requires more psy-chological investigation before a test can be conveniently applied and properly interpreted.

PERCEPTION OF SPACE AND TIME

The observer was given a standard line, 10 cm. in length, drawn near the top of a piece of paper, and was required to place this on the left-hand side of a sheet of letter paper of the same width, and draw in a corresponding position a line of the same length. His line was then folded under and he repeated the trial. The results (93 cases) were:

	Error in mm.		
	Av.	*v*	*V*
Average error........................	6.5	3.4	0.9

The constant error was on the average +0.08 mm., that is, there was in the group no appreciable tendency to over-estimate or under-estimate the line.

As the sheet of paper was only 20 cm. wide, the observer may have guided himself by the distance from the edge of the paper. It would save time (especially in the subsequent calculations) to make only one trial. We expect hereafter to amplify this test as follows: Give the student a sheet of letter paper (about 25 × 20 cm.) with a line 5 cm. in length drawn horizontally 20 cm. from the bottom of the sheet. The student is required to reproduce this line in the same position on a similar sheet, and afterwards to draw from the middle of the line he has drawn a vertical line of the same apparent length, and then to bisect the left-hand angle and, perhaps, tri-sect the right-hand angle and divide the vertical line in the middle. The test can be made quickly, but it would be somewhat tedious to measure the errors.

The accuracy with which intervals of time can be judged was measured by giving the student an interval of 10 seconds, marked at the beginning and end by taps, and letting him make a tap when an apparently equal interval had elapsed. The results (90 cases) were:

TIME IN SEC.

	Av.	*v*	*V*
Average errors.....................	1.57	0.81	0.26

The constant error for the group was on the average −0.18 sec. The errors are almost too small to be measured by the method used (an ordinary watch or stop chronoscope), and it would seem desirable either to increase the time to 30 seconds or to use chronographic methods of giving the signals and measuring the times. This test is one easily and quickly made, and strictly psychological in character. But the interpretation of the results is not obvious, and it might perhaps be omitted by those not specially concerned with psychology or amplified by those who are.

MEMORY

The experiment already described in which we required a student to draw twice a line as nearly as he could the same length as a standard line of 10 cm. was made at the beginning of the series. About three-quarters of an hour later when all the tests had been completed, he was reminded of the line he had drawn and told to draw from memory a line of the same length. We have thus a good test of recollection (the observer not knowing at the time that he would be asked to remember) easily made and giving a quantitative result. The average error of recollection was 7.3 mm. (21 cases only), and the constant error under +0.2 mm., practically none. The error is but slightly larger than in the case of immediate comparison of the lines, but the number of students tested was small.

Like all tests of memory, the results are somewhat complex, and cannot readily be compared with other work not made by exactly the same method. But it is desirable that a test of ordinary or casual memory be made and the conditions fixed by agreement. As in some of the other experiments on our list, the average result of this test gives the accuracy of the class tested, but the place of the individual in the series is very inadequately determined by a single trial.

We also tested immediate memory by reading aloud eight numerals and requiring the student to repeat them, making the determination three times with different numerals. The average number correctly given (without regard to order) was 6.92.

The errors can be counted in three ways, with regard to omissions, substitutions, and mistakes in order or position. It is tedious and difficult to count up the mistakes in order or position, and we give only the total number of numerals remembered. This test can be made in various ways; one can use numerals, letters, words or nonsense syllables, read them or show them, etc. We prefer numerals in spite of the elaborate work with nonsense syllables undertaken by Ebbinghaus and by Müller and Schumann. Jastrow uses additional tests of memory, and it would certainly be desirable to compare auditory and visual memory. It would also be useful to test memory by reading aloud a paragraph (say 200 words) and requiring the student to reproduce it. The experiment is easily made, but it is somewhat difficult to calculate the errors. Perhaps the papers might simply be graded on a scale of 10 with regard to verbal and logical memory.

AFTER-IMAGES AND IMAGERY

After-images were tested by allowing the observer to see in a dark room for fifteen seconds a white light of determined area and intensity. The area was a cross with arms 1 cm. square, 30 cm. distant from the eyes, and the intensity (light through ground glass which absorbed about one-half) was from a 100 candle power incandescent electric lamp at a distance of 30 cm. Of the 75 students tested 73.3% saw an after-image. The average total duration from the disappearance of the light to the disappearance of the first image, and the duration of the latent period before any image appeared, were as follows:

	Av.	*v*	*V*
Duration of image in secs..................	44.2	25.2	3.0
Duration of latent period (34 cases)..........	16.2	9.4	0.2

The latent period is long because the student is not likely to notice the first positive image and oscillations. With 61.8% of the students the after-image, after disappearing, reappeared. With 29.1% it appeared three or more times; with 7.3% four or more times, and with 3.8% five times. The after-image, when first seen, was sometimes positive and sometimes negative, and the colors varied greatly, being distributed in the first phase noticed as follows:

> Negative or dark, 33.3%; light or white, 29.4; blue, 13.7; purple, 9.8; green, 5.9; yellow, 3.9; red, 2.0; miscellaneous, 2.0.

We included after-images in our series in part because it was a subject being especially investigated in the laboratory. We think it an advantage for each laboratory to undertake, in addition to certain tests made everywhere, some special tests, so that a larger field may be covered, and the best tests selected by survival of the fittest. Our results with after-images seem to show that the test is a good one. We get definite results, combined with great individual differences. The differences depend on attention, power of observation, etc., and, perhaps, on inherent differences in the nervous system, which may prove typical when correlated with our other determinations.

Imagery was tested by letting the student fill in a blank containing the questions printed below. The answers are given in percentages (95 subjects) after the questions.

Think of your breakfast table as you sat down to it this morning; call up the appearance of the table, the dishes and food on it, the persons present, etc.

Then write answers to the following questions:

(1) Are the outlines of the objects distinct and sharp?

Yes, 86.5%; No. 6.2%; miscellaneous, 7.3%.

(2) Are the colors bright and natural?

Yes, 83.3%; No, 10.4%; miscellaneous, 6.3%.

(3) Where does the image seem to be situated? In the head? Before the eyes? At a distance?

In the head, 28.7%; before the eyes, 36.2%; at a distance, 33%; miscellaneous, 2.1%.

(4) How does the size of the image compare with the actual size of the scene?

Same, 53.7%; smaller, 45.3%; miscellaneous, 1%.

(1) Can you call to mind better the face or the voice of a friend?

Face, 75%; voice, 14.6%; miscellaneous, 10.4%.

(2) When "violin" is suggested, do you first think of the appearance of the instrument or the sounds made when it is played?

Appearance, 76.8%; sounds, 23.2%;

(3) (*a*) Can you call to mind natural scenery so that it gives you pleasure? (*b*) Music? (*c*) The taste of fruit?

	Yes, Per Cent	No, Per Cent	Miscellaneous, Per Cent
Scenery..........................	94.6	4.3	1.1
Music...........................	89.1	9.8	1.1
Taste of fruit....................	68.1	28.6	3.3

(4) Have you ever mistaken a hallucination for a perception, *e.g.*, apparently heard a voice or seen a figure when none was present? If you answer "yes" describe the experience on the back of this sheet.

Yes, 74.7%; No, 25.3%.

As we have already had occasion to state those tests that are of special interest to the psychologist are often ones with which it is difficult to get definite results. The student has had no practice in introspection and even a trained psychologist may find it difficult to fill in such a blank. For this reason we have added to several of the questions proposed by Mr. Galton others admitting of more definite answers. On the whole we think it desirable to make this test. A discussion of results would lead us beyond the limits of a general article.

Conclusions

Our experience with these tests leads us to recommend that they be made a part of the work of every psychological laboratory. When used with freshmen on entering college the record is of interest to the man and may be of real value to him. It is well for him to know how his physical development, his senses, his movements and his mental processes compare with those of his fellows. He may be able to correct defects and develop aptitudes. Then when the tests are repeated later in the college course and in subsequent life the record of progress or regression may prove of substantial importance to the individual. The making of the tests brings the psychological laboratory into relation with a large number of students and with other departments of the university, shows the modern methods of anthropometry and experimental psychology, and may lead to a more serious study of these on the part of a larger number of students.

The psychological laboratory can also be brought into mutually helpful relations with the community by extending the tests to any who wish to have them made. Children in the schools might be tested with special advantage. For this purpose tests are especially useful which can be made simultaneously on a large number of observers. Physicians might find it an advantage to have records made of their patients. The tests are well suited for civil service examinations. If a small fee were charged in these cases it might suffice to support an assistant, the larger part of whose time would be spent in scientific work. In any case the making of the tests is good practice for advanced students preliminary to, or in addition to, special research. By bringing the laboratory into relations with the community we add to its influence and at the same time secure the material needed for research.

We have only studied 100 individuals and regard this paper rather as an investigation of methods than as a summary of results. We think that an hour used in tests should be divided between physical, psychophysical and mental measurements. We regard it as important that work in physical anthropology, which is a subject sure to be recognized before long by all our universities, should be intimately associated with the work in experimental psychology. We are not able to suggest any radical improvement in the tests selected or in the methods of making them; but in reviewing the individual tests we have called attention to difficulties and suggested improvements. The work is one now only begun, but likely to develop and requiring investigation and discussion from diverse points of view.

We do not at present wish to draw any definite conclusions from the results of the tests so far made. It is of some scientific interest to know that students entering college have heads on the average 19.3 cm. long, that 15% have defective hearing, that they have an average reaction-time of 0.174 sec., that they can remember seven numerals heard once, and so on with other records and measurements. These are mere facts, but they are quantitative facts and the basis of science. Our own future work and that of others must proceed in two directions. On the one hand we must study the interrelations of the traits which we define and measure. To what extent are the several traits of body, of the senses and of mind interdependent? How far can we predict one thing from our knowledge of another? What can we learn from the tests of elementary traits regarding the higher intellectual and emotional life? On the other hand we must use our measurements to study the development of the individual and of the race, to disentangle the complex factors of heredity and environment. There is no scientific problem more important than the study of the development of man, and no practical problem more urgent than the application of our knowledge to guide this development.

15

MEASUREMENTS OF THE ACCURACY OF RECOLLECTION

Printed in *Science*, **2**: 761–766, 1895.

We know that ordinary observation and recollection are not altogether reliable. We do not credit all the stories that we hear, even though we may not doubt the good faith of the narrators; we see that conflicting evidence is offered in courts of justice when no perjury is intended; we regard as partly mythical records supposed for many centuries to describe historical events. But we do not know how likely it is that a piece of testimony is true, now how the degree of probability varies under different conditions. If we could learn this by experiment the result would be a contribution to psychology, and would at the same time have certain important practical applications.

I have tried in various ways to secure a quantitative determination of the reliability of recollection and evidence, and will here report on the answers to some questions asked the Junior class in psychology in Columbia College in March, 1893. The questions were answered in all or in part by the fifty-six students present.

Several simple questions were first asked and the students allowed in each case one-half minute to consider and write the answer. They were also requested to assign the confidence which they felt in the correctness of their answer—a if quite certain, b if tolerably certain, c if doubtful, d if the answer were a guess.

The first question was "What was the weather a week ago to-day?" The answers were pretty equally distributed over all kinds of weather which are possible at the beginning of March. Of the 56 answers, 16 may be classed as "clear," 12 "rain," 7 "snow," 9 "stormy," 6 cloudy and 6 partly stormy and partly clear.[1] It seems that an average man with a moderate time for reflection cannot state much better what the weather was a week ago than what it will be a week hence. Yet this is a question that might naturally be asked in a court of justice. An unscrupulous attorney can discredit the statements of a truthful witness by cunningly selected questions. The jury, or at least the Judge, should know how far errors in recollection are normal and how they vary under different conditions.

When asked "what was the weather two weeks ago?" 20 students

[1] On the day in question it snowed in the morning and cleared in the afternoon.

answered "clear," and 18 "stormy." The confidence in this case was slight, only two being sure that their answers were correct and 8 having some confidence, while the others were doubtful or did not answer at all.

We ought not, indeed, to conclude from these conflicting answers that no inference as to the weather on those days can be drawn. Almost nothing could be inferred from any single answer, but the answers taken together give information of a degree of exactness which may be defined. We can, however, better consider this matter in connection with questions requiring a quantitative answer.

Three questions were asked with a view to learning the ordinary accuracy of observation: "Do chestnut trees or oak trees lose their leaves the earlier in the autumn?" "Do horses in the field stand with head or tail to the wind?" "In what direction do the seeds of an apple point?" The questions were all answered correctly more often than incorrectly, but only by a moderate majority. Thus 30 students thought that chestnut trees lose their leaves the earlier in the autumn, and 21 were of the opposite opinion; 34 students thought that horses in the field stand with tails to the wind, and 19 thought they stand facing it. Thus in only about three cases out of five will a college student answer such a question correctly.

Each class of persons would, of course, have a different index of precision. In the present cases country boys would probably do better, whereas in other directions, as in judging of character, they might not do so well. This opens up an interesting direction for research. Is the ordinary observation of men or women better? of students in classical or scientific courses? etc.

The degree of confidence may be noticed. The students were sure their answers were correct in all 34 times, and in these cases they were, in fact, correct 27 times. They were somewhat or quite doubtful in all 70 times, and in these cases were correct 37 times, scarcely more than a majority. Their judgment of their own accuracy was therefore of some value, and the degree of confidence can with advantage be taken in ordinary testimony. But there is great individual difference in this respect. Some observers are nearly always sure that they are right, whereas others whose decision is equally or more likely to be correct are much less confident. In other and more elaborate experiments I have found that when an observer is entirely doubtful, for example, as to which of two weights is the heavier, and makes a guess, his guess is more likely to be right than wrong. This opens an opportunity for determining the part played by subconscious inference in the decisions of daily life, as in judging the character from the face.

As regards the direction in which the seeds in an apple point, 24 answers were "upward," or "toward stem"; 18 "toward center"; 13 "downward," and 3 "outward." The reader may be left to decide whether or not he knows in what direction the seeds in fact point, and what information he can obtain from these answers.

Two questions were asked, the answers to which measure the ordinary accuracy of information: "Was Luther or Michel Angelo born the earlier and by how many years?" "In what year did Victor Hugo die?" Michel Angelo was assigned the earlier year in 29 of the 45 answers. The average of the answers placed his birth 12 years before that of Luther, which was nearly the correct value (8 years). The average departure from the correct value was 54 years, which measures a considerable degree of ignorance.

The average assigned the death of Victor Hugo 12 years too early, with an average departure from the true date of 13 years. The median would here give a more correct date, as the average is unduly influenced by a few who assigned a very early date. The extreme values, indeed, betray great ignorance. One student thought Hugo died in 1790, another that he is still alive. One student thought that Michel Angelo was born 300 years earlier than Luther.

Three questions were asked intended to determine the average accuracy in estimating weight, distance and time. These were the weight of the text-book (James' *Briefer Course* in Psychology) used by the class, the distance between the two buildings on the college grounds and the time usually taken by students to walk from the entrance door of the building to the door of the lecture room. The results are shown in the accompanying table, there being given the approximate actual magnitude, the average estimate with the constant error, the average departure of the estimates from the average estimate and from the actual magnitude and the median.

Estimation of	Actual magnitude	Average estimate	Constant error	Average residual	Average error	Median estimate
Ounces........	24	17	− 7	5	8	16
Feet..........	310	356	+46	179	162	250
Seconds.......	35	66	+31	36	40	60

It thus appears that in these cases there was a marked tendency to under-estimate weight and to over-estimate time. Length was over-estimated, but to a less degree. For the magnitudes used the average variation was about one-third of the weight and one-half of the distance or time. The actual errors were larger in the case of weight and time, but not in the case of distance. The middle estimate or median value is in all cases smaller tlan the average. The degree of confidence of the observer does not in these cases seem to measure objective accuracy.

Curves are subjoined showing the distribution of the estimates. The residuals are divided into classes of the size of one-half the theoretical probable errors, and the ordinates represent the percentages of the whole number of observations falling within each class.

The curves approach the bell-shape required by the theory of probabilities, but not very closely. The departures are partly due to the limited number of observations (56 in each case), and the tendency

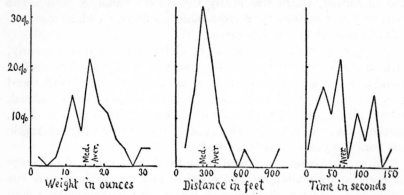

FIG. 1.—The distribution of errors in estimating weight, distance and time.

to estimate in round numbers; in estimating time $\frac{3}{4}$ of the estimates were $\frac{1}{2}$, 1 or 2 minutes. But there is a large constant error, and in addition there is an excess of large positive errors which makes the average in all cases larger than the median. This tendency obtains in nearly all variations and measurements and has not received the attention it deserves. The average weight of men may be 150 pounds, and there are men weighing 300 pounds, but none weighing 0. In actual measurements it is probable that large positive errors occur more frequently than negative errors of the same size.

When students were asked what was said during the first two minutes of the lecture in the same course given one week before, the accounts were such that the lecturer might prefer not to have them recorded. From the testimony of the students it would appear that two minutes sufficed to cover a large range of psychological and other subjects, and to make many statements of an extraordinary character.

The last task set was to draw in a scale of about $\frac{1}{4}$ inch to the foot a ground plan of the entrance hall of the building in which the class met, ten minutes being allowed. The students were also asked to state about how many times they had passed through the hall. All the students (with some possible exceptions) had passed through the hall about an equal number of times, but the average estimate of 4,022 had an average variation of 2,669 times. It might be supposed that the number of times was in any case sufficient to impress a tolerably exact recollection of the hall, but the drawings vary to such an extent that any one taken at random would be likely to give an entirely false impression. An examination of the many drawings, however, leaves on the mind a fairly exact idea of the hall, and it would be possible to make a composite drawing which would be found to approach a correct ground plan. Three of the ground plans (supposed to be drawn on the

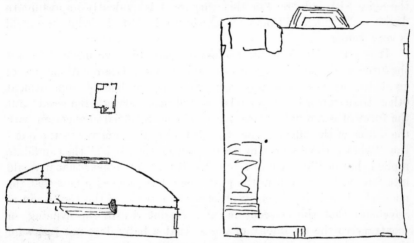

Fig. 2.—Ground-plans of a hall drawn from memory (scale 1:96).

same scale and here reduced about one-half) are subjoined. This is worth the while if only to emphasize the worthlessness of many hundred casual observations as compared with one measurement.

Psychology is continually gaining ground as a natural and even as an exact science, and some progress is made when in any direction the surmise of daily life is superseded by systematized facts and measurements.

It is sometimes said that the useful applications of the material sciences have no parallel in the case of the mental sciences, but I venture to maintain that psychological experiments may have a high degree of practical value. Thus, determinations such as those here described are useful in various ways.

It would be of value to an individual and to those having dealings with him if he could be assigned a definite index of precision. This could be determined early in life, and the effects of environment and methods of education could be determined. It is generally acknowledged that children should be treated as individuals and not as bits of stone to be shaken together until they become marbles, equally round. We consequently need to study methods which will discover individual differences early in the life of the child. Education may properly be devoted to overcoming defects which would interfere with usefulness, but perhaps its more important function is to strengthen qualities which the individual possesses and which may be developed so as to serve his welfare and that of society. From the point of view of science, private benevolence and State aid should be directed less to supplying the cripples with crutches than to supplying the agile with ladders. For this purpose it is evidently important to devise tests which will demonstrate natural aptitudes while the child is very young.

It is especially desirable to devise some objective method to test the fitness of candidates for the civil service. Examinations are of great importance in merely securing some method of appointment other than reward for personal or political services rendered. But the form of examination has often only an artificial connection with the duties of the official. The story is told that in answer to the question "what is the distance of the moon from the earth?" the candidate replied that he did not know, but that it was not so near that it would interfere with his work in the post-office. It is, indeed a fact that the man who had independently observed (contrary to the testimony of novelists) that the crescent moon does not rise in the evening, or (contrary to the testimony of poets) that a baby does not reach for the moon, would discover mental qualities of greater importance for most work than the man who remembered the number of miles from the earth to the moon. Of course the accuracy of observation would only be one of a number of tests which could be applied. The candidate for postoffice clerk whose eyesight is good; who can accurately judge of the weight of a letter; who can make many similar movements in succession without becoming fatigued; whose range of perception is large so that he can perceive at a glance the address on an envelope; whose reaction-time is short, so that he can quickly distribute the letters, etc., would probably be a more efficient public servant than one who passed a slightly better examination in grammer and arithmetic. Stress should be laid on the advantages of obtaining quantitative results. In this case the candidates can be arranged in order without any chance of prejudice or mistake on the part of the examiner. The report would show that *A* has passed a better examination than *B*, and that the chances are (say) nine to one that this result is correct.

As a last example of the usefulness of measurements of the accurcay of observations and memory I may refer to its application in courts of justice. The probable accuracy of a witness could be measured and his testimony weighted accordingly. A numerical correction could be introduced for lapse of time, average lack of truthfulness, average effect of personal interest, etc. The testimony could be collected independently,[1] and given to experts who could affirm for example that the chances are 19 to 1 that the homicide was committed by the defendant, and 4 to 1 that it was premeditated.

A proper application of measurement and the theory of probabilities to the affairs of daily life would add greatly to intellectual detachment and clearness of view. It would be salutary to have in mind the probable error of the newspaper one is reading. The historian could assign the probable accuracy of each event which he narrates, in the same manner as the physicist assigns a probable error to his measurements. We should know what reliance we can place on the stories we hear, and our own memory of past events. When the relative probabilities of the various conflicting claims of business, politics and religion are expressed in simple numerical formulas, a great part of the wasted energy of life may be directed to useful ends. It is a long way to travel, but we should advance when and how we can.

[1] The independently formed verdict of three jurors, if concordant, would probably have more validity than the unanimous verdict of twelve jurors in consultation. Questions of such great practical importance as this could be definitely settled by the proper psychological experiments.

16

ON RELATIONS OF TIME AND SPACE IN VISION

A paper read before the Physical Section of the American Association for the Advancement of Science, August, 1899.
Printed in *The Psychological Review*, **7**: 325–343, 1900. The note which follows the paper and which comments on a research report by Professor Raymond Dodge was printed in *The Psychological Review*, **7**: 507–508, 1900.

In the ordinary vision of daily life the eyes, the head and the whole body are in continual movement. There are no distinct and lasting images on the retina; the physical conditions are those of the photographic plate when the camera is constantly moved hither and thither. But the world that we see appears to each of us distinct and unshifting. When I glance across the room—along a row of books covering its side, for example—images follow one another on each retinal element in rapid succession, but I see this time continuum as a space continuum with all the objects duly arranged side by side.

When black and white surfaces are moved across the retina with the color-wheel at the rate of fifty white stimuli per second, a gray, as every one knows, is seen. When, however, the eye moves so that the line of sight passes over black and white surfaces at the same rate, there is no fusion whatever, the surfaces being seen distinctly side by side. No fusion occurs even when 1,000 stimuli per second fall upon each retinal element.

When colored surfaces are moved one after the other across a limited part of the retina, under conditions described below, they do not seem to follow each other on the same field, but the colors are seen spread out side by side or intermingled in a larger field than is actually presented. The arrangement in space of the stimuli varies greatly with different observers, each seeing them in a way peculiar to himself. Thus in the elaboration of a time series into a spatial continuum the same stimuli are followed by perceptions different for each observer.

These phenomena are important from several points of view. They indicate that the fusion of stimuli—and indeed all the phenomena of color vision—are not the result of chemical processes in the retina, but are cerebral phenomena dependent on complex factors. The individual differences under unusual experimental conditions indicate that the processes of vision are not organically fixed, but are the result of

338

individual experience and adjustment. The perception of a time series
as a spatial continuum shows that our perceptions are not "copies"
of a physical world, but are mental phenomena dependent on utility
and the whole content of present and past experience.

SECTION I. PERCEPTION WITH THE MOVING EYE

That in ordinary vision the spatial world of perception is recon-
structed from a series of changes in time of the retinal images is an
observation which, so far as I am aware, has not hitherto been made.

FIG. 1.—Black and white bars which do not fuse when the line of sight is moved over
them.

But when once stated the fact is obvious and scarcely needs confirmation by special experiments. The results, however, when stated in
quantitative terms, show a remarkable sensitiveness in the visual
mechanism.

When the eyes are moved horizontally through an angle of about
45° once a second, from a distance of about 5 m., sweeping over an
arc of about 4 m., on which are black and white lines 2 mm. wide, as
shown in the figure, stimulations at the rate of one thousand per second
fall on each retinal area. There is no fusion into a gray, or blurring
of the lines, so long as the eyes are kept in focus for the arc. The white
lines stimulating the retina in rapid succession are seen clearly side
by side exactly as when viewed with the stationary eye, except that
the field of distinct vision is enlarged.

When the eyes move so that the line of sight passes over the field
at the rate of about 2 m. per second, going from a white to a black
surface, it will in $\frac{1}{50}$ sec. move over 4 cm. According to our experience with the color-wheel there is fusion when one stimulation of the
retina follows another at an interval of $\frac{1}{50}$ sec., or less, and if the
same conditions obtained with the moving eye the white edge would
not be seen, but white and gray would extend 4 cm. and more into
the black. But as a matter of fact the white edge is seen with perfect
distinctness, there being no fusion whatever. If one looks at the ground
when riding in a trolley-car all the objects are fused, but it is easy to
move the eyes so quickly in the opposite direction that the objects are

distinctly seen. If when the car stops the line of sight is moved over the ground at the same rate there is no fusion whatever.

The rate of stimulation by movements of the eye cannot be increased greatly beyond that given above, and the limits of distinct vision are not set by the inability of the retina to respond to the stimuli, but by the "minimum visible" and the maximum rate of movement.[1] More than a thousand interruptions per second give a series of sharply defined retinal processes. Vibrations fuse into a continuous tone when there are thirty or less per second, but two noises can be distinguished when separated by an interval of about .002 sec. Touches fuse at about the same interval. It is always stated that hearing and touch respond more accurately to successive changes in stimuli than vision, but this is apparently not the case.

The head can be moved more quickly than the eyes, and the whole body can also be turned more quickly than the eyes. I am not aware of attention having been called to this fact, which is of some interest in view of the phenomena here described. When the head or body is turned quickly objects in the field of vision appear to move in a direction opposite to that of the line of sight, and this is the more marked the quicker the movement. When the eyes only are moved the field does not shift,[2] or if so the apparent motion is very slight. When the line of sight is moved by turning the head so that it passes over black and white bars at such a rate that there are about fifty stimuli per second there is no fusion. But when the movement is more rapid the field begins to move and there is then blurring and finally gray.

The fact that we see clearly and side by side objects over which the line of sight moves rapidly is evident. I have no doubt that the explanation I have given is correct—namely, that the visual mechanism is sufficiently sensitive to respond to more than 1,000 stimuli per second, and that we perceive a series of time changes on the retina as a spatial continuum because for our reactions it is in fact a spatial continuum. The only other possible explanations seem to be that the moving eye makes a series of jumps, seeing at each stop a distinct field, or that the distinctness of the field is an illusion, being really a

---

[1] Conflicting results as to the rate of movement of the eye have been obtained by Lamansky (*Pflüger's Archiv*, 2: 418–422, 1869), Erdmann und Dodge (*Ueber das Lesen*, Halle, 1898) and Huey (*Am. Journ. of Psych.*, 2: 283–302, 1900).

[2] James (*Psychology*, 2: 173) is apparently mistaken in stating that it does, not discriminating movements of the eyes from movements of the head and trunk. The difference in the case of the moving eyes and the moving head may in part be due to the fact that with the eyes all objects in the field of vision maintain their relative positions, whereas when the head is moved nearer objects move over further ones, and we learn to regard a moving field as natural and a thing to be ignored.

memory image. But these suggestions are invalid. It can be readily observed that the eye does move continuously over the field. Further the field of distinct vision[1] is only about 1°, and to see all parts of an arc of 90° by separate steps the eye would need to stop some ninety times. It takes about ⅕ sec. for the eye to stop and fix a field, and it is of course absurd to suppose that it could stop frequently in the half second needed to sweep over the arc. Finally if one had in fact only a few distinct images in the course of the movement it would remain true that a series of successive images is seen as a space continuum.[2]

The second alternative, that the distinct vision with the moving eye is an illusion, is at least conceivable. In daily life one does not notice that at each moment only a very small part of the field of vision is distinct. But this phenomenon is in fact explained by the constant movements of the eyes and the clear vision accompanying the movements—not conversely. Further it can be shown experimentally that when the eye sweeps over an object it is seen distinctly even though the observer may not know what it is. In this case if fusion occurred, as it does when the field is in motion, it would not, e.g., be possible to discriminate red and green bars from white and black bars. Finally the perception as a space continuum of a series of changes in the time of stimulation is confirmed by the experiments with a moving field described below.

SECTION 2. THE FUSION OF MOVING OBJECTS

The fact that the sense of vision responds to changes in stimulation as accurately as the other senses is not in itself surprising. I have always thought[3] that the phenomena of binocular vision, of contrast, of after-images, etc., are far too complicated to be attributed chiefly to the retina, and have never cared for the physiological mythology of the Young-Helmholtz and Hering theories of color vision. Assuming it to be true as a matter of experience that the moving eye responds accurately to changes in time of stimulation, it does not seem to me that this fact particularly requires explanation. On the contrary we

[1] I do not find any measurements of the field of distinct vision, beyond the estimates of Weber and of Erdmann and Dodge. The fovea is said by Kölliker to be from 0.18 to 0.225 mm. in diameter, by Dimmer 1.1 mm. or more.

[2] In reading a line of printed text the eyes do stop as they sweep over the page. This, however, is not because there is any blurring of the letters with the moving eyes, but owing to the limited amount that can be simultaneously perceived and the time it takes to perceive it.

[3] I have said: "The writer finds most satisfaction in assuming that the continuity of physical vibration is transmitted through the retina to the brain, where inertia, summation and inhibition intervene to produce the changes which are correlated with consciousness." PSYCHOL. REV., 1, 326, 1894.

need to explain why lights fuse when in motion. In this connection it may be suggested that vibrations producing a simple tone fuse at 30 or fewer per second, which is at nearly the same rate that black and white fuse on the color-wheel. When a slowly vibrating tuning-fork is touched with the finger we also have a partly continuous sensation. The conditions with these different senses are thus somewhat analogous. We have under certain conditions fusion with comparatively few changes per second, and under other conditions can discriminate stimuli much closer together. I maintain that we should attribute the phenomena of perception chiefly to utility. We perceive what it is useful for us to perceive in order to direct our actions so as to preserve ourselves and attain our ends, and we usually perceive things in the way that is most conducive to these purposes. A general principle such as this does not of course obviate the need of investigating the conditions in the different cases, but it may lead us to consider that it is circumstances in which our senses fail in utility that need explanation rather than cases in which they fail to give copies of an external world, which is itself only the chief case of the interpretation of perceptions in accordance with maximum utility.

We can discriminate two noises separated by $\frac{1}{500}$ sec., but vibrations fuse into tones varying in quality when separated by much longer intervals. We notice very small differences in pitch, and the qualitative differences are evidently more useful to us than would be a series of sounds at varying rates. Beats on the other hand, though at the same rate as the vibrations giving tones, do not fuse perfectly.

In the case of vision a great loss in efficiency would result if the organs concerned could not respond to changes in the image as rapidly as these are brought about by movements of the eye. There would be confusion just at the time when clear vision might be of special importance. The processes of vision and of movement have developed in harmony, and the sensitiveness of the retina and of the brain centers is as great as is needed. The comparative slowness with which the eyes can be moved is perhaps due to the fact that a greater rapidity would be of no use, as it could not be followed by the retina and brain.

In the case of moving objects on the contrary, it is not necessary and would probably be disadvantageous for us to see the separate phases. The savage is concerned with the fact that a panther is springing toward him or a deer running away, not with the successive positions of the limbs of the creatures as instantaneous photography would exhibit them. Moving objects in nature are seen as wholes as they should be for our convenience. When we produce motion by machinery or in the laboratory with the color-wheel we also naturally have fusion, but I doubt whether we do produce complete fusion with the color-wheel. It is assumed that we do, but I have never seen it. There is on the color-wheel always an appearance of glitter or translucence similar to that in binocular fusion. I have never been able to make gray in a color-wheel from red and green (with the necessary correction of blue), but when it is as nearly gray as it can be got I see both red and green with an appearance of translucence. Neither do I see a gray when red and green are mixed by reflection or diffraction; there is in this case an oscillation comparable to the conflict of the fields in binocular rivalry. If I am correct in these observations it is evident that we do not have complete chemical fusion on the retina.

I may refer in this connection to another phenomenon of the color-wheel, which I observed some years ago, but have not described. When we mix black with white we get a blue-gray. This is well known, and is said to be a case of the Purkinje phenomenon, according to which lights are said to become bluer as they are made fainter.[1] But if we throw a shadow on the same white that we are mixing with the black (say a perfect black from a black hole) we can get a gray evidently lighter or darker than the gray from fusion, but this cannot be matched, the shadow being yellow-gray as contrasted with the blue-gray on the color-wheel. The intermittent stimulation of the color-wheel seems to produce the blue,[2] and Talbot's law can scarcely be exactly correct. This experiment also indicates that in the fusion of successive stimuli we have not a chemical process in the retina, at least not such a simple one as is assumed.

The phenomena of after-images are not at variance, as might perhaps be supposed, with the ability of the eye to respond to very rapid time changes in the environment. A perceptible after-image is only produced by a certain minimum quantity of light,[3] and with the moving eye in ordinary vision the time that any object is fixed is extremely short, while the intensity of the light is usually small.[4] It is exactly the delicacy of the visual mechanism which would lead us to expect an after-image when the light is unusually intense or fixed for an unusually long time. It is a general principle that a nervous

---

[1] As a matter of fact the Purkinje phenomenon does not occur when the intensity of the colors is altered, but only when the eye is accommodated for a fainter light. I accidentally discovered this fact in trying to demonstrate the phenomenon to my classes in a light room. It has been described by Hering (*Pflüger's Archiv*, 60: 519–542, 1895).

[2] The degree of blue is, however, independent of the rate of intermission.

[3] *Cf.* FRANZ, THE PSYCHOLOGICAL REVIEW, *Monograph Supplements*, No. 12, 1899.

[4] As a matter of fact the after-image appears only after a latent period, which contradicts the ordinary theory that it is simply the continuation of the commotion produced by the stimulus on the retina.

system sufficiently delicate to respond to ordinary stimuli is over-stimulated and perhaps injured by extraordinary stimulation. Thus after-images, like the expression of the emotions in certain cases, are not useful reactions but pathological conditions. I can at present see an after-image obtained about six years ago.[1] This is not a purely retinal brand, because it can be made more distinct and, I think, permanent by acts of attention.[2] After-images do not in any way contradict the sensitiveness of the visual mechanism to rapid time changes, but on the contrary the indications that they are cerebral phenomena, and the fact that being useless they are ignored in our ordinary vision, support the general point of view of this paper.

Section 3. The Perception of Moving Objects

When the color-wheel is turned so slowly that fusion does not occur there is a flicker if the sectors differ in intensity, and the colors

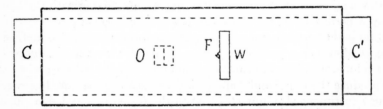

Fig. 2.—Simple apparatus for studying the perception of moving objects.

intermingle. My research was originally concerned with experiments on moving objects and commingling colors, which led to the results on perception with the moving eye already described. Four methods were used to exhibit the stimuli, and it is desirable to describe these in some detail, as they may be used for various purposes.

(1) The phenomena may be produced by very simple means with sufficient accuracy for demonstration. All that is needed is a black screen about 30 cm. long and 10 cm. wide with a slit perpendicular to the long side 5 cm. long and 1 cm. wide. The screen is so attached to a board that a long card (*CC'*) can be slid beneath it. On the card are attached colors or shapes (*O*) which are seen as they pass the window (*W*). The card can be moved with the hand at rates varying up to about 5 m. per second with a mean variation of about one tenth.[3] Thus if green and red bars each one cm. wide be pasted on the card, green can be exhibited for about .01 sec. and the same retinal elements immediately afterwards stimulated by red for the same period.

(2) In order to secure greater accuracy and convenience in these experiments

---

[1] *Cf.* my article on "The Perception of Light" in *System of Diseases of the Eye,* Philadelphia, 1897.

[2] Newton made a similar observation. *Cf.* his letter to Locke in Brewster's *Memoirs of the Life of Sir I. Newton,* Edinburgh, 1855.

[3] Fullerton and Cattell: *The Perception of Small Differences,* Philadelphia, 1892.

and for other psychological purposes I had constructed[1] an instrument which may be called a wheel chronoscope. It consists of a wheel, one meter in diameter with a rim about 9 cm. wide. Cards or colors placed on the outside of the rim pass by the slit (S) and may be seen by the observer on the far side of the instrument. It is

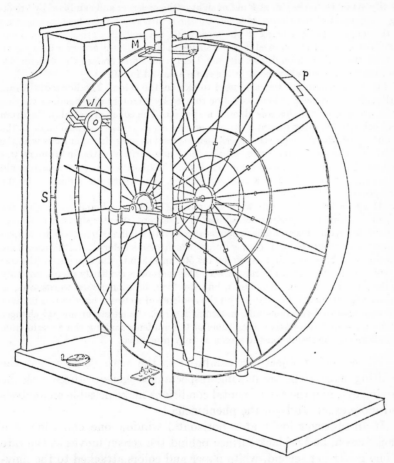

FIG. 3.—Wheel chronoscope for studying the perception of moving objects.   The rate of motion, size of field, etc., can be accurately adjusted.

thus possible to exhibit a color or a series of colors for an interval dependent on the rate at which the wheel moves and the size of the colored surfaces. The intensity of the light and the size of the field can also be varied, thus permitting experiments on the relations of time, area, intensity and color in vision. The instant at which the color reaches the slit can be recorded by keys at C, thus permitting experiments on the time of discrimination, etc. The wheel can be revolved at a constant rate by a motor or can be turned by the fall of the weight W. The latter method was used in the present experiments. The wheel is in this case held in position by the electro-

[1] By J. D. Brown, Camden, N. J. The instrument can be supplied by the instrument maker of the department of psychology of Columbia University.

magnet M. When the current is broken the weight falls and the wheel swings like a pendulum. At and near the dead point the rim is moving at a nearly uniform rate and at this point the colors pass the slit in the screen. The rate can be adjusted by the weight W, and was in these experiments 1 m. per second. The object can be readily attached to the rim at P out of sight of the observer and exhibited by breaking the current of the electro-magnet. On the return swing the wheel is caught up to the magnet, the slit being in the meanwhile covered. If a green surface 5 cm. wide is attached at P, followed by a red surface 5 cm. wide, the observer has over an area of the retina through the slit, say 1 cm. wide, first green exhibited for 50σ ($\frac{1}{20}$ sec.) and then following it in the same area red for 50σ.

(3) A chronograph[1] was also used to exhibit the colors. The horizontal drum with a circumference of 95 cm. could be rotated by a motor or by hand, at varying rates, usually so that this was about 1 m. per sec. The colors attached to the drum were exhibited as they passed a slit in a screen. An extension was also made to the drum so that the colors passed by a slit, and the colors only. In other cases with the wheel chronoscope or the chronograph, the black surface of the instrument was seen moving before the colors came into view. The black was as perfect as it could be made, but it suggested a moving surface, which has an influence on the perception.

(4) In order to do away with the moving background and to exhibit the phenomena simultaneously to a number of observers, the stereopticon was used. The colors were in this case gelatine films attached to a falling screen which dropped before the stereopticon and to a pendulum which swung before it. In this case there appeared on the screen first say green for 50σ and then in the same area (the size of which could be regulated) red for 50σ. This method is evidently useful, not only for demonstrating these phenomena, but also for exhibiting colors, words, etc., in various experiments to be made by all the students of a class. I have in this manner also demonstrated reaction-time, muscular fatigue, the effects of mental changes on the pulse and respiration, etc., some of the students making the experiments, and all seeing the results on the screen as they proceeded.

When moving objects are exhibited by the methods described, the resulting perceptions are in some respects analogous to those with the moving eye, and the experimental conditions make possible an analysis and more exact study of the phenomena.[2]

If an observer looks at a horizontal window one cm. wide in a black screen, and a black surface behind the screen moves at the rate of one meter per second, white paper and colors attached to the moving surface are seen as they pass by the window in the screen. If a piece of white paper is used 10 cm. in length it is in view for one-tenth of a second as it passes the window. If the eyes do not move, and they cannot make a movement in one-tenth of a second, a retinal field

[1] I was so fortunate as to buy three excellent chronographs for $10 each, they having been made for an unsuccessful system of synchronous telegraphy.

[2] I may perhaps be permitted to make in this connection an incidental remark on behalf of experiment in psychology. The chief observations in this paper could have been made by any one at any time, but as a matter of fact they were not made except as the result of a quantitative experimental investigation, continued at intervals for about ten years.

corresponding to the size of the window is stimulated by the light. The physical conditions are the front edge of the light moving over the field in one-hundredth of a second, then the stimulation of each retinal element for one-tenth of a second by the white light, and finally the second edge of the white moving over the field. We have a series of changes in time which might conceivably be followed by a corresponding series of time changes in the nervous system and in consciousness. As a matter of fact we know that the sensation does not exactly follow rapid changes in stimulation. Lights following one another at intervals of one-hundredth of a second fuse, and we should not expect to see the white surface moving over the field, but a fusion of the white and black. We also know that there is a time threshold for vision.[1] If a white surface is exposed to view for a very short time it is not seen. When the time is, say, one-thousandth of a second, it is seen as a gray which increases in brightness until the time of exposure is one- to two-tenths of a second, when the sensation is a maximum. As the time of exposure is taken longer the sensation diminishes. Then we also know that after the objective light has been cut off the sensation may be followed by an after-image.

When consequently a white surface is exposed in the manner described, we might perhaps expect to see a field the size of the window, which would be at first gray and after gradually increasing in brightness would fade away. What I in fact see is a field larger than the window, very bright in the middle and shading through gray into black at each side. A process physically and physiologically in time is given in perception as a spatial continuum. This is evidently a phenomenon similar to that already described when with the moving eye objects successively stimulating the same retinal areas are seen side by side.

The experiment can be varied in many ways, and the results can be made more obvious. If the white surface is on one side 5 cm. and on the other 10 cm. in length we have the conditions shown below in Fig. 4. The left hand side of the field of vision is stimulated for one-twentieth, and the right hand side for one-tenth of a second, and the field is of the same size on both sides. The right hand side appears to me, however, to be perhaps 3 cm. broad, about twice as large as the left hand side and much brighter. There is a contrast effect, making the field darker near the middle on the left hand side and at the edges the white fades away indeterminately. In all these experiments a cloud-like or phantom-like image is seen which is difficult to draw or to describe.

[1] Cattell: "Ueber die Trägheit der Netzhaut und des Sehcentrums," *Philos. Stud.*, **3**: 94–127, 1885.

When colors are used—say green for one-twentieth of a second followed by red for the same time—we have the rapid moving across the field of the edges of the colors, and the retinal area stimulated first by red and then by green. The observer does not, however, see first green in the field, followed by a mixture, followed by red, but the colors are seen simultaneously on a field larger than the window. I see below green fading away indeterminately into black with bright white in the middle commingling with green below and red above, the red fading into black. The white is brighter than white paper, much brighter than the gray obtained by mixing green and red on the color-wheel. The lines are never sharp, the colors being transfused, the one appearing spread over the other. The appearance of the image changes from time to time; after many experiments I do not now see the extension of the image beyond the size of the window as clearly as formerly, only seeing it distinctly when the moving areas are of different sizes on the two sides.

The experiments on moving objects exposed to view for a short time I have varied in many ways, regarding the rate of motion, the time of exposure, the area of exposure, the number of stimuli, the different colors in varying combinations, the shape of the field, the intensity of illumination, the motion of the field before the stimulus appears, movements of the eyes during exposure and other factors. With so many variables the details become complicated, and it is perhaps best to postpone their consideration, as they do not affect the chief conclusions of the present paper.

The individual variation of the perception is, however, a matter of fundamental importance. With exactly the same stimulus different observers have entirely different perceptions. When the moving field is exhibited for the first time to the observer under the conditions described, he not knowing the character of the stimulus, the perception is usually extremely vague, a mere cloud of light perhaps, the size, shade and brightness of which cannot be described. When the same stimulus is exhibited a second time it is usually perceived more distinctly. The attention has a more definite direction, and the memory image fuses with the effects of the stimulus. After three or four trials the observer ordinarily has a fairly definite perception, and then usually continues to have the same perception as the stimulus is repeated. There may, however, be a sudden change in the way in which the stimulus is perceived. When the observer is told what is actually exhibited or what others see, some observers have the same perception as before, while with others it is completely changed.

In the figure on pp. 350–351 the results of the fifth exposure with ten observers and two different stimuli are reproduced. The stimuli are shown on the right hand side of the figure—in the one case a white area 5 cm. broad on the one side and 10 cm. broad on the other, in the second case green 5 cm. broad followed by red 5 cm. broad. The rate of motion was 1 m. per sec. and the field was consequently exposed for 0.1 sec., the area of exposure was 1 cm. wide and 8 cm. long, viewed from a distance of about 30 cm. The drawings of the observers are reduced to one-half. They are more or less schematic, it being difficult or impossible for the observer to draw just what he sees, the outlines being less definite and sharp than the figures indicate.

I have not selected the most variant results, but those of ten advanced students tested consecutively. It is evident that the same stimulus after being exhibited five times is perceived by the observers in entirely different ways. As has already been stated, we have physically lights moving across the field of vision and lasting 0.1 sec. Physiologically we have a limited field of the retina over which the light moves, and from each retinal element for 0.1 sec. a gradual increase in the commotion of the nervous system which gradually subsides. Nearly all the observers perceive a field larger than is exhibited and the time changes in the nervous system are given in consciousness as a space continuum, e.g., the increase in the commotion of the nervous system as the time of stimulation is increased is perceived as a spatial shading from black through gray to white. But in the area of the figure and in the arrangement of the parts the observers differ completely.

With the stereopticon I have exhibited moving colors on the screen to classes of about thirty students of psychology and have secured results analogous to the above. It is more difficult to reproduce the apparent areas, as the screen is not at the same distance from the observer as the paper on which he draws or at the same distance from all the observers. But the general results are the same. Colors exhibited consecutively are seen simultaneously side by side, arranged and intermingled in very different ways.

These experiments show how absurd it would be to suppose that a perception is in any way a copy of the physical world or the correlate of a simple physiological process. The physical change is exactly the same and the physiological process is nearly the same for all observers, but the perceptions are entirely different. The artificial conditions of the experiment may perhaps give us some indication of what happens to each of us in learning to perceive the physical world as we do perceive it, and may also lead us to consider that there may be more individual variation in the perception of the same physical world than we commonly assume. The variations of different observers and of the same observer at different times indicate that the percep-

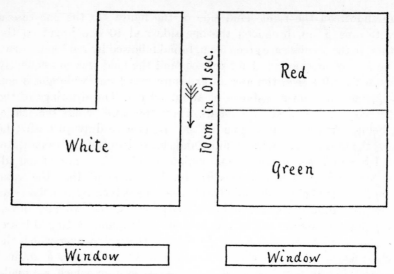

FIG. 4.—The stimuli as described in the text are shown above.   On the right hand page is shown the way these stimuli looked to ten different observers.

tion of a series of time changes in the retina as a spatial continuum must be learned by the individual, and may lead us to realize what a complete chaos the visual world must present to the infant.

In these experiments the eye cannot begin to move during the exposure of the stimulus, as the time is one-tenth of a second, while it takes about two-tenths of a second for the eye to move in answer to a stimulus. If the time of exposure is as long as 0.2 sec. then the eye may move with the stimulus and the field of the retina stimulated may be larger than the window. Zöllner[1] observed that a circle moved under a narrow slit in a screen appears like an ellipse, and von Helmholtz[2] explains the fact by movements of the eye. He remarks: "Um die Figur erkennen zu können, muss man ihr eben mit dem Auge folgen." But this, as Zöllner himself had previously shown, is incorrect; the phenomenon may occur through movements of the eye or without any movements. If the circle is 5 cm. in diameter and the window 1 cm. in width, we see an ellipse wider than the slit or even a circle 5 cm. in diameter, although the eyes are perfectly stationary. The eyes can be kept stationary by fixing a white spot on the edge of the window; if the eyes move, the movement is betrayed by a motion of the after-image.

[1] *Poggendorff's Ann.*, 117: 477–484, 1862. Since the present article was written a study of the illusion has been published by Mr. C. C. Stewart (*Am. Journ. of Psychol.*, 11: 240–243, dated Jan., 1900).

[2] *Physiologische Optik*, 2d Ed., p. 749, 1895.

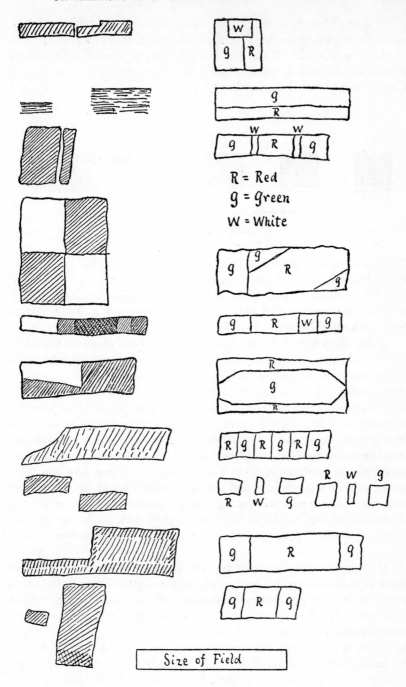

R = Red
g = Green
W = White

Size of Field

If three white squares (whose sides are 2 cm. and which are separated from each other by 2 cm.) are moved across the field of vision at the rate of about 10 cm. per second, and are viewed with the eyes motionless through a window one cm. wide, I see simultaneously the three squares crowded together and blurred as shown in the figure.

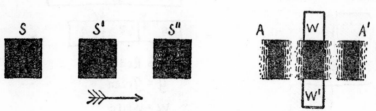

FIG. 5.—The squares at the left appear as shown at the right when seen as they pass the window (ww') of the size indicated.

If the motion is more rapid the squares overlap, and finally coincide. If the motion is slower the squares are seen to move across the field, but the perception is not that of one square replacing the preceding on the same field, but of three squares moving along and separated from each other by 2 cm.

These phenomena, again, are similar to those of perception with the moving eye. When the line of vision passes over objects which successively stimulate the same retinal areas we do not see a change in the same field, one object taking the place of the other, but the objects following each other in time are seen contiguous to each other in space. So when objects move and successively stimulate the same retinal area, they may be seen side by side and spread over a larger area than is stimulated. But there is the difference, already discussed, that with the moving eye there is no fusion or blurring, however rapid the change in stimulation, and the space relations of the objects remain the same whatever the rate of movement, whereas when the objects move there is partial fusion when the rate is 10 cm. per second, and the apparent space relations vary with the rate of motion.

The phenomena described for vision also hold for touch. If the finger is moved along a rough edge, as the teeth of a saw, the same points of the skin are touched consecutively, but an extended object is perceived. Here, as in the case of vision with the moving eye, we have the muscular sense as a factor in the total perception. But when the finger is stationary and the edge moves over the finger we have the perception not so much of one touch after another on the finger as of an extended moving object. In this case the illusion that the finger is moving is very strong.

Some of the results of this research may be summarized as follows:

(1) When objects are moved slowly over a limited visual field, while the eyes are stationary, they are not seen one after the other at the place where they are exhibited, but seem spread out over a larger area than can be seen. When successive white or colored surfaces pass over a limited field of vision so rapidly that the eye cannot be moved while they are in view, the stimuli do not seem to follow one another, but are perceived simultaneously side by side, variously arranged and commingled. What is physically a stimulus lasting a certain time and physiologically a series of changes in time is psychologically an area in which the colors are spread out side by side, and the processes in time are a spatial continuum. The colors appear in this case to cover a larger area than is exhibited.

(2) Observers differ greatly in their perception of exactly the same physical stimulus under these artificial conditions. On the first exposure there is usually no definite perception, but as the experiment is repeated the observer tends to perceive the stimulus always in the same way, although two observers rarely or never have the same perception. The perception with some observers alters greatly when they know what the stimulus is or what others see; with other observers it is not altered. These phenomena indicate that visual perceptions are built up by the individual in the course of experience and may differ greatly in different individuals. For the infant the visual world is probably a chaos.

(3) When the eyes are moved so that the line of sight passes over objects, we have one after another stimulating the same retinal field, but we perceive the objects simultaneously side by side. A series of physiological processes in time is perceived as a spatial continuum. The same phenomena obtain for touch. In the case of vision the changes in the field may be very rapid—more than one thousand per second—and yet there is no fusion. We have, however, movement of the field and partial fusion when the head is shaken. The different results with the moving eye and with objects in motion (the retinal processes being the same) prove that the phenomena of fusion and color-vision are cerebral and mental rather than retinal.

(4) In general these experiments show that perceptions are not "copies" of a physical world or the "inner side" of special physiological processes, but are in large measure the result of experience and utility. The phenomena of vision as a whole require this conclusion, but the facts here described, showing that changes in time are perceived as extension in space, appear to be of fundamental importance for psychology and for epistemology.

VISION WITH THE MOVING EYE

A brief note printed in *The Psychological Review*, **1**: 507–508, 1894, which comments on certain differences between the above report and a paper published by Raymond Dodge under the title, "Visual Perception during Eye Movement," *The Psychological Review*, **1**: 454–465, 1894.

In view of Professor Dodge's experiments, published in the present number of the REVIEW, I am uncertain as to the validity of the hypothesis advanced by me to explain the lack of fusion in vision with the moving eye.[1] I had planned similar experiments, but was unable to make them, although I held my paper for a year,[2] in the hope of being able to do so. Having made the observation that there is no fusion in the vision of daily life when the eye is in constant motion, I attempted to explain the fact by assuming that the visual organs respond to retinal changes more rapidly when the eye moves than when the objects are in motion. Professor Dodge finds that there is fusion when objects are exposed only when the eye is moving. It would follow from this that the hypothesis discussed in my paper, but there rejected, must be accepted or at least considered. This is, that there is clear vision only in the pauses of movement, there being no peripheral perceptions while the eye is moving and the apparent distinctness of the field being an illusion. This hypothesis will not interfere with the chief conclusion of my paper, for, as I said, "if one had in fact only a few distinct images in the course of the movement, it would remain true that a series of successive images is seen as a space continuum." Indeed, if it turns out to be true that we have no perceptions corresponding to the retinal changes while the eye is moving, but supply centrally the perception that we should have if the eye were at rest, this would further support my argument for the dependence of perceptions on utility and experience rather than on the nature of the physical stimuli.

[1] This REVIEW, **7**: 325–343, July, 1900.
[2] It was presented to the Physical Section of the American Association for the Advancement of Science in August, 1899.

17

THE TIME OF PERCEPTION AS A MEASURE
OF DIFFERENCES IN INTENSITY

A paper prepared at Columbia University and printed in English in *Philosophische Studien*, **19**: 63–68, 1902. It was contributed to a Festschrift presented to Wilhelm Wundt by his former students upon his seventieth birthday. The Festschrift comprises volumes 19 and 20 of the Philosophische Studien.

When a student at Leipzig under Professor Wundt, I made some experiments on the time required to estimate the size of lines of different lengths and in briefly communicating the results said:

Mit den horizontalen Linien stellte ich eine ziemlich grosse Zahl von Versuchen an, da ich das Verhältniss zwischen der Länge der Linie und dem mittleren Fehler (psychophysisches Gesetz) einerseits und dem Fehler und der zum Urtheil gebrauchten Zeit anderseits kennen zu lernen wünschte. Ich halte es indessen für wünschenswerth, die Zahl der Versuche noch weiter zu vermehren, bevor ich die Resultate veröffentliche).[1]

The problem here indicated has always seemed to me important and I have taken it up on several occasions,[2] but the solution requires a larger number of routine experiments than I have found time to carry out. I may, however, take this occasion to present some preliminary results of a research begun at Leipzig and following lines laid down by the eminent founder and director of the Leipzig Laboratory.

Weber's work on the relation between the magnitude of the stimulus and the just noticeable difference and Fechner's deduction of a logarithmic relation between stimulus and sensation have been followed by a large number of experimental researches and an extensive literature. In the experiments and discussion I have shared.[3] I have argued that in most of our experiments we have measured the error of observation, which determines the accuracy of perception, but does not measure the intensity of sensation. This holds for experiments

---

[1] Philos. Studien, IV, S. 250. 1888.

[2] Proceedings of the American Psychological Association for 1893. Professor Münsterberg has, however, anticipated me in the publication of experiments on the length of lines, cf. A psychometric investigation of the psychophysic law. Psychological Review, vol. I, p. 45–51. 1894.

[3] On the perception of small differences (with Professor G. S. Fullerton), University of Pennsylvania, 1892. On Errors of Observation. Amer. Journ. of Psychol. 1893.

by the methods of average error and of right and wrong cases. The method of just observable difference appears to me to have been used ambiguously. On the one hand, it may be reduced to the method of right and wrong cases, when the wrong cases are but few and the determination is difficult. On the other hand, the observer may seek to make the differences equally noticeable, in which case the results are analogous to those of the method of mean gradation and really estimate differences in sensation. Such estimates are, however, inexact, lacking an objective criterion. Different observers or the same observers at different times vary greatly in their estimates of equally noticeable differences. It seems that these estimates may be based on the known objective relations of the stimuli, and consequently can not be used to determine a relation between the sensation and the stimulus.

It is, however, possible to approach the problem from a new direction. An observer can not decide with any certainty when the difference in one pair of sensations is equal to the difference in another pair, but the time it takes to perceive a difference can be measured. The smaller the difference between two sensations, the greater is the time required to perceive it. When differences require equal times for discrimination, the discrimination is equally difficult, and the differences are equal for consciousness. A gray physically midway between white and black looks more like white than black, but observers differ greatly in the gray that they select as midway between white and black. If, however, we measure the time required to discriminate black from a gray reflecting 50% of the light, we find it to be shorter than the time required to discriminate the gray from white. We can in this way find the gray equally difficult to discriminate from white and black, and this is the gray which for consciousness is midway between white and black. By the same method it is possible to make a complete scale of equal increments in sensation between white and black, and for the range of intensity or quality in any sense.

I have made experiments with intensities of light and sound, with differences in color and with lines, but will here record only the first mentioned. I should, however, like to call attention to the fact that apart from the measurement of sensation the method offers an excellent way to test differences in sensibility. For example, a person with normal color-vision takes about as long to discriminate red from green, as to discriminate yellow from blue. A person who belongs to one of the classes of red-green color-blindness takes a much longer time to discriminate red from green than to discriminate yellow from blue. This method of testing color-blindness follows closely the actual requirements of the railway service for stopping trains by color signals, in which case the determination of color-blindness is of practical importance.

In the experiments on the intensity of light, I used various methods. These included a method of securing a given physical difference by altering the angle of incidence of the rays of light, which constitutes, I believe, a new form of photometer, having certain advantages. I found it, however, most convenient to use gray surfaces, reflecting a known percentage of the light. These surfaces were washed with Indian ink. The ink was made as black as possible, and one piece of drawing paper was washed; then a drop of water was added to the ink, another piece was washed, and the process was continued until the wash became imperceptible. In this way 211 shades between black and white were obtained. These grays (in cards 5 cm. sq.) were then tested by various photometric methods. The series proved to have a fairly regular gradation, except that the steps increased toward the white end, the gray 95 steps from white being midway between white and absolute black.

Such a series of grays[1] is suitable for testing the accuracy of discrimination and its variation under different circumstances, as with the intensity of the stimulus, in memory, etc. The physical differences are smaller than can be perceived, and if an observer arranges the grays as nearly as possible in the order of brightness, errors occur which measure the accuracy of discrimination. Thus in ten trials— the first two by the present writer and the others by eight different observers—the errors of displacement were as follows: 6.63, 7.97, 6.04, 6.2, 7.44, 7.81, 8.29, 8.77, 9.68, 11.5. The arrangement can be made in about an hour, and, as there are over 200 separate judgments, the average has a probable error of only about 0.5. Observers differ within the extremes of about 1.2 which agrees with other determinations. For the more accurate observers the error is 6 cards, or about $\frac{1}{35}$th of the range between black and white. The degrees that appeared just noticeable when these were selected were between 13 and 32, but errors occurred in the case of the larger number.

When the results of the ten series are combined and the relation of the error of displacement to the intensity is considered, it is found that while the error increases with the stimulus, it does so more slowly than required by Weber's law. The average displacement for each of seven groups of 30 cards (allowance being made for the longer steps between the brighter cards) was, approximately, 13.61, 10.06, 12.14, 10.03, 6.46, 5.09, 2.98.

[1] A hundred grays forming equal physical steps could be selected that would be preferable to this series of 211 cards.

In the table are given: (I) the approximate percentage of light reflected from the middle gray in each of the seven groups, that is the magnitude of the stimulus; (II) the error of observation in terms of percentages of light between white and an absolute black; (III) the error of observation in terms of the magnitude of the stimulus to the nearest whole fraction; (IV) the error of observation in terms of percentages of the magnitude, and (V) the error of observation in terms of percentages of the square root of the magnitude.

I	II	III	IV	V
85	5.44	$\frac{1}{16}$	6.4	59
68	4.02	$\frac{1}{16}$	5.9	49
56	4.85	$\frac{1}{14}$	8.7	65
44	4.01	$\frac{1}{11}$	9.1	60
32	2.58	$\frac{1}{12}$	8.1	46
20	2.03	$\frac{1}{10}$	10.2	45
8	1.19	$\frac{1}{7}$	14.9	42

It appears, consequently, that as the stimulus increases the error of observation increases, but not so rapidly as the stimulus, being about $\frac{1}{7}$ with the weakest and $\frac{1}{16}$ with the strongest stimulus. It increases much more nearly in direct proportion to the square root of the stimulus, in accordance with the hypothesis I have proposed in place of Weber's law. This hypothesis—The error of observation tends to increase as the square root of the magnitude, the increase being subject to variation whose amount and cause must be determined for each special case—has not as yet received the consideration which the experimental evidence and theoretical explanation seem to me to warrant.

The photometric cards were made, as has been stated, for experiments in which differences in intensity were to be measured by the time of perception. Two gray surfaces, each 3 × 3 cm. and of different intensities, were mounted side by side; the card was thus 6 × 3 cm. and, viewed from a distance of 40 cm., was of convenient size for distinct vision. It was exposed by means of a dropping screen on the general plan of the gravity chronometer used by me at Leipzig. The screen was, however, of aluminium, and was drawn down by a long spiral spring, so that the rate of motion when the card was exposed was about 10 m. per sec. The exposure appeared to be instantaneous, the card being uncovered in 3σ and the registration being made with exactness. The Hipp chronoscope was used in the usual manner, being carefully regulated, so that its variable and constant errors were smaller than 1σ. The observer reacted with right or left hand in accordance with the character of the stimulus—whether, *e.g.*, the brighter card was to the right or left. For white the card was painted with zinc oxyde, and a nearly absolute black was secured by using a hole in a black box.

In the following table are given in σ the times of discrimination and movement of two observers (including the writer, C), when the differences in the lights were as stated. Each entry is the result of 100 measurements. The mean variation was between 10 and 20σ in the different series, and the probable error of each is consequently between 1 and 2σ. The first three and the last four differences were used simultaneously.

Lights	Times		Differences	
	C	X	C	X
100: 0	231	243		
100:50	282	283	51	40
50: 0	240	246	9	3
100:75	311	317	80	74
75:50	274	293	43	40
50:25	268	285	37	41
25: 0	239	263	8	20

It will be seen by the table that white was discriminated from black and the movement made in 231 and 243σ. When the differences were made smaller the times became longer, and the probable errors and the agreement between the two observers prove the validity of the method. A gray midway between white and black could be more quickly discriminated from black than from white, and equal objective differences are more quickly discriminated when the magnitudes are smaller.

As has been indicated a large number of experiments would be required to determine by this method degrees of intensity equally easy to discriminate and consequently equal for consciousness. I have also made preliminary experiments with sounds, lines and colors, but, as it is uncertain when I shall complete them, it seems desirable to take advantage of the present occasion to publish the method.

18

STATISTICS OF AMERICAN PSYCHOLOGISTS

A paper contributed to a commemorative volume in honor of G. Stanley Hall upon the twenty-fifth anniversary of his attainment of the Doctorate in Philosophy, and presented to him by his students. It was printed in a special number of the *American Journal of Psychology*, **14**: 310–328, 1903.

To have the privilege of joining with other former students of President Hall in this volume, I must detach from an unfinished study of American men of science some statistics regarding our psychologists.

I have discussed in various papers the importance to psychology of the study of individual differences and have given some results of a research in which I am taking as the material one thousand students of Columbia College,[1] one thousand eminent men of history,[2] and one thousand American men of science.[3] The thousand men of science have been selected from some 4,000 included in a biographical dictionary that I am compiling, who, in turn, were selected from a list containing some 10,000 names.

On the lists are the names of 313 who appear to me to have contributed to the advancement of psychology. Among them are many whose work is unimportant, and several who have scarcely accomplished anything beyond teaching or the writing of a text-book. There are not included, however, those who have printed a minor study and have not again been heard from, nor most of those working in other sciences whose results may be valuable for psychology, but belong elsewhere. Excluding from the group nearly all those whose work is not primarily in psychology, or in psychology combined with philosophy or education, there remain 270. Omitting those whose work seems to be of the least value, and those whose addresses I have not been able to find or from whom I have no returns, I have taken a group of 200 for consideration. The first 150 or so have been selected objectively

[1] Physical and Mental Measurements of the Students of Columbia University (with Dr. Livingston Farrand). *Psychol. Rev.*, 3: 618–648, 1896. *Cf.* also "The Correlation of Mental and Physical Tests," C. Wissler. Monograph Supplement to the *Psychol. Rev.*, No. 16, 1900.

[2] *The Popular Science Monthly*, 57: 359–377, February, 1903.

[3] *Science*, N. S., 18: 561–570, April 10, 1903. Towards the cost of computation in connection with this research, I have received a grant of two hundred dollars from the Esther Herrman Research Fund of the Scientific Alliance of New York.

in the manner described below, the last fifty are practically those that were left. For certain purposes four groups of fifty each have been used, the first group consisting of those whose work is supposed to have the greatest merit, the second group ranking next, etc.

I have distributed scientific men among twelve principal sciences—mathematics, physics, chemistry, astronomy, geology, botany, zoölogy, physiology, anatomy, pathology, anthropology, and psychology. As there are about 200 psychologists among some 4,000 students of science, the psychologists are about one-twentieth of the scientific workers of the country. They are about equal in number to the astronomers; they are more numerous than the physiologists, anatomists, or anthropologists, and are fewer than the workers in the other principal sciences.

In each of these sciences I have asked ten leading representatives to arrange the students in that science in the order of merit. I did this (1) to select for special study the thousand regarded as the most meritorious; (2) to be able to discuss distribution in relation to merit, and to correlate merit with various qualities; (3) to learn the meaning and validity of such judgments, and (4) to have on record the order with a view to reference or possible publication ten or twenty years hence.

The memorandum sent to those who were asked to make the arrangement was as follows:

MEMORANDUM

The undersigned is making a study of American men of science. The first problem to be considered is the distribution of scientific men among the sciences and in different regions, institutions, etc., including the relative rank of this country as compared with other countries in the different sciences, the relative strength of different universities, etc. It is intended that the study shall be continued beyond the facts of distribution to what may be called the natural history of scientific men.

For these purposes a list of scientific men in each science, arranged approximately in the order of merit, is needed. This can best be secured if those who are most competent to form an opinion will independently make the arrangement. The average of such arrangements will give the most valid order, and the degree of validity will be indicated by the variation or probable error of position for each individual.

It is obvious that such an order can be only approximate, and for the objects in view an approximation is all that is needed. The judgments are possible, because they are as a matter of fact made in elections to a society of limited membership, in filling chairs at a university, etc. By merit is understood contributions to the advancement of science, primarily by research, but teaching, administration, editing, the compilation of text-books, etc., should be considered. The different factors that make a man efficient in advancing science must be roughly balanced. An effort may be made later to disentangle these factors.

In ranking a man in a given science his contributions to that science only should be considered. Thus, an eminent astronomer may also be a mathematician, but in ranking him as a mathematician only his contributions to mathematics should be regarded. In such a case, however, mathematics should be given its widest interpretation. It is more difficult to arrange the order when the work cannot readily be compared, as, for example, systematic zoölogy and morphology, but, as already stated, it is only expected that the arrangement shall be approximate. The men should be ranked for work actually accomplished,—that is, a man of sixty and a man of forty, having done about the same amount of work, should come near together, though the man of forty has more promise. It may be possible later to calculate a man's value with allowance for age.

In case there is noted the omission of any scientific man from the list who should probably have a place in the first three quarters, a slip may be added in the proper place with his name and address. In case there are names on the list regarding which nothing is known, the slips should be placed together at the end. The slips, as arranged in order, should be tied together and returned to the undersigned.

It is not intended that the lists shall be published, at all events not within ten years. No individual list will be published. They will be destroyed when the averages have been calculated, and the arrangements will be regarded as strictly confidential.

The attitude of those asked to make the arrangement was itself a matter of some slight psychological interest. Most of those asked consented, but for one reason or another a considerable number failed. For example, the ten psychologists whom I selected proved to be the ten at the head of the list. All but one of these undertook to make the arrangement; but one gave it up on account of the difficulty, one arranged the names in groups instead of serially, and two delayed the matter. For these substitutes were secured. Many of those who made the arrangement stated that they had but little confidence in its validity; but the results of combining the ten series show that the judgments do have a certain validity, which is itself measurable.

The table gives the results for the fifty psychologists esteemed the most meritorious. The first column, printed in heavy type, gives the serial order in which they stand, the second column the positions as deduced from the average of the ten arrangements, and the third column the probable errors of these positions. The four remaining columns give the probable error obtained by the easiest method, and the order when the figures are compiled in accordance with the different methods described below. It should be distinctly noted that these

TABLE I.—ORDER, POSITIONS AND PROBABLE ERRORS ASSIGNED TO THE FIRST FIFTY AMERICAN PSYCHOLOGISTS

Order	Positions	P.E.	p.e.	Orders		
				II	III	IV
1	1.0	0.0	0.0	1	1	1
2	3.7	0.5	0.6	2	2	2
3	4.0	0.5	0.4	3	3	3
4	4.4	0.6	0.6	4	4	4
5	7.5	1.0	0.9	5	5	6
6	7.5	1.2	1.3	6	8	5
7	7.6	0.4	0.3	9	9	9
8	9.2	1.5	1.2	7	6	7
9	9.6	0.6	0.7	10	10	10
10	11.6	3.0	2.3	8	7	8
11	12.3	1.0	1.1	11	11	11
12	16.8	1.7	1.4	12	12	13
13	17.1	1.6	1.6	14	13	16
14	17.9	2.1	2.3	13	14	12
15	18.7	1.4	1.5	15	15	14
16	19.3	1.3	1.4	19	17	17
17	19.6	1.6	1.6	18	18	15
18	21.6	2.7	2.4	16	16	19
19	21.8	1.2	1.3	20	21	18
20	22.4	1.6	1.3	21	20	20
21	24.5	3.4	3.4	17	19	21
22	27.0	2.0	2.0	23	25	22
23	29.5	4.8	3.9	22	22	23
24	37.5	2.4	2.5	26	24	26
25	37.7	5.4	5.0	24	23	24
26	40.4	6.5	7.3	27	26	27
27	41.6	6.2	7.0	25	27	25
28	42.9	4.1	4.2	30	28	32
29	44.7	4.1	4.2	29	29	31
30	44.9	4.1	4.6	34	30	38
31	45.5	4.5	4.4	31	31	35
32	46.4	4.8	4.9	32	32	33
33	47.1	5.2	5.7	37	33	30
34	48.0	5.5	5.5	28	34	28
35	49.3	6.6	7.4	35	35	29
36	49.6	4.9	4.8	38	36	39
37	49.9	5.9	6.0	33	37	34
38	51.1	5.3	5.3	40	38	40
39	52.6	5.7	6.1	39	39	37
40	53.3	5.7	5.8	36	40	41
41	54.5	4.1	4.6	41	41	42
42	54.5	5.6	6.9	52	42	45
43	56.2	5.3	5.9	42	43	53
44	56.5	6.6	8.0	43	44	43
45	58.6	4.6	5.1	45	45	48
46	59.0	5.0	4.6	46	46	46
47	59.0	7.1	8.7	51	47	51
48	59.2	5.7	6.9	44	48	36
49	59.2	6.2	7.1	47	49	44
50	59.6	3.7	4.0	49	50	49

figures give only what they profess to give, namely, the resultant opinion of ten competent judges. They show the reputation of the men among experts, but not necessarily their ability or performance. Constant errors, such as may arise from a man's being better or less known than he deserves, are not eliminated. There is, however, no other criterion of a man's work than the estimation in which it is held by those most competent to judge. The posthumous reputation of a great man may be more correct than contemporary opinion, but very few of those on this list of psychologists will be given posthumous consideration. I am somewhat skeptical as to merit not represented by performance, or as to performance unrecognized by the best contemporary judgment. There are doubtless individual exceptions, but, by and large, men do what they are able to do and find their proper level in the estimation of their colleagues.

It will be noticed that the probable errors tend to increase from the top of the list downward. These errors show the validity of position and also the amount of difference between the men. No. 3, with a grade of 4 and a probable error of 0.5, has about one chance in three of being higher than the grade of No. 2, or of being lower than that of No. 4. The chances are more than 10,000 to one that he is not as high as No. 1,[1] or as low as No. 5. At the bottom of the list the probable errors show that the positions are probably correct within about ten places. The chances are about one in four that No. 40 does not belong among the first fifty psychologists.

The men at the top of the list differ much more from each other than the men at the bottom. The average probable error of the first ten is less than one, and they cover a range of about ten points; the average probable error of the last ten is about six, and they cover a range of about five points. If we may assume that the differences between the men are directly as the difference in grade and inversely as the probable error, there is about twelve times as much difference between the individuals near the top of the list as between those near the bottom. It is as easy for a man towards the bottom to gain twelve places in the estimation of his colleagues, as for a man near the top to gain one place. There is about as much difference between No. 1 and No. 2, as between No. 2 and No. 8, which again is about equal to the difference between No. 24 and No. 50.[2]

The table indicates that the differences are not continuous, but

---

[1] No. 1, having a probable error of 0, has his position determined in the negative direction only by the positions and probable errors of Nos. 2, 3 and 4.

[2] I am quite willing that these statements shall be regarded as rough approximations. There are certain theoretical questions involved which I hope to discuss on a subsequent occasion.

that there is a tendency towards the formation of groups or species. This may be due to accidental breaks in the series, but similar breaks in approximately the same places occur in other sciences. Among the psychologists, and in several other sciences, there is one man who stands distinctly at the head, completely separated from those next to him. Should No. 1 die, his place would not be taken by No. 2, but Nos. 2, 3, and 4, and others would each be raised a little. This man is a great genius, who has an international, and will have a posthumous reputation. Then, among the psychologists we have a distinctly marked group of three; they are men who doubtless have a reputation beyond their own science and their own country. There is next a group of seven, so well marked that it is very unlikely that any one of them belongs above or below this group. There is next an equally distinctly marked group of twelve. The break at the end of this group is eight whole points, and would be fifteen points did not the individual Nos. 21, 22, and 23 partly bridge it. Nos. 21 and 23 have comparatively large probable errors, and in my opinion belong to the upper group. No. 22 appears to me to belong to the upper group by ability, and to the lower group by performance, and will probably join later one or the other group. There is, consequently, a well-marked break separating the first 20 or 23 psychologists from those below. The chances are very great[1] against Nos. 19 or 20, being as low as the grade of No. 24. The break is also shown in the probable errors, which increase almost suddenly from about 2 to about 6. The average age of the group from No. 12 to No. 23, is 40 years. It appears to me that not more than three or four of those in the lower group will ever pass over to the upper group. There is about the same percentage further down in the second and third fifties who are nearly as likely to enter the first group. We thus seem to have two main groups or types; the leaders, and the men of moderate attainments, the leaders being about one-tenth of the whole number. The leaders are again broken into four groups—say, of great genius, of moderate genius, of considerable talent, and of talent.[2] It appears that analogous groups are found in other sciences, and it is probable that they also exist in other lines of intellectual activity and performance.

The lower group, from 24 to 50, and on down to the end of the 200, shows no further break and no very great increase in mediocrity.

---

[1] More than a million to one. It seems fair to emphasize the accuracy of this determination, showing that psychology even in cases as complicated as this can rival in exactness the physical sciences.

[2] The two lower groups are not, however, uniform; they include two or three men who would rank higher for their contributions to philosophy, and two or three who are young and will almost certainly advance to a higher group.

The group is heterogeneous and may be divided into three main sub-groups—psychologists of moderate ability who have found their level; young men who may improve their positions, even going to the top of the list; and students of other subjects, almost exclusively philosophy or education, who have made, or are supposed to have made, contributions to psychology.

In the average positions given in the table, the ten arrangements are included without omissions. Those who made the arrangements do not, however, possess equal information or judgment, and here again it is possible to measure traits that at first sight appear to be scarcely comparable. The table gives the average variation of the judgments of each observer from the average of the judgments of the ten observers. Data are given for groups of ten (I, the ten psychologists highest on Table I, etc.), which show a considerable degree of constancy. The observer A is always more accurate than any other

TABLE II.—MEASUREMENTS OF THE ACCURACY OF JUDGMENT OF TEN OBSERVERS

	A	B	C	D	E	F	G	H	I	J	Av.
I............	1.6	5.2	2.3	3.1	1.9	2.8	1.8	2.4	5.0	2.6	2.87
II...........	4.9	7.0	8.7	7.8	6.3	4.2	10.2	6.1	7.0	5.1	6.73
III..........	7.1	11.1	13.5	12.4	24.2	16.2	12.5	12.0	16.9	27.6	15.35
IV...........	13.8	18.0	16.7	18.4	18.8	18.1	22.7	25.4	21.9	25.5	19.93
V............	12.1	17.4	21.1	21.1	13.2	26.6	21.7	24.7	22.9	25.5	20.63
Av...........	7.9	11.74	12.46	12.56	12.88	13.58	13.78	14.12	14.74	17.26	13.1
V............	-5.20	-1.36	-0.64	-0.54	-0.25	$+0.48$	$+0.68$	$+1.02$	$+1.64$	$+4.16$	±1.60

observer, except in one case in the fifty. The validity of judgment of the ten observers varies from 7.9 to 17.26, or about as 1 : 2, which is approximately the variability that I have found in normal individuals in other mental traits, accuracy of perception time of mental processes, memory, etc. The departures from the mean reliability of judgment, given in the last line of the table, indicate that accuracy of judgment tends in a general way to follow the normal distribution of the probability curve. As the validity of the judgments vary to a measured degree, the arrangements made by the individuals should be weighted. I have not undertaken the somewhat tedious calculations necessary; they would not considerably alter the order, but would make it somewhat more exact, at the same time decreasing the probable errors.

Taking the individual departures from the mean of the ten estimates in each case (the residuals or errors), and reducing them to a common standard, we secure the distribution of the 500 "errors" shown in the figure. The curve is fairly regular, but asymmetrical. The judgments do not follow the distribution of the probability curve and do not represent the typical case of errors due to a large number of independent and small causes equally likely to be positive or negative. The average judgment would give a man a lower grade than the median judgment, and this again is lower than the mode or most common judgment. This means that in judging the position of a man, the individual judgments are more likely to depart considerably from the average in placing him too low than too high. This is especially the case for men near the top of the list. The judgments do not, how-

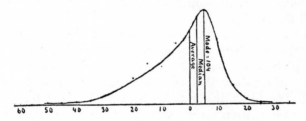

FIG. 1.—Distribution of "errors" of judgment.

ever, depart abnormally from the mean. According to Chauvenet's criterion, there should not be in 500 observations any over about five times the probable error. There are in this series but three departures larger than this, which all occur near the top of the list, and in the negative direction. The regular character of the curve seems to show that the extreme judgments are not abnormal. There is no evident group or species, due to ignorance, prejudice or the like, such as might conceivably have existed.

Under these circumstances, we may ask, what is the most probable position of the individuals? Should we take the average, median or mode, or possibly some compromise, such as would be obtained by omitting certain of the more divergent judgments? It seems to me that any of these procedures would be correct, but that the meaning would be different in each case. The average is what it professes to be—the average judgment; here a single unfavorable judgment is more likely to be large than a favorable one, and a single judgment may pull a man down further than it can lift him up. The median is also what it professes to be—the middle judgment, omitting the divergent judgments and not taking into account the size of the departures. The mode, or most common judgment, comes out clearly as the result of 500 measures, but would not in the case of the ten judgments for each individual. It has seemed to me that in many psychological measurements, there is something to be said for a compromise between the average and the median.[1] The curve of distribution is usually asymmetrical, and the more divergent measures may be due to abnormal conditions. Experimenters have been led to reject observations that appeared to be abnormal, and have sometimes done so in a way that has invalidated their results. I can see no theoretical objection to a criterion such as Chauvenet's, or to the plan used by me of rejecting in each series a certain fixed number of the more divergent results, the average of the entire and of the corrected series being given. It is an advantage to do away with incorrect or even abnormal values in an objective manner, and so far as normal values are eliminated, we are simply adopting a compromise between the mean and the median.

In the case before us, the regular character of the curve of distribution and the fact that the departures are scarcely larger than the theory of probabilities would lead us to expect in the case of an orthodox distribution, show that the more divergent judgments are not abnormal. The most divergent errors were in the cases of Nos. 10 and 21, and it appears to me that there is some slight chance that each of these extreme judgments is correct—a larger chance, indeed, than the theory of probability indicates. On the other hand, the incidence of these extreme judgments on the individual seems unfair. If we had a hundred judgments of each individual, we might expect one so divergent, but its effect would be nearly eliminated in the average. When a hundred judgments are given to ten individuals, we may expect that there is some slight chance that one of these individuals should be considerably lower than his grade indicates; but the incidence on a particular individual seems to be a matter of chance. Thus, No. 10 is by a single divergent judgment carried down two places and given a probable error three times as large as he would otherwise have. The use of the median or the omission of the more divergent judgments by Chauvenet's criterion, or otherwise, tends to give most the individuals a higher grade, but scarcely alters the position of any one beyond the limits already indicated by the probable error.[2]

I have used in my discussion, the simple averages from all the judgments. In the table, however, is given the order of the individuals when the two highest and the two lowest judgments are discarded

[1] Psychometrische Untersuchungen. Philos. Stud. 8: 316 f., 1886.

[2] One disadvantage in the use of the median or in the adoption of any criterion rejecting the more divergent observations, is that it becomes difficult or impossible to assign a probable error. Attention should be called to the fact that the probable errors deduced by the ordinary formulas, and given in the table, do not hold for a curve of distribution such as we have here. They must be regarded as approximations only.

(Order II), when Chauvenet's criterion is approximately applied[1] (Order III), and when the median is taken (Order IV).

A careful consideration of the individual figures leads me to believe that the use of all the judgments is quite satisfactory, the exceptional judgments not altering the positions to a considerable extent, or beyond the limits of the probable errors except in one case. I am inclined to believe, however, that the most valid order is that in which the six most accordant judgments were used, and the order next in validity is that in which Chauvenet's criterion is applied.[2] The median seems to be the least satisfactory determination, as, owing to the comparatively small number of observations, the position is determined by chance.

There are given two probable errors. The former (P.E.), has been deduced by way of the squares of the residuals, the latter (p.e.) by multiplying the mean variation by 0.28.[3] There is really but little difference in the results, and in view of the character of the curve of distribution, I doubt whether this is significant. It seems to me to be a waste of time to use the method of least squares in such cases.

The curve of distribution of the men on the list approaches roughly the distribution of the probability curve at the positive end. We have, as a matter of fact, only fifty psychologists on the table given above, and if we assume that all the psychologists of the country form a "species," we have only the upper fourth or fifth of the distribution. On the average about one hundred psychologists were arranged in the order of merit by the ten observers, but the number varied from 53 to 175. I have counted out the order and the probable errors up to 120 places, but after about 75 places they have not much validity. When an individual was not included on one of the lists, he was given a grade about midway among those omitted; but this procedure is inexact and tends to decrease unduly the probable errors. It would be of interest to secure the complete curve of distribution, but it is scarcely possible to do this, as the men in the lower half are not known to those who make the arrangements. In this case the sizes of the probable errors depend on the ignorance of the observer as well as on the similarity in merit of the men. I am myself fairly well acquainted with the work of our minor psychologists. When I undertake to

[1] That is, variations are omitted that are more than about three times the probable error, there being ten estimations in each series.

[2] The difficulty with Chauvenet's criterion is that the probable error is not very exactly determined in a series of ten judgments. Thus, if two divergent judgments in the same direction occur in a series of ten, the probable error is so enlarged that the divergent judgments are not eliminated, whereas they would be eliminated if we used the average probable error of the adjacent individuals.

[3] *I. e.* $\dfrac{\text{Av. E.} \times 0.845}{\sqrt{n-1}}$

rearrange the men, there is but little variation in the position of those near the top of the list, while the variations increase constantly as I go downward. Ten arrangements made by the same individual, would give an order and probable errors analogous to those of the table, but this is an experiment that cannot be made accurately, as the observer remembers his previous arrangements, thus introducing a large constant error. I, however, regard my own judgment as subject to a probable error somewhat similar in size to that given in the table as deduced from ten observations. This subjective probable error increases continuously as I go down the list, and I assume that there is no descending half on the negative side of the curve of distribution. Starting from the median man there is a rough approximation to the probability curve on the positive side, but on the negative side the curve continues to rise, but with increasing slowness. This refers to the great majority of those on the negative side of the median, their work being simply mediocre or unimportant. There are, however, a few individuals in each science whose work is inaccurate or bad. They belong to a different "species," and are scarcely comparable with the others. There would be some agreement as to their order, and they would form a descending curve. They are, however, far too few to balance those above the median. It should be noted that while for men whose work is well known the order and probable errors nearly coincide with their performance and ability, in the case of men who are imperfectly known, the probable errors are a function of this ignorance. If the men below the median were as well known as those above, the probable errors might not continue to increase as we go down. Among my students those weak in psychology do, in a general way, seem to balance those who are good, in accordance with the distribution of the probability curve. But the students on the minus side do not become professional psychologists. However, even if we assume that all the people of the country are psychologists of a sort, their distribution seems to be represented more nearly by the positive half of the probability curve than by the whole curve.

It is claimed by Mr. Galton and others that the probability curve represents the normal distribution of ability, the idiots balancing the geniuses, etc. But I am not sure that this is correct. For example, it seems to me that in poetic ability the great poets differ fully as much from the poor poets, as these do from the mass of mankind, and that the latter do not differ so much among themselves in poetic ability as do poets. Poetic ability would thus be distributed as suggested for psychological ability. Ability and performance may not be due to a large number of small causes equally likely to be positive or negative, but there may be a certain standard ability which may be increased by a few relatively large causes, hereditary and environmental, but not correspondingly decreased.

It is my intention to make a somewhat elaborate study of the natural history of American men of science. I am at present, however, only able to give in regard to the psychologists some statistics of their academic origin, course and destination. The accompanying table

TABLE III.—THE NUMBERS OF AMERICAN PSYCHOLOGISTS WHO HAVE STUDIED AT DIFFERENT INSTITUTIONS

	A.B.					Gd. stud.					Ph.D.					G.T.
	I	II	III	IV	T	I	II	III	IV	T	I	II	III	IV	T	
Columbia.....	2	1	4	3	10	2	1	2	4	9	3	5	9	6	23	42
Harvard......	2	6	2	1	11	7	5	4	0	16	4	4	5	2	15	42
Clark.........	..	..	..	..	...	2	3	4	4	13	4	5	5	4	18	31
Cornell.......	0	0	0	2	2	1	1	0	1	3	3	4	10	5	22	27
Yale..........	1	2	1	3	7	1	2	2	0	5	2	3	2	4	11	23
Princeton.....	3	6	2	4	15	..	..	..	..	...	1	3	0	1	5	20
Penn.........	3	3	0	2	8	0	1	2	1	4	1	2	1	1	5	17
Hopkins......	..	..	..	..	...	2	1	1	1	5	7	1	0	0	8	13
Amherst......	4	1	1	3	9	..	..	..	..	..	..	..	..	..	...	9
California.....	3	0	3	0	6	..	..	..	..	...	0	0	1	0	1	7
Indiana.......	2	2	0	3	7	..	..	..	..	..	..	..	..	..	...	7
Brown........	0	1	4	0	5	..	..	..	..	...	0	0	1	0	1	6
Chicago.......	0	0	2	0	2	..	..	..	..	...	0	1	2	1	4	6
Michigan.....	1	1	0	1	3	0	0	1	0	1	0	0	0	1	1	5
Nebraska.....	2	1	0	2	5	..	..	..	..	..	..	..	..	..	...	5
Rochester.....	1	2	0	1	4	..	..	..	..	..	..	..	..	..	...	4
Vermont......	2	0	2	0	4	..	..	..	..	..	..	..	..	..	...	4
Wesleyan.....	2	1	1	0	4	..	..	..	..	..	..	..	..	..	...	4
Williams......	2	1	1	0	4	..	..	..	..	..	..	..	..	..	...	4
Wisconsin.....	0	0	1	2	3	..	..	..	..	..	0	0	0	1	1	4
Lafayette.....	1	1	1	0	3	..	..	..	..	..	..	..	..	..	...	3
Stanford......	0	1	2	0	3	..	..	..	..	..	..	..	..	..	...	3
Berlin........	..	..	..	..	...	13	10	6	3	32	1	1	0	1	3	35
Leipzig.......	..	..	..	..	...	7	5	4	2	18	9	4	2	2	17	35
Heidelberg....	..	..	..	..	...	4	5	1	0	10	0	1	1	0	2	12
Göttingen.....	..	..	..	..	...	3	2	1	1	7	..	..	..	..	...	7
Freiburg......	..	..	..	..	...	2	0	1	1	4	1	1	0	1	3	7
Bonn.........	..	..	..	..	...	1	2	0	0	3	0	0	1	1	2	5
Jena..........	..	..	..	..	...	1	1	1	0	3	0	0	1	1	2	5
Strasburg.....	..	..	..	..	...	0	0	3	1	4	0	0	1	0	1	5
Zurich........	..	..	..	..	...	1	1	0	0	2	0	0	1	0	1	3
Paris.........	..	..	..	..	...	5	7	2	0	14	..	..	..	..	...	14
Cambridge....	0	0	0	1	1	2	1	0	1	4	..	..	..	..	...	5
Total.......	31	30	27	28	116	54	48	35	20	157	36	35	43	32	146	419

contains data regarding the education of the two hundred psychologists. There are given the numbers that took the A.B. or equivalent degree from various institutions, the numbers that pursued graduate studies without taking the doctor's degree at the given institution, and the numbers that were given the doctor's degree. Institutions are included that were attended by three or more students. Most of those who took the bachelor's degree pursued graduate studies, and they may be entered in the three different divisions. Those who took the doctor's degree were also graduate students at the institution granting it, but they are not entered under this heading in the table. Many pursued graduate studies at two or more universities and are included under each. There are consequently duplications in the second division, but not in the first or third. When a man has taken a bachelor's degree from more than one institution, he is credited to the first, and if the work at the second was specialized he is credited as a graduate student. The spirit rather than the letter of the classification has thus been followed. Each division of the table is divided into four columns, numbered I, II, III, IV, under which are the figures for the four groups into which the men have been classed, the fifty selected as the best being in the column under I, etc.

The most interesting fact shown by the tabulation appears to be the very large number of institutions—seventy-six—from which the 200 psychologists have come. The origin of the men is in general independent of the college at which they were educated, as is also their rank among psychologists. Harvard, with its strong department of philosophy and psychology, has not produced three times as many psychologists as Rochester, Vermont, Wesleyan, or Williams, though it has given its Bachelor's degree to far more than three times as many students. Yale, where philosophy and psychology have been required studies under able professors, has not produced twice as many psychologists as each of the colleges mentioned. Cornell has only produced half as many. Of the eleven psychologists from Harvard, only two are in the first fifty, and of the seven from Yale, only one. Some institutions have produced more than their share of psychologists, as Indiana and California, but probably not more than the theory of chance distribution would lead us to expect, except in the cases of Princeton and Amherst. At these two colleges there appears to be an influence strong enough to direct men to psychology.

There is, perhaps, no other information so desirable for applied psychology and sociology as knowledge of the extent to which the performance in life of the individual is due to what Mr. Galton has called nature and nurture, respectively. Our present knowledge is scanty and ambiguous, so that it is possible to hold extreme views without coming into conflict with facts. It may plausibly be argued that a man's career is chiefly prescribed by his equipment at birth, or chiefly by his environment, education, and opportunity. It appears to me that certain aptitudes, as for music, mathematics, etc., are chiefly innate, and that kinds of character and degrees of ability are largely innate. But I have been inclined to believe that the direction of performance was largely determined by circumstance, that a man who is a psychologist might, by a comparatively slight and accidental alteration in conditions, have become a zoölogist, or a lawyer, or a man of business, and have been almost equally successful in any career. This view seems to me, however, to be traversed by these statistics, which, as far as they go, indicate that psychologists are born, not made.

After the men have graduated from college, and when their work has been chosen, they are gathered for their special studies into a few universities. It does not seem, however, that they are turned into psychologists at these universities. They simply select for study the universities that have reputation and facilities, being often attracted by fellowships or the hope that the university will assist them in securing positions. The direction of the work is sometimes determined or influenced by the university, the merit of the work but slightly, if at all. Harvard, Clark, Columbia, Cornell, and Yale have contributed to the first group 4, 4, 3, 3, 2 doctors, respectively, and to the second group, 4, 5, 5, 4, 3. There are relatively more men in the third and fourth groups from Columbia and Cornell, which is in part due to the fact that Columbia has conferred the degree frequently in education, and Cornell in philosophy, and the men being ranked for their contributions to psychology come in the lower hundred. It should also be stated that my returns for Columbia are probably more complete than for the other universities. This would not affect the first hundred, but the total influence of Harvard shown by my statistics to be equal to that of Columbia, is probably somewhat greater. Harvard, Clark, and Columbia have had, according to the table, almost exactly the same number of graduate students; if, however, we add together the students under President Hall at the Johns Hopkins and Clark Universities, they surpass in numbers and in rank those of any other institution.

It will be noted that our psychologists have studied in Germany in large numbers, no less than thirty-five, both at Leipzig and at Berlin. Leipzig has exerted much the greater influence, having conferred seventeen doctorates on men who studied there from one to five years. Men record themselves as having pursued graduate studies at German universities when the time was a semester or less, whereas here it is practically always at least one year. It is noticeable that more men of the first group have studied and taken their degrees in Germany, and that the numbers decrease as the groups become lower. I should not interpret this as meaning that men are made better psychologists by going to Germany. Men of greater ability and enterprise are perhaps more likely to go to Germany, but the facts of the table are largely due to the circumstance that the older men have studied in Germany in much larger numbers than those who are younger.

The two hundred psychologists come originally from 76 institutions, they gather together for graduate study at a comparatively small number of universities, and are again widely dispersed. Nearly all the men are engaged in teaching, being distributed among 57 colleges and universities, 14 normal schools, and six other schools. There is, indeed, not a single person on the list who has not been engaged in teaching, though three or four have only given lecture courses incidentally. There are at present only eight who do not earn their livings by teaching or administrative educational work. I can give in quantitative terms the strength of the work in psychology in different institutions, but it may be wiser to postpone publication of the figures until all the sciences can be treated together.

It is fortunate for psychology that there are in this country so many teaching positions to be filled. Still, the conditions present certain serious drawbacks. The time of the men is occupied in teaching, and in administrative, clerical, or missionary work, which, together with their great dispersal, is not favorable to the cultivation of a spirit of scholarship and research. There is but small opportunity for natural selection, a kind of panmixia obtaining. In other sciences larger numbers of men are needed for school work, and from these the better can be selected for the college and university positions. In most sciences there is applied work, into which those who prove inept for research can overflow.

It appears to me that psychology in America has received fewer contributions from those not professionally engaged in teaching it than is the case in other countries. In Great Britain there has always been a group of men, largely selected from the wealthy classes, who have not earned their livings by teaching, but have devoted themselves to research and authorship. Psychology in Germany has received important and numerous contributions from physiology, physics, neurology, and other sciences to an extent not approached in America.

In order to compare our productivity with that of other nations, I have counted up the first thousand references in the index to the twenty-five volumes of the *Zeitschrift für Psychologie*. These are the papers published in, or reviewed by, the journal, and are doubtless supposed to be the more important contributions to psychology. In the table are given the numbers of contributions from each nation and a classification of the subject-matter. Germany leads in productivity, though German contributors are favored in the original articles and also in the reviews of the *Zeitschrift*. This appears to be especially the case under the heading "Physiological" (which includes pathological and physical papers). The French experimental papers include 48 by M. Binet, and if the classification had been carried to the end of the alphabet, the French contributions would have been relatively much fewer. I should infer from the table that America leads decidedly in experimental contributions to psychology, that we are about equal

TABLE IV.—CLASSIFICATION OF CONTRIBUTIONS TO PSYCHOLOGY

	Experimental	Theoretical	Physiological	Total
German..................	93	99	290	482
French..................	102	56	34	192
American................	111	31	11	153
English.................	7	25	31	63
Italian.................	9	9	39	57
Swiss...................	8	7	6	21
Belgian.................	8	5	4	17
Spanish.................	0	0	8	8
Dutch...................	2	2	0	4
Scandinavian............	1	1	1	3
Total................	344	235	424	1,000

to Great Britain in theoretical contributions, but are almost doubled by France and Germany, and that we are decidedly inferior to Germany, France, Great Britain, and Italy in contributions of a physiological and pathological character. The thousand contributions counted up extend into the *F*'s or to rather more than one-fourth of the index. Thus, somewhat less than six hundred American contributions in the course of ten years have been published in, or reviewed by, the *Zeitschrift*. There were not, during this period, as many as two hundred American psychologists. But in a general way it appears that each of our psychologists has on the average made a contribution of some importance only once in two or three years.

19

EXAMINATIONS, GRADES AND CREDITS

Printed in *The Popular Science Monthly* (now Scintffc Monthly), **66**: 367–378, (Feb.) 1905.

The determination of individual differences, the improvement of useful traits and the assignment of men to the work for which they are fit are among the most important problems in the whole range of pure and applied science. The extraordinary growth of the material sciences with their applications during the nineteenth century requires as its complement a corresponding development of psychology. It would under existing conditions be intolerable to erect a building without regard to the quality and strength of materials, to use at random a wooden beam or a steel girder; yet we often do much this thing in selecting men for their work and adjusting them to it.

In examinations and grades we attempt to determine individual differences and to select individuals for special purposes. It seems strange that no scientific study of any consequence has been made to determine the validity of our methods, to standardize and improve them. It is quite possible that the assigning of grades to school children and college students as a kind of reward or punishment is useless or worse; its value could and should be determined. But when students are excluded from college because they do not secure a certain grade in a written examination, or when candidates for positions in the government service are selected as the result of a written examination, we assume a serious responsibility. The least we can do is to make a scientific study of our methods and results.

Grades assigned to college students have some meaning, though just what this is remains to be determined. Dr. Wissler[1] has shown that there is a decided correlation in the standing in different subjects. A man who receives a high grade in Latin is likely to receive a high grade in Greek, and almost as likely to receive a high grade in mathematics or gymnastics. This seems to indicate that the grades are assigned for moral traits, or for the general impression made by the man, as much as for ability and performance in a given subject. Professor Thorndike and his students[2] have found a similar relation-

---

[1] "The Correlation of Mental and Physical Tests," Monograph Supplement to *The Psychological Review*, No. 16.

[2] Summarized in "Educational Psychology," Lemcke and Büchner, 1903.

ship in school grades and in the New York State Regents' examinations. Professor Dexter[1] has shown that a man who is given a high standing in college is more likely than others to find his name in "Who's Who in America." Phi Beta Kappa men (on the average the upper seventh of the class) are twice as likely to be there as others, and the first man in his class is five times as likely.[2]

It is evident that subjects differ greatly in examinability. The results of an examination in mathematics, for example, can be graded with considerable accuracy; they give fairly definite information as to the man's mathematical aptitudes, and mathematical ability is largely innate, so that here the boy is father to the man. The mathematical tripos at Cambridge is a real test. Of the fifty senior wranglers in the first half of the last century a very large number have attained eminence. For example, two of them, Sir George Gabriel Stokes and Dr. N. M. Ferrers, who died within a month preceding the writing of this paragraph, maintained both in mathematical performance and general efficiency the position of, say, first in a hundred given them as the result of a student examination. Two facts should, however, be borne in mind. The senior wrangler is given great opportunity by being made a fellow, and the examination is on three years of solid work. The results of examinations in scrappy courses lasting half a year are not nearly so valid.

Subjects such as literature and psychology do not lend themselves to written examinations so well as mathematics. I have had the same papers in psychology graded by different examiners and have found great variations in the results. There is some validity in the order of excellence, but scarcely any in the absolute grades, the variation of the grades for the same paper by different examiners being as large as the variation of different papers by the same examiners. I have not, however, confirmed this result by sufficient data. One of our courses in psychology is given by different instructors, each of whom sets and grades papers for the same student. The grades assigned are A, B, C, D and F—excellent, good, fair, poor and failure. Four instructors gave twenty-one men a total of 15 A's, 38 B's, 27 C's, 4 D's and 1 F. When, however, we average the grades of the four instructors, we get $3B+$, $17C+$ and $1D+$. All the grades are alike within the unit used, except four, and the probable errors of three of the four show that they are as likely as not to fall within this grade,

---

[1] "High Grade Men in College and Out," POP. SCI. MON., March, 1903.

[2] It must, however, be remembered that the kind of people who are put in a book such as "Who's Who" are largely those who talk about things rather than those who do things—the class that receives part payment for its services in notoriety.

while the probable error of the remaining grade gives it but moderate validity.

It seems scarcely possible to determine what students are fitted for a college course by means of a written examination; and I fear that the systematization of entrance examinations under the auspices of a board will be harmful to secondary education.[1] The German method, which has made some progress here, of leaving the decision to the school seems much better. If we can not accept the recommendation of the school, I should prefer to see the candidate passed upon by two psychological experts. If their independent judgment agreed, I should have more confidence in this than in the results of any written examination. In general, I should admit to college any students who were not pronounced unfit by expert opinion, dropping of course those who subsequently proved themselves unfit. Requiring all students to pass an examination in Latin composition and the like is as out of place in a modern university as an ichthyosaurus on Broadway.[2]

Our college entrance requirements and examinations are a serious injury to secondary education, and they select very imperfectly the men who should have a college education. Of 262 students who entered Columbia College in 1900, only 50 completed the regular four-year course in the college. Civil service examinations often exclude the fit from the public service. In Great Britain the method is carried to an extreme, and the results depend as much on the coach as on the candidate. Almost anything is better than appointments for party service; but past performance, character, habits, heredity and physical health are much more important than the temporary information that can be but imperfectly tested by a written examination. I should not be willing to select a fellow or an assistant in psychology by such a method, and to select a professor would be nearly as absurd as to choose a wife as the result of a written examination on her duties. To devise and apply the best methods of determining fitness is the business of the psychological expert, who will probably represent at the close of this century as important a profession as medicine, law or the church.

I am at present working at the problem of assigning grades for

[1] Since this was written Professor Thorndike has compiled statistics, not as yet published, which indicate that students who pass these examinations with the lowest grades are as likely to do well in college as those having much higher grades. Those rejected would probably do equally well.

[2] In the discussion now in progress at Cambridge concerning the requirement of Greek at entrance, Professor Jebb ridiculed New Zealand as a Greekless land, because one of its citizens is alleged to have called Andromache "Andromach." Professor Jebb in his speech called New Zealand a part of Australia; yet he does not regard himself as illiterate.

moral, mental and physical traits,[1] but shall here confine myself to a discussion of college grades. The literature is very scanty. I can only refer to two papers,[2] both of which are slight.

Grades are usually assigned on a scale of 100, some institutions, as Harvard and Columbia, reporting only the five groups into which the men are divided. The starting point in all grades is the fact that the written papers or the results of the term's work can be arranged more or less accurately in the order of merit.[3] The assignment of quantitative grades to a qualitative series or its division into groups is usually done in an arbitrary manner, and, so far as I am aware, no attempt has hitherto been made to assign probable errors. It is obvious that our grades should be standardized. Our colleges are in the position of a grocer who should let each of his clerks give to customers without weighing and without knowledge of market prices what he believed to be a dollar's worth of tea.

The simplest method of assigning grades is to arrange a hundred papers as nearly as may be in the order of merit and to give the poorest paper the grade 1, the next poorest the grade 2, and so on, until the best paper receives the grade 100. The 100 cases would not be exactly representative of the entire group with which we are concerned; but if we had 100,000 cases, the error from this source in giving the poorest 1,000 the grade of 1, etc. would be entirely negligible. It is possible to calculate how likely it is that in a random group of 100 cases we should find two, three or more men to whom the lowest or any other grade should be assigned. Each instructor forms a rough estimate of the group of students with which he is concerned, and can with a probable error that might be determined assign its place in the series to each case.

If men are arranged in this way in the order of merit and each is assigned his position in the series from 1 to 100, the differences between them will not be equal. If a hundred men are placed in a row according to height, the line passing along the tops of their heads will not be a straight line. The men in the middle of the row will differ but little from one another, and the differences will become continually greater towards the ends. Fig. 1 (page 380) shows the approximate distribution in stature of 1,052 English women, measured

[1] Cf. articles in *Science* (N. S. **17**: 561–570, 1903) and *Am. Jour of Psychol.* (**14**: 310–328, 1903).

[2] "American Titles and Distinctions," W. Le Conte Stevens, THE POPULAR SCIENCE MONTHLY, **63**: 312–320, 1903. "The Education of Examiners," E. B. Sargent, *Nature*, **70**: 63–65, 1904.

[3] Many instructors doubtless let the grade represent the percentage of questions correctly answered. This is a possible but fallacious method in a subject such as mathematics; in a subject such as psychology it is impossible.

for Professor Karl Pearson. Their average height was about 5 feet 2½ inches; 18.3 per cent of the whole number were between 62 and 63 inches, and one half of them were within about 1½ inches of the average, the probable error. The ordinates or vertical lines are proportional to the number of women falling within the limits of an inch. Thus 16.3 per cent were between 63 and 64 inches; 11.5 per cent between 64 and 65 inches, etc., only two falling between 70 and 71 inches. The women near the average tend to differ in height by about ⅟₂₀₀th of an inch, while the tallest or shortest of the thousand tend to differ by half an inch or more. This curve, showing the dis-

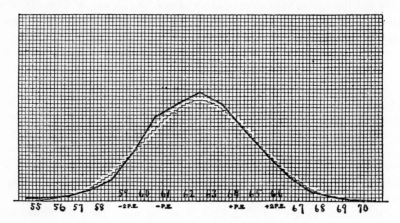

FIG. 1.—Distribution of stature of women in inches.

tribution in height, corresponds closely with the fainter and more regular curve on the figure which represents the distribution of events due to a large number of small causes equally likely to affect them in one of two ways, the curve of error of the exponential equation whose properties have been discussed by Gauss, Laplace and other mathematicians.

If the performances of students in examinations are assumed to vary in the same way as their height, then we can if we like place them in classes which represent equal differences. Thus by the Harvard-Columbia method of grouping into five classes, if we put half the men into the middle class, *C*, and let *B* and *D* represent an equal range, we should give about 23 per cent of both *B*'s and *D*'s and about 2 per cent of both *A*'s and *F*'s. This, however, gives too few men in the *A* and *F* classes for our purposes. If we make the range of the unit 20 per cent smaller, we obtain the distribution shown in Figure 3, according to which of ten men, four would receive *C*, two *B*, two *D*, one *A* and one *F*. It departs slightly from the theoretical distribution, but certainly not so much as the theoretical distribution departs from the actual distribution. It appears to be the most convenient classification when five grades are used; one in ten being given honors and one in ten being required to repeat the course corresponding fairly well with the average practise and being a convenient standard.

It is maintained by Dr. Galton, Professor Pearson and others that ability and performance are distributed in accordance with the curve

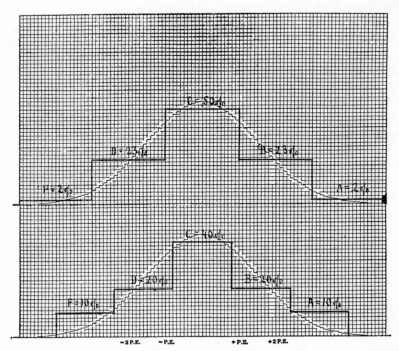

Fig. 2.—The upper surface shows the theoretical distribution of grades, the lower that most convenient in practise.

of error. It does not seem to me that this is the case. If ability for scholastic work were distributed in this way at birth, it would not remain so among college students, who are a selected group. Those unfit are less likely to be found in college and those particularly competent are more likely to be there. This would tend to give us for college students a skew curve in the negative direction. In spite of this factor, I believe that the main skew is in the opposite direction, and that ability is distributed somewhat like wages which are roughly proportional to it. If the average earnings of men in this country are $600 a year, it is clear that the positive deviations from the average are many times the negative deviations. There may be a certain minimal ability necessary for survival, and variations and sports may occur to an extent in the positive direction not possible in the negative direction. There are certain "constant errors," such as a college education, which divide men into different "species." In so far as students are graded on the lines of the probability curve, this may measure the attitude of the examiner rather than the distribution of the men in merit.

But we do not need theorizing so much as facts, which should be secured without delay. In the papers quoted above I have shown that it is possible to transform a qualitative series into one giving measures of differences. If the same thousand examination papers were read and graded independently by ten examiners, the variation in the grades of the same paper by different examiners would give us a measure of the differences between the papers, which would be inversely as the variation of the grades. I have in this way made a curve for the distribution of scientific performance in a selected group, and the same methods should be applied to merit in examinations.

In the meanwhile I am able to give the grades actually assigned in several cases. The accompanying table shows the grades given to 200 students in each of five courses in Columbia College, and the figure shows the averages and the grades in English _A_ and Mathematics _A_. The average grade is a little above _C_, the median grade is nearly midway between _C_ and _B_, and more than two thirds of all

PERCENTAGE OF STUDENTS RECEIVING

	A	B	C	D	F
Eng. _A_	4.5%	41.5%	44.5%	4.5%	5%
Eng. _B_	4	40	39	6.5	10.5
Math. _A_	11	24	24	22	19
Hist. _A_	10.5	28	28.5	20	13
Econ. _A_	9	36	33	17.5	4.5
Average	8	33.9	33.8	14.1	10.4

the grades are either _C_ or _B_. Eight per cent of the grades are _A_ and ten per cent are _F_, which approximates closely to the standard recommended above. The average of the grades assigned in these courses does not vary considerably, but the distribution is different. In the courses in English the distribution tends to follow the normal curve of error, with the failures as a separate group or species. In the courses in mathematics and history the groups are more nearly equal in size, except in the case of "excellent." Here the range of ability is presumably greater in _D_ and _F_ than in _B_ and _C_. The distribution in economics is intermediate. The fact that the courses in English, though given by different instructors, correspond closely shows that within a department certain standards may be followed; and this would be possible for the whole college or for the educational system of the country. It is only necessary to adopt the standards and then to teach people how to apply them.

8   33.9   33.8   14.1

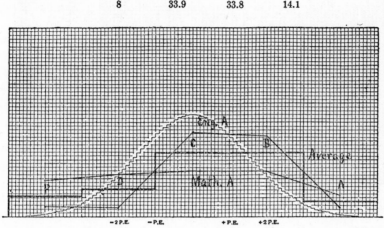

FIG. 3.—The distribution of the average grades assigned in five courses, with the details for introductory courses in English and Mathematics.

I have also counted up the average grades assigned to 200 students in their first ten courses. In the table and curve, A represents the range between A and $B + \frac{1}{2}$, B the range to $C + \frac{1}{2}$, etc. Here

	A	B	C	D	F
Average grade	A	B	C	D	F
Per cent of students	2.5	34	46.5	16.5	0.5

the grades tend to be bunched, the differences between the men being partly obliterated by the combination of the grades in different courses.

In the next table and in the figure are given the grades of 15,-275 papers assigned by the examiners of the College Entrance Examination Board in 1904. The grades are in this case given on a centile scale. The curve is decidedly skewed in the negative direction, the most frequent grades being between 60 and 75. There is a considerable variation in the different subjects. Thus 10.6 per cent of the candidates are given a grade above 90 in Greek and only 2.7 per cent in history; 34.9 per cent are given a grade below 50 in mathematics and only 19.1 per cent in English. It is obvious that such grades should be standardized. It may be remarked incidentally that it is easy to select examiners by a competitive examination. If twenty candidates grade the same sets of papers, those whose grades are nearest the average of all the grades are likely to be the most competent examiners.

Rating	100–90	89–75	75–60	59–60	49–40	39–0
Per cent of papers	6.1	21.4	32.6	12.1	11.1	16.7

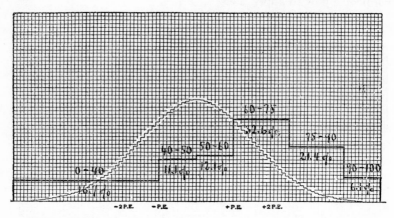

FIG. 4.—Distribution of grades of the college entrance examination board.

In these cases, and in all grades with which I am acquainted, there is a tendency to grade students above the average. Professor Pearson finds that in estimating the health of English boys, teachers place twice as many above "normally healthy" as below, and he seems to regard it as gratifying that English boys should be more than normally healthy. We look on our own students as better than the average and in any case give them the benefit of the doubt. We call things "fair" that are only average, and then the word "fair" comes to mean average. Then we assign the grade "fair" to students who are below the average, and a "fair" student comes to mean a poor student. In assigning grades such words should be avoided; we should learn to think in terms of the average and probable error.

If grades are given on a centile system, the grade should mean the position of the man in his group; thus 60 should mean that in the long run it is more likely than anything else that there would be forty men better and fifty-nine not so good. The average probable error should be determined and a probable error should be attached to the grades; thus the grade 60 ± 10 means that the chances are even that there are between thirty and fifty men in the group who are better. The probable error becomes smaller as we depart from the average man; I estimate on the basis of a few experiments that it is over 10 in the middle of the scale. If this proves to be correct on the basis of more extended data, it is needless to grade more closely than on a scale of 10, though the first decimal would have some meaning when the grades are combined. If a hundred men are divided into ten groups of 10 each, the men in the middle groups will differ less from each other than those towards the ends, and if we wish to let the groups represent approximately equal ranges of merit, we can, as explained above, make five groups, A, B, C, D and F, putting 40 men in C, 20 men in both B and D and 10 in both A and F.

The determination of the validity of the grades given to college students and their standardization appear to me to be important because I regard it as desirable that students should be credited for the work they do rather than for the number of hours that they attend courses. By our present method a student who fails gets no credit at all, while a student who is nearly as bad (and perhaps worse) gets as much credit towards his degree as the best student in the class. In our graduate faculties we credit men for work they do, and this principle is also adopted in the secondary schools that have broken the "lock step." Just now we hear much about the need of shortening the four year college course. Men can not do the work of four years in three by attending more courses each year, but some men accomplish as much in three years as others do in four, and many men, if they had an adequate motive, would do as much in three years as they now do in four.

We find among our graduate students that the better men can obtain the doctor's degree in about half the time required by the poorer men, while in exceptional cases the range is greater. I have found in various fundamental traits that can be measured, such as accuracy of perception, reaction-time and memory, that ordinary individuals differ about as 2:1. It seems that the best men (say the first ten) in our classes differ from the poorest (say the last ten) in about this ratio. If, therefore, men are divided into five groups representing nearly equal ranges of ability and we give the C, or middle group, a credit of three points for a three hour course, it would be just to give the A group 4 points, the B group $3\frac{1}{2}$ points, the D group $2\frac{1}{2}$ points, and the F group 2 points or less.

In Columbia College sixty points are required for the bachelor's degree, a point being an hour's attendance at lectures or recitations, or two hours of laboratory work. Students are expected to attend classes for about 15 hours a week and usually receive the degree in four years; there are, however, some who attend 20 hours a week and receive the degree in three years. At Harvard College 54 points are required, and I understand that about half the students now accomplish the work in three years. When 60 points are required for the degree, and if credits as proposed above were assigned, the 200 students of Columbia College whose grades have been compiled on

the basis of half the work for the degree would be required to attend
a total number of hours, as follows:

Grades	A	B	C	D	F
Per cent of students	2.5	34	46.5	16.5	0.5
Hours for degree	40–45	45–55	55–65	65–75	75+

This would be a just assignment of credits to the best of our
present knowledge. It would permit about one third of the best students to secure the degree by an attendance of from 15 to 18 hours
a week for three years. If, however, it is thought that this gives
too great a reward for good work and too great a penalty for deficiency, the credits and deductions could be halved. This would
give for these students an attendance, as follows:

Grades	A	B	C	D	F
Per cent of students	2.5	34.5	46.5	16.5	0.5
Hours for degree	47.5–52.5	52.5–57.5	57.5–62.5	65.5–67.5	67.5+

Or, if the grades were standardized on the lines here proposed, the
percentages would become:

Grades	A	B	C	D	F
Per cent of students	10	20	40	20	10
Hours for degree	47.5–52.5	52.5–57.5	57.5–62.5	62.5–67.5	no degree

It would also be possible to introduce the principle of giving extra
credit for good work in a less radical manner, for example, by allowing a credit of three points to students who receive the highest grade
in at least five courses. The application of the principle in any form
would be an important educational advance, but a method such as
this would not be nearly so fair and accurate as the plan here recommended. It would affect only a few men and would be more dependent
on chance. The amount of credit in the plan recommended can be so
adjusted that a given percentage of students can receive any credit
desired; those receiving the highest grade (the first ten per cent in
the long run) could be awarded, on the average, an extra credit of 2,
3, 5, 10 or 20 points, as may be decided, and all others would receive
credits in proportion.

I see no serious objection to the plan. The aberrancy of grades
in different subjects would be a drawback, but not so serious as the
existence of "snap courses" under the present system. The adoption
of the plan would tend to the standardization of grades, and the apparent objection might prove to be a real advantage. If it is objected
that it would lead students to work too much for grades, this would

simply mean, if grades are properly assigned, that it would lead them to do better work. The present method, where the grade is simply a kind of prize or punishment putting one man before another, seems to have objections; I have some sympathy with the students who call "*C*" the "gentleman's grade." But if grades had some real meaning, they would be no more invidious than the payment of a salary of $3,000 to one man and of $5,000 to another. If it is said that the method is unfair because grades can not be given in accordance with exact deserts, it may be replied that this is true of all salaries and the like. Although a single grade is subject to a considerable probable error, the error of the average of a number of grades decreases as the square root of the number. Thus, if the probable error of a single grade is one place (that is, if a man receives *C*, the chances are even that he deserves a higher or a lower grade), the average of 25 grades (about the number of college courses taken for the degree) would be subject to a probable error of only one fifth of a place. Lastly it may be said that the bookkeeping is very simple—the credits for 400 students can be compiled by an ordinary clerk in one day.

The assignment of credits in accordance with the work done by the student rather than for the number of exercises he attends appears to be in accord with common sense and justice. If after four years' study one man has the qualifications for the B.A. and another for the M.A., each should be given his appropriate degree. It may be well for one student to attend exercises for twelve hours a week and for another to be eighteen hours in attendance, but if each accomplishes the same amount of work they should be given the same credit. The plan would prove an excellent stimulus to good work and would attract to the college that adopted it the best class of students.

I should myself not only like to give students credit for the degree in accordance with the work they do, but I should also like to see tuition fees charged in proportion. In this case conduct and character should be included as well as merit in class work. More of the endowment of the institution should be used for those whose education is the greater service to the community, while those whose presence in a college interferes with its work should not be supported at the public expense. If the tuition fee is $150, it should be apportioned as follows:

Grades	A	B	C	D	F
Per cent of students	10	20	40	20	10
Tuition fee	$100–120	$120–140	$140–160	$160–180	$180–200

But I fear that it will be even more difficult to convince trustees than faculties that psychology is becoming an exact science.

20

A STATISTICAL STUDY OF AMERICAN MEN OF SCIENCE

Printed in *Science*, **24**: 658–665, 699–707 and 732–742, 1906. It also formed, under the same title, the first part of the supplement to "American Men of Science: A Directory," (Second Edition) 537–563, 1910.

THE SELECTION OF A GROUP OF ONE THOUSAND SCIENTIFIC MEN

The psychologist, like the student of other sciences, can view his subject from different standpoints and pursue it by various methods. He may get what knowledge he can of mental processes by introspection, or he may use objective methods. He may confine himself to the "inner life," or he may study the individual in all his psychophysical relations. He may give verbal descriptions, or he may make measurements. He may describe static mental life, or he may study the lower animals and human beings from a dynamic and genetic point of view. He may attempt to determine facts and laws that hold for mental life in general, or he may attend to individual differences. He may ignore the practical applications of his science, or he may investigate them. Psychology has until recently concerned itself chiefly with the first of these various alternatives. But its recent progress and future development seem to the present writer to depend particularly on the second. In this case, our two main methods, which can often be combined, are experiment and measurement in the laboratory, and the inductive and statistical study of groups of individuals. In recent years great progress has been made in both directions. Experimental psychology has become a science coordinate with the other great sciences, and statistics have been extended to include sociological and moral phenomena.

The intensive study of groups of individuals has, however, only been begun. The origin of the method may be attributed to Quetelet, whose "Essai de physique sociale" was published in 1835, and its principal development to Dr. Francis Galton, whose "Hereditary Genius" (1869) has been followed by a series of books and articles, including "English Men of Science" (1874). Another work bearing closely on the subject matter of the present paper is Alphonse de Candolle's "Historie des sciences et des savants depuis deux siècles" (1873). Other extensive studies of groups of individuals are: Dr. Paul Jacoby's "Etudes sur la sélection" (1881), which has as its subject matter the 3,311 Frenchmen of the eighteenth century whose biographies are included in the "Biographie universelle," Professor A. Odin's "Genèse des grands hommes" (1895), which is a study of 6,382 French men of letters; Mr. Havelock Ellis's "A Study of British Genius" (1906, published in the *Popular Science Monthly*, February–September, 1901), which considers 859 men and 43 women of eminence, and Dr. F. A. Woods's "Mental and Moral Heredity in Royalty" (1906, published in the *Popular Science Monthly*, August, 1902–April, 1903), which treats 832 members of royal families.

I have myself selected as material for study three groups: a thousand students of Columbia University;[1] the thousand most eminent men in history;[2] a thousand American men of science.[3]

Each of these groups seems to me favorable for such work. The students of Columbia College are measured, tested and observed in our laboratory; we are able to follow their academic courses and their careers in after life. The lives of the most eminent men of history are to a certain extent public property, open to statistical investigation and psychological analysis. A thousand scientific men in the United States will doubtless be willing to assist in furnishing the material needed, which is in any case accessible from other sources.

The accompanying table, which with most of the data to be discussed refers approximately to January 1, 1903, shows how American men of science are distributed among the principal sciences by various agencies.[4] There are in the table certain facts that require allowance

[1] "Physical and Mental Measurements of the Students of Columbia University" (with Dr. Livingston Farrand). *Psychol. Rev.*, **3**: 618–648, 1896. Cf. also the dissertation for the doctorate of Clark Wissler, "The Correlation of Mental and Physical Tests," *Psychol. Rev.*, Monograph Supplements, **16**: iv + 62, 1901.

[2] "A Statistical Study of Eminent Men," *Pop. Sci. Mon.*, **53**: 359–378, 1903.

[3] "Homo Scientificus Americanus: Address of the president of the American Society of Naturalists," SCIENCE, N. S., **17**: 561–570, 1903. "Statistics of American Psychologists," *Am. Jour. of Psychol.*, **14**: 310–328, 1903. Towards the cost of computation in connection with this research, I have received a grant of two hundred dollars from the Esther Herrman Research Fund of the Scientific Alliance of New York.

[4] The distribution among the sciences of those in the "Biographical Directory of American Men of Science" (published this year by The Science Press, New York) differs rather more than I had expected from this estimate, which was based on the first thousand entries that were written. There are in the "Directory" 4,131 names, of whom 131 are students of philosophy, education, economics and sociology, leaving just 4,000 in the twelve sciences under consideration. They are distributed among the sciences as follows: mathematics, 340; physics, 672; chemistry, 677; astronomy, 160; geology, 444; botany, 401; zoology, 441; physiology, 105; anatomy, 118; pathology, 357; anthropology, 91; psychology, 194. These figures were not at hand when it was necessary to select the thousand men of science for this research. The numbers under physics and pathology are increased

or at least mention. The American Chemical Society and the doctorates conferred in chemistry represent in part professional work in
applied science. Under the special societies there are duplications, as

TABLE I.—THE NUMBER OF AMERICAN MEN OF SCIENCE AND THEIR DISTRIBUTION
AMONG THE SCIENCES

	Special societies	Fellows of association	Members of academy	University professors	Doctorates in five years	Contributors to *Science* 13 vols.	Who's Who	Biographical dictionary (estimated)
Mathematics	375	81	1	136	61	35	46	380
Physics	149	167	23	105	69	155	73	556
Chemistry	1933	174	12	143	137	73	166	656
Astronomy	125	40	12	41	16	48	51	212
Geology	256	121	13	55	32	161	174	436
Botany	169	120	7	57	53	94	70	416
Zoology	237	146	17	83	72	243	131	620
Physiology	96	10	2	53	18	22	25	156
Anatomy	136	10	0	56	1	13	18	116
Pathology	138	14	5	68	4	44	56	224
Anthropology	60	60	3	4	5	56	37	92
Psychology	127	40	1	37	63	58	21	136
Total	3801	983	96	838	531	1002	868	4000

Reduced to per Thousand

Mathematics	99	32	10	162	113	35	53	95
Physics	39	170	240	125	128	155	84	139
Chemistry	506	177	125	171	265	73	191	164
Astronomy	33	41	125	49	30	47	59	53
Geology	68	123	136	66	60	161	200	109
Botany	45	122	73	68	99	94	81	104
Zoology	63	149	177	99	134	243	151	155
Physiology	25	10	21	63	34	22	29	39
Anatomy	36	10	0	67	2	13	21	29
Pathology	36	14	52	81	8	44	64	56
Anthropology	16	61	31	5	9	56	43	23
Psychology	34	41	10	44	118	57	24	34

scientific men may belong to more than one society. The American
Mathematical Society and the Association of American Anatomists
have been rather liberal in the admission of members. As mathematics
and the medical sciences are required subjects for large groups of

by the inclusion under these sciences of engineers and physicians. The chief discrepancy is that there are fewer zoologists than was indicated by the preliminary
estimate or by the other data of the table.

students, there are many teachers, but this has not produced a proportional number of investigators. The membership of the National Academy represents to a certain extent the interests of the passing scientific generation, the doctorates the interests of the coming scientific generation.

In selecting a group of a thousand scientific men, the number in each science was taken roughly proportional to the total number of investigators in that science, the numbers being: chemistry, 175; physics, 150; zoology, 150; botany, 100; geology, 100; mathematics, 80; pathology, 60; astronomy, 50; psychology, 50; physiology, 40; anatomy, 25; anthropology, 20.

The individuals were selected by asking ten leading representatives of each science to arrange the students of that science in the order of merit. There were for each science slips made with the names and addresses of all those known to have carried on research work of any consequence. The total number assigned a position was 2,481, distributed among the sciences as follows: Mathematics, 201; physics, 261; chemistry, 389; astronomy, 165; geology, 257; botany, 213; zoology, 290; physiology, 101; anatomy, 89; pathology, 251; anthropology, 72; psychology, 192. These numbers included duplications when a man was given a place in more than one science.

The memorandum sent to those who were asked to make the arrangement was as follows:

MEMORANDUM

The undersigned is making a study of American men of science. The first problem to be considered is the distribution of scientific men among the sciences and in different regions, institutions, etc., including the relative rank of this country as compared with other countries in the different sciences, the relative strength of different universities, etc. It is intended that the study shall be continued beyond the facts of distribution to what may be called the natural history of scientific men.

For these purposes a list of scientific men in each science, arranged approximately in the order of merit, is needed. This can best be secured if those who are most competent to form an opinion will independently make the arrangement. The average of such arrangements will give the most valid order, and the degree of validity will be indicated by the variation or probable error of position for each individual.

It is obvious that such an order can be only approximate, and for the objects in view an approximation is all that is needed. The judgments are possible, because they are as a matter of fact made in elections to a society of limited membership, in filling chairs at a university, etc. By merit is understood contributions to the advancement of science, primarily by research, but teaching, administration, editing, the compilation of text-books, etc., should be considered. The different factors that make a man efficient in advancing science must be roughly balanced. An effort may be made later to disentangle these factors.

In ranking a man in a given science his contributions to that science only should be considered. Thus, an eminent astronomer may also be a mathematician, but in ranking him as a mathematician only his contributions to mathematics should be regarded. In such a case, however, mathematics should be given its widest interpretation. It is more difficult to arrange the order when the work can not readily be compared, as, for example, systematic zoology and morphology, but, as already stated, it is only expected that the arrangement shall be approximate. The men should be ranked for work actually accomplished, that is, a man of sixty and a man of forty, having done about the same amount of work, should come near together, though the man of forty has more promise. It may be possible later to calculate a man's value with allowance for age.

In case there is noted the omission of any scientific man from the list who should probably have a place in the first three quarters, a slip may be added in the proper place with his name and address. In case there are names on the list regarding which nothing is known, the slips should be placed together at the end. The slips, as arranged in order, should be tied together and returned to the undersigned.

It is not intended that the lists shall be published, at all events not within ten years. No individual list will be published. They will be destroyed when the averages have been calculated, and the arrangements will be regarded as strictly confidential.

The ten positions assigned to each man were averaged, and the average deviations of the judgments were calculated. This gave the most probable order of merit for the students in each science, together with data for the probable error of the position of each individual. The students of the different sciences were then combined in one list by interpolation, the probable errors being adjusted accordingly. The list contains 1,443 names, of whom the first thousand are the material used in this research.

It should be distinctly noted that the figures give only what they profess to give, namely, the resultant opinion of ten competent judges. They show the reputation of the men among experts, but not necessarily their ability or performance. Constant errors, such as may arise from a man's being better or less known than he deserves, are not eliminated. There is, however, no other criterion of a man's work than the estimation in which it is held by those most competent to judge. The posthumous reputation of a great man may be more correct than contemporary opinion, but very few of those in this list of scientific men will be given posthumous consideration. I am somewhat sceptical as to merit not represented by performance, or as to performance unrecognized by the best contemporary judgment. There are doubtless individual exceptions, but, by and large, men do what they are able to do and find their proper level in the estimation of their colleagues.

In order to obtain the 10 arrangements in each science, or 120 in all, it was necessary to ask the assistance of 192 scientific men. Twenty-three of these did not reply to my letter; 16 declined to make the arrangement, usually on the ground that it was not feasible; 23 consented, but afterwards gave it up or did not send the slips in time, and 10 made arrangements that could not be used, in most cases because the names were arranged in groups instead of being ordered serially. As the arrangement resulted, those who made it and those who were asked but failed were distributed in the different hundreds of the thousand, as shown in Table II.

TABLE II.—THE STANDING OF THOSE WHO MADE THE ARRANGEMENTS AND OF THOSE WHO WERE ASKED BUT FAILED

	I	II	III	IV	V	VI	VII	VIII	IX	X	XI	Total
Observers........	47	26	20	9	6	3	1	1	3	4	0	120
Failed...........	29	20	10	5	1	0	3	1	0	1	2	72
Total..........	76	46	30	14	7	3	4	2	3	5	2	192

Thus 76 of those who proved to be in the first hundred men of science were asked to make the arrangement and 47 of them did so. Only twelve of those who made the arrangement are not in the first five hundred. In anthropology, for example, there are only twenty representatives in the list, of whom but two would probably be in the first hundred, and of the twelve sciences there are only three that would be expected to have more than ten in the first hundred. It is therefore, evident that the ten scientific men who gave the judgments in each science are among the leaders in that science. But their standing must of necessity vary with the different sciences, one half of all the anthropologists having made the arrangement and only two thirty-fifths of all the chemists.

Those asked to arrange the names were distributed among different institutions, as shown in Table III.

Thus 23 scientific men connected with Harvard University were requested to sort out the slips; this was done by 7 of them. Sixty-six and five tenths of the thousand, as the list resulted, are at Harvard University; about 10 per cent of them made the arrangement, which is about 30 per cent of those asked. Seventeen of the 39 scientific men at the University of Chicago were asked to make the arrangement, of whom fifteen accomplished it and two did not. Or 38 per cent of all its men made the arrangement, who were 88 per cent of those asked. The numbers are in most cases too few to give a correct measure of the cooperativeness in such a scheme of the different institutions, but, so far as they go, they are not altogether without interest. They are not, however, printed here for that purpose, but in order to show the geographical distribution of those who made the arrangement. It appears that different institutions are fairly well represented, there being no great preponderance of any one of them. Of the 120 who made the arrangement 89 are connected with the 17 institutions given in the table, although these institutions contain only 450 of the 1,000 scientific men. They, however, have, as will be shown later, a much larger proportion of the more eminent scientific men.

TABLE III.—THE DISTRIBUTION AMONG INSTITUTIONS OF THOSE WHO WERE ASKED TO MAKE THE ARRANGEMENTS

	Number in 1,000	Number asked	Per cent asked	Number of observers	Per cent of observers	Per cent of those asked
Harvard	66.5	23	.35	7	.10	.30
Columbia	60.0	20	.33	13	.21	.65
Chicago	39.0	17	.44	15	.38	.88
Cornell	33.5	6	.18	4	.12	.67
Geological Survey	32.0	7	.22	4	.12	.57
Depart. of Agriculture	32.0	3	.09	3	.09	1.00
Hopkins	30.5	13	.43	5	.16	.38
Yale	26.5	8	.30	6	.23	.75
Smithsonian Institution	22.0	9	.41	5	.23	.55
Michigan	20.0	9	.45	7	.35	.78
Wisconsin	18.0	3	.17	2	.11	.67
Pennsylvania	17.0	10	.59	6	.35	.60
Stanford	16.0	3	.19	3	.19	1.00
Princeton	14.5	3	.21	0	0	0
New York University	9.5	5	.53	4	.42	.80
Clark	7.0	5	.71	3	.43	.60
New York Bot. Garden	6.0	2	.33	2	.33	1.00
One at each institution	....	46	.08	31	.06	.67
Total	...	192	...	120		

Those who made the arrangements are not likely to possess equal information, impartiality and good judgment. If there were only two arrangements of each group it would not be possible to decide objectively which is the better. We have, however, ten arrangements, and the average is more likely to be correct than any one of them. The conditions are the same as in the case of observations in the physical sciences. As the personal equation of the astronomer is determined by comparing his observations with those of other astronomers, so here we can measure the accuracy of judgment of each observer by determining how far it departs from the average judgment.

I have counted up the departures of each of the ten observers from the average result for one of the groups, namely, the fifty psychologists. The data are given in Table IV by groups of ten.

The observer *A* is always more accurate than any other observer, except in one case in the fifty. The validity of judgment of the ten observers varies from 7.9 to 17.26, or about as 1:2, which is approximately the variability that I have found in normal individuals in other mental traits, such as accuracy of perception, time of mental processes, memory, etc. The departures from the mean reliability of judgment, given in the last line of the table, indicate that accuracy of judgment tends in a general way to follow the normal distribution of the probability curve, though with so few cases this may be accidental. As the validity of the judgments varies to a measured degree, the arrangements made by the individuals could be weighted. I have not undertaken the somewhat tedious calculations necessary; they would not considerably alter the order, but would make it somewhat more exact, at the same time decreasing the probable errors.

There is here measured for the first time, I think, the accuracy or reliability of judgment. This is obviously a complex and imperfectly analyzed trait, depending on a large number of varying conditions. A man's judgment may be good in some directions or from certain points of view, and bad in other ways. Still we understand vaguely

TABLE IV.—MEASUREMENTS OF THE ACCURACY OF JUDGMENT OF TEN OBSERVERS

	A	B	C	D	E	F	G	H	I	J	Average
I..........	1.6	5.2	2.3	3.1	1.9	2.8	1.8	2.4	5.0	2.6	**2.87**
II..........	4.9	7.0	8.7	7.8	6.3	4.2	10.2	6.1	7.0	5.1	**6.73**
III..........	7.1	11.1	13.5	12.4	24.2	16.2	12.5	12.0	16.9	27.6	**15.35**
IV..........	13.8	18.0	16.7	18.4	18.8	18.1	22.7	25.4	21.9	25.5	**19.93**
V..........	12.1	17.4	21.1	21.1	13.2	26.6	21.7	24.7	22.9	25.5	**20.63**
Av..........	**7.9**	**11.74**	**12.46**	**12.56**	**12.88**	**13.58**	**13.78**	**14.12**	**14.74**	**17.26**	**13.1**
A..........	*−5.20*	*−1.36*	*−0.64*	*−0.54*	*−0.25*	*+0.48*	*+0.68*	*+1.02*	*+1.64*	*+4.16*	*±1.60*

what is meant by good judgment and value the trait highly in ourselves and in others. Thus most people complain that they have a bad memory, but I have never heard any one acknowledge that he had a bad judgment. It appears that the measurement of the reliability of judgment of individuals may have wide-reaching applications in civil service examinations and in all cases where individuals are selected for special purposes, a balanced judgment being nearly always more important than the kind of information that can be tested by a written examination. I have measured the accuracy of observation and memory[1] and Dr. F. B. Sumner has measured the validity of beliefs.[2] When we learn to look upon our observations, recollections, beliefs and judgments objectively, stating in numbers the probability of their correctness and assigning probable errors to them, there will be an extraordinary change in our attitude in religion, politics, business and all the affairs of life.

There are two cases in which these judgments were subject to special conditions which it may be worth the while to notice—that in which a man of science gave his own position and that in which he gave the positions of his immediate colleagues. In sending out the slips, nothing was said as to whether it was expected that a man should include his own name. Of the 120 who made the arrangement, 34 gave positions to themselves; 20 assigned positions to themselves lower than that resulting from the average judgment, twelve higher positions and two the same positions. On the other hand, 22 gave themselves positions higher than the average grade (which is lower than the position, being related to it somewhat as the average is to the median), ten lower and two the same. The judgments were somewhat more accurate than the average judgments. In 21 cases the departures from the mean were less than the average departures and in 13 cases they were larger. It thus appears that there is on the average no constant error in judging ourselves—we are about as likely to overestimate as to underestimate ourselves, and we can judge ourselves slightly more accurately than we are likely to be judged by one of our colleagues. We can only know ourselves from the reflected opinions of others, but it seems that we are able to estimate these more correctly than can those who are less interested. There are, however, wide individual differences; several observers overestimate themselves decidedly, while others underestimate themselves to an equal degree.

We tend to overestimate the positions of our immediate colleagues, though the departure from the average judgment is not considerable. Here again there are decided individual differences; thus one man assigned positions to six of his colleagues, all of which were above the average, and another assigned positions to five of his colleagues, all of

[1] "Measurements of the Accuracy of Recollection," Science, N. S., **2**: 761–766, 1895.

[2] "A Statistical Study of Belief," *Psychol. Rev.*, **5**: 616–631, 1898.

which were below the average. Most of us also overestimate those whose lines of research are similar to our own.

These factors affect the order of the names in the list but slightly, though they increase the probable errors. A more considerable variation is due to the fact that the names were divided among twelve sciences, whereas the lines between the sciences are artificial. A man's work may not fall naturally in one of these conventional sciences, or it may fall in two or more of them. In such cases he is likely to receive a lower position than he deserves. It is not clear how this difficulty could have been avoided, for if more departments of science had been used, the overlapping would have been greater.

TABLE V.—THE NUMBERS OF THOSE WHO WERE ASSIGNED A POSITION IN MORE THAN ONE SCIENCE

	Mathematics	Physics	Chemistry	Astronomy	Geology	Botany	Zoology	Physiology	Anatomy	Pathology	Anthropology	Psychology	
Mathematics..........		1		3	1							1	6
Physics..............	11		1	4	1								17
Chemistry............		3			3			2		1			9
Astronomy...........	9												9
Geology..............				1		1	2		2				6
Botany...............			1		2					1			4
Zoology..............					4			3	15	1			23
Physiology...........			2						1	4		2	9
Anatomy.............							4	3		1		1	9
Pathology............			3					2	1				6
Anthropology........					1				4		1		6
Psychology...........								1			1		2
	20	4	7	8	12	1	6	11	23	8	1	5	106

Table V gives the cases in which the thousand scientific men were given places in the lists of two or more sciences, even though in the science in which they were given the lower position they did not come within the thousand, but only in the 1,443 who made up the total list. The horizontal lines of the table give those who were assigned the higher position in the science named, and the vertical lines those who were assigned the lower position. Thus there was one man whose higher position was in mathematics, but who was also given a position in physics, and there were eleven men who are primarily physicists and secondarily mathematicians. There are 93 men who have a position in two sciences, five who have a position in three sciences and one who has a position in four sciences. It thus appears that about one tenth of our scientific men do work of some importance in more than one of the twelve sciences here defined.

The chief interest of the table is that it gives a certain measure of the relationships of the sciences. Thus mathematics, physics and astronomy, on the one hand, and zoology, anatomy and physiology, on the other, are the most closely interrelated groups. This might have been foreseen, but the table gives the definite relations. There are but few who are anatomists only, whereas botany is the science which is the least likely to be combined with any other. One of the most serious obstacles to the advancement of science is the lack of men who are expert both in an exact and in a natural or biological science.

There are in all the leading countries academies of science, whose membership is supposed to consist of their most eminent scientific men, and one of the principal functions of such academies appears to be the election of members as an honor. The methods of selection used in this research are more accurate than those of any academy of sciences, and it might seem that the publication of the list would be as legitimate as that of a list of our most eminent men selected by less adequate methods. But perhaps its very accuracy would give it a certain brutality.

Of the first hundred scientific men on the list who are eligible, 61 are included among the 97 members of the National Academy of Sciences, and of the first 30 men on the list 28 are members of the academy. The elections to the academy tend to follow the list pretty closely in the order in which men are arranged in the separate sciences —usually falling within the probable error of position. But the academy has no method of comparing performance in different sciences, and if one science has less than its proper representation, the disparity is likely to increase rather than to decrease. Thus there are in the country about half as many astronomers as botanists, but there are twice as many astronomers in the academy. The second principal variation in the membership of the academy is due to the fact that men do not always retain the positions that they hold when elected. Apart from the somewhat greater accuracy, the superiority of this list consists in the assignment of probable errors of position. Thus the probable error at the close of the first hundred is about 25 places, that is, there are about 25 men not in an ideal academy of a hundred, whose chances of belonging there are at least one in four. A list such as this would also give us academies of any desired size—the sixty most eminent men of science, as in the Paris Academy, the hundred or thereabouts as in the National Academy, or the 450 or thereabouts, as in the Royal Society.

While under existing conditions of sentiment, the publication of a list of our thousand leading men of science in the order of merit with the probable errors would not be tolerated, I have indicated those who are included in the thousand in my "Biographical Directory of American Men of Science," a work of reference that may be regarded as a by-product of this study. I did this with some hesitation, but it seemed best to place on record those who were the subjects of this research, more especially as this could be done without any invidiousness. The probable error toward the end of the list is about 100 places, so there are one hundred others who have at least one chance in four of belonging to this group. Further, several scientific men of standing were omitted from the lists as originally drawn up, and were not considered in making the arrangements. Consequently, while each of those indicated in the Biographical Directory is probably one of the leading thousand American men of science, there are others not indicated who belong to this group. This, however, is a minor factor, and we have with sufficient accuracy for statistical purposes a group of the leading thousand American men of science arranged in the order of merit with the probable errors of position known.

THE MEASUREMENT OF SCIENTIFIC MERIT

Many of the problems that the writer had in view in the present research might be solved by the study of any group of a thousand American men of science, so long as they had been objectively selected. The objective selection of a group sufficiently large for statistical treatment is, however, essential. As cases can be quoted to illustrate the cure of nearly every disease by almost any medicine, so examples can be given in support of any psychological or sociological theory. The method of anecdote, as used by Lombroso, may be readable literature, but it is not science. A thousand names might have been selected by lot from all the scientific men of the country, assuming a list to have been available, but a group of the thousand leading men of science arranged in the order of merit has certain advantages. Information in regard to them can be better obtained than in the case of those who are more obscure. Correlations can be determined between degrees of scientific merit and various conditions. The comparison with a similar group selected ten or twenty years hence, or with a similar group of British, French or German men of science, would give interesting results. The list itself, if printed after an interval of twenty years, would be a historical document of value. Lastly, the data can be so used as to carry quantitative methods a little way into a region that has hitherto been outside the range of exact science. It is the last problem that I wish to take up in this paper.

It will be remembered that we have in each science the workers in that science arranged in the supposed order of merit by ten competent judges, who made their arrangements independently. If the ten arrangements agreed exactly, we should have complete confidence in the result, except in so far as it was affected by systematic or constant errors. If there were no agreement at all, the futility of any attempt to estimate scientific merit would be made clear. The conditions are naturally intermediate. There is a certain amount of agreement and a certain amount of difference of opinion. Thus taking, for example, the ten astronomers—I, II, III, etc.—whose average positions were the highest, the order given to them by each of the ten observers, A, B, C, etc., is as shown in Table I.

TABLE I.—THE ORDER ASSIGNED TO TEN ASTRONOMERS BY TEN OBSERVERS

	I	II	III	IV	V	VI	VII	VIII	IX	X
A	1	2	4	3	10	6	9	5	11	8
B	1	4	2	5	6	?	9	3	8	7
C	1	4	?	5	2	*16	6	17	7	*21
D	?	2	4	3	1	5	7	13	8	6
E	1	*9	2	5	6	3	8	4	7	11
F	1	4	10	2	5	6	3	7	8	11
G	1	3	5	*16	2	6	7	13	4	8
H	1	3	5	7	6	4	9	?	8	2
I	1	2	8	4	10	6	7	3	11	5
J	1	2	4	5	12	8	3	6	13	7
AV.	1.0	3.5	4.8	5.5	6.0	6.6	6.8	7.8	8.5	8.6
av.	1.0	2.9	4.8	4.3	6.0	5.5	6.8	7.8	8.5	7.2
m.v.	0.0	1.4	1.9	2.4	2.8	2.3	1.7	4.3	1.9	3.4
P.E.	0.0	.45	.59	.84	.84	.85	.48	1.15	.54	1.09
p.e.	0.0	.39	.57	.68	.79	.69	.48	1.28	.54	.96

Here we find complete agreement that I is our leading astronomer. He has been selected as such by nine competent judges from the 160 astronomers of the country.[1] The probability that this is due to chance is entirely negligible. II stands next in scientific merit. He is placed second by four of the observers, third by two, fourth by three and ninth by one. The conditions are similar to observations in the exact sciences. The average position or grade is 3.5, and the probable error of this position is 0.45, *i.e.*, the chances are even that this grade is correct within one half of a unit. The grade of the astronomer who stands third is 4.8, and that of the astronomer who stands fourth is 5.5. There is consequently one chance in about fifty that II deserves

[1] In three cases where a question mark appears the astronomer did not give a position to himself. In one case the name was not included among the slips.

a grade as low as that of III, and one in about one thousand that he deserves a grade as low as that of IV. The order thus has a high degree of validity, and this has itself been measured. As we go further down the list, the probable errors tend to increase, the order is less certain, and the difference in merit between a man and his neighbor on the list is less. The variations in the sizes of the probable errors are, as a rule, significant. When the error is small the work of the man is such that it can be judged with accuracy; when it is larger it is because the work is more difficult to estimate.

The probable errors depend on the assumption that the individual deviations follow the exponential law, and they do so in sufficient measure for the purposes in view. For those near the top of the list, the distribution of errors is "skewed" in the negative direction, that is, there are relatively more large negative than positive errors. Thus in the table there are four judgments marked with a star, the deviation of each of which is more than three times the average deviation, and these observations would be omitted by an approximate application of Chauvenet's criterion. If these four observations are omitted, the grades of the ten astronomers are those given in the second line of averages. The omitted judgments are not extremely divergent, barely exceeding the limits set by Chauvenet's criterion, and I do not regard them as invalid. Indeed, I believe that in view of the presence of systematic errors in these estimates the chance that they represent correct values is greater than that assigned by a strict application of the theory of probabilities. But the incidence of an extreme judgment might in special cases do injustice to an individual, and in the order used Chauvenet's criterion has been applied.[1] This means that a compromise has been adopted between the median and the average judgment; but the departure from the average judgment is small, affecting less than one fifth of the individuals and only to a slight degree. The average deviations and probable errors used are those found when all the judgments are included. Two probable errors are given in the table, the first obtained through the error of mean square, the second by taking it as directly proportional to the average devia-

[1] Among the some 15,000 observations under consideration several variations might be expected to occur in a normal distribution as much as six times as large as the probable error, and among the 1,500 or more individuals, several might be expected to deserve positions departing considerably from those assigned. But assuming that we have "normal errors" to deal with, there is no reason why the particular individuals on whom the divergent errors fall should receive them rather than any other individuals. Such errors should apparently be distributed among all the individuals. Similar conditions must occur in the case of errors of observation in the exact sciences, but so far as I am aware their significance has not been considered.

tion. The differences are not significant, and for work of this character I regard it as useless to calculate the probable errors by the ordinary formula. I have published elsewhere[1] a more technical discussion of the treatment of errors or deviations of this character, and may return to the subject at some subsequent time. The theory of errors commonly applied in the exact sciences is too crude for psychology, and probably for the sciences in which it is used. Progress here will be blocked until there are psychologists who are mathematicians or mathematicians who are psychologists.

In order to illustrate further the serial distribution and the probable errors, I have made a diagram for the fifty psychologists. The grade of each, no judgments being omitted, is shown by the vertical mark, and the length of the line indicates the probable error or range within which the chances are even that the true position falls. Thus the psychologist who stands first on the list, was, like the astronomer, given this position by the independent judgment of all. The psychologist who stands second has, as shown on the diagram, a position of 3.7 and a probable error of 0.5 i.e., the position of 3.7 is the most probable, but the true position is equally likely to be within the short horizontal line, between 3.2 and 4.2, or outside it. It must, however, be remembered that the chances of the true position being far outside the range of this line decrease very rapidly. Over it is roughly drawn the bell-shaped curve of the normal probability integral. The true position is along the base line covered by this curve, and the chances of its being at any given point are proportional to the ordinate or height of the curve above the base line. There is only one chance in about six that the true grade is above 2.7 or below 4.7, and only one chance in about 150 that the true grade is above 1.7 or below 5.7. It will be seen from the diagram that while the positions of the psychologists II, III and IV are the most probable, the relative order is not determined with certainty. On the other hand, the chances are some 10,000 to one that each of these psychologists stands below I and above V.

It is evident that the probable errors increase in size as we go down the list. The curve of distribution drawn over No. XL indicates that the chances are even that the true position falls between the grades of XXXIV and L and that there is one chance in four that he does not belong among our fifty leading psychologists. The increase in the size of the probable errors is irregular, it being more difficult to assign a position to some men than to others.

It will be noted that the psychologists fall into groups, the first twenty being set off from the next group, though the two groups are

[1] *Am. Journ. of Psychol.*, **14**: 312–328, 1903.

bridged over by three cases. At this point also the probable errors become almost suddenly about three times as large. There are altogether about 200 psychologists in the country, and it looks as if the first tenth forms a separate group of leaders. There is a similar, though less marked group of the first twenty astronomers, but these groups seem to be partly accidental. There is, however, as shown below, an inflection point in the curve of distribution after about the first tenth of our scientific men. The first twenty psychologists fall into four distinct groups, and there are groupings in the other sciences, They do

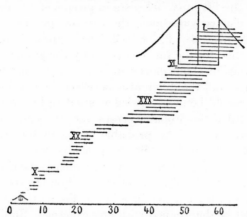

Fig. 1.—The positions and probable errors of the fifty psychologists.

not, however, appear to be sufficiently marked to lead us to distinguish species, such as men of genius and men of talent. It is, however, possible that the complicated conditions may ultimately be analyzed so as to give such groups.

The probable errors not only tell the accuracy with which the psychologists can be arranged in the order of merit, but they also measure the differences between them. This, indeed, I regard as the most important result of this paper, as science is advanced chiefly by the extension of quantitative methods, and it might not have been foreseen that it would be possible to measure degrees of scientific merit. Our data are concerned with the recognition of scientific performance, not with abstract ability, if such a thing is conceivable. Merit is in performance, not in non-performance, and expert judgment is the best, and in the last resort the only, criterion of performance.

The difference in scientific merit between any two of the psychologists whose positions and probable errors are shown in the chart is directly as the distance between them and inversely as their probable errors. If two of them are close together on the scale, and if the probable errors are large, the difference between them is small, and conversely.

If the psychologists II and III were separated by 0.5 and their probable errors were 0.5, as is approximately the case, then the difference between them is so small that there is one chance in four that the position of III is above the grade of II. If again the psychologists XL and XLIX were separated by 6 and their probable errors were 6, as is approximately the case, then there is again one chance in four that the true position of XLIX is above the grade of XL. The difference between II and III is thus about the same as that between XL and XLIX.

If we take the fifty psychologists in groups of 10, and thus partly eliminate the chance variations, the average probable errors of the five groups are 0.7, 1.8, 4.2, 5.8, 6.2. These probable errors are subject to a correction for the range covered by the grades. Thus the first ten cover a range of about eleven points, and the last ten a range of about six points, and the differences between the psychologists at the top of the list would be nearly twice as great as between those at the bottom of the list if the probable errors were the same. When we take account of both factors, the probable errors in the five groups are 0.6, 1.9, 1.8, 6.4 and 10.7. While the probable errors are determined with a considerable degree of exactness, which is itself measured, the ranges covered by the grades seem to depend on the special conditions in the science; they are not the same in the different sciences, and their validity can not be determined with any exactness. Subject, however, to a considerable probable error, the range of merit covered by the fifty psychologists is inversely as the figures given, and reduced to a scale of 100 would be: 55.6, 17.5, 18.5, 5.2 and 3.2.

Thus we can say that the psychologists at the top of the list are likely to differ from each other about 18 times as much as the psychologists at the bottom of the list. We have no zero point from which we can measure psychological merit. Men who are 6 ft. 2 in. tall are likely to differ from each other about ten times as much as men who are about 5 ft. 8 in. tall, though the difference in their height is only as 68:74. Even though we assumed the zero point to be where psychological performance begins or at the survival minimum of human ability, we should only obtain relative differences.

The astronomers and the psychologists have been used as illustrations. The number of students of astronomy and of psychology in the country does not differ greatly, and it is assumed that they represent an equal range of scientific merit. It is possible that it requires more ability to be an astronomer than to be a psychologist, and it is equally possible that, in view of the larger endowments, longer history and more conventional problems, less ability will suffice for the astronomer. The curves of distribution might also vary; for example, it might be relatively easier to be an astronomer of moderate performance, but more difficult to be a great astronomer. There are indications of such differences, but the data at hand do not disclose them with any degree of certainty.

There are 100 geologists and 100 botanists on the list, who are about one fourth of all the geologists and botanists of the country. These are assumed to cover about the same range of scientific merit as the astronomers or the psychologists. The average difference between the geologists would consequently be about half that between the astronomers, and the probable errors of position should theoretically be about twice as large. The anthropologists are the smallest class of scientific men, numbering in all about ninety, of whom 20 are included in the thousand under consideration. They are again assumed to cover a range of performance equal to that of the astronomers or geologists, the average difference between them being two and a half times as great as between the astronomers or five times as great as between the geologists. The chemists are the most numerous class of scientific men, 175 being included in the thousand. There are 150 physicists, 150 zoologists, 80 mathematicians, 60 pathologists, 40 physiologists and 25 anatomists.

In the accompanying table are given the grades and probable errors of the twenty men of science who were assigned positions at the head of each of the twelve sciences. All the anthropologists are thus included in the table, but only two fifths of the astronomers, one fifth of the geologists, etc. In cases in which an individual stands relatively higher in another science a star is attached.

It will be observed that the grades are, as a rule, lower than the positions. As has been stated, the distribution of the judgments or errors in the upper part of the list is "skewed" in a negative direction, so that the average judgment is lower than the median judgment. Further down the list this tendency disappears, and towards the bottom, not given in the table except for the anatomists and anthropologists, the "skew" is in the opposite direction. Chauvenet's criterion has been applied; it causes but an insignificant difference in the order, and for statistical purposes the extra calculations involved were superfluous. As has been explained, however, the incidence of a divergent judgment, which might be due to ignorance or prejudice, might be unjust to an individual. The probable errors have been obtained by taking them directly proportional to the average deviation and assuming that there were always ten judgments. In the comparatively few cases where there were less than ten judgments the probable errors of the average are too small, but the differences are not significant. In the measurement of scientific merit, we are concerned not with the

TABLE II.—GRADES AND PROBABLE ERRORS OF THE TWENTY MEN OF SCIENCE WHO STAND FIRST IN EACH OF THE SCIENCES

	Mathematics		Physics		Chemistry		Astronomy		Geology		Botany		Zoology		Physiology		Anatomy		Pathology		Anthropology		Psychology	
	Av.	P.E.	Av.	P.E.	Av.	P.E.	Av.	P.E.	Av.	P.E.	Av.	P.E.	Av.	P.E.	Av.	P.E.	Av.	P.E.	Av.	P.E.	Av.	P.E.	Av.	P.E.
I	2.5	.6	1.6	.7	3.6	.6	1.0	0	2.5	.4	2.9	.8	2.7	.2	2.0	.3	1.5	.3	1.0	0	1.7	.2	1.0	0
II	3.3	3.0	3.2	2.5	4.4	.5	*2.9	.4	3.3	.4	3.3	.5	3.2	1.0	2.6	.3	*1.8	.2	3.9	.3	2.6	.2	3.0	.5
III	3.7	.7	8.7	2.7	5.5	1.7	*4.3	.6	5.4	1.6	5.0	1.6	4.3	1.3	*4.3	.5	5.7	1.0	3.9	1.5	2.7	.8	3.2	.4
IV	5.7	.5	9.0	.8	6.8	1.2	4.8	.5	7.0	2.2	6.7	1.1	4.6	.9	5.7	.5	6.6	1.3	4.8	.6	4.5	.4	4.4	.6
V	5.7	1.6	9.6	7.9	8.8	1.5	5.5	.7	8.8	1.2	7.1	3.9	7.0	.9	6.1	.6	*6.7	.9	8.6	1.7	4.6	1.1	6.2	.9
VI	*5.7	3.9	11.5	1.8	9.7	1.4	6.0	.8	11.3	1.9	7.5	.6	8.9	.9	6.2	1.1	7.0	1.2	11.1	1.5	7.2	1.0	7.1	1.2
VII	9.2	1.0	*11.7	6.7	9.8	1.6	6.8	.4	12.2	1.5	8.1	2.6	12.6	5.2	7.5	1.1	8.0	1.2	12.0	2.7	8.4	.7	7.2	2.3
VIII	9.6	3.6	11.8	2.1	11.4	1.7	7.2	1.0	17.1	2.3	8.5	.8	13.1	1.5	10.3	1.5	*8.5	1.4	13.3	.7	8.5	.9	7.5	1.2
IX	12.1	2.0	12.0	5.3	15.5	2.9	7.8	1.2	17.1	2.5	11.3	1.7	13.4	1.8	13.0	.9	*8.8	.8	16.9	5.6	10.4	1.6	8.0	.3
X	13.1	1.5	12.2	1.7	15.8	1.5	8.0	.5	18.3	2.5	12.3	1.8	14.1	1.8	13.0	.8	*15.2	1.7	17.6	3.7	11.0	.8	9.5	.6
XI	14.0	1.3	13.5	1.7	16.4	6.1	10.2	.3	19.3	4.5	13.2	1.3	17.3	5.0	15.2	1.7	*15.7	1.7	18.0	2.5	11.4	1.5	12.3	1.1
XII	14.6	2.0	14.2	6.2	16.8	3.6	11.0	.3	19.4	3.7	13.7	1.9	17.6	5.2	15.7	2.2	*16.2	2.2	18.5	2.6	15.8	2.4	14.7	1.4
XIII	14.7	3.1	14.8	8.0	17.8	3.7	13.6	1.1	19.4	4.6	14.8	1.3	*19.1	5.0	19.1	3.1	*16.4	3.1	19.6	4.1	17.5	1.8	17.1	1.5
XIV	17.4	1.7	18.3	3.5	19.8	3.7	14.2	1.2	19.5	2.9	16.3	1.9	19.7	2.2	20.1	2.6	16.8	2.6	*20.6	2.2	18.0	1.2	17.9	2.3
XV	19.1	3.4	19.4	4.8	20.7	1.5	14.3	.4	21.5	2.9	19.8	2.0	20.1	2.9	21.2	2.2	18.5	2.2	22.7	3.6	18.6	1.8	18.1	2.3
XVI	21.5	2.8	19.5	2.2	21.3	3.4	17.0	.7	22.1	2.3	20.2	3.2	20.4	3.4	*21.3	2.7	18.6	2.3	25.5	2.5	19.1	1.6	18.7	1.5
XVII	21.8	3.1	19.7	5.6	22.0	4.6	21.4	1.2	22.2	1.5	23.9	3.9	20.8	3.1	21.8	2.0	18.8	4.0	26.8	2.7	19.5	1.4	19.2	1.1
XVIII	*22.8	2.6	21.1	2.3	24.7	2.5	22.7	1.2	*24.8	5.1	27.2	4.0	20.8	3.5	22.4	3.0	19.3	1.5	27.4	4.4	20.5	1.7	19.6	1.6
XIX	23.1	2.9	21.2	3.7	25.3	6.4	22.9	3.0	26.5	3.5	27.9	3.2	23.0	3.2	24.4	2.4	21.1	1.9	27.5	4.5	21.8	1.5	20.0	3.4
XX	23.8	2.6	22.1	4.9	25.4	12.7	23.3	2.6	*27.4	4.5	27.9	4.5	24.4	2.3	*25.4	3.7	22.7	3.7	29.9	4.0	22.0	3.6	20.4	1.3

probable error of the average, but with the average probable error, which does not depend on the number of cases. Figures for both might be given, but they are so nearly alike and so lacking in significance that it is not worth while.

As the table shows, there are in astronomy, pathology and psychology men who are placed distinctly at the head. In the other sciences those who stand first have grades varying from 1.6 to 3.6. In most cases the differences in grade are less than the probable errors, or not much larger, and the position is not determined to a single place, though it is determined with a theoretically high degree of validity within a very few places. Various groupings occur, which seem to represent the existing conditions of the sciences. Thus there are breaks of two or more units after chemists 4 and 8; physicist 2; zoologists 4 and 6; geologists 2, 5 and 7; botanist 8; mathematicians 3, 6 and 8; pathologists 1, 4, 5 and 9; psychologist 1; physiologists 7 and 9; anatomists 2 and 9, and anthropologist 5. On the other hand, there are cases in which consecutive numbers are bracketed or practically bracketed. Thus mathematicians 4, 5 and 6 have a grade of 5.7. These various groupings appear to be about what the probable errors would lead us to expect.

The probable errors tend to increase as we go down the lists, but with considerable irregularity. This irregularity is in part due to normal variability where the number of observations is small and the average deviations are relatively large, but the larger departures are usually significant, it being easier to assign a position to some men of science than to others. Thus, for example, it is not easy to compare a man who has made one or two important discoveries with a man who has accomplished a large mass of useful work.

The tendency of the probable errors to increase is, however, significant. It is easier to assign the order at the top of the list, and the difficulty increases as we go downward. This subjective fact is measured by the probable errors. It is in part due to less knowledge of those whose work is less important. I know of no way to eliminate this factor or to measure its influence. But the main factor is the real differences between the men, and these are assumed to be inversely as the probable errors and directly as the differences in grade.

In Table III are given all the probable errors averaged in six groups for each of the sciences. In the first and second groups are included one tenth of those in each science, and in the remaining groups one fifth. That is, the probable errors are divided into five equal groups, but the first group is divided into two subgroups, in view of the fact that the probable errors of the first tenth are distinctly smaller than those of the second tenth. In the middle part of the table the probable errors have been adjusted to the ranges covered by each group, and in the lower part these figures have been reduced to a common standard of a thousand, so that the results for the different sciences may be comparable.

TABLE III.—PROBABLE ERRORS IN EACH OF THE SCIENCES, THE MEN OF SCIENCE BEING DIVIDED INTO SIX GROUPS

	Mathematics	Physics	Chemistry	Astronomy	Geology	Botany	Zoology	Physiology	Anatomy	Pathology	Anthropology	Psychology	Average	P.E.
Crude Probable Errors														
I {	1.8	3.8	2.5	.4	1.7	1.6	2.4	.4	.4	.9	.2	.5		
{	2.2	4.0	5.7	.8	3.5	2.7	4.1	.9	.9	3.0	.3	.9		
II	4.1	8.5	6.9	1.3	5.2	4.8	6.8	2.0	1.3	3.7	.9	1.8		
III	4.5	10.1	13.4	3.8	6.7	7.6	9.8	3.0	2.1	6.8	1.6	4.2		
IV	6.0	9.4	15.0	3.6	7.0	8.7	9.6	2.9	2.7	5.9	1.6	5.8		
V	6.4	8.5	13.9	3.2	6.7	8.3	9.6	2.9	3.4	6.0	2.0	6.2		
Probable Errors Corrected for the Range														
I {	1.3	3.1	2.0	.4	.9	1.3	1.9	.3	.2	.5	.2	.4		
{	1.8	2.8	3.4	.9	3.6	1.7	3.3	.7	1.7	2.8	.3	.9		
II	3.0	6.2	5.0	.8	7.0	4.2	5.3	1.5	.8	3.3	.6	1.9		
III	7.1	14.0	16.4	6.3	6.4	8.2	11.3	2.9	3.6	8.6	.9	1.8		
IV	7.3	28.5	22.7	3.9	8.3	8.3	15.3	2.6	2.6	12.6	3.2	6.4		
V	6.2	24.8	25.3	4.6	7.3	15.6	17.0	4.2	3.8	6.2	2.1	10.7		
The Same Reduced to a Common Standard for the Thousand Men of Science														
I {	16	21	11	8	9	13	13	8	8	8	10	8	11.1	.8
{	22	19	19	18	36	17	22	18	68	47	15	18	26.6	2.9
II	37	41	29	16	70	42	35	38	32	55	30	38	38.6	2.2
III	89	93	94	126	64	82	75	73	144	143	45	36	88.7	6.4
IV	91	190	129	78	83	83	102	65	104	210	160	128	118.6	9.1
V	78	165	145	92	73	156	113	105	152	103	105	214	125.1	8.4

If the range of ability is the same in each science and if the difficulty of assigning the order in each science is the same, then the figures in the lower third of the table should tend to be the same in the different sciences. As the averages include from 2 to 35 cases, they are subject to a probable error which varies considerably. Thus, to take, for example, an intermediate case—the botanists—the probable errors of the six entries in the upper part of the table are: 0.25, 0.33, 0.18, 0.28, 0.22, 0.25. They thus seem to be determined with considerable validity. When the probable errors are adjusted for the ranges, a considerable "chance" variation is introduced. If the figures were broken up into groups of different sizes, the results would be different. The figures in the last three groups of each of the sciences seem scarcely to be significant of real differences in the sciences, though they to a certain extent measure the actually existing conditions.

The figures in the table give the validity with which the positions are determined, and at the same time measure the relative differences between the men in the several groups. Thus the first tenth of the chemists have on the average their positions determined relatively to other chemists with a probable error of two places and the last fifth with a probable error of 25 places. In relation to the first hundred scientific men, a chemist in this group has his position determined on the average (apart from the error due to the interpolation) with a probable error of 11 places, whereas in relation to the last 200 scientific men, the place is determined with a probable error of 145 places.

The figures also show that the average differences between the chemists who are in the first tenth are about eight times as great as between the chemists towards the middle of the list and about twelve times as great as between the chemists towards the bottom of the list.

As has been stated, there are considerable variations in the figures for the different sciences. In general, however, those in the first hundred differ from each other about ten times as much as those in the last four hundred, among whom there are no constant differences. It is scarcely safe to draw inferences from the variations in the different groups and in the different sciences. If the probable errors in one science were consistently higher than in another, it would mean that in the former science it is more difficult to make the arrangement, which might be due to greater diversity in the work to be compared or to greater similarity in the men. The greater similarity in the men would probably be due to there having been relatively too many men included in that science. But such consistent differences do not appear. Thus the psychologists have the largest probable error in the last group, but the smallest in the third group, and the mathematicians have the second smallest probable error in the last group, but the second largest in the first group. In so far as these figures are significant, they might mean that our able psychologists are more able than our able mathematicians, whereas our lesser psychologists are less able than our lesser mathematicians. It is probably true that our leading psychologists would compare more favorably with those of Germany, France and Great Britain than our leading mathematicians, but inferences as to the variation in the distribution of ability in the different sciences can not be made from the data at hand with any considerable degree of validity. It would, however, be of interest to have comparable data for different nations and for different periods.

The workers in the twelve sciences have been combined into one series by interpolation, it being assumed that the range of ability in each science is the same. The probable errors have at the same time been increased to correspond with a thousand cases, as shown in Table III. This makes the probable errors relatively correct, but does not allow for the additional chance variations caused by the interpolation. The list is of considerable interest, as it enables us to compare with more or less accuracy men of science working in diverse directions.

TABLE IV.—THE ORDER, THE SCIENCE, THE GRADE AND THE PROBABLE ERROR OF EACH OF THE FIRST FIFTY MEN OF SCIENCE ON THE LIST

Order	Science	Grade	P.E.	Order	Science	Grade	P.E.
I	Astron.	?	0	XXVI	Chem.	55.4	7.8
II	Path.	?	0	XXVII	Chem.	56.0	9.3
III	Psychol.	?	0	XXVIII	Physics	58.0	17.7
IV	Physics	10.7	4.8	XXIX	Zool.	59.3	6.2
V	Zool.	18.0	1.3	XXX	Physics	60.0	5.2
VI	Chem.	20.5	3.2	XXXI	Psychol.	60.0	9.8
VII	Zool.	21.3	6.9	XXXII	Anat.	60.0	12.3
VIII	Physics	21.3	18.2	XXXIII	Physics	64.0	53.4
IX	Geol.	25.0	4.7	XXXIV	Path.	65.0	4.2
X	Chem.	25.1	2.4	XXXV	Physiol.	65.0	7.0
XI	Zool.	28.7	8.6	XXXVI	Psychol.	65.0	7.3
XII	Bot.	29.0	8.1	XXXVII	Path.	65.0	24.7
XIII	Zool.	30.7	5.9	XXXVIII	Chem.	65.1	9.9
XIV	Math.	31.3	7.0	XXXIX	Bot.	67.8	10.6
XV	Chem.	31.4	9.8	XL	Geol.	70.0	21.8
XVI	Bot.	33.0	5.3	XLI	Math.	71.3	5.9
XVII	Geol.	33.3	4.7	XLII	Math.	71.3	19.6
XVIII	Chem.	38.8	6.9	XLIII	Bot.	71.3	39.2
XIX	Math.	41.3	37.1	XLIV	Bot.	75.5	6.2
XX	Math.	46.3	8.7	XLV	Physics	76.7	11.8
XXI	Zool.	46.7	6.0	XLVI	Physics	78.7	14.2
XXII	Physiol.	50.0	7.7	XLVII	Path.	80.0	10.7
XXIII	Bot.	50.0	15.9	XLVIII	Physics	80.0	35.3
XXIV	Chem.	50.2	8.3	XLIX	Bot.	81.1	27.2
XXV	Geol.	54.4	16.2	L	Physics	81.3	11.2

The order, grades and probable errors of the fifty who stand first are given to illustrate the method. We can thus say that the work of a certain physicist is equal in value to the work of a certain zoologist, or that a certain chemist has one chance in four of being as competent as a certain pathologist, a result that would not be possible by direct comparison. The various factors which limit the exactness of the method should be kept in mind, but we have at least the beginning of a method which with further effort can be made more accurate.

Similar methods can be applied to comparing the value of performance in fields even more diverse than the several sciences.

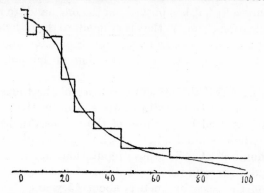

Fig. 2.—Distribution of the thousand men of science.

In the accompanying curve—which is based on substantially the same figures as are given in Table III, except that a man is given a position only in the science in which he stands the highest—is shown the distribution of the thousand men of science. The 1,000 scientific men are divided into ten groups, the range of eminence or merit covered by each hundred being proportional to the space it occupies on the axis of the abscissas, and the number of each degree of ability being proportional to the ordinates. The range of merit covered by each hundred becomes smaller and there are more of each degree of merit as we pass from the first to the second hundred and so on for the first five hundred, after which the differences become very small. The first hundred men of science cover a range of merit about equal to that of the second and third hundreds together, and this again is very nearly equal to the range covered by the remaining seven hundred. The average differences between the men in the first hundred are about twice as great as between the men in the second and third hundreds, and about seven times as great as between the men in the remaining groups. Or the differences among the first hundred are almost exactly ten times as great as among the last five hundred, who differ but little among themselves. It would be desirable to compare this distribution with that of the normal probability integral and with the salaries paid to scientific men, but the data are not as yet at hand.

The Distribution of American Men of Science

From a conventional point of view the distribution of men of science would not be regarded as a psychological problem, perhaps not even as a scientific problem. But in recent years the distribution of plants and animals has received increasing attention in botany and zoology, and apart from its pertinence as a correct description of the world in which we live, it has proved, on the one hand, to have certain practical applications, and, on the other hand, to throw light on certain general problems of heredity and evolution. Similar results may accrue from a scientific study of the distribution of human ability and performance.

The birthplace and the present residence of the thousand leading men of science of the United States are shown on the table on page 414, the divisions used being those of the census. Figures are given separately for the five hundred (I–V) who are more distinguished and for the five hundred (VI–X) whose reputations are less, followed by the totals and their number per million of the population. As the average age of the scientific men is about 45 years, their birth rate is referred to the census of 1860.[1] Thus the first line of the table shows that 29 of the 1,000 scientific men were born in Maine, and four now reside there. Of the 29 scientific men born in the state, 19 are among the 500 who are more eminent and 10 among the 500 who are less eminent. The number born was at the rate of 46.1 per million of the population at the approximate time of their birth, or one for each 22,000. The scientific population of the state is now only at the rate of 5.7 per million of the population, or scarcely more than one for each 200,000.

There are striking variations in the origin and in the present residence of scientific men throughout the United States. Massachusetts and Boston have been the intellectual center of the country. The birth rate of these leading men of science is in Massachusetts 108.8 per million population; it is 86.9 in Connecticut, and decreases continually at greater distances from this center. It is reduced to about one half in the surrounding states—46.1 in Maine, 46 in New Hampshire, 57.1 in Vermont and 47.2 in New York. There is a further reduction to one half in Pennsylvania—to 22.7—and this proceeds as we go southwards, the rate being 8.8 in Virginia, 5 in North Carolina, 2.8 in Georgia, 2.1 in Alabama, 1.3 in Mississippi and 1.4 in Louisiana. In the north central states the conditions are intermediate between New York and Pennsylvania. Thus the birth rate per million is 32.1 in Ohio and 36 in Michigan. Here again it decreases as we go southward. The rate is 45.1 in Wisconsin, 24.5 in Illinois, 11.8 in Missouri and 6.9 in Kentucky. Westward the total number of scientific men is too small and the population has been too rapidly increasing for the figures

[1] This is not exact, as the age distribution is not symmetrical, and the rate of increase of the population in the different states is not uniform, but the results are as nearly correct as is necessary.

to be reliable. Each individual should be considered in connection with the population at the time of his birth, but even in this case the validity of the results would be small.

Of the 1,000 scientific men, 126 were born in foreign countries—34 in Canada, 38 in Great Britain and 19 in Germany. The birthplace of seven is not known. The number per million is for the native population 13.2, and for the foreign-born population 12. These figures have, however, no significance, as the foreign-born population contains a much larger proportion of adult males. The percentage of the white native population in the United States over 40 years of age is 18.4, and of white foreign-born is 44.4. The native population consequently produces more than twice as many scientific men as the foreign-born even without regard to the excess of males among the foreign-born, the inclusion of the colored races among the native-born and the fact that many of the foreign-born have been called to this country on account of their scientific standing. The different nations contribute scientific men in very unequal measure, the numbers per million foreign-born being as follows: Switzerland, 68.9; Scotland, 37.9; England, 29.6; Canada, 28.7; Austria-Hungary, 10.4; Russia, 7.4; Germany, 7.1; Sweden, 5.2; Italy, 2.1; Ireland, 1.8; France, 0. These differences can not be attributed to race, as they do not represent the scientific productivity of these nations, but only of the classes that have emigrated to this country. While it is not possible to deny that the variations are dependent on the kinds of family stocks, it is probable that they are due in much larger measure to social and economic conditions. The native-born sons of Irish-born parents may not be inferior in scientific productivity to other classes of the community.

The inequality in the production of scientific men in different parts of the country seems to be a forcible argument against the view of Dr. Galton and Professor Pearson that scientific performance is almost exclusively due to heredity. It is unlikely that there are such differences in family stocks as would lead one part of the country to produce a hundred times as many scientific men as other parts. The negroes have a racial disqualification, but even this is not proved. The main factors in producing scientific and other forms of intellectual performance seem to be density of population, wealth, opportunity, institutions and social traditions and ideals. All these may be ultimately due to race, but, given the existing race, the scientific productivity of the nation can be increased in quantity, though not in quality, almost to the extent that we wish to increase it.

There may be no significant difference in the distributions of the first and second groups of 500. Some states have produced men of higher average standing than others, but the differences are within

TABLE I.—DISTRIBUTION OF THE THOUSAND MEN OF SCIENCE

	Birthplace			Per million 1860	Residence			Per million 1900
	I–V	VI–X	Total		I–V	VI–X	Total	
North Atlantic Division.								
Maine	19	10	29	46.1	0	4	4	5.7
New Hampshire	7	8	15	46.0	2	6	8	19.4
Vermont	9	9	18	57.1	0	2	2	5.8
Massachusetts	60	74	134	108.8	74	70	144	51.3
Rhode Island	4	1	5	28.6	7	1	8	18.7
Connecticut	26	14	40	86.9	27	16	43	47.3
New York	99	84	183	47.2	93	99	192	26.4
New Jersey	9	19	28	41.6	17	18	35	18.5
Pennsylvania	32	34	66	22.7	28	37	65	10.3
South Atlantic Division.								
Delaware	0	2	2	17.8	0	1	1	5.4
Maryland	12	14	26	37.8	24	23	47	39.5
District of Columbia	1	2	3	39.9	69	50	119	426.9
Virginia	5	8	13	8.8	8	2	10	5.4
West Virginia	1	0	1	.....	2	1	3	3.1
North Carolina	1	4	5	5.0	3	3	6	3.2
South Carolina	2	3	5	7.1				
Georgia	1	2	3	2.8	0	1	1	1.4
South Central Division.								
Kentucky	6	2	8	6.9	1	2	3	1.4
Tennessee	5	1	6	5.4	2	1	3	1.5
Alabama	1	1	2	2.1	1	1	2	1.1
Mississippi	1	0	1	1.3				
Louisiana	1	0	1	1.4	0	1	1	.7
Texas	0	3	3	4.9	2	5	7	2.3
North Central Division.								
Ohio	42	33	75	32.1	13	21	34	8.2
Indiana	17	11	28	20.7	4	8	12	4.7
Illinois	24	18	42	24.5	36	27	63	13.1
Michigan	12	15	27	36.0	22	5	27	11.1
Wisconsin	11	24	35	45.1	11	12	23	11.1
Minnesota	1	3	4	23.2	3	10	13	7.4
Iowa	6	14	20	29.6	5	2	7	3.1
Missouri	4	10	14	11.8	7	14	21	6.7
North Dakota	...	...	...	.....	0	2	2	6.2
South Dakota	...	...	...	.....	0	2	2	3.9
Nebraska	1	1	2	69.3	4	5	9	8.4
Kansas	5	2	7	65.3	2	3	5	3.4
Western Division.								
Montana	...	...	...	.....	0	2	2	8.2
Wyoming	...	...	...	.....	0	1	1	10.8
Colorado	0	3	3	87.2	3	5	8	14.8
New Mexico	...	...	...	.....	0	2	2	10.2
Arizona	...	...	...	.....	1	1	2	16.3
Washington	1	0	1	86.2				
California	5	6	11	28.9	23	30	53	35.7
Alaska	...	...	...	.....	0	1	1	15.7
Hawaii	1	0	1					
Philippine Islands	...	...	...	.....	2	1	3	
Total	**432**	**435**	**867**	27.6	**496**	**498**	**994**	13.3
Canada	11	23	34	28.7	1	1	2	
Brazil	...	...	...	.....	1	0	1	
Cuba	...	...	...	.....	0	1	1	
England	10	15	25	29.6	1	0	1	
Ireland	2	1	3	1.8				
Scotland	6	3	9	37.9				
Wales	0	1	1	10.7				
West Indies	0	1	1	69.1				
Germany	15	4	19	7.1				
Austria-Hungary	4	2	6	10.4				
Norway	1	0	1	2.9				
Sweden	2	1	3	5.2				
Denmark	0	2	2	12.9				
Switzerland	4	4	8	68.9				
Russia	4	2	6	7.4				
Italy	...	1	1	2.1				
Spain	0	...	...	137.3	1	0	1	
Turkey	...	1	...	.....				
India	4	0	4	193.3				
China	1	1	2	18.7				
Total	**64**	**62**	**126**	.....	**4**	**2**	**6**	
Grand total	**496**	**497**	**993**	.....	**500**	**500**	**1000**	

the range of possible chance variations. Thus Maine has produced 19 men of the first rank and 10 of the second. But if 29 pennies are tossed up, there is one chance in 14 or 15 ($P = .068$) that there will be 19 or more heads. It is, however, true, as a matter of fact, that Maine, Connecticut, Ohio, Indiana and Illinois have produced men of decidedly higher average standing than New Jersey, Wisconsin, Iowa and Missouri. Those born in Germany are considerably above and those born in Canada are below the average, and the figures may here represent a real difference in the classes drawn to this country.

The fact that there is not a significant difference in the average standing of scientific men born in different regions of the country tends to support the conclusion that scientific performance is mainly due to environment rather than to innate aptitude. If the fact that Massachusetts has produced relatively to its population four times as many scientific men as Pennsylvania and fifty times as many as the southern states were due to a superior stock, then we should expect that the average standing of its scientific men would be higher than elsewhere; but this is not the case. Like most arguments intended to disentangle the complex factors of "nature and nurture," this, however, is not conclusive. If scientific ability were innate, each tending to reach his level in spite of environment, then a potentially great man of science would become such wherever born, and we might expect a favorable environment to produce mediocre men, but not great men. But this argument is answered by the small number of scientific men from certain regions of the country. Differences in stock can scarcely be great enough to account for this; it seems to be due to circumstance. A further analysis of the curves of distribution might throw light on the problem. Thus it might be that the men of greatest genius were independent of the environment, while men of fair average performance were produced by it. Examples might be given in favor of this view, but I can not see that it is supported by the forms of the curves of distribution. I hope at some time to take up the question from a study of individual cases, but I have not as yet the data at hand. My general impression is that certain aptitudes, as for mathematics and music, are mainly innate, and that kinds of character and degrees of ability are mainly innate, but that the direction of performance is mainly due to circumstances, and that the environment imposes a veto on any performance not congenial to it.

The present distribution of the 1,000 men of science is somewhat the same as their origin. The population of the country has more than doubled since 1860, and the number of these scientific men per million population is consequently less than half the number per million at the period of their birth. There are in Massachusetts 144 of the 1,000,

which is 51.3 per million of the population, according to the census of
1900. The numbers then decrease to 26.4 per million in New York,
10.3 in Pennsylvania, 13.1 in Illinois, 8.2 in Ohio, 3.1 in Iowa, 1.1 in
Alabama, 0.7 in Louisiana and 0 in Mississippi. The most striking
development has been the attraction to Washington of a large group
of scientific men, 119 of the thousand, nearly all in the service of the
government. This number has been almost exactly supplied to the
country by the excess of scientific men born abroad—120. This leaves
an equal balance between the gains and losses of other parts of the
country. The greatest gain has been made by California, which has
drawn 42 of the scientific men from other states; Illinois and Maryland
have each gained 21. Other states have gained considerably in proportion to their total scientific population—New Jersey 7, Minnesota 9,
Missouri 7, Nebraska 7 and Colorado 5. These gains appear to be
significant, attributable to the establishment and growth of universities.

Massachusetts, New York and Pennsylvania have remained
nearly stationary. Massachusetts has gained ten of the scientific men
and New York nine, while Pennsylvania has lost one. The conditions
in New York are by no means creditable to that state, in view of its
great increase in wealth. Outside New York City, the state has lost
31 men of science, nearly one third of those it has produced, and half
the others are concentrated at Ithaca. The conditions are somewhat
similar in Massachusetts and Pennsylvania, outside Boston, Cambridge
and Philadelphia.

The rural New England states, Maine, New Hampshire and
Vermont, have lost 48 of the 62 scientific men whom they have produced. This is a loss that they can ill afford; it signifies a distinct
decadence. Had each of these states provided an income of $50,000
to retain these men in their service, they would have been repaid
manyfold, commercially as well as intellectually. The conditions in
some of the north central states are also ominous, though more likely
to improve. Thus Ohio has lost forty-one of its scientific men, more
than half of those whom it has produced; Indiana has also lost more
than half and Iowa just half. The south remains in its lamentable
condition of scientific stagnation, but we may hope that material
progress will be followed by an intellectual awakening. All these
figures become more impressive when we remember that they indicate
performance in scholarship, in literature and in art, as well as in
science. It would be well if they were widely known, as they would
tend to awaken civic pride and to improve the conditions of intellectual
activity.

The average standing of the scientific men residing in different
parts of the country varies a little more than the standing of those

produced in different regions and is perhaps less likely to be due to chance variations. This appears to be somewhat paradoxical from the point of view of the theory of probabilities. The fact that of the 75 scientific men born in Ohio, 42 belong to the first group and 33 to the second is a natural result of chance distribution, and the fact that of the 34 scientific men remaining in the state, 13 belong to the first group and 21 to the second might equally well be the result of chance distribution. But apparently it is not. Ohio has lost more than half the scientific men it has produced; it has lost two thirds of its better men and one third of its more mediocre men. The state has not provided for its scientific men, and has provided less adequately for the better men than for those who are not so good. Indiana has lost three fourths of its men of the first class and one fourth of those of the second class. The three rural New England states have lost seventeen eighteenths of their men of the first class and one half of those of the second class. These conditions are significant and serious.

Other states have improved their positions. Thus, thanks to its great university, Michigan has 22 men in the first group as compared with five in the second. Thanks again to its universities, Illinois has increased its number of scientific men from 42 to 63, of whom 36 are in the first class. California, Missouri and Minnesota have, on the other hand, called men who are below the average.

The large centers of scientific population in Massachusetts and New York have about maintained their positions, having produced men of about average standing and their resident men of science being of about average standing. Massachusetts has, however, gained a little and New York has lost a little. Of the 119 scientific men in Washington, 69 are in the first group and 50 in the second. This appears to me to be a fact of very great importance. It is commonly said that less able scientific men are attracted to the government service, that those who are able leave it for university positions and that those who stay are not encouraged to do their best work. Such statements are refuted by these statistics. The average performance of the scientific men at Washington is higher than in Massachusetts or in New York. This conclusion is most gratifying to those of us who believe that the future of scientific research depends largely on its support by the nation, the states and the municipalities.

The writer has on various occasions called attention to the economic conditions which limit scientific research. As one of the objects of the present work is to improve these conditions, it may be well to repeat here the argument. Our economic system rests on the free exchange of services. A state of society may some day be reached in which each will aim to give as much as he can and to take as little, but at present it appeals to our sense of fairness that each should ask for his services what someone else is willing to pay. In the increasing complexity of our society this method is working two serious injustices. One of these is the formation of monopolies. Thanks chiefly to the applications of science, many services can now be supplied at a cost less than people would be willing to pay. When free competition is excluded, either by the conditions of the case or by ingenious combination, people may be made to pay more than a fair return for certain services. The problems of monopoly are being discussed on all sides, and remedies are being sought in all directions; but the injustice which in a way is the converse of monopoly has scarcely been noticed. This is the case in which an individual gives services without an adequate return, owing to the fact that they are not rendered to a single individual or group who will pay for them, but to society as a whole. A surgeon may ask for an operation for appendicitis as large a fee as his patient is willing to pay, but should he after years of research discover a method of preventing appendicitis altogether, he would receive no payment at all, but would, on the contrary, give up all future fees for the operation. The surgeons who by risking and sacrificing their lives discovered how to suppress yellow fever have received no return for their great work.

The two most important services for society—the bearing and rearing of children and creation in science and art—are exactly those for which society gives no economic returns, leaving them dependent on instincts which are in danger of atrophy. This state of affairs not only does injustice to the unrewarded individual, but works immeasurable harm to society—a greater injury probably than all existing monopolies. There are more than a hundred thousand physicians in the United States who are practising on their patients for fees, while there are scarcely two hundred who are studying seriously the causes of disease and the methods of preventing it. The conditions are similar in law and in all professions and trades. The scientific investigator is usually an amateur. He has wealth or earns his living by some profession, and incidentally does what he can to advance science for love of the work. This has its good side in producing a small group of men who are not subject to purely commercial standards. But this is after all a minor factor, and the scientific man is likely to look for fame, which is scarcely more ideal than money and can be supplied to but few. Satisfaction in the work itself is the best reward for work; but no one can know that his work is of value except by the reflected appreciation of others, and in the existing social order the simplest and probably the most adequate expression of this appreciation is direct payment for the service rendered.

The methods that society has devised to meet this situation, apart from the conferring of honors and fame, are recent and inadequate. Copyrights and patents are the most direct acknowledgment of property in ideas. They have accomplished a good deal, and their scope should be extended. At present only a small part of discovery is covered by the patent office, and this perhaps not the part requiring the greatest genius. It is, however, leading, especially in Germany, to the development of discovery on a sound commercial basis. It is said that one chemical firm employs three hundred doctors of philosophy to carry on scientific investigations. Research has hitherto been forwarded mainly by the universities, where again Germany has led the way. The professorship is given as a reward for successful investigations, and the holder of a chair is expected to devote himself to investigation as well as to teaching. There is a tendency to permit certain professors to engage almost exclusively in research. Thus the astronomical observatories of Harvard, Chicago and California universities are purely research institutions. A further step has been taken in the endowment of institutions, such as the Carnegie Institution and the Rockefeller Institute, explicitly for research. The most logical and important advance, however, consists in the direct conduct of research by the government. As the government should control monopolies, so it should conduct the work which is not for the benefit of a single individual, but for the people as a whole. There are, of course, no end of difficulties in the control of monopolies or the conduct of research by a municipality, state or nation; but it is exactly these difficulties that it is our business to overcome. We may congratulate ourselves that our national government is at present accomplishing more for research and the applications of science than the government of any other nation, and that the men of science working under the government are doing their full share for the advancement of science.

Table II gives the cities in which five or more of the thousand scientific men were born, and the cities in which five or more of them now reside. The tendency towards concentration which we know to exist is here measured. Two hundred and twenty-seven of the scientific men were born in places producing five or more, and 782 of them live in places where there are five or more. This is, of course, natural, and probably desirable; scientific work is accomplished where men gather together. Still the fact that three fourths of our scientific men live in 39 places—with a good many more in the suburbs—leaves rather a scanty number for the rest of the country. We have, however, more separate scientific centers than foreign countries, and by this circumstance we both gain and lose. The lack of men of distinction in whole regions and large cities is a serious indictment of our civiliza-

TABLE II.—DISTRIBUTION IN DIFFERENT PLACES

	According to birthplace			Per million 1860
	I–V	VI–X	Total	
New York, N. Y.	33	25	**58**	*71.2*
Boston, Mass.	24	19	**43**	*241.8*
Philadelphia, Pa.	12	16	**28**	*49.5*
Baltimore, Md.	9	11	**20**	*94.1*
Cincinnati, O.	6	6	**12**	*74.5*
Brooklyn, N. Y.	3	8	**11**	*39.4*
Chicago, Ills.	5	3	**8**	*73.2*
Buffalo, N. Y.	3	4	**7**	*86.2*
St. Louis, Mo.	2	5	**7**	*43.5*
Cambridge, Mass.	4	2	**6**	*230.2*
Cleveland, O.	4	2	**6**	*140.5*
Salem, Mass.	1	5	**6**	*269.6*
Milwaukee, Wis.	1	4	**5**	*110.5*
Newark, N. J.	3	2	**5**	*69.5*
San Francisco, Cal.	2	3	**5**	*88.0*
Total	**112**	**115**	**227**	

	According to residence			Per million 1900
	I–V	VI–X	Total	
Washington, D. C.	69	50	**119**	*426.9*
New York, N. Y. ⎱	61	54	**115**	*56.1*
Brooklyn, N. Y. ⎰	1	3	**4**	*3.4*
Cambridge, Mass.	30	22	**52**	*576.8*
Chicago, Ills.	29	16	**45**	*26.5*
Baltimore, Md.	22	16	**38**	*74.6*
New Haven, Conn.	24	10	**34**	*314.7*
Philadelphia, Pa.	14	20	**34**	*26.3*
Boston, Mass.	14	19	**33**	*58.8*
Ithaca, N. Y.	17	15	**32**	*2436.1*
Ann Arbor, Mich.	20	5	**25**	*1723.1*
Madison, Wis.	7	11	**18**	*939.2*
Berkeley, Cal.	8	9	**17**	*1286.5*
Palo Alto, Cal.	9	7	**16**	*9650.2*
Princeton, N. J.	8	6	**14**	*3590.6*
Minneapolis, Minn.	3	8	**11**	*54.3*
St. Louis, Mo.	6	5	**11**	*19.1*
Worcester, Mass.	7	4	**11**	*229.6*
Cleveland, O.	6	4	**10**	*26.2*
Columbus, O.	3	7	**10**	*79.6*
San Francisco, Cal.	1	9	**10**	*29.1*
Columbia, Mo.	1	8	**9**	*1592.6*
Lincoln, Nebr.	4	5	**9**	*224.0*
Syracuse, N. Y.	0	9	**9**	*83.0*
Cincinnati, O.	2	6	**8**	*24.5*
Bryn Mawr, Pa.	2	5	**7**	*?*
Evanston, Ills.	5	2	**7**	*363.4*
Middletown, Conn.	2	5	**7**	*730.0*
Bloomington, Ind.	3	3	**6**	*928.8*
Brookline, Mass.	4	2	**6**	*300.8*
Charlottesville, Va.	5	1	**6**	*930.7*
Iowa City, Ia.	4	2	**6**	*751.2*
Mt. Hamilton, Cal.	4	2	**6**	*?*
Northampton, Mass.	2	4	**6**	*321.8*
Providence, R. I.	5	1	**6**	*34.2*
Albany, N. Y.	3	2	**5**	*53.1*
Amherst, Mass.	3	2	**5**	*994.9*
Chapel Hill, N. C.	3	2	**5**	*4549.6*
Lawrence, Kans.	2	3	**5**	*460.3*
New Brunswick, N. J.	2	3	**5**	*249.9*
Total	**415**	**367**	**782**	

tion. The existence of cities such as Brooklyn and Buffalo is an intellectual scandal.

Of the 866 men native to the United States, 224 were born in the cities which in 1900 had a population of more than 25,000. These places had in 1860 a population of about 4,500,000 as compared with a rural population of about 27,000,000. The urban population was about one sixth of the rural population and produced more than a quarter of the scientific men. The urban birth rate was 50 and the

TABLE III.—DISTRIBUTION ACCORDING TO PRESENT POSITION OF THE THOUSAND MEN OF SCIENCE

	I	II	III	IV	V	VI	VII	VIII	IX	X	Total
Harvard..............	19	8.5	3	6.5	3.5	6	4.5	5.5	3.5	6.5	66.5
Columbia.............	7	6	6.5	4.5	5	4.5	5.5	6	4	11	60
Chicago..............	7	10	3	6	2	2.5	3	2	1.5	2	39
Cornell..............	3	6	3	2	3	1.5	3	3.5	4	4.5	33.5
U. S. Geological Survey.	6	3	4	4	4	1	3	3	2	2	32
U. S. Department Agriculture.............	3	4	2	4	3	2	3	3	3	5	32
Johns Hopkins........	9	2	5.5	0	1.5	2	4.5	0.5	1	4.5	30.5
California............	1	2	2	4	3	4	1	5	1	4	27
Yale.................	2	5.5	3	3.5	5.5	2	1	0	2	2	26.5
Smithsonian Institution................	3	2	4	4	2	0	1	3	1	2	22
Michigan.............	1	3	6	3	3	0	0	1	1	2	20
Mass. Inst. Tech......	1	2	2.5	4	2	3	2	0	0	3	19.5
Wisconsin............	1	3	1	2	0	3	2	4	2	0	18
Pennsylvania.........	2	1	1	3.5	2.5	1.5	1	2	0.5	2	17
Leland Stanford, Jr....	3	1	1	1	3	2	2	1	1	1	16
Total...											459.5

Princeton..	14.5
Minnesota, Ohio State...	10
New York University..	9.5
Missouri, Nebraska, Northwestern..................................	9
National Bureau of Standards, U. S. Navy, Am. Mus. Nat. History......	8
Carnegie Institution, Clark, Iowa, Syracuse, Virginia, Wesleyan.........	7
Bryn Mawr, Cincinnati, Dartmouth, Illinois, Indiana, N. Y. Botanical Garden, Smith....	6
Brown, Kansas, North Carolina, Texas, Washington (St. Louis).........	5
Field Columbian Museum, General Electric Co., St. Louis, Western Reserve, Pennsylvania State, Rutgers....	4
Lehigh...	3.5
Philadelphia Acad. Nat. Sciences, Amherst, Case, College of City of New York, Colorado College, Colorado University, Haverford, Purdue, Rockefeller Institute, Simmons, Tufts, Vassar, Worcester...........	3
Grand Total..	730

rural birth rate was 23.8. The superior position of the towns is doubtless due to a more favorable environment, but it may also be in part
due to the fact that the parents of these scientific men were the abler
clergymen and others of their generation who were drawn to the
cities.

Table III gives the institutions with which three or more of the
scientific men are connected, and in the case of institutions in which
there are more than fifteen the details of their rank are shown, I, II,
etc., representing the first hundred, the second hundred, etc. I give
this table with some hesitation, but it appears that in the end it will
be for the advantage of scientific research if it is known which institutions obtain and retain the best men. Harvard has 66,5 of the scientific
men, the half (0.5) being used when a professor is emeritus or gives
only part of his time to an institution. Columbia follows with 60, and
Chicago comes next with 39. In both the U. S. Geological Survey and
the Department of Agriculture there are 32. About half of the scientific
men are connected with 18 institutions. Harvard has not only the
largest number of scientific men, but they are also of the highest
rank, 19 being in the first hundred and 8.5 in the second hundred.
John Hopkins has nine in the first hundred and Columbia and Chicago
each has seven. A table such as this might have some practical influence if the data were made public at intervals of ten years.

Table IV gives the institutions at which the 1,000 men of science
pursued their studies. A man is credited for his degree to the first
institution at which he took it, but in the case of graduate study, he
may have attended several institutions. He is not, however, credited
as a graduate student to the institutions from which he received the
doctorate.[1] The total influence of Harvard is 237, of the Johns Hopkins
171, of Yale 93, of Columbia 78 and of Cornell 74. About one tenth
of the men of science received their bachelor's degree from Harvard
and about the same number their doctor's degree from the John Hopkins. It is not certain that a preponderance of scientific men has been
produced at any institution as compared with the total number of
students, and it appears that those who attend the larger universities
are not of higher average performance than others. Thus of the 106
who have taken the bachelor's degree at Harvard, 55 are in the first
rank and 51 in the second. Yale, Cornell and Michigan have produced
men above the average rank, and the excess is such that it is probably
significant, though the departures fall within the limits of possible
chance variation. On the whole, however, there is no significant difference in rank between the 515 men who attended the larger institutions

[1] The doctorates include the comparatively few cases in which the degree of
doctor of science has been conferred in course

TABLE IV.—ATTENDANCE OF THE THOUSAND MEN OF SCIENCE AT DIFFERENT INSTITUTIONS

	Bachelor's degree			Graduate study			Ph.D.			Grand total
	I–V	VI–X	Total	I–V	V–IX	Total	I–V	VI–X	Total	
Harvard............	55	51	106	38	36	74	30	27	57	237
Johns Hopkins........	12	15	27	27	15	42	50	52	102	171
Yale................	35	17	52	9	4	13	14	14	28	93
Columbia............	12	16	28	9	3	12	11	27	38	78
Cornell..............	19	12	31	4	13	17	10	16	26	74
Michigan............	23	12	35	4	4	8	8	2	10	53
Princeton............	11	12	23	5	7	12	4	4	8	43
Chicago.............	0	2	2	3	11	14	12	11	23	39
Mass. Inst. Tech......	13	13	26	3	6	9	0	0	0	35
Amherst.............	12	11	23	2	3	5	0	1	1	29
Clark...............	0	0	0	5	11	16	4	8	12	28
Pennsylvania.........	5	10	15	2	2	4	3	6	9	28
Wisconsin...........	4	10	14	1	4	5	2	2	4	23
California...........	5	7	12	3	3	6	3	1	4	22
Wesleyan............	9	7	16	2	3	5	0	0	0	21
Indiana..............	4	4	8	2	4	6	4	0	4	18
Nebraska............	5	5	10	4	2	6	1	1	2	18
Williams............	6	8	14	0	2	2	0	1	1	17
Dartmouth...........	5	5	10	2	1	3	0	1	1	14
Oberlin..............	6	4	10	2	2	4	0	0	0	14
College City N. Y.....	7	4	11	1	1	2	0	0	0	13
Geo. Washington......	3	2	5	2	0	2	3	3	6	13
Brown..............	4	4	8	1	2	3	0	0	0	11
Iowa................	2	4	6	1	2	3	1	0	1	10
Toronto.............	5	13	18	3	3	6	0	0	0	24
Edinburgh...........	2	1	3	0	3	3	2	3	5	11
Cambridge...........	2	0	2	3	5	8	0	0	0	10
Berlin...............	...	...	...	53	42	95	11	11	22	117
Leipzig..............	...	...	...	30	15	45	27	12	39	84
Göttingen............	...	...	...	18	18	36	19	14	33	69
Heidelberg...........	...	...	...	27	14	41	7	8	15	56
Munich..............	...	...	...	13	5	18	6	7	13	31
Strasburg............	...	...	...	13	4	17	3	3	6	23
Freiburg.............	...	...	...	10	5	15	3	1	4	19
Bonn................	...	...	...	10	4	14	2	2	4	18
Zürich...............	...	...	...	5	6	11	1	2	3	14
Vienna..............	...	...	...	9	3	12	0	0	0	12
Würzburg............	...	...	...	4	3	7	3	2	5	12
Paris................	...	...	...	21	7	28	0	1	1	29
Total..............	266	249	515	351	278	629	244	243	487	1631

and those who attended smaller colleges or none. It might be supposed that abler students would be attracted to a university such as Harvard, and that they would have greater opportunities there, but this appears not to be the case. So far as it goes, this favors the theory that men of science are born such and are not dependent on the environment for the quality of their performance. It may, however, be that relatively more men of mediocre ability are led to take up scientific work at an institution such as Harvard, whereas only those of genius are likely to break through the barrier of an unfavorable environment.

The conditions are similar in the case of the doctor's degree. Of the 487 men who have received it from the larger institutions, 244 are of the first rank and 243 of the second; nor do any institutions excel, unless it be Leipzig and Göttingen. Those who pursue graduate studies at institutions from which they do not take the degree are of distinctly higher standing than the average A.B. or Ph.D. This is probably because the abler and more energetic men have attended several institutions, more especially abroad, many of them having worked in foreign universities even after having obtained scientific distinction.

The thousand men of science under consideration pursued their graduate studies on the average from fifteen to twenty years ago. Since that time a considerable change has occurred in the relative numbers of students attracted to different institutions. Owing to the improvement of our universities relatively fewer students now frequent foreign institutions. The number of doctorates conferred in the natural and exact sciences during the past nine years is as follows: Johns Hopkins, 147; Chicago, 145; Columbia, 137; Harvard, 129; Yale, 120; Cornell, 94; Pennsylvania, 85; Clark, 75. There is then a drop to universities that have conferred fewer than 25 degrees in the sciences during this period. Relatively more work is done in the sciences in some institutions than in others. Thus the percentage of degrees in the sciences in these universities is as follows: Clark, 95; Cornell, 58; Johns Hopkins, 54; Columbia, 49; Chicago, 48; Pennsylvania, 43; Harvard, 42, and Yale, 41.

Table V shows the institutional origin of men who have pursued different sciences. The Johns Hopkins University has excelled relatively in chemistry, physics, zoology and physiology; Harvard in zoology and botany; Columbia in zoology, botany and mathematics; Cornell in physics and botany; Clark in psychology, and Michigan in botany and pathology. Of the foreign universities, Berlin has excelled in physics, Leipzig in psychology and Göttingen in chemistry and mathematics.

The table also shows that men are more likely to pursue graduate studies and to take the doctor's degree in some sciences than in others.

Of the fifty psychologists, 35 have received the doctor's degree from the institutions given in the table, and of the 150 zoologists 90 have received it, whereas only two of the 25 anatomists and only five of the 60 pathologists have received a non-technical higher degree from these universities. While important improvements in the practise of surgery and medicine have been made in this country, it must be admitted that we are not doing our share for the advancement of pathology, anatomy and physiology.

TABLE V.—SUBJECTS OF THE THOUSAND MEN OF SCIENCE WHO HAVE PURSUED GRADUATE STUDIES OR TAKEN THE DOCTOR'S DEGREE AT DIFFERENT INSTITUTIONS

	Graduate study													Ph.D.													Grand total
	Chemistry	Physics	Zoology	Geology	Botany	Mathematics	Pathology	Psychology	Astronomy	Physiology	Anatomy	Anthropology	Total	Chemistry	Physics	Zoology	Geology	Botany	Mathematics	Pathology	Psychology	Astronomy	Physiology	Anatomy	Anthropology	Total	
Johns Hopkins...	3	8	5	4	3	5	7	2	..	3	2	..	42	18	24	22	9	1	8	1	6	2	10	1	..	102	144
Harvard.....	10	8	13	8	12	10	1	7	1	3	1	..	74	9	2	20	7	10	3	..	4	..	..	..	2	57	131
Columbia....	3	4	..	2	..	1	..	1	..	..	1	..	12	5	5	9	1	5	6	..	2	2	2	..	1	38	50
Cornell......	1	4	3	2	3	2	..	..	..	1	1	..	17	1	14	2	..	5	1	..	3	..	..	..	..	26	43
Yale........	3	2	2	4	..	1	..	1	..	..	..	..	13	8	2	2	5	1	5	..	2	1	2	..	..	28	41
Chicago......	2	4	1	..	3	..	1	..	2	1	..	..	14	1	1	11	3	2	3	..	..	..	1	1	..	23	37
Clark........	1	2	6	..	5	..	..	..	1	1	..	..	16	..	1	2	..	..	1	1	5	..	1	..	1	12	28
Princeton.......	..	1	6	..	..	1	..	2	1	..	1	..	12	1	3	2	..	..	1	..	1	..	..	..	..	8	20
Michigan....	..	4	2	..	..	1	..	1	..	..	..	..	8	..	2	1	..	4	..	3	..	..	..	..	..	10	18
Pennsylvania	..	..	1	..	..	..	2	1	..	..	..	..	4	3	1	3	..	1	..	..	1	..	..	..	..	9	13
California....	1	1	1	..	..	..	1	2	..	..	..	..	6	1	..	..	1	2	..	..	..	..	..	..	..	4	10
Indiana........	..	2	1	..	1	..	..	2	..	..	..	..	6	..	..	2	1	1	..	..	..	..	..	..	..	4	10
Berlin.......	18	24	5	3	5	5	10	14	3	4	3	1	95	3	12	1	..	..	2	..	1	3	..	..	..	22	117
Leipzig......	10	2	7	3	2	4	2	8	..	5	1	1	45	11	2	8	1	3	4	..	9	..	1	..	..	39	84
Göttingen....	10	5	1	3	..	9	3	5	..	..	..	..	36	17	2	..	2	..	12	..	..	..	..	..	..	33	69
Heidelberg...	18	2	2	8	..	3	2	4	..	1	..	1	41	12	..	..	3	..	..	..	..	..	..	..	..	15	56
Munich......	10	..	2	2	..	..	1	1	..	1	1	..	18	5	..	1	3	2	..	..	..	..	1	1	..	13	31
Strasburg....	4	1	4	..	2	1	2	..	2	..	1	..	17	..	2	1	..	1	1	..	..	1	..	..	..	6	23
Freiburg......	3	1	5	1	..	..	2	2	..	1	..	..	15	1	..	2	..	..	..	..	1	..	..	..	..	4	19
Bonn........	2	..	..	..	7	..	..	1	1	2	..	1	14	..	1	..	..	2	1	..	..	..	..	..	..	4	18
Zürich.......	6	3	1	..	..	1	..	..	..	..	..	..	11	2	..	..	1	..	..	..	..	..	..	..	..	3	14
Vienna.......	1	1	..	..	..	10	..	..	..	..	..	..	12	..	..	..	..	..	..	..	..	..	..	..	..	0	12
Würzburg....	2	..	3	..	..	1	..	..	1	..	..	..	7	..	4	1	..	..	..	..	..	..	..	..	..	5	12
Paris........	5	4	3	3	..	4	3	6	..	..	..	..	28	..	..	..	..	..	..	1	..	..	..	..	..	1	29
Total......	113	83	74	43	38	53	47	59	12	24	13	4	563	98	78	90	36	41	49	5	35	10	18	2	4	466	1029

It would be desirable to compare the scientific men and the scientific work of the United States with those of other nations, and I hope to collect data on this subject. It is my impression from such information as is on hand that we produce from one seventh to one tenth of the world's scientific research, but that we have not produced one tenth of its recent great discoveries or of its contemporary great men. With our vast population and unlimited resources, it would be shameful and intolerable to let the future be no better than the present. It is obvious that we should collect without delay the information that would tell us where we stand among the nations.

It is not altogether without interest to find that it is possible to reduce to order facts which might be supposed to be outside the range of the natural and exact sciences. The present articles are, however, only a beginning of a study of scientific men as a group and of the conditions on which scientific performance depends. We have in a large measure explored the material world and subdued it to our uses; it is now our business to secure an equal increase in our knowledge of human nature and to apply it for our welfare. If he is a benefactor to mankind who makes two blades of grass grow where one grew before, his services would be immeasurably greater who could enable two men of science to flourish where there had been but one.

21

A FURTHER STATISTICAL STUDY OF AMERICAN MEN OF SCIENCE

Printed in *Science*, **32**: 633–648 and 672–688. 1910.
It also formed, under the same title, the second part of the supplement to "American Men of Science: A Directory." (Second Edition) 564–596, 1910.

The advancement of science and the improvement of the conditions under which scientific work is done are of such vast importance for society that even the most modest attempt to introduce scientific method into the study of these conditions has some value. It is truly both exhilarating and appalling to face the opportunities and responsibilities of science and of scientific men. The applications of science have quadrupled the wealth which each individual produces and have doubled the length of human life. In many cases the gain has been greater than this. In transporting freight or printing a newspaper, the products of each man's labor have been multiplied a hundredfold; in equal measure the danger from smallpox, cholera and the plague has been diminished.

As intercommunication increases between the nations, bringing them all within the circle of our civilization, and as the total population of the earth grows, the number of scientific advances becomes continually larger and the value of each of ever greater magnitude. It is thus an economic law that the means of subsistence tend to increase more rapidly than the population.[1] When the applications of electricity increase the efficiency of each individual on the average by twenty per cent—as may now be the case in civilized countries—the economic value would be in the neighborhood of twenty billion dollars a year. In comparison with a sum so inconceivable, the cost of science since the days of Faraday and Henry is altogether insignificant. In the United States at present there are scarcely more than a thousand men engaged in serious research work, and they do not on the average devote more than half their time to it. Throughout the world there

[1] This inversion of the law of Malthus, to which the writer has called attention on several occasions (*e. g.*, SCIENCE, December 18, 1896) has recently been given a most interesting expression by Professor T. H. Norton (*The Popular Science Monthly*, September, 1910). Both the number and the value of scientific advances being directly proportional to the total population, the means of subsistence tend to increase as the square of the population.

may be seven to ten times as many. The investigations of these men may cost a total of $20,000,000 a year, perhaps one thousandth of what may be gained by the applications of electricity, or one hundredth of what is saved by the use of the phosphorus match.

But man does not live alone by the applications of electricity and the use of the phosphorus match. Science has given us a new heaven as well as a new earth, for it has checked not only poverty and disease, but also superstition, ignorance and unreason. It has done away with slavery and with the need of child labor; it has made excessive manual labor by women or by men unnecessary. By giving the possibility of leisure and education to all it has made democracy possible. Finally science has not only given us leisure, but also the means to occupy that leisure in a worthy manner; its intellectual and emotional appeal is almost equal to the art and religion which were so much earlier in their origin.

Science has been more successful in the production of wealth than in its distribution and use, and it has been more effective in its control of the material world than of human conduct; but this is a natural result of necessary lines of development. The methods which have slowly extended from physics and chemistry to the more complicated phenomena of biology will give us sciences of psychology, sociology and anthropology and applications of these sciences commensurate with their dominant importance. Science has, indeed, already profoundly altered not only the material conditions of life but also social relations and mental contents and attitudes. The conditions of heredity and circumstance which determine the whole course of life are subject to its control. We need only to obtain the knowledge and to apply it. If an improvement of ten per cent in the cereal crop will yield a billion dollars a year, in what terms of money should an increase of ten per cent in the annual output of science be stated?

The application of scientific methods to the advancement of science is in one sense the beginning of science and in another one of its latest undertakings. We are at present almost wantonly ignorant and careless in regard to the conditions which favor or hinder scientific work. We do not know whether progress is in the main due to a large number of faithful workers or to the genius of a few. We do not know to what extent it may be possible to advance science by increasing the number of scientific positions or how far such an increase might be expected to add to the number of men of genius. We do not know to what extent increased salaries, better facilities and greater leisure would favor the quantity and quality of our work. We do not know to what extent non-rational sanctions, such as reputation, offices, titles, degrees, prizes, membership in exclusive societies and the like are effective. We do not know whether it is wise to combine teaching with research or applied with pure science. We do not know whether it is better for the professor and investigator to have a moderate salary, a life position and a pension, or to engage in severe competition for large prizes; whether obedience and discipline should be prescribed or the largest individual liberty allowed. We know but little as to the kind of education, methods of work and mode of life, which are most favorable to scientific productivity. In the face of endless problems of this character we are as empirical in our methods as the doctor of physic a hundred years ago or the agricultural laborer to-day. It is surely time for scientific men to apply scientific methods to determine the circumstances that promote or hinder the advancement of science. We should begin where and when we can; even though the results of the first efforts may appear somewhat trivial, we may proceed in the confident belief that in the end the advancement of science will become an applied science.

In a series of three articles published in the numbers of SCIENCE for November 23 and 30 and December 7, 1906, the writer described the methods which he used to select a group of a thousand leading American men of science, the application of these methods to the measurement of scientific merit, and the origin and distribution of the group. About seven years having elapsed since the selection of the group treated in these articles and a second edition of the "Biographical Directory of American Men of Science" being in preparation, it seemed desirable to repeat the process of determining the thousand leading scientific men in the United States. It is worth while to learn what changes have taken place in the composition of this group and in the distribution of the scientific men among various institutions and in different parts of the country. A list of scientific men as nearly contemporary as might be was also wanted for some further studies of the conditions of heredity and environment which are favorable to scientific productivity.

The methods used to select the group of a thousand leading men of science were substantially the same as before and need not be redescribed in detail. The scientific men were distributed among twelve sciences as previously. It was intended that the number in each science should be proportional to the total number of investigators in that science, and it was as nearly so as is needful for the purpose in view. The distribution was as follows: Chemistry, 175; physics, 150; zoology, 150; botany, 100; geology, 100; mathematics, 80; pathology, 60; astronomy, 50; psychology, 50; physiology, 40; anatomy, 25; anthropology, 20.

In each science twice as many names were selected and written on slips with the addresses and positions. The ten men of science who stood at the head of the list in each science in the previous arrangement were asked to arrange the names in that science in the order of merit. The memorandum of instructions read: "It is obvious that such an order can be only approximate, and for the objects in view an approximation is all that is needed. The judgments are possible, because they are as a matter of fact made in elections to a society of limited membership, in filling chairs at a university, etc. By merit is understood contributions to the advancement of science, primarily by research, but teaching, administration, editing, the compilation of text-books, etc., should be considered. The different factors that make a man efficient in advancing science must be roughly balanced."

There were thus at hand in each science ten arrangements of those known to have done research work in the order of the value of their work, as estimated by those having expert knowledge. The ten positions assigned to each individual were then averaged, and the workers in each science were arranged in order. The lists for the twelve sciences were interpolated to form a combined list of a thousand scientific men. A second group in each science and a second group of a thousand scientific men were in like manner obtained. This was not done before, and the second thousand has less validity than the first thousand. It has, however, a certain interest for purposes of comparison.

The average of ten judgments is not necessarily more correct than any one of these judgments; the conditions are similar to observations in the exact sciences. One good observation may have more validity than the average of a number of observations made under less favorable conditions. But if ten scientific men concerning whose competence it is not possible to discriminate in advance make a judgment, we may take the average as the most probable value. If we had but a single judgment we should not know its validity, but with ten judgments the probable error can be calculated. These probable errors tell us not only the limits within which the place of an individual in the series is likely to be correct, but also measure the differences between the individuals.

This method of converting a qualitative series into a series of quantitative differences may be illustrated by the case in which it was used by the writer for the first time.[1] Some two hundred shades of gray were made, giving approximately equal differences in illumination between white and black. In such a series the grays toward the white end appear more alike than those toward the black end, and two adjacent grays are indistinguishable. Psychologically it is a qualitative series. If now the grays are arranged in the order of brightness a

[1] "The Time of Perception as a Measure of Differences in Intensity," *Philos. Studien*, **19**: 63–68, 1902.

number of times by the same or different observers and the average position in the series of each gray is determined, the mean variation is inversely proportional to the psychological differences between the grays. There is thus determined the quantitative differences in the perception and its relation to the physical differences between the lights. The same methods have been used in the Columbia laboratory of psychology to measure the validity of beliefs, the beauty of pictures, differences in traits of character, literary skill and efficiency in various performances.

The method used enables us to measure not only differences in scientific merit, but also the accuracy of judgment of those who make the arrangements. It would be possible to determine whether those more eminent have the more accurate judgments, at what age the individuals are most competent and the like. As a matter of fact, the judgments in the present case were made by those most eminent in each science who were willing to undertake the task. Of the ten in each science who were placed at the head of the list in the previous study,[1] or 120 in all, 80 consented to undertake the arrangement, and of these 68 sent in valid lists. Others in the order of eminence were then asked until ten lists were obtained in each science. This study has thus only been made possible by the cooperation of those whose time is of much value. My personal obligations to them are very great.

The names of those selected for arrangement included all who were known to have done research work of any consequence, and those who arranged them were asked to add any who had been omitted. Some names deserving consideration were doubtless neglected and consequently would not find a place in the first or second thousands as ultimately selected. Each of those included in the first group is probably among the leading thousand scientific men in the United States, but there are a few others who belong to this group though not included. It might be a service to science to print the list of our thousand leading scientific men in the order of merit together with the probable error of each position, but it would require courage to do this, and perhaps it would not be possible to obtain the arrangement if it were to be made known. In the "Biographical Directory of American Men of Science" those are indicated by stars who belong either to the group as selected seven years ago or as selected now. Those who have won a place in the group can be identified by a comparison of the two editions of the book. Those who have lost their places in the group can not be known.

---

[1] Six were not asked owing to their illness or absence from the country. These conditions also account for a number of those who did not reply to the latter or did not consent to make the arrangement.

The arrangements of each of the two lists extended over a period of some months. The first list may be dated as approximately of January 1, 1903, and the second list as approximately of January 1, 1910. The distributions given in the previous paper refer approximately to January 1, 1906, the residences and positions used being those given in the first edition of the directory. For the present list, the residences and positions are those of January 1, 1910. It would be better if the arrangement of the first list and the distributions referred to the same date, but it was not possible to work up the data more promptly, as the writer was able to attend to the compilation of the directory and the statistics only during the summer months. In collecting and compiling the data he has had the very valuable assistance of Professor V. A. C. Henmon, of the University of Wisconsin, and of Mr. E. K. Strong, Jr., fellow in psychology in Columbia University.

Those included in the list of 1903 who died prior to 1910 number 58. It is a roll of honor which may be given here:

1903 (in part)

BOLTON, HENRY CARRINGTON	*Chemistry*
RHOADS, EDWARD	*Physics*

1904

BEECHER, CHARLES E.	*Geology*
DROWN, THOMAS MESSENGER	*Chemistry*
HATCHER, JOHN BELL	*Geology*
HERRICK, CLARENCE LUTHER	*Zoology*
PALMER, ARTHUR WILLIAM	*Chemistry*
DE SCHWEINITZ, EMIL ALEXANDER	*Chemistry*

1905

BRACE, DEWITT BRISTOL	*Physics*
ELDRIDGE, GEORGE HOMANS	*Geology*
ELLIS, JOB BICKNELL	*Botany*
EWELL, ERVIN E.	*Chemistry*
MATTHEWS, WASHINGTON	*Anthropology*
PACKARD, ALPHEUS SPRING	*Zoology*
PRESCOTT, ALBERT BENJAMIN	*Chemistry*
WARDER, ROBERT BOWNE	*Chemistry*
WOOD, EDWARD STICKNEY	*Chemistry*

1906

LANGLEY, SAMUEL PIERPONT	*Physics*
MacCALLUM, JOHN BRUCE	*Anatomy*
MILLER, EDMUND HOWD	*Chemistry*
MORGAN, ANDREW PRICE	*Botany*
PAULMIER, FREDERICK CLARK	*Zoology*
PEIRCE, JAMES MILLS	*Mathematics*
PENFIELD, SAMUEL LEWIS	*Mineralogy*
RUSSELL, ISRAEL COOK	*Geology*
SHALER, NATHANIEL SOUTHGATE	*Geology*

1907

ATWATER, WILBUR OLIN............................. *Chemistry*
CALDWELL, GEORGE CHAPMAN..................... *Chemistry*
CARROLL, JAMES..................................... *Pathology*
CLARK, GAYLORD PARSONS........................ *Physiology*
GARDINER, EDWARD GARDINER..................... *Zoology*
GATSCHET, ALBERT SAMUEL....................... *Anthropology*
HEILPRIN, ANGELO................................. *Geology*
NEWELL, WILLIAM WELLS.......................... *Anthropology*
REES, JOHN KROM................................. *Astronomy*
SAFFORD, JAMES MERRILL.......................... *Geology*

1908

ANTHONY, WILLIAM ARNOLD....................... *Physics*
ASHMEAD, WILLIAM HARRIS....................... *Zoology*
AUSTIN, PETER TOWNSEND......................... *Chemistry*
BROOKS, WILLIAM KEITH.......................... *Zoology*
DAVENPORT, GEORGE EDWARD..................... *Botany*
GIBBS, OLIVER WOLCOTT........................... *Chemistry*
JOHNSON, SAMUEL WILLIAM....................... *Chemistry*
KELLERMAN, WILLIAM ASHBROOK.................. *Botany*
LEE, LESLIE ALEXANDER........................... *Zoology*
MASCHKE, HEINRICH............................... *Mathematics*
MASON, OTIS TUFTON............................. *Anthropology*
SNOW, FRANCIS HUNTINGTON...................... *Zoology*
UNDERWOOD, LUCIEN MARCUS..................... *Botany*
WHITEHEAD, CABELL............................... *Chemistry*
YOUNG, CHARLES AUGUSTUS....................... *Astronomy*

1909

DUDLEY, CHARLES BENJAMIN....................... *Chemistry*
HARRIS, WILLIAM TORREY.......................... *Psychology*
HOUGH, GEORGE WASHINGTON..................... *Astronomy*
NEWCOMB, SIMON................................. *Astronomy*
STEARNS, ROBERT EDWARDS CARTER.............. *Zoology*
STRINGHAM, WASHINGTON IRVING................. *Mathematics*
TUFTS, FRANK LEO................................. *Physics*

The death rates for the six past years have been 6, 9, 9, 10, 15 and 7, on the average 9.3 per thousand. The rates for those under and over fifty, respectively, were approximately 3 and 21. The number of cases is too small for reliable data, but they show a youthful scientific population. In Great Britain there are annually elected into the Royal Society fifteen new fellows, and a membership of about 450 is maintained. The death rate is consequently over 30. It has been claimed that scientific men live longer than the average, and they probably do, but this can not be proved from the age at which they die, unless the age at which they become scientific men is known. If, however, we assume that scientific men live to the average age, we can from the age at which they die determine the age at which they become scientific men or reach a given degree of eminence.

In addition to those who died, there were removed from the thousand nine foreign men of science, who are no longer residents of the United States, and one other man whose address is unknown. There would thus be 68 vacancies on the list of 1910 to be filled by new men. In the order of the list, there is a probable error which increases from about 10 places at the top to about 100 places at the bottom. Consequently if the same scientific men were rearranged under the same conditions, each of those in the last hundred would be subject to a chance of one in four or more of being dropped from the list. In a general way 37 from the last hundred, 15 from the next to last, or ninth hundred, five from the eighth hundred and one from the seventh hundred—58 in all—might be expected to drop from the thousand as a result of rearrangement.

Apart from the 68 who died or were removed and the 58 changes due to a chance variation, there were 143 on the list of 1903 who failed to find a place on the list of 1910. These are the scientific men who did not maintain their positions in competition with their colleagues. There were 269 who attained a place on the list of 1910 for the first time. It seems best to remove from this group those who would probably have been given a place on the list of 1903, but were not considered at the time. They number 31, of whom only one is a foreigner who came to this country in the period of seven years.

There were 126 foreign-born men of science on the list of 1903. While the majority came to this country before attaining scientific reputation, a large number were called from Canada, Great Britain, Germany and other countries to fill positions in our universities, of whom seven were among our leading hundred men of science. The members of this group have added greatly to the scientific strength of the country, not only by the research that they have accomplished, but also because they have brought familiarity with the educational methods of other nations, and high ideals of scholarship and of the dignity of the career of the scientific man and university professor. It is surprising and truly most unfortunate that while nine leading foreign men of science have returned to their native countries during the past seven years, only one has come to America—one scientific man among seven million immigrants. There is no way by which the abundant wealth of the country could be used to greater advantage than by bringing to it men of promise and men of distinction.

We have then a group of 238 scientific men, who in the course of seven years have attained a place among the leading thousand, and a group of 201 who have lost their places. These two groups deserve careful consideration. Together with the other groups added to and taken from the list, they are distributed geographically in respect to birthplace and residence, as shown in Table I.

TABLE I.—BIRTHPLACE AND RESIDENCE OF THOSE ADDED TO AND DROPPED FROM THE LIST

	Birthplace							Residence						
	Men added			Men dropped				Men added			Men dropped			
	New	Old	Total	Out	Dead	Gone	Total	New	Old	Total	Old	Dead	Gone	Total
North Atlantic.														
Maine	5	1	6	8	2	0	10	1	1	2	1	1	0	2
New Hampshire	3	0	3	5	1	0	6	1	0	1	1	0	0	1
Vermont	2	1	3	3	1	0	4	0	0	0	1	0	0	1
Massachusetts	24	3	27	21	9	0	30	40	3	43	23	6	0	29
Rhode Island	3	1	4	0	1	0	1	2	1	3	1	2	0	3
Connecticut	6	0	6	5	2	0	7	14	2	16	4	4	0	8
New York	31	5	36	43	18	0	61	31	7	38	49	9	2	60
New Jersey	3	1	4	6	1	0	7	5	0	5	6	2	0	8
Pennsylvania	13	1	14	14	4	0	18	10	3	13	19	5	1	25
South Atlantic.														
Delaware	0	0	0	1	0	0	1	0	0	0	1	0	0	1
Maryland	2	0	2	4	0	0	4	11	2	13	6	2	0	8
Dist. of Col.	1	0	1	3	0	0	3	23	3	26	24	11	1	36
Virginia	7	0	7	5	1	0	6	0	0	0	1	0	0	1
West Virginia	2	0	2	0	0	0	0	1	0	1	0	0	0	0
North Carolina	0	0	0	0	1	0	1	3	0	3	1	0	0	1
South Carolina	3	0	3	1	0	0	1	0	0	0	0	0	0	0
Georgia	1	0	1	0	0	0	0	0	0	0	0	1	0	1
Florida	1	0	1	0	0	0	0	0	0	0	0	0	0	0
South Central.														
Kentucky	2	0	2	2	1	0	3	0	0	0	2	0	0	2
Tennessee	2	0	2	2	0	0	2	0	0	0	2	0	0	2
Alabama	1	1	2	0	0	0	0	0	0	0	0	0	0	0
Mississippi	1	0	1	0	0	0	0	0	0	0	0	0	0	0
Louisiana	0	0	0	0	0	0	0	1	0	1	1	0	0	1
Texas	2	0	2	1	0	0	1	2	0	2	2	1	0	3
Oklahoma	0	0	0	0	0	0	0	0	0	0	0	0	0	0
Arkansas	0	0	0	0	0	0	0	0	0	0	0	0	0	0
North Central.														
Ohio	19	4	23	15	6	0	21	9	1	10	6	2	0	8
Indiana	11	1	12	3	0	0	3	5	0	5	6	0	0	6
Illinois	10	4	14	8	1	0	9	25	3	28	15	3	0	18
Michigan	17	0	17	8	1	0	9	5	0	5	2	2	3	7
Wisconsin	11	0	11	10	0	0	10	12	1	13	0	0	0	0
Minnesota	5	0	5	1	1	0	2	2	1	3	4	0	0	4
Iowa	8	1	9	3	0	0	3	1	0	1	3	0	0	3
Missouri	5	0	5	4	0	0	4	6	0	6	1	0	0	1
North Dakota	0	0	0	0	0	0	0	0	0	0	1	0	0	1
South Dakota	0	0	0	0	0	0	0	1	0	1	0	0	0	0
Nebraska	1	0	1	1	0	0	1	4	0	4	3	1	0	4
Kansas	0	0	0	1	0	0	1	2	0	2	1	1	0	2
Western.														
Montana	0	0	0	0	0	0	0	0	0	0	0	0	0	0
Wyoming	0	0	0	0	0	0	0	0	0	0	1	0	0	1
Colorado	0	0	0	1	0	0	1	2	0	2	1	0	0	1
New Mexico	0	0	0	0	0	0	0	0	0	0	1	0	0	1
Arizona	0	0	0	0	0	0	0	1	0	1	1	0	0	1
Utah	0	0	0	0	0	0	0	0	0	0	0	0	0	0
Nevada	0	0	0	0	0	0	0	0	0	0	0	0	0	0
Idaho	0	0	0	0	0	0	0	0	0	0	0	0	0	0
Washington	0	0	0	0	0	0	0	0	0	0	0	0	0	0
Oregon	1	0	1	0	0	0	0	1	0	1	0	0	0	0
California	4	0	4	2	0	0	2	14	1	15	10	3	0	13
Alaska	0	0	0	0	0	0	0	0	0	0	0	1	0	1
Hawaii	0	1	1	0	0	0	0	0	1	1	0	0	0	0
Philippines	1	0	1	0	0	0	0	2	0	2	0	0	0	0
Panama	0	0	0	0	0	0	0	0	1	1	0	0	0	0
Canada	8	1	9	6	2	5	13	0	0	0	0	0	1	1
England	0	0	0	6	2	1	9	0	0	0	0	1	0	1
Scotland	3	1	4	2	0	1	3	0	0	0	0	0	0	0
Wales	0	0	0	1	0	0	1	0	0	0	0	0	0	0
Ireland	1	0	1	0	1	0	1	0	0	0	0	0	0	0
Germany	5	1	6	1	1	0	2	0	0	0	1	0	0	1
Switzerland	0	0	0	0	1	1	2	1	0	1	0	0	1	1
Belgium	0	1	0	0	0	0	0	0	0	0	0	0	0	0
Austria	0	0	0	0	0	1	1	0	0	0	0	0	0	0
Russia	3	0	3	2	0	0	2	0	0	0	0	0	0	0
Sweden	1	1	2	0	0	0	0	0	0	0	0	0	0	0
Norway	1	0	1	0	0	0	0	0	0	0	0	0	0	0
Japan	1	1	2	0	0	0	0	0	0	0	0	0	0	0
China	0	0	0	1	0	0	1	0	0	0	0	0	0	0
Unknown	7	0	7	1	0	1	2	0	0	0	0	0	0	0
Total	**238**	**31**	**269**	**201**	**58**	**10**	**269**	**238**	**31**	**269**	**201**	**58**	**10**	**269**

Massachusetts still retains its leadership in the production of scientific men, but it has lost ground in the course of the past seven years, while the north central states have gained. In the list of 1903, the birth rate of scientific men was at the rate per million population of about 50 in Maine, New Hampshire and Vermont, 109 in Massachusetts and 87 in Connecticut. If for purposes of comparison we increase the 238 new men to a thousand and again by 22.6 per cent to allow for the increase in population of the country between 1860 and 1870, the corresponding figures (referred to the census of 1870) would be: Maine, New Hampshire and Vermont, about 40; Massachusetts 85, Connecticut 57. By the same method of comparison the figures have decreased in the central Atlantic states, as follows:

New York.. 47 to 36
New Jersey...................... .... 42 to 17
Pennsylvania.. 23 to 19
Maryland... 38 to 13

On the other hand, the north central states show an increase, the figures being:

Ohio... 32 to 35
Indiana.. 21 to 34
Illinois........... .... 24 to 20
Michigan... 36 to 74
Wisconsin.. 45 to 54
Minnesota...................... .... 23 to 59
Iowa... 30 to 34
Missouri... 12 to 15

The cases are too few to give exact quantitative data, but a comparison of the north Atlantic and the north central states is significant. The former have lost seriously in their production of scientific men, while the latter have gained in every case except Illinois. Michigan rivals Massachusetts and surpasses every other state. New York on the list of 1903 surpassed every north central state, whereas the new men on the list of 1910 equal or exceed those from New York in six of the eight north central states. The big cities—New York, Philadelphia, Baltimore and Chicago—have lost ground. The birth rate per million inhabitants on the basis of 1,000 scientific men has fallen as follows:

New York... 71 to 33
Philadelphia....................................... 49 to 23
Baltimore.. 94 to 19
Chicago.. 73 to 17

These cities, in spite of their vast wealth and great universities, and the fact that the ambitious and successful are drawn to them, are failing to produce scientific men. For the thousand of 1903, it was found that the urban birth rate was 50 and the rural birth rate 24. The 238 new men are too few to give reliable figures, but it seems that the cities are failing to produce scientific men, and presumably other men of intellectual performance, to an extent that is ominous.

Nebraska, Kansas and the states west to the Pacific have not improved, as the writer would have anticipated from the students in psychology who have worked with him. Probably the gain in the north central states is now extending westward and will show later. The southern states, though still lamentably deficient in their productivity of scientific men, have improved decidedly. They have produced 22 scientific men among the 238, as compared before with 48 among the 1,000.

Among the 238 men who have obtained a place on the list, 23 were born abroad, as compared with 126 among 1,000 on the list of 1903. The percentage from Canada and Germany is the same and it is larger from Russia. In the case of other countries the numbers are too small to be significant, except England, from which country there were 25 in the list of 1903 and not a single one among the new men on the list of 1910. As has been already noted, only one foreigner has been called to this country of such scientific standing that he would have clearly deserved a place on the list of 1903. Nearly all the foreign-born scientific men acquired their scientific reputation after coming to this country. Fifteen of the 23 were wholly or partly educated in the United States.

A comparison of the first and eighth columns in the table will show which states have retained fewer men than they have produced and which have drawn on other states. Thus the three rural New England states have produced 10 men and have retained but two, while Massachusetts has produced 24 and has at present 40. New York has exactly as many as it has produced, 31, though of course the individuals are not all the same. The District of Columbia must depend on other parts of the country for its scientific men; the number it has obtained, 23, is just the number born abroad, so the balance is even among the states. Illinois has called men from other states, Wisconsin and Missouri have maintained nearly an even balance, while the other central states have lost their men—Michigan 12 of 17, Ohio 10 of 19, Indiana 6 of 11 and Iowa 7 of 8. It seems a pity that these wealthy states can not retain the men they produce or make an equal exchange with other states. The western states have tended to add to the number of men they have produced, thus California has produced 4 and acquired 10 more. The southern states have lost their men. Their increasing wealth has led to greater productivity, but they have not yet learned the importance of retaining and securing scientific men.

Reviewing the table with reference to those who have obtained a place on the list or have been dropped from it, we find that Massachusetts and Connecticut, which already had of all the states the largest percentages of scientific men in their populations—51 and 47 per million—now show the greatest gains. Nearly one fourth of the new men on the list reside in these two states, which have but 5 per cent of the population of continental United States. At the same time, a comparatively small percentage of their scientific men have failed to maintain their places on the list, so that their net gains have been 22, or about 12 per cent. The figures refer to new men who have obtained places among the thousand in the course of the past seven years or to those who have lost their places on the list, and not to men who have maintained their places and have removed from one state to another. These two states have been fortunate in the possession or skilful in the selection of young men of ability; and credit should be given to their three great educational institutions—Harvard, the Massachusetts Institute and Yale. Another center of scientific activity and growth is found in the states of Illinois and Wisconsin, and is there also due to three leading universities. Illinois has 28 and Wisconsin 13 of the men added, while of those dropped from the list Illinois has 18 and Wisconsin none. The two states have a net gain of 23 men, or about 28 per cent. Missouri also shows a gain, while the other north central states remain about stationary.

New York, New Jersey and Pennsylvania have more men who have died or been crowded off the list of the first thousand scientific men than have attained places on it. The net loss has been 22 in New York, 3 in New Jersey and 12 in Pennsylvania. This is a sinister record for this center of vast wealth with its richly endowed universities. These three states can but ill bear comparison with the two progressive centers in the northeast and north central states.

The District of Columbia has 26 of the men added and 36 of the men dropped out. It has suffered more serious losses from death than any other region. Washington and the scientific bureaus under the government have lost somewhat. Large appropriations are made and useful work is done, but there seems to be a lack of men of genius and a paucity of important discovery. The Smithsonian Institution under Henry, Baird and Langley, the Geological Survey under Powell, the Naval Observatory when Newcomb and Hall were there, had promise and distinction which they lack to-day.

The western states have about maintained their creditable position, while the southern states have fallen still further behind. South

Carolina, Georgia, Florida, Mississippi, Alabama, Louisiana, Tennessee and Kentucky had among them only 10 scientific men in the list of 1903. One man has been added and six lost. This record must be characterized as discreditable. The policy which leaves the south almost without scientific leaders is most foolish, even from the strictly utilitarian point of view. It appears that here too "he that hath, to him shall be given: and he that hath not, from him shall be taken even that which he hath."

The institutions with which two or more of the men added to the list are connected, together with those dropped, are given in Table II. As has been already indicated, Harvard, the Massachusetts Institute of Technology and Yale in New England, and Chicago, Illinois and Wisconsin in the north central region have been particularly fortunate in the possession of younger men who have acquired scientific reputation in the course of recent years. The same institutions have been equally happy in not having many men who have lost their positions on the thousand. This double success can not be attributed to chance, but must indicate skill in the selection of men or an environment favorable to good work. The Johns Hopkins and Stanford also stand well. Columbia, Cornell and California are the three universities which have lost the most. While Harvard and Yale have about three times as many men who have won a place as have lost it, Columbia has twice as many who have been dropped from the list as have been added to it. In the other universities and colleges the changes have been smaller, but they have considerable significance and deserve careful consideration. When we remember that seven adjacent states have not a single one of these men within their borders, it is not a small thing for institutions such as the University of North Carolina or Goucher College to have two of them. We may well ask why Pennsylvania should compare so unfavorably with Yale, or Minnesota with Wisconsin.

Among the non-teaching institutions there is the same direct correlation between the men added and dropped. Institutions which have a good record in one case have it also in the other. It seems almost incredible that it should be possible to measure the efficiency with which an institution is conducted by such simple means, yet the differences can not be attributed to chance. The Carnegie Institution has the largest gains, though in view of its resources and exemption from inherited survivals, it does not compare favorably with some universities. The Bureau of Standards, the Philippine Islands Bureau of Science and the Rockefeller Institute have done well. The Department of Agriculture has lost about twice as many men as it has gained and the Smithsonian Institution with its dependent bureaus about four times as many.

TABLE II.—INSTITUTIONS WITH WHICH THE MEN ARE CONNECTED WHO HAVE BEEN ADDED AND DROPPED

Institution	Men added			Men dropped			
	New	Old	Total	Out	Dead	Gone	Total
Harvard	22	1	23	6	3	0	9
Chicago	13	1	14	3	1	0	4
Wisconsin	11	1	12	0	0	0	0
Yale	11	1	12	0	4	0	4
Johns Hopkins	9	1	10	5	1	0	6
Illinois	8	2	10	3	1	0	4
Mass. Inst.	8	1	9	2	0	0	2
Carnegie Inst.	8	0	8	1	0	0	1
Columbia	8	0	8	12	3	1	16
Stanford	6	1	7	1	0	0	1
Dept. of Agr.	6	0	6	11	0	0	11
Michigan	5	0	5	0	2	3	5
Cornell	5	0	5	6	1	0	7
Princeton	5	0	5	3	1	0	4
Geol. Survey	4	1	5	3	1	0	4
Bur. of Standards	4	0	4	0	0	0	0
California	4	0	4	4	2	0	6
Missouri	4	0	4	1	0	0	1
Nebraska	4	0	4	2	1	0	3
Bryn Mawr	3	1	4	0	0	1	1
Western Reserve	3	1	4	0	0	0	0
Amer. Museum	3	0	3	1	0	0	1
N. Y. University	3	0	3	2	0	0	2
Pennsylvania	3	0	3	4	0	0	4
Minnesota	2	1	3	3	0	0	3
Brown	2	0	2	1	1	0	2
P. I. Bur. of Sci	2	0	2	0	0	0	0
Catholic	2	0	2	1	0	0	1
Cincinnati	2	0	2	2	0	0	2
Goucher	2	0	2	0	0	0	0
Indiana	2	0	2	1	0	0	1
Kansas	2	0	2	0	1	0	1
North Carolina	2	0	2	0	0	0	0
Northwestern	2	0	2	3	1	0	4
Ohio	2	0	2	2	1	0	3
Rockefeller Inst.	2	0	2	0	0	0	0
Smithsonian Inst.	2	0	2	4	5	0	9
Texas	2	0	2	2	0	0	2
Washington (St. Louis)	2	0	2	0	0	0	0
Wellesley	2	0	2	1	0	0	1
Elsewhere	46	18	64	111	28	5	144
Total	238	31	269	201	58	10	269

TABLE III.—THE INSTITUTIONS FROM WHICH MEN GRADUATED WHO WERE ADDED TO OR DROPPED FROM THE LIST

	Men added			Men dropped		
	A.B.	Ph.D.	Total	A.B.	Ph.D.	Total
Harvard....................	20	27	47	17	4	21
Chicago....................	5	27	32	0	1	1
Yale.......................	15	13	28	5	2	7
Hopkins...................	5	22	27	2	17	19
Cornell....................	9	12	21	7	5	12
Columbia..................	4	14	18	8	8	16
Wisconsin.................	8	4	12	2	1	3
Michigan..................	8	2	10	6	0	6
Mass. Inst................	7	2	9	3	0	3
Minnesota.................	6	2	8	0	0	0
California	5	2	7	2	1	3
Stanford...................	3	4	7	0	0	0
Brown.....................	5	1	6	2	1	3
Ohio State................	6	0	6	0	1	1
Nebraska..................	5	0	5	3	1	4
Clark.....................	0	4	4	0	2	2
Lehigh....................	4	0	4	1	0	1
Princeton..................	3	1	4	4	1	5
Amherst...................	3	0	3	6	1	7
Indiana....................	3	0	3	1	0	1
Pennsylvania..............	1	2	3	3	3	6
Syracuse...................	2	1	3	3	1	4
Texas.....................	3	0	3	0	0	0
Elsewhere.................	70	7	77	79	12	91
Total.....................	200	147	347	154	62	216
Leipzig....................	0	10	10	0	4	4
Göttingen..................	0	5	5	0	6	6
Berlin.....................	0	3	3	0	3	5
Heidelberg.................	0	3	3	0	5	5
Edinburgh.................	2	1	3	1	2	3
Elsewhere.................	11	6	17	3	11	14
Total.....................	13	28	41	4	31	35
Total.....................	213	175	388	158	93	251
None......................	19	57	76	42	107	149
Unknown..................	6	6	12	1	1	2
Grand Total...............	238	238	476	201	201	402

Table III gives the institutions at which three or more of the 238 scientific men who obtained a place on the list of 1910 received their degrees. The table also gives data for the 201 men who were dropped from the list. Of 232 of the new men whose education is known, all but 19 have the bachelor's degree and all but 57 the doctorate of philosophy or science. Some of those who did not receive the bachelor's degree were educated abroad and have its equivalent, and many of those not holding the doctorate of philosophy are doctors of medicine or have pursued university studies. Among the 1,000 on the list of 1903, 758 are known to have received the bachelor's degree and 544 the doctor's degree. The percentage of those holding the bachelor's degree has increased from 76 to 92, and of those holding the doctor's degree from 54 to 75. Our educational methods are thus becoming more completely standardized or conventionalized. The two men who stood first on the list of 1903, Simon Newcomb and William James, had neither the regular college nor the regular university education. Whether this was favorable or harmful to their genius is unknown; but it is probable that our present educational methods do not favor individuality and its early expression.

Harvard stands very clearly in the lead in its influence. Of the 232 men, 20 have received from it their first degree and 27 the doctorate of philosophy or science. Yale is the only university in the same class with Harvard as regards the bachelor's degree, and Chicago and the Johns Hopkins are the only ones as regards the doctor's degree. It is a curious fact that while Columbia and Yale have conferred in the past thirteen years about the same number of doctorates in the natural and exact sciences (189 and 179, respectively) as have Chicago, the Johns Hopkins and Harvard (245, 220 and 178, respectively), each can claim only about half as many of the new men who have obtained places among the thousand. Pennsylvania has the worst record in this respect, having conferred 133 doctorates and having only two doctors among the men added to the list. The 13 men who received the doctorate of philosophy from universities not given on the table received it from 11 different institutions, and the 81 bachelors not accounted for on the table received their degrees from no fewer than 70 colleges.

The colleges of the state universities have done better than those of the Atlantic seaboard. Thus Michigan and Wisconsin have each produced eight of the bachelors, while Princeton and Amherst have produced three, Dartmouth two and Williams one. In the list of 1903, Princeton and Amherst each had 23 bachelors among 758. The technical schools of the east have been more productive than the colleges; thus the Massachusetts Institute has seven and Lehigh four of the new men. Harvard, Yale and Cornell owe their good record to their scientific and technical courses. It is to be feared that the eastern college with "its frivolous amateurism and futile scholasticism" exerts influences actually prejudicial to the scientific career.

Leipzig, Berlin, Göttingen and Heidelberg are the four German universities which this time as last have conferred the largest number of degrees. Among 175 of the newer men 21 have received the doctorate of philosophy from these four universities, whereas among 544 in the list of 1903, 112 received it from the same institutions. In about ten years the percentage of foreign degrees has decreased to nearly one half, and it is in course of further reduction. The number of foreign men of science educated abroad and coming to this country has, as shown above, also decreased. In so far as these changes are due to the improvement of our universities and to the increase in the number of native scientific men they are gratifying. None the less there is an aspect of the movement which is unpromising. It is not desirable that we should become more provincial than we are.

The education is known of 200 of the 201 men who dropped from the list. About 25 per cent of these fall out through the probable error of arrangement, but in general they are those who have failed to maintain their scientific standing in competition with their colleagues. Twenty per cent of those on the list of 1903 were dropped from it; of those on the list who hold the bachelor's degree 21 per cent were dropped, and of those who hold the doctor's degree 17 per cent were dropped. Those holding the doctor's degree thus have a small advantage; but this is only because the younger men are more likely to have the doctor's degree and at the same time more likely to maintain their positions.

Harvard had on the list of 1903, 106 of the bachelors and 57 of the doctors. It has now made a gain of three bachelors and 23 doctors. Chicago has made a notable gain, having added five of its bachelors and 27 of its doctors to the list and having lost but one doctor. Yale also has a good record, having increased its bachelors by 10 and its doctors by 11. The Johns Hopkins had 102 doctors on the previous list, nearly twice as many as Harvard and four times as many as Yale. It has lost 17 and added 22, and is thus still far in advance in the number of leading scientific men for whom it has provided higher education. Cornell has gained two bachelors and seven doctors. Columbia has added four bachelors and has lost twice as many; it has added 14 doctors and has lost eight; thus it has gained but two men on the list. The state universities, especially Wisconsin, have good records. Princeton, Amherst, Syracuse and Pennsylvania have lost more men than they have gained. The German universities have done well, having added more men than they have lost, in spite of the fact that the number of students studying in Germany has so greatly decreased. These figures are in part accidental, but they certainly throw a new light on the standards and efficiency of our universities.

Table IV shows the distribution of the 238 new men among the twelve sciences in relation to their positions in the thousand and the relation of their ages to the positions. The additions to each science are in the neighborhood of 25 per cent and the departures from this average are within the limits of chance variation, but only 14 per cent of the astronomers and 16 per cent of the geologists are new, while 37.5 per cent of the physiologists are new. Astronomy and geology are the sciences which were the most forward in the last generation, and this would lead us to expect a smaller number of changes apart from deaths.

TABLE IV.—DISTRIBUTION OF THE MEN ADDED ACCORDING TO THEIR POSITIONS IN THE THOUSAND AND IN RELATION TO THEIR AGES

Science	I	II	III	IV	V	VI	VII	VIII	IX	X	No.	Per cent
Math	0	3	1	1	3	2	3	2	2	4	12	26.2
Physics	0	2	1	3	3	7	8	5	8	7	44	29.3
Chem	0	1	1	3	2	5	6	9	8	9	44	25.1
Astr	0	0	0	1	0	1	2	1	0	2	7	14.0
Geol	0	0	0	1	2	3	4	1	4	1	16	16.0
Bot	0	0	3	2	0	2	5	4	6	1	23	23.0
Zool	0	0	2	0	3	1	5	6	4	8	29	19.3
Physiol	0	1	1	0	2	1	2	0	1	7	15	37.5
Anat	0	0	0	1	0	1	0	0	0	4	6	24.0
Path	0	0	1	1	3	3	4	3	2	0	17	28.3
Anth	0	0	0	0	2	0	0	1	1	1	5	25.0
Psychol	0	0	0	1	1	1	1	1	2	4	11	22.0
Number	0	7	10	14	21	27	40	33	38	48	238	23.8
25–29	0	0	0	1	1	1	1	1	0	1	6	
30–34	0	4	2	2	5	4	5	6	7	10	45	
35–39	0	1	4	7	10	13	15	11	14	17	92	
40–44	0	2	4	3	3	9	12	9	9	11	62	
45–49	0	0	0	0	1	0	3	3	6	6	19	
50–54	0	0	0	0	0	0	2	0	2	3	7	
Not known	0	0	0	1	1	0	2	3	0	0	7	
Number	0	7	10	14	21	27	40	33	38	48	238	

None of the new men attains a place in the first hundred, seven reach the second hundred, ten the third and fourteen the fourth. Those who reach the highest positions are in the mathematical and exact sciences; men of exceptional ability advance more rapidly than in the natural and descriptive sciences.[1] Their success probably depends more on innate genius and less on persistent work. There are more "prodigies" in mathematics than in any other science, and they

[1] In the complete list of the thousand the youngest man among the first 20, among the first 50 and among the first 100 is in each case a mathematician.

are more likely to maintain their promise. In this and in certain other respects mathematics is related to music and chess.

Nearly all the men obtain recognition between the ages of 30 and 45. They do their work earlier and have their ideas still earlier. Those who do not have their ideas before they are thirty are not likely to have them, and those who do not do good work under forty-five are not likely to do it. Not a single man over fifty-five has attained a place on the list, and only one man over forty-five has attained a place as high as the fifth hundred. The average age of those added to the thousand is 38.1 years and of those dropped from it 53.6 years. The corresponding median ages are 37.9 and 50.9 years. The writer knows a number of men who think that they have been hindered from doing research work by teaching or other distractions and intend to take up such work later, as when they retire on a pension, but they will almost inevitably fail.

While those added to the thousand are comparatively young, there are only six under thirty years of age, and only the same number in the complete list of the thousand leading scientific men. This is significant and disquieting. A man of genius is likely to do his work at an early age and to receive prompt recognition. Kelvin was appointed full professor at Glasgow at 22, Thomson at Cambridge at 26, Rutherford at McGill at 27. Men of science of this age and rank simply do not exist in America at the present time; nor is it likely that we are faring better in scholarship, in literature and in art. It will be shown further on that the increase in the number of scientific men of standing is only about one half so large as the increase in the population of the country.

It is sometimes urged that our men of genius are drawn into medicine, law and business owing to the large financial rewards of these pursuits. Any one acquainted personally with some of those who earn or get the largest money returns will probably doubt whether they are in fact men of genius superior to our scientific men. The hundred physicians who have the largest incomes selected from the hundred thousand physicians of the country, and the hundred multi-millionaires selected from the million men of business, do not obviously surpass in ability or character the hundred leading scientific men selected from five thousand.

It is indeed probable that the conditions existing in this country are paralleled in Great Britain, Germany and France. In no country does there seem to be a group of younger men of genius, ready to fill the places of the great men of the last generation. This holds not only for science but also for other forms of activity. There is no living peer of Lincoln, Bismarck or Cavour. An Academy of Letters is just now being planned in Great Britain, and its proposed membership is trivial compared with what it might have been in the middle of the Victorian era. It may be argued that we suffer from an illusion of perspective, that many a newspaper writer is the equal of the men of letters of the past, that our young doctors of philosophy would discover laws of motion if Newton had not anticipated them. But it would appear to be a sufficient answer to write the names of Kipling, Barrie, Shaw, Wells and Chesterton besides the names of Carlyle, Ruskin, Mill, Spencer, Tennyson, Browning, George Eliot, Meredith, Dickens and Thackeray, or the names of the leading British, German or French scientific men now active with the corresponding list for forty years ago.

It is doubtless a question of relativity. By the nature of things there can only be a limited number of famous men, and it is not fair to compare a period of twenty years with the most productive period of all history. Both physical science and biological science have been rewritten within a generation, and it is possible that our scientific advance is more rapid to-day than it ever was before. None the less it is ominous for the future that there should be only six men of science of standing in the country who are under thirty years of age, and that the number of scientific men of standing should increase more slowly than the population.

There may be a racial senescence such as we seem to find in comparing the peoples of the Mediterranean with the Scandinavians and Sclavs, but it would be contrary to all our biological knowledge to suppose that the human stock could alter in a generation. In this period the number of individuals who have the education opening the gates to a scientific career has at least quadrupled. But eminent men are lacking; and this we must attribute to changes in the social environment rather than to deterioration of the stock.

The progress of science opposes a real barrier to its further advance. This is not because all the great discoveries have been made. The field of science is not a circumscribed territory which can be completely explored, but rather an area which the larger it becomes, the greater is the contact with the unknown and the more numerous and momentous are the problems pressing for solution. But as the known country becomes larger, each explorer has further to go before he reaches the undiscovered regions, and as he travels over the well-mapped land he loses the strength and vigor required for daring exploration. In plain English, the young man who must spend his early manhood in acquiring knowledge has passed the age at which he is most likely to have new ideas. The inherent difficulty we exaggerate by our educational methods. By our requirements for degrees, by our system of examinations, by our insistence on irrelevant information and ridicule of desirable ignorance and promising mistakes, we crowd on fat when the athlete should be relieved of every superfluous ounce. The doctor's thesis is supposed to be the first productive work; it is completed at the average age of twenty-eight years and is likely to be the working over of the old ideas of an old professor. In the meanwhile the creative instinct has atrophied.

Racial senescence, the lack of emotional stimuli and the accumulations of knowledge will probably set limits to the further advance of science. In the presence of racial senescence we should be entirely helpless, but it is possible that there is no such thing. Twenty years ago the Chinese were called a senile race, but such a statement could not be justified to-day. In a way our stock is as young as any, and the germ plasm may increase as much in complexity as it has since the amœba. Still a highly specialized organism is likely to become unplastic and extinct, and apart from physical exhaustion of the stock there is likely to be a social senescence. This is closely related to the lack of emotional stimuli. Great men and great achievements are likely to be associated with national excitement, with wars, revolutions the rivalry or consolidation of states, the rise of democracy and the like. Such stirring events will probably disappear from the world civilization of the future, and it may be impossible to devise artificial stimuli adequate to arouse men from a safe and stupid existence. But exactly because within a century the great achievements of science may belong to the past, where the great creations in poetry, art and religion may perhaps now only be found, it is our business to do the best we can to assure the race of an adequate endowment policy.

It is probable that we do not attract to the scientific career the best possible men. There is perhaps no harm in our fellowships and underpaid assistantships, though a subsidized theological education seems to have drawn inferior men to the church. Those who carry on investigation for the benefit of society should be paid for their services by society, and the average doctor's thesis is worth at least $500. We must open the scientific career to many in order to catch in our net the few who count. But large prizes are lacking at both the beginning and the end of the scientific career. It is too closely bound up with college teaching and routine administration; its modest preferments are too often purchased by subservience rather than by independence, by neglect of research rather than by devotion to it. Permanent tenure of office so long as no offense is given, small advancements by the favor of a superior, long vacations and retirement on a pension, are not the rewards to attract the best men or to lead men to do their best work.

The apprentice system in which the beginner assists the expert is the best educational method, and if the right spirit exists on both sides it is the method most conducive to fruitful research. But the teaching of large classes of students having no real interest in the subject is not favorable to investigation. It not only takes the time and strength of the teacher, but to lecture continually "als dictirt euch der heilig' Geist" cultivates an attitude of superficial omniscience subversive of both the caution and the daring which should animate the investigator.

Three fourths of our leading scientific men hold teaching positions and earn their livings by teaching. The accomplishment of research work is usually a factor in the original appointment, and to this extent investigation is encouraged in the graduate schools of our universities. But the reward offered—usually an instructorship at about $1,000 a year—is small, and it is not adjusted to discriminate between men of possible genius and the commonplace squatter. The appointment once received, men are likely to advance by a kind of civil service routine, being on the average assistant professors with a salary of $1,800 at the age of 37 and full professors a little later at a little higher salary. The small advances in salary which may thereafter be given have but little connection with successful research. At the age of sixty-five the professor is no longer regarded as worth his salary, and is put aside on a pension at a time of life when men in other callings earn more than ever before. The only reward open to the professor is the presidency or some other executive position which takes him away from research work.

Money is certainly not the main thing in the world, but the desire for money is by no means so materialistic as is commonly assumed. The pursuit of wealth is an idealistic passion; it is rarely for the gratification of sensual pleasures and usually at the sacrifice of these. It is closely associated with the family—the creation of a home, the education of children, their establishment in life, the transmission of family sanctions and traditions. The pursuit of fame or reputation is usually far more selfish. It is further the case that we measure performance in terms of money. In each career those who do the best work are likely to receive the largest money rewards. These are consequently not only desirable as improving the conditions of living and of the family, in giving security for the future and in providing facilities for further work, but they are also ideal symbols of useful service. If the university president receives three times the salary of the professor and the professor's salary depends on the president's favor, the office of the professor is degraded. If the scientific man in the government service receives the salary of a clerk and is subject to the orders of a superior, he will be treated like a clerk and in the end will deserve no better treatment. As the writer has said:[1] "Professors and scholars are not sufficiently free or sufficiently well paid, so there is a lack of men who deserve to be highly rewarded, and we are in danger of sliding down the lines of a vicious spiral, until we reach the stage where the professor and his scholarship are not respected because they are not respectable."

University professors and scientific men doubtless belong to the privileged classes. If their salaries are too small in comparison with the incomes of the classes, they are ample in comparison with the wages of the masses. But the salaries and rewards are not adjusted to performance. In Germany the docents in the universities have had a meager support, but the professorship has been maintained as a high office. Promotion to it has not as a rule accrued through favor, through length of service, or even through personal presentability or skill in teaching, but as a reward for research work in which a man is judged by his peers. To this method of university administration must in large measure be attributed the primacy of Germany in research during the past century. In Great Britain and in France also the exceptional man has received exceptional honors.

In this democracy we face conditions into which the other nations are likely to follow us. Geheimarts, knights and academicians may become no more reputable than our LL.D's. As scientific men increase in numbers and their work becomes more highly specialized, it becomes more and more difficult to use fame and social distinction as rewards. The most plausible expedient would appear to be the establishment of research positions in our universities, in our endowed institutions and in the government service, better paid and more free than any now existing. By the will of Senator Vilas, the University of Wisconsin will have ten professorships with salaries of $10,000 and freedom from routine teaching. If each large university has such a scheme, the vacancies being filled by the professors and the position and salary being for life, a comparatively small expenditure would go far toward attracting exceptional men to the academic and scientific career and stimulating them to do exceptional work.

The difficulty confronting us is that our competitive system of payment does not apply to services rendered to society. The physician must promote health, the lawyer prevent litigation and the editor conserve decency at their own cost and to their own cost. The scientific man is not directly paid for his research work; he often has difficulty to find a charity that will publish it. The man of letters was formerly

[1] "The Case of Harvard College," *The Popular Science Monthly*, **76**: 604–614, June, 1910.

dependent on a patron, but thanks to the printing press, the increase of the reading public and the copyright laws, his condition has improved. The patent office has been of assistance to discovery; its scope should be extended to cover, for example, the production of new varieties of plants and animals, and, if possible, the production of new kinds of ideas. But methods should be devised by which scientific work will be rewarded in some direct proportion to its value to society—and this not in the interest of the investigator, but in the interest of society.

At the same time we must remember that human nature is extremely complicated and imperfectly understood. The fine flower of genius may wither in the sunshine more quickly than in the shade. Children are loved and cherished in direct proportion to the sacrifices made for them. There is a subtle distinction between play and work. It might happen that the joy of creation in art and science would be crushed by professionalism. The dominant motives of conduct vary from age to age, from land to land, from group to group, from individual to individual. But in spite of our ignorance of the causes of conduct we may have some confidence that among the restless nations of the west, poverty, celibacy, obedience and obscurity are exotic ideals which can not be used to make the scientific career attractive.

In addition to the 269 men added to the thousand, whose origin, education, distribution, ages and standing have been considered, there were 731 men on the list of 1903 who retained places on the list of 1910. Some of them maintained about the same places as before, some improved their positions and some dropped down to lower places on the list. The number of places that each individual moved up or down is known. A gain or loss of a hundred places at the bottom of the list would not be significant, as the probable error of the change would be about $100 \times \sqrt{2}$. A gain of a hundred places at the top of the list, where the probable error is under twenty places, would represent a certain and important advance in the estimation in which the work of the individual is held. The value of gains or losses in different points in the series is inversely as the probable error corrected by the range, and it is thus possible to represent the gains or losses of individuals wherever they occur in comparable figures. If a gain of one place in the last five hundred is taken as the unit, a gain of one place in the upper hundreds would be approximately as follows: $V = 1.5$; $IV = 2$; $III = 3$; $II = 6$, and $I = 10$. Dividing further the first hundred, a gain in the lower fifty equals 8, and gains in the two upper twenty-fives, respectively, equal 10 and 14. On such a scale the gain or loss of each individual has been assigned. It is a truly dramatic figure expressing with almost brutal conciseness the efforts, the successes and the failures of seven years of a man's life.

The gains and losses of those on the list of 1903, apart from the 68 who died or removed from the country, are shown in the accompanying curve:

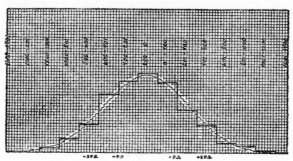

FIG. 1.

It is a tolerably symmetric surface of distribution, in view of the limited number of cases and the complicated conditions. 357 men improved their positions and 575 lost ground, of which latter 201 dropped out of the thousand. The average loss was 113 places, these being places in the lower five hundred, equal to one tenth as many places in the first hundred. Apart from this average change in one direction, or constant error, there was an average change of position, or variable error, which referred to the age groups in 305 places. This variable error is due to two factors—the chance error of arrangement (say 141) and the real change in the position of the men—and is equal to the square root of the sum of their squares. The real variable error is consequently 270. Men on the list thus lost on the average 113 places, and from this average there was a loss or gain of position, which on the average amounted to 270 places.

The removals from the list would tend to give higher positions to those remaining on it. If the 68 removals were equally distributed over the list, they would allow on the average an advance of 34 places to each man, or, weighting the places, an advance of 73 places of the value of those in the lower five hundred. Instead of such an advance, there was an average loss of 113 places and consequently a total average loss of 186 places. With a gross variable error of 305 places there might be expected to be dropped from the list about 155 men, apart from any negative constant error or any positive advance due to the deaths.

In a stationary scientific population it might be reasonable to assume that the losses by death would be filled by those below the thousand and that those in the thousand would maintain the same or an improved average position, while only so many would be dropped from the thousand as are accounted for by the variable error. In an increasing scientific population, however, the standard of the thousand would become higher. If there were an increase of ten per cent in the number of scientific men in the course of seven years, then there should be 110 of the same rank as the first hundred in the thousand of 1903 and 1,100 of the same rank as the thousand. A man in the lower part of the list who maintained his absolute position would lose nearly a hundred places in relative position, and, apart from the variable error of position, 91 of those in the thousand would drop to the eleventh hundred. As a matter of fact the average loss in position was 113 places, and the number dropped from the list was 46 in excess of those accounted for by the variable error. According to this argument, the increase in the number of scientific men of standing in seven years would be from 5 to 11 per cent, or about one half the increase of the population. There has certainly been no increase in the number of scientific men of standing commensurate with the increase in the instructors, students and endowments of our universities, with the larger appropriations for scientific work under the government, or with the new foundations for research.

Table V gives the gains and losses of the thousand scientific men of the list of 1903 (apart from the 68 who died or removed from the country) in reference to their standing and their present ages. It thus appears that in each hundred of the thousand the men were more likely to lose in position than to gain, but that those in the first hundred lost the least and those in the upper hundreds lost less than the average. Of those in the first hundred 44 gained in position and 46 lost, the average loss being 53 places. They were not subject to the competition of an increasing population, and only seven men not on the list of 1903 attained places among the second hundred. It thus appears that even men of established reputation do not maintain their positions, they do not advance as they grow older, and death removes more eminent men whose places they might fill. The losses tend to increase as the men are of lower rank, but the differences are not considerable. The variable error being 305 places, the probable error of the figures given in the table is rather large.

In the case of age it is clear that the younger men in the thousand are likely to improve their positions, while the older men are likely to fall back. The nine men now under thirty-five have, on the average, gained 364 places and the 77 now between thirty-five and thirty-nine have, on the average, gained 144 places. Of those under forty, 54 gained and 32 lost. In the next five-year period men are about as likely to lose as to gain, whereas older men are likely to lose. There appears to be a plateau between the ages of those now between fifty-five and seventy-four; in the course of the seven preceding years they

TABLE V.—GAINS AND LOSSES IN REFERENCE TO POSITION AND TO AGE

Position	1–100	101–200	201–300	301–400	401–500	501–600	601–700	701–800	801–900	901–1000		Totl.
Number	90	91	95	92	91	92	97	93	94	97	.....	932
No. gained	44	40	37	34	35	28	40	31	26	42	.....	357
No. lost	46	51	58	58	56	64	57	62	68	55	.....	575
Constant error	−53.3	−93.9	−99.4	−64.5	−115.8	−160.8	−95.3	−165.0	−182.9	−89.1		

Age	30–34	35–39	40–44	45–49	50–54	55–59	60–64	65–69	70–74	75–85	Not xn'n.	Total
Total number	9	77	187	194	155	104	85	52	38	24	7	932
No. gained	6	48	94	79	60	23	17	14	11	1	4	357
No. lost	3	29	93	115	95	81	68	38	27	23	3	575
Constant error	+364	+144	+29	−103	−134	−276	−268	−262	−227	−438		
Variable error	*485*	*328*	*366*	*284*	*308*	*285*	*252*	*299*	*258*	*185*		

have about the same record. They tend to lose about 250 places or about twice the average of all the men on the list. The 24 men who seven years ago were sixty-eight years of age or older have nearly all lost in position. It is not likely that any one of them has done anything to lower his scientific reputation; but men of the younger generation have accomplished work of greater importance, or the work of older men is forgotten because it is less contemporary. It thus appears that under existing conditions in this country, scientific men are likely in the course of seven years to lose about 100 places. Men who have obtained recognition among the thousand are likely to gain if under forty; if between forty and fifty they are likely to lose, and if over fifty-five they are likely to lose more than the average.[1]

The average age of the thousand scientific men on the list of 1910 is 48.12 years. The age distribution is as follows:

Age	Number
25–29	6
30–34	54
35–39	155
40–44	214
45–49	176
50–54	137
55–59	82
60–64	68
65–69	40
70–74	33
75–79	13
80–84	7
Unknown	15

In Table VI is given the average age of the men in the ten groups of one hundred making up the thousand for the lists of 1903 and 1910.[2] The probable errors of the averages are less than one year. It thus appears that the more eminent scientific men are likely to be older; but the differences are small apart from the first hundred, who in 1903 were 5.1 years older than the average, and in 1910 6.7 years older. Scientific men do not become more eminent as they grow older unless they have obtained a good position at a comparatively early age.

The men on the list of 1910 are, on the average, three years older than those on the list of 1903. An increase in age would be expected, as we have to do with a youthful and increasing scientific population.

[1] The coefficient of correlation between age and gain in position is −31.7. It is, however, doubtful whether the Galton-Pearson method can be used to advantage in such cases.

[2] The list for 1903 used for ages consisted of the 1,000 scientific men who stood first before the adjustments had been made to secure a fixed number in each science.

Some part of the increase in age is probably caused by the long period of education now likely to precede productive scientific work, but it is not easy to analyze the factors. In so far as the increased age is due to higher standards through increasing competition, it is gratifying; in so far as it is due to the postponement of scientific productivity it is unfortunate.

TABLE VI.—AVERAGE AGE ACCORDING TO POSITION IN 1903 AND 1910

	Average age			Average age	
	1903	1910		1903	1910
I.....................	50.12	54.78	VI...................	43.70	46.40
II....................	49.76	48.94	VII..................	41.97	45.60
III...................	47.04	48.34	VIII.................	42.36	47.82
IV....................	45.38	48.62	IX...................	43.50	45.94
V.....................	44.09	48.50	X....................	42.32	46.14
			Average.............	**45.02**	**48.11**

For the list of 1903 data have been compiled in regard to the ages at which academic degrees were received. The average age at which 758 men received the bachelor's degree was 22.2 years, and the average age at which 544 men received the doctorate of philosophy or science was 28.4 years. The corresponding median ages were 21.8 and 26.9 years. Table VII shows the details in reference to the different sciences and the ten groups of a hundred composing the thousand. The age differences are small, but men have received the bachelor's degree at an earlier age who have become pathologists than those who have become anatomists or botanists. The chemists have received the doctor's degree at the earliest age and the anatomists and botanists at the latest. The mathematicians have received the doctorate at exactly the average age, not earlier, as the writer would have anticipated.

In the different sciences there are decided differences in the proportion of those who have received academic degrees. Only half the pathologists have the bachelor's degree and one twelfth the doctorate of philosophy, their education having been in the medical school. Of 50 psychologists 46 hold the bachelor's and 37 the doctor's degree. The doctor's degree is held by nearly two thirds of the zoologists, while it is held by less than half the geologists and less than a third of the astronomers.

There is a small but definite correlation between standing and the age at which the men received their degrees—the more eminent the men the earlier the age. Those in the first hundred have received both the bachelor's and the doctor's degree at the earliest age, the former

0.6 and the latter 1.5 years below the average. The second hundred are the next youngest, the ages for the two degrees being 0.3 and 1.1 below the average. Those in the lower two hundred were 0.6 year older than the average in receiving the first degree and 0.8 year older in the case of the second degree. There is no correlation between standing and the possession of one or the other of the degrees.

TABLE VII.—AGES AT WHICH THE BACHELOR'S DEGREE AND THE DOCTORATE OF PHILOSOPHY WERE RECEIVED ACCORDING TO SCIENCE AND TO POSITION IN THE THOUSAND

	Bachelor		Ph. D.	
	No.	Age	No.	Age
Mathematics	67	21.9	64	28.4
Physics	112	22.1	87	28.6
Chemistry	132	21.6	114	26.7
Astronomy	34	21.6	14	29.3
Geology	85	22.8	43	28.5
Botany	83	23.7	56	30.5
Zoology	117	22.6	96	28.8
Physiology	29	21.7	19	26.7
Anatomy	15	23.7	2	30.5
Pathology	30	20.7	6	27.2
Anthropology	8	22.0	6	27.5
Psychology	46	21.7	37	27.6
No. or average	**758**	**22.2**	**544**	**28.4**
I	74	21.6	57	26.9
II	77	21.9	52	27.3
III	80	22.3	56	27.7
IV	74	22.2	52	27.5
V	74	22.2	53	28.2
VI	74	22.0	63	29.3
VII	79	22.4	52	28.6
VIII	76	22.2	58	28.8
IX	74	22.8	49	29.3
X	76	22.8	52	29.1
No. or average	**758**	**22.2**	**544**	**28.4**

Our thousand leading men of science are occupied as shown in Table VIII. 738.5[1] are engaged in teaching, or have been so engaged, and now fill administrative educational positions or have retired from active service. Nearly three quarters of our scientific men earn their livings by teaching, and a large proportion of the others have done so.

[1] The decimal here and elsewhere refers to a man who gives part of his time to teaching or to the institution to which he is credited.

In this country, as in Germany, the advancement of science depends mainly on those who hold chairs in our colleges and universities. Some ten per cent of our scientific men are engaged in work for the government, among whom the geologists predominate. Only six per cent earn their livings by direct applications of science. Apart from one

TABLE VIII.—OCCUPATION OF THE THOUSAND MEN OF SCIENCE ACCORDING TO SCIENCE AND TO POSITION

	Teaching	Government work	Applied science	Research institutions	Museums and academies	Botanical and zoological gardens	Amateurs	State work	Physicians	Architects	Artists	Editors	Missionaries	
Mathematics	77	1	1	....	....	....	....	....	....	....	1	..		80
Physics	104	18	22	6	....	....	....	....	....	....	....	....		150
Chemistry	126.5	12	28	8.5	....	....	....	....	....	....	....	....		175
Astronomy	38	5	..	4	....	....	3	....	....	....	....	....		50
Geology	52.5	30.5	8	1	2	....	1	5	....	....	....	....		100
Botany	66	12	..	6	2.5	12.5	1	....	....	....	....	....		100
Zoology	112.5	14	..	3	15.5	1	2	....	....	1	..	..	1	150
Physiology	37	1	..	2	....	....	....	....	....	....	....	....		40
Anatomy	21	....	..	2	1	....	1	....	....	....	....	....		25
Pathology	51	4	..	3	....	....	....	2	....	....	....	....		60
Anthropology	7.5	8	..	....	3.5	....	1	....	....	....	....	....		20
Psychology	45.5	0.5	..	....	....	....	1	..	1	1	....	....		50
	738.5	106	59	35.5	24.5	13.5	11	5	3	1	1	1	1	1000
1– 100	79	7	1	6	3	2	2	?	?	?	?	?	?	100
101– 200	78	12	2	4	1	....	1	....	....	....	....	....		100
201– 300	80.5	12	3	2	1.5	....	....	....	....	....	....	....		100
301– 400	67	18	8	1	2	3	....	....	....	....	....	....		100
401– 500	69	11	5	4	4	2	1	....	....	....	....	....		100
501– 600	78	9	7	....	2	3	....	....	....	....	....	....		100
601– 700	67.5	11	5	8	3	2.5	2	....	....	....	....	....		100
701– 800	72	12	9	3	3	....	....	....	....	....	....	....		100
801– 900	69.5	6	11	4.5	3	1	4	....	....	....	....	....		100
901–1000	78	8	8	3	2	....	1	....	....	....	....	....		100
	738.5	106	59	35.5	24.5	13.5	11	....	....	....	....	....		1000

actuary, this work is in applied chemistry, engineering and mining. There is no one who earns his living by applications of the natural sciences. Research institutions, nearly all of recent foundation, employ 35 men. There are 24 connected with museums, academies and libraries and 12 with botanical gardens. Only eleven among the thousand may be classed as amateurs, and these include several married women who should perhaps be given a separate place. This contrasts with Great Britain, where Darwin, Huggins, Rayleigh and many other great scientific men, not needing to earn their livings, have devoted their lives to scientific research. Only three physicians not connected with medical schools have done scientific work of consequence. One architect, one artist, one editor and one missionary appear on the list, but no lawyer or man of business. It seems that in this country the time has gone by when science can be advanced by any except by those engaged in certain definite professions, while these professions require men, with a few exceptions, to earn their livings by teaching or by applied science.

The standing of those in the different professions does not show a considerable difference. There are in the upper three hundred relatively more men engaged in teaching and in the research institutions, and fewer in applied science, but the differences are scarcely significant, except that those engaged in applied science are of somewhat lower standing. Those in the government service and the officers and curators of museums and botanical gardens are of average standing.

There were 19 women on the list of 1903. None of them died but seven were not placed on the list of 1910. This is a somewhat larger proportion than in the case of the men, but the figures are too small to have significance. Six women found a place for the first time on the list of 1910, the highest being in the fifth hundred. It thus appears that women have not improved their position in science in the course of seven years, and it is not an important one, only 18 women among 982 men, with none in the first hundred, two in the second, two in the third and three in the fourth. There are now nearly as many women as men who receive a college degree; they have on the average more leisure; there are four times as many women as men engaged in teaching. There does not appear to be any social prejudice against women engaging in scientific work, and it is difficult to avoid the conclusion that there is an innate sexual disqualification. Women seem not to have done appreciably better in this country than in other countries and periods in which their failure might be attributed to lack of opportunity. But it is possible that the lack of encouragement and sympathy is greater than appears on the surface, and that in the future women may be able to do their share for the advancement of science.

Table IX gives the distribution on January 1, 1910, of the thousand leading scientific men of the country and the gain or loss of each state in a period of about four years. The distribution of the second thousand is also shown. In respect to the first thousand, the main facts have already been considered in connection with the men who have acquired or lost places in the group. This table shows in addition the changes which have occurred as the result of men removing from

TABLE IX.—DISTRIBUTION OF THE FIRST AND SECOND THOUSANDS

	First thousand			Second thousand	
	No.	Gain or loss	Per million 1900	No.	Per million 1900
North Atlantic.					
Maine........	3	− 1	14.3	5	7.2
New Hampshire........	8	0	19.4	8	19.4
Vermont........	1	− 1	2.9	6	17.4
Massachusetts........	165	+21	58.7	103	36.7
Rhode Island........	9	+ 1	20.9	11	25.7
Connecticut........	50	+ 7	55.0	32	35.2
New York........	183	− 9	25.1	166	22.8
New Jersey........	26	− 9	13.2	29	15.3
Pennsylvania........	60	− 5	9.5	69	10.9
South Atlantic.					
Delaware........	0	− 1	0	4	21.7
Maryland........	39	− 8	32.8	30	25.2
Dist. of Columbia........	109	−10	391.0	111	399.2
Virginia........	10	0	5.4	14	7.5
West Virginia........	2	− 1	2.0	3	3.1
North Carolina........	7	+ 1	3.7	7	3.7
South Carolina........	0	0	0	3	2.2
Georgia........	0	− 1	0	1	0.4
Florida........	0	0	0	3	5.7
South Central.					
Kentucky........	0	− 3	0	5	2.3
Tennessee........	1	− 2	0.5	8	3.9
Alabama........	2	0	1.1	2	1.1
Mississippi........	0	0	0	1	0.7
Louisiana........	4	+ 3	2.9	1	0.7
Texas........	4	− 3	1.3	10	3.2
Oklahoma........	0	0	0	2	5.0
Arkansas........	0	0	0	1	0.7
North Central.					
Ohio........	34	0	8.2	39	9.3
Indiana........	11	− 1	4.4	21	8.3
Illinois........	77	+14	15.9	87	18.0
Michigan........	25	− 2	10.3	31	12.8
Wisconsin........	36	+13	17.4	14	6.7
Minnesota........	13	0	7.4	20	11.4
Iowa........	6	− 1	2.7	15	6.7
Missouri........	24	+ 3	7.7	19	6.1
North Dakota........	1	− 1	3.1	4	12.5
South Dakota........	1	− 1	2.4	2	4.9
Kansas........	5	0	3.4	14	9.5
Nebraska........	6	− 3	5.6	11	10.3
Western.					
Montana........	0	− 2	0	3	12.3
Wyoming........	0	− 1	0	1	10.9
Colorado........	9	+ 1	16.6	13	24.1
New Mexico........	0	− 2	0	1	5.1
Arizona........	4	+ 2	34.2	2	16.4
Utah........	0	0	0	5	18.1
Nevada........	0	0	0	1	21.4
Idaho........	0	0	0	2	12.4
Washington........	0	0	0	6	11.6
Oregon........	1	+ 1	2.4	1	2.4
California........	50	− 3	33.6	38	25.6
Hawaii........	2	+ 2	12.9	1	6.5
Porto Rico........	0	0	.....	1	
Panama........	1	+ 1	.....	0	
Philippines........	4	+ 1	.....	8	
Canada........	1	− 1	.....	0	
Mexico........	0	0	.....	1	
Cuba........	1	0		0	
Brazil........	1	0	.....	0	
Argentine........	2	+ 2	.....	0	
Peru........	0	0	.....	2	
France........	1	+ 1	.....	0	
Germany........	0	0	.....	1	
Switzerland........	1	+ 1	.....	0	
Turkey........	0	0	.....	1	
Number........	1000	....	.....	1000	

one state to another who have retained their places on the list. Massachusetts, as has been noted, gained 14 men owing to the fact that 43 of the new men reside in that state, while but 29 were lost to it through death or through dropping below the standard. In addition it has gained seven men, the excess of those having places on both lists who have moved into the state above those who have left it. Its total gain in scientific men of standing is consequently 21, and it has 58.7 of these scientific men per million of its population according to the census of 1900, as compared with 51.3 about four years ago. The increase in the number of scientific men is nearly 18 per cent. This is an honorable record. It is commonly assumed that Boston has yielded to New York City the position of literary center of the country, and if the facts were not known the same assumption would probably be made in regard to science. As a matter of fact Boston has 126, New York 120 and Washington 110 of our leading scientific men. In comparison with population and with wealth, Boston is far in advance of New York, though it is Cambridge and Harvard University which give Boston its preeminent position.

New York and Pennsylvania have in part retrieved the loss due to men dropping out of the first thousand by calling men of this rank from other states. Though they have lost, respectively, 22 and 12 through the failure of their men to maintain their position, they have drawn an excess of 13 and 7 from other states, so that their total losses are 9 and 5. It appears that the immense wealth of these states has been but sparingly used to bring new men to them, whereas the conditions are such that those residing there are more likely to lose than to gain in scientific position. It may be unsafe to draw sweeping conclusions from such figures, but they certainly indicate that residence in these states is unfavorable to scientific productivity. It may perhaps be the case that the salaries are below the expensive standards of living and that opportunities for commercial and hack work are tempting, so that men are drawn away from research. The District of Columbia has lost nine men. Eleven have been removed by death, and this loss has not been made good by men improving their positions or going to reside in Washington. In view of the increasing appropriations made by the government for scientific work and the endowment of the Carnegie Institution this is not a favorable record.

Illinois and Wisconsin show the gains due to men who have improved their positions, there being no significant changes due to removals. The same is generally true in regard to the gains or losses in the other north central states and in the west and south. The numbers are too small to be as a rule significant. Missouri and Louisiana have each gained three men, Arizona two and Colorado one. Ohio and

Minnesota are exactly stationary. Indiana, Michigan, Iowa, Texas and California have in each case lost from one to three men. The southern states (except Louisiana) have been losing even the few scientific men whom they had.

Table IX shows also the distribution of the thousand scientific men standing below the first thousand. The men are not as well known and they can not be arranged as accurately in the order of merit. They were not independently selected from a larger group by the judges, but were those not assigned a place in the first thousand. The first five hundred were selected from the thousand with a tolerable degree of validity, but the second five hundred can only be regarded as representative of the scientific men who have done research work, but are not of the rank of the first fifteen hundred. The men are, however, arranged in the order of merit, and probable errors can be assigned to the positions as in the case of the first thousand. The number from each science is the same as in the case of the first thousand.

It is an honor to belong to this second group of a thousand men; they deserve well who have accomplished research work and have obtained recognition as scientific men. But those who are young have far greater promise than those who are older. All young men of ability must pass through the second thousand before they reach the first, though they are likely to escape notice in a period which may be short. The group is thus heterogenous, including those who may become our leading men of science and those who have attained a mediocre though creditable position beyond which they will not advance. The same conditions hold for the lower hundreds of the first thousand. In the preceding paper the scientific men were divided into two groups of 500 each, and no considerable differences were found in their origin or distribution. This appears to have been in part due to the heterogeneous character of the second group. Thus Massachusetts had 74 men in the first five hundred and 70 in the second, while New York had in the two groups 93 and 99, respectively. But in the intervening period more men in Massachusetts than in New York have retained or improved their positions. It thus appears that Dr. F. A. Woods[1] is correct in holding that Massachusetts has not only produced more scientific men, but also men of higher standing.

The second thousand includes those who have dropped down from the first thousand (201), to whom consideration has already been given. The others have been divided into those above and those below the median age (42 years), but the conditions are almost too complicated to admit of analysis, and it seems to be scarcely worthwhile to

[1] "American Men of Science and the Question of Heredity," SCIENCE, N. S., **31**: 205–209, 1910.

give the figures. In New York 43 are below and 68 above the median age; in Illinois 37 below and 28 above, and in California 9 below and 18 above. The excess of older men in New York may be attributed to its earlier development and to the fact that older men, especially in applied science, tend to reside in New York City. Chicago is of more recent origin and has called younger men to its universities. In Massachusetts and the District of Columbia there are about equal numbers below and above the median age. Older men reside in Boston and Washington, and younger men have been called to the institutions of learning in the former city and to the government service in the latter. The eight scientific men in the Phillippines are all below the median age.

The men of the second thousand are more equally and widely distributed over the country than those of the first thousand. The regions and institutions which are the strongest in numbers tend to have also the larger share of men of the higher rank. Thus Massachusetts has 165 men of the first thousand and 103 men of the second thousand; Connecticut 50 of the first and 32 of the second. The educational institutions of these states have called and kept good men. They have relatively more in the first thousand than in the second, as they have relatively more in the first hundred than of lower rank. New York has a smaller preponderance of the better men. In the District of Columbia the scientific men are drawn equally from the first and second thousands. Thanks to the recent development of its great university, Wisconsin has 36 men in the first thousand and 14 in the second. The superior men are in the majority in Missouri, but the other north central states have fewer men of the first rank than of the second. California has 50 men of the first thousand and 38 of the second. In general the western and southern states which have but few scientific men have relatively more of the second thousand. It is of course important to have even men of this rank. There are advantages and disadvantages in concentrating the better men in a few regions and institutions. The standards of the men in both thousands are becoming higher, though more slowly than would be wished.

The distribution of our scientific men is almost entirely determined by educational and scientific institutions, including under the latter the government bureaus. Table X shows the institutions with which three or more of those among our thousand leading men of science are connected, together with the gain or loss in a period of about four years. The table also gives the ratio of the number of leading scientific men in each institution to the total number of instructors, to the total number of students, to the value of buildings and grounds and to the current income. Harvard, Wisconsin, the Carnegie Institution, Illinois

Yale and Chicago have made the most notable gains. Columbia, California, the Geological Survey, the Smithsonian Institution and the Department of Agriculture have suffered the most severe losses. Four years ago Harvard had 66.5, Columbia 60 and Chicago 37 of our leading scientific men, as selected three years previously. After this short period it has resulted that Harvard has 31.5 more than Columbia and Chicago the same number. Such changes are only to a small degree due to the probable errors of the arrangements, though in the case of Columbia the fact that last time there were 11 and this time but two men in the last hundred may be attributed in part to the probable error and account in part for the loss of that university. There is also a different kind of chance variation due to the date to which the census refers. Thus since January 1, Harvard has lost two of its greatest men, while the losses of Columbia occurred earlier and certain important positions were vacant at that time. It is, however, a fact not without significance that Columbia and California, in which faculty control is regarded by the administration as less important than executive efficiency, have suffered the most serious losses, whereas Harvard and Yale, where the methods of appointment and promotion are more democratic, show most gratifying advances. Yale has disproved the assertion that a faculty is not able to select its own members. The Smithsonian Institution and the government bureaus, which are somewhat autocratically controlled, show serious losses, but these should be in part at least attributed to the inadequate salaries. The gain of 50 per cent in the Bureau of Standards shows that losses are not inevitable.

Wisconsin and Illinois are the state universities which have made the most notable progress. Wisconsin has moved ahead of Michigan and is nearly equal to the Johns Hopkins and Cornell. The gain of almost 200 per cent at Illinois is in the main due to the departments of chemistry and mathematics, to the heads of which the university was so wise as to call men of high scientific standing. Michigan has a gain of 3.5, Missouri of two and Indiana of one. Minnesota and Kansas are exactly stationary. Ohio has a loss of one, Iowa and Texas of two and California of 8.5.

The Johns Hopkins has gained three men, which is satisfactory in view of its limited endowment and the high standards it has always maintained. The Massachusetts Institute of Technology has gained 5.5, Cornell 1.5, Pennsylvania 1, Princeton 2 and Stanford 5. We may hope for a considerable further advance at Princeton in the near future. It will be noted that in general the larger institutions have gained, and this relative gain represents a greater absolute gain as the standard of the thousand becomes continually higher with the increase of the numbers of scientific men.

Among universities with which fewer scientific men are connected, Western Reserve has gained four men and Brown, Missouri and Tulane have each gained 2, whereas Nebraska has lost 3 and Wesleyan, Syracuse, Northwestern, Cincinnati and Texas have each lost two. Bryn Mawr, Vassar and Wellesley have gained and Smith has lost. Small changes of this character are not necessarily significant, as they may be accounted for by the chance error of arrangement or the chance date to which the data refer. Still in each case the change is probably a real one and of importance when considered in relation to the total number of professors in the institution. The gain of a scientific man of standing is worth more to an institution than a building costing $100,000.

Table X gives also the ratio of the number of scientific men of the thousand in each institution to the total number of instructors, to the total number of students, to the value of the buildings and grounds and to the income for current expenses, the figures being based on the report of the commissioner of education for 1909.[1] The institutions vary greatly. One half of all the instructors at Clark are among our leading men of science, whereas in certain institutions there is but one in fifty. The institutions which stand the highest are Clark, the Johns Hopkins, Chicago, Stanford, Bryn Mawr, Harvard, Wesleyan, Case and Princeton. These institutions have at least one scientific man of standing among each ten instructors. It is of interest to note that the five institutions that have the best record are of comparatively recent establishment. They have given a relatively more prominent position to science than the older institutions and have selected better men. At certain other institutions the ratios are: Yale, 10.6; Michigan, 12.3; Wisconsin, 13.2; Columbia, 13.3; Cornell, 16.5; California, 21.3; Pennsylvania, 25.2. The institutions having more than

---

[1] Unfortunately the figures in the report do not seem to be uniformly accurate. For example, the value of the buildings of Columbia University are reported by the commissioner of education at $2,238,800, and those of the U. S. Military Academy at $20,000,000, whereas the buildings on the Columbia campus have apparently cost much more than those at West Point. The treasurer gives the assessed value of the Columbia buildings (apart from Barnard College, Teachers College and the College of Pharmacy) as over $6,000,000. The commissioner of education reports the total receipts of Columbia University, exclusive of gifts for endowment, to have been $5,572,943, whereas the treasurer reports for the same year an income for the Columbia College corporation of $1,614,166. The correct figures have been substituted in the case of Columbia, but it is to be feared that other figures in the report are misleading. The writer considered using the figures collected by the Carnegie Foundation, but these also seem to be difficult to interpret. Thus Illinois is said to have an annual income (for running expenses) of $1,200,000 and to spend $491,675 on salaries of teachers, and Pennsylvania to have an annual income of $589,226, and to spend $433,311 on salaries.

TABLE X.—THE NUMBER OF SCIENTIFIC MEN CONNECTED WITH INSTITUTIONS WHEN THERE ARE THREE OR MORE

	No.	Gain or loss	Ratio to instr.	To students	To buildings and grounds	To income
Harvard	79.5	+13.0	7.8	49.2	138,364	24,729
Chicago	47.5	+ 8.5	6.0	114.9	187,741	35,986
Columbia	48.0	−12.0	13.3	96.7	259,954	45,989
Yale	38.0	+11.5	10.6	90.3	....	34,142
Cornell	35.0	+ 1.5	16.5	113.9	122,966	41,106
Johns Hopkins	33.5	+ 3.0	5.6	21.8	186,095	10,121
Wisconsin	30.0	+12.0	13.2	150.7	126,104	50,499
Dept. Agric.	28.0	− 4.0				
Geol. Surv.	25.5	− 6.5				
Mass. Inst.	25.0	+ 5.5	10.1	58.5	53,480	20,850
Michigan	23.5	+ 3.5	12.3	200.8	87,649	57,539
Stanford	21.0	+ 5.0	6.9	80.3	333,810	39,571
Carnegie Inst.	19.0	+12.0				
California	18.5	− 8.5	21.3	191.9	281,761	81,387
Pennsylvania	18.0	+ 1.0	25.2	229.0	....	56,368
Illinois	17.0	+11.0	29.2	251.9	111,971	99,647
Princeton	16.5	+ 2.0	9.8	79.7	....	24,964
Smithsonian	16.0	− 6.0				
Bur. of Stan.	12.0	+ 4.0				
Missouri	11.0	+ 2.0	14.7	259.4	157,591	54,870
Minnesota	10.0	0	20.1	264.9	387,008	133,348
Ohio State	9.0	− 1.0	22.1	281.7	323.889	85,784
New York	8.5	− 1.0	28.1	446.5	435,294	49,062
Amer. Museum	7.5	− 0.5				
Clark	8.0	+ 1.0	2.0	17.7	66,562	17,585
West. Reserve	8.0	+ 4.0	24.5	126.3	187,996	30,496
Bryn Mawr	8.0	+ 2.0	7.2	52.5	243,649	37,185
N. Y. Bot. Gar.	8.0	+ 2.0				
Brown	7.0	+ 2.0	12.9	141.9	257,142	65,813
Indiana	7.0	+ 1.0	43.0	353.0	85,842	50,349
Virginia	7.0	0	10.4	112.0	306,714	36,194
Northwestern	7.0	− 2.0	44.6	319.3	....	134,191
Rockfeller Inst.	6.0	+ 3.0				
North Carolina	6.0	+ 1.0	15.7	131.0	103,833	27,191
Nebraska	6.0	− 3.0	36.1	544.3	210,225	101,509
Dartmouth	5.5	− 0.5	15.4	224.1	345,454	55,338
Washington (St. Louis)	5.0	+ 1.0	27.4	211.6	....	113,408
Kansas	5.0	0	36.2	442.0	220,000	91,775
Iowa State	5.0	− 1.0	30.6	494.4	328,938	109,620
Syracuse	5.0	− 2.0	46.8	627.2	550,051	148,350
Case	4.0	+ 1.0	8.8	111.3	207,500	12,204
Field Museum	4.0	+ 1.0				
Tufts	4.0	+ 1.0	54.2	279.5	....	54,501
Vassar	4.0	+ 1.0	25.3	254.5	616,421	145,015
Smith	4.0	− 1.0	29.2	393.0	329,875	90,212
Cincinnati	4.0	− 2.0	42.3	348.5	367,030	68,624
Wesleyan	4.0	− 2.0	8.5	80.5	220,616	25,613
Wistar Inst.	3.0	+ 3.0				
Tulane	3.0	+ 2.0	52.0	365.6	601,297	54,967
Wellesley	3.0	+ 1.5	35.3	427.3	423,841	127,937
Conn. Sta.	3.0	+ 1.0				
Pittsburgh	3.0	+ 1.0	61.0	414.3	309,844	122,529
Colorado Coll.	3.0	0	19.0	225.3	362,667	29,166
Gen. Elect. Co	3.0	0				
G. Washington	3.0	0	61.6	502.6	111,500	58,437
Worcester	3.0		16.7	162.6		
Texas	3.0	− 2.0	28.6	611.0	340,234	110,691
U. S. Navy	3.0	− 4.0				

forty instructors to one scientific man of standing are George Washington, Pittsburgh, Tufts, Tulane, Syracuse, Northwestern, Indiana and Cincinnati. These differences are truly remarkable and should be widely known in the interest of scientific education and the advancement of science. Institutions differ in the relative strengths of their departments, but it will be found that those which have men of distinction in the natural and exact sciences also have such men in other subjects. Students should certainly use every effort to attend institutions having large proportions of men of distinction among their instructors. It will be ordinarily the case that in such institutions the younger instructors are also of higher standing. Scientific men, especially those beginning their careers, should try to accept positions only where the higher standards obtain.

In general the institutions which have a large proportion of scientific men of distinction among their instructors will also have a large number in comparison with the student attendance. But institutions vary greatly in the number of students for each instructor—from 3.9 at the Johns Hopkins to 18.1 at Chicago.[1] For each scientific man among the thousand, the numbers of students are: Clark, 18; Johns Hopkins, 22; Harvard, 49; Bryn Mawr, 52; the Massachusetts Institute, 58; Princeton and Stanford, 80; Yale, 90; Columbia, 97. These are the institutions which have at least one scientific instructor of distinction for each hundred students. The institutions not having one such instructor for five hundred students are Syracuse, Texas, Nebraska and George Washington.

There are extraordinary differences or discrepancies in the relation between the value of the buildings and grounds of different institutions and their annual incomes for current expenses as given in the report of the commissioner of education. Some institutions, as Michigan and Illinois, are said to spend nearly as much annually on their educational work as the total value of their buildings and grounds, whereas others, as New York, Stanford and Tulane, are said to spend scarcely more than a tenth as much. Apparently but little reliance is to be placed on such figures. In so far as they are correct the Massachusetts Institute has one scientific man of standing for each fifty-three thousand dollars invested in buildings and grounds. The other institutions having at least one scientific man for each hundred thousand dollars so invested are Clark, Michigan and Indiana. The institutions having but one scientific man of standing for four hundred thousand dollars or more invested in buildings and grounds are Vassar, Tulane, Syracuse, New York and Wellesley. The Johns Hopkins supports one leading scientific man for each ten thousand dollars that it spends. The other institutions which have at least one scientific man for each twenty-five thousand dollars spent annually are Clark, the Massachusetts Institute, Harvard and Princeton. Vassar, Northwestern and Minnesota are the institutions that spend the most in proportion to the number of their scientific men.

Men who stand toward the upper end of the list are of far greater consequence than those toward the bottom. Here too Harvard shows

---

[1] These remarkable differences are confirmed by the report from the Carnegie Foundation, which gives the ratio as 3.7 and 17.4.

its primacy and in unmistakable terms. Of our hundred leading men of science nineteen are at Harvard, as compared with nine at Chicago and seven at Columbia and the Johns Hopkins.[1] Of the second hundred Harvard has 10.5, Chicago 15, Columbia 6 and the Johns Hopkins 3.

It is not possible to estimate the value of a great scientific man in terms of other men. It may even be argued with plausibility that the progress of science depends exclusively on the few men of genius, while the mass of scientific men erect obstacles, and are only of use as a group which on occasion supplies the great man. But in a comparison of this kind we have in mind men such as Galileo, Newton, Laplace and Darwin. In the list of a thousand living American men of science, those in the lead are not incomparable with the others. As a matter of fact, we undertake to measure them by the salaries we pay. These are obviously imperfectly adjusted to merit, and there are kinds of merit other than scientific distinction. If, however, a university pays its more distinguished professors three times as much as its younger assistant professors, it estimates the one to be worth three times as much as the other. In the case of the salaries and earnings of psychologists, it appears that those in the first hundred of the thousand earn about three times, and those in the second and third hundreds about twice as much as those in the lower half of the list. With numerous individual exceptions—some men of high standing even paying for the privilege of doing scientific work, while some men of medium standing may receive comparatively large salaries[2]—we find that the salaries increase with distinction and roughly measure it, placing it about three times as high in the upper hundred as in the lower third of the list. It is also the case that the range of merit in the curve of distribution covered by the first hundred is almost exactly equal to the range covered by the second and third hundreds, and each of these is equal to the range covered by the remaining seven hundred.[3] It may not be possible to fix a zero point at which scientific merit begins, but it can plausibly be placed at a point below the first thousand, about equal to the range of merit covered by the other

[1] The membership of the National Academy of Sciences corresponds closely with these figures—18 at Harvard, 9 at Chicago, 8 at Columbia and 7 at the Johns Hopkins.

[2] It is scarcely necessary to point out again the failure of our competitive system to reward scientific research, but it may be illustrated by an example. Lord Kelvin made a large fortune by his inventions and engineering advice; he earned a modest salary as professor at Glasgow; he was paid nothing for his great contributions to mathematical physics, though he might have earned large sums in the time devoted to these. His technical work was doubtless worth far more to society than he was paid for it, but it was worth less than his scientific research. In his three lines of work he was paid inversely as the value of his services.

[3] Cf. p. 552 above.

three groups. In this case the merit of those toward the bottom of each of the three groups in the thousand—the first hundred, the second and third hundreds, and the last seven hundred—would be as 3:2:1.

In order, therefore, to sum up in one figure the strength of a university or department, weights have been assigned to the men on this basis—a man in the lower four hundred being the unit, those in the other hundreds were assigned ratings as follows: VII and VI = 1.2; V = 1.4; IV = 1.6; III = 1.9; II = 2.2; and I = 3. The first hundred were subdivided, the lower fifty being assigned 2.5, and the upper twenty-fives, respectively 3 and 4. These ratings scarcely measure the real value of the men to society; they are nearly all paid less than they are worth, and the greater the performance of a man the more out of proportion is the payment for his services. They do, however, give with tolerable accuracy the value attached to men in our competitive system. A university can obtain a man of the first rank for from $5,000 to $7,500, or a man in the lower hundreds of the list for from $2,000 to $2,500. It is further the case that a moderate alteration in the weights adopted would not considerably alter the comparative results.

The scientific strength of our strongest institutions rated in the manner described, together with the gain or loss in a period of four

TABLE XI.—THE SCIENTIFIC STRENGTH OF THE LEADING INSTITUTIONS

	Weighted number	Gain or loss
Harvard	146.0	+16.3
Chicago	94.6	+18.0
Columbia	79.3	−13.3
Hopkins	63.4	+ 4.2
Yale	61.7	+12.2
Cornell	57.6	+ 4.6
Wisconsin	49.0	+22.3
Geol. Survey	43.8	−12.2
Dept. Agric	40.9	− 4.9
Mass. Inst	37.7	+ 9.5
Michigan	37.1	− 3.5
California	32.4	− 5.0
Carnegie Inst	30.9	+19.4
Stanford	30.0	+ 4.8
Princeton	28.6	+ 7.5
Smithsonian Inst	26.0	− 7.3
Illinois	25.0	+16.7
Pennsylvania	24.4	− 4.5
Bur. of Standards	18.9	+ 0.1
Clark	16.0	+ 2.0

years is shown in Table XI. Thus Harvard has a total scientific strength equivalent to 146 men in the lower part of the thousand and has made a gain equivalent to 16.3 such men in the course of about four years. In general the figures in this table correspond with those in the preceding table, but they tell us more. They take account not only of the number of men gained or lost, but also of the rank of these men and of the changes which have taken place through men improving their standing or failing to maintain it.

If only the number of men is considered, Columbia and Chicago are equal and Harvard has made a larger gain than Chicago within the past four years. But Chicago has increased the number of men in the first hundred by two and in the second hundred by five. When we count up the total scientific strength, we find that Chicago is in advance of Columbia by the equivalent of 15.3 men and has gained more than Harvard by the equivalent of 1.7 men. Wisconsin and Illinois also show larger gains than Harvard. While Yale has more scientific men in the thousand than the Johns Hopkins, and Stanford than California, the order of the institutions is in each case reversed when the effective strengths are calculated. The figures on the table appear to be significant and important, and it would be well if they could be brought to the attention of those responsible for the conduct of the institutions to which they relate.

Assuming the validity of the method of weighting used or, at all events, its relative validity for purposes of comparison, considerable reliance may be placed on the figures given in the table. The probable error of a man assigned a weight of one is greater owing to the break at the bottom of the thousand, and this is the largest factor in the probable error of the total. Men just coming within the thousand and men just falling below it are of almost equal merit yet the former are counted and the latter are not. Still the probable error of a man assigned the weight of one is less than 0.5. When the errors are algebraically added the probable error of the sum increases as the square root of the number, and we may assume the probable errors of the figures given in the table to be not greater than one half of their square root. Thus in the case of Harvard, we may assume that the chances are even that its real strength is between 142 and 152 and its real gain between 14.3 and 18.3.

The scientific strength of an institution does not necessarily measure its total strength. Common observation would lead us to believe that the Johns Hopkins and Cornell are relatively stronger in the natural and exact sciences than Harvard and Yale. We may perhaps assume that the relative strength of a university in different departments tends to be proportional to the number of research degrees conferred. Data concerning these the writer has each year collected and analyzed.[1] Chicago has in the past thirteen years conferred exactly half its doctorates of philosophy in the exact and natural sciences. The percentages for the other universities which confer most of these degrees are: Cornell, 63; Johns Hopkins, 57; Yale and Pennsylvania, 43; Harvard and Columbia, 39. On this basis, the total strength of these universities, the unit as before being a man in the lower part of the thousand scientific men, is:

Harvard	374.4
Columbia	203.2
Chicago	188.2
Yale	140.7
Johns Hopkins	111.1
Cornell	91.9
Pennsylvania	56.7

These figures represent with tolerable accuracy the strength of each institution, so far as the subjects leading to the doctorate of philosophy are concerned. They do not, however, give adequate recognition to the professional schools, schools of law being practically ignored. Harvard has the strongest schools of law and medicine and has a school of theology, so its primacy would not be affected if these were fully accounted for. In its strength Harvard is nearly double Columbia and Chicago, which come close together. Each of these universities has nearly double the strength of the Johns Hopkins, which again has double the strength of Pennsylvania.

The figures at hand enable us to measure the strength of the scientific departments of the different universities. They are given in Table XII for the ten strongest departments in each of the twelve sciences, together with the gain or loss within the period of four years. The institutions are arranged in the order of strength of the department, but when this is less than four the figures are omitted to avoid giving possible information as to the standing of individuals. The probable errors of the figures given in the table are somewhat less than one half their square root. Thus the strength of the department of mathematics at Chicago is equivalent to 16.8 men on the lower part of the list, and the chances are even that this figure is correct within two places. The gain in four years has been equivalent to 2.8 such men, and this figure is likely to be correct within 0.8. A gain of this kind may be due to the calling of new men or to the winning of higher places by the same men.

It should be kept in mind that the figures refer only to men included in the first thousand, and that these are graded for distinction

[1] Cf. for the last report SCIENCE, N. S., **32**: 231–238, August 19, 1910.

TABLE XII.—THE TEN STRONGEST DEPARTMENTS IN EACH SCIENCE TOGETHER WITH THEIR GAIN OR LOSS IN A PERIOD OF ABOUT FOUR YEARS

Mathematics			Physics		
Chicago	16.8	+2.8	Harvard	19.6	+6.1
Harvard	14.2	+1	Bur. Stand	15.9	+3.4
Columbia	8.4	−1.3	Princeton	9.6	+3.9
Yale	8.1	+1.2	Hopkins	9.4	+3.2
Illinois	8	+8	Chicago	9.3	+4.1
Princeton	6.9	+2.7	Columbia	9.1	−8.9
Cornell	6.9	+0.1	Mass. Tech	9	+2.8
Wisconsin	6.7	+6.7	Cornell	8.3	−1.6
Mass. Tech	4.1	+1.9	Carnegie	8.1	+4.9
Stanford			Dept. Agr	6.1	−0.9

Geology			Botany		
Geol. Surv	40.3	−5.3	Harvard	18.3	+ 3.2
Yale	9.6	+0.4	N. Y. Bot	13.5	0
Harvard	7.9	−1.2	Dept. Agr	13	−11.6
Chicago	7.4	−1.3	Chicago	12.9	+ 2.3
Wisconsin	6.4	+2.2	Cornell	10	+ 2.8
Smithsonian	5.1	+1.3	Stanford	5.9	+ 22.
Cornell	4.9	−0.3	Wisconsin	5.2	+ 1.1
Hopkins	4.6	+1.5	Mo. Bot	5.2	+ 1.4
Stanford			Carnegie	5.1	+ 5.1
Columbia			Hopkins		

Anatomy			Pathology		
Hopkins	6.8	−1.0	Harvard	16.5	+4.1
Harvard	4.9	−0.3	Hopkins	11.5	+1
Michigan			Chicago	7	+2
Wistar			Columbia	6.2	+0.2
Wisconsin			Rockefeller	6.1	+1.5
Minnesota			Michigan	6	−1.3
Columbia			Penna	4.8	−0.3
Missouri			New York		
Penna			P. I. Bur. Sci		
Chicago			Wisconsin		

Chemistry			Astronomy		
Mass. Tech	19	+5.9	Chicago	8.9	+1.9
Yale	13.6	+4.4	California	8.7	−1.2
Dept. Agr	12.8	+6.5	Harvard	7.9	+1.4
Harvard	11.3	−2.5	Carnegie	6.8	+3.6
Hopkins	11	+3.6	Yale		
Cornell	8.9	−0.7	Columbia		
Columbia	8.5	+1.4	U. S. Navy		
Illinois	8.3	+7.3	Wisconsin		
Wisconsin	8.2	+1.8	Penna		
Chicago	8.1	+2.4	Michigan		

TABLE XII.—The Ten Strongest Departments in Each Science Together with Their Gain or Loss in a Period of About Four Years.—*(Continued)*

Zoology			Physiology		
Harvard	22	+3.3	Harvard	9.9	+0.1
Columbia	18.1	+1.4	Yale	7.1	+2.2
Chicago	13.8	+1.6	Hopkins	6.1	−1.1
Am. Museum	10.9	−2.6	Rockefeller	4.9	+2.7
Cornell	8.8	+2.3	Chicago	4.6	+1.4
Yale	8.3	+2.3	W. Reserve	4.2	+4.2
Stanford	7.6	+0.9	California	4	+1.8
Dept. Agr	7.6	+0.7	Wisconsin		
Smithson	6.5	−2.4	Cornell		
Princeton	5.5	+2	New York		

Anthropology			Psychology		
Smithson	10.1	−3.3	Columbia	11	+1.4
Columbia			Harvard	10.2	0
Harvard			Clark	5.2	+0.5
Field Mus			Cornell	5	+0.5
California			Chicago	4.4	+2.8
Am. Museum			Iowa		
Brooklyn			Wellesley		
Clark			Wisconsin		
			Stanford		
			Indiana		

in scientific work, ability in teaching and administration being given a subordinate place. A university may conceivably have a department consisting of men of moderate scientific standing, but of personal distinction and superior teaching ability. Some universities even have collegiate professors who are not supposed to permit research work to distract them from teaching and the personal oversight of students. The writer believes that such men belong to the past rather than to the present generation. Under existing conditions scientific men of ability and character will be investigators, and there is a high correlation between these traits and teaching skill. However, this is one of the numerous questions awaiting scientific solution.

Another factor not taken into account by the figures is the age of the men. As a matter of fact, this should not be considered in the present strength of an institution or department, for if a man of forty and a man of sixty have about the same position, they may be regarded as of about equal value for the present. There are drawbacks and advantages of both youth and age which nearly balance each other or regarding which we have at present no exact information. The writer would prefer the merits and faults of the younger men. However this may be, the departments or institutions having the younger men are in a better position as to the future.

In some cases the strength of the departments should be considered in relation to other factors. Thus, to take an example, the Bussey Institution, the Arnold Arboretum and the Museum of Comparative Zoology are parts of Harvard, whereas the New York Botanical Garden and the American Museum of Natural History are not parts of Columbia, though their heads and other officers may be professors at Columbia, and their facilities may be used for graduate study to the same extent as the Harvard institutes and museums. Or to take another example from the institution with which the writer is connected, the School of Pharmacy has but small educational connection with Columbia, but its professors would be added to the strergth of its departments, whereas the Union Theological Seminary, now adjacent to Columbia, is closely affiliated with it educationally, but the professors would not be counted in its strength.

The geologists of the U. S. Geological Survey form the strongest group of men in the same science and under the same institution. The zoologists of Harvard stand next with about half the strength. There then follow in order the physicists of Harvard, the chemists of the Massachusetts Institute, the botanists of Harvard, the zoologists of Columbia, the mathematicians of Chicago, the pathologists of Harvard and the physicists of the Bureau of Standards. These are the departments which have a strength equivalent to fifteen or more men of standing.

Reviewing the sciences in order, it appears that in mathematics Chicago and Harvard are far in the lead, followed by Columbia, Yale and Illinois, the advance of the last institution being noteworthy here and in chemistry. In physics Harvard has double the strength of any other university and has gained largely. Columbia, which four years ago stood first, has lost more than any university in any department. In chemistry, the Massachusetts Institute of Technology stands clearly first, followed by Yale, Harvard and the Johns Hopkins. In astronomy, the great observatories—Yerkes, Lick and Harvard—give their universities precedence. The Mt. Wilson Observatory of the Carnegie Institution has entered this group, while the U. S. Naval Observatory has dropped from it. In geology the U. S. Survey overshadows the universities, among which Yale, Harvard, Chicago and Wisconsin are in the lead. In botany Harvard is far in advance, followed among universities by Chicago and Cornell. The New York Botanical Garden and the Department of Agriculture stand next to Harvard. The Department of Agriculture has, however, suffered severe losses within four years and is now as strong in chemistry as in botany. In zoology Harvard, Columbia and Chicago have by far the strongest departments. The American Museum of Natural History is twice as strong as the U. S. National Museum. In physiology, under which physiological chemistry and pharmacology are included, Harvard is followed by Yale and the Johns Hopkins. In anatomy the Johns Hopkins is followed by Harvard and Michigan. In pathology Harvard is followed by the Johns Hopkins, which precedes Chicago, Columbia and Michigan. The dependencies of the Smithsonian Institution employ nearly half the anthropologists of the country, but they have lost ground in recent years. Columbia, Harvard, California and Clark are the only universities with adequate departments. In psychology Columbia and Harvard have about double the strength of Clark, Cornell and Chicago.

Reviewing the same figures from the point of view of the institutions, the primacy of Harvard among our universities is unchallenged. It stands first in physics, botany, zoology, physiology and pathology; second in mathematics, geology, anatomy, anthropology and psychology, and third in chemistry and astronomy. In every science of the twelve, it is so nearly first that a small change would place it there. This is a remarkable record, and all honor should be given to the men responsible for it. The departments of Chicago and Columbia stand next to Harvard with about half its strength. Chicago stands first in mathematics and astronomy; second in botany and third in geology, zoology and pathology. Columbia stands first in anthropology and psychology, second in zoology and third in mathematics. The departments at Chicago and Columbia are much more unequally developed than at Harvard. This, however, is not a disadvantage, as with limited resources it is probably desirable for a university to have certain strong departments rather than to have all of equal mediocrity. The departments of mathematics, geology, botany and zoology at Chicago and of zoology, anthropology and psychology at Columbia are well developed, while in certain other sciences these universities stand at the bottom of the list or even fail to be included among the ten strongest departments. The Johns Hopkins stands first in anatomy, second in pathology and third in physics and in physiology. Yale stands first in geology (which includes mineralogy) and second in chemistry and physiology. The Massachusetts Institute of Technology stands first in chemistry.

The most important recent development of science has been the establishment of endowed institutions for research. The astronomical observatories, often officially but loosely connected with universities, are of earlier origin. Botanical gardens as centers of research also have a long history. There is every argument for similar institutions in each science, either as integral parts of universities, in affiliation with them or as independent institutions; and they are probably being established as rapidly as men can be found to do the work. In all our leading universities there are professors whose attention is devoted to advanced students and investigation, and their laboratories may be regarded as research institutions. Then there are specially endowed foundations, such as the Bussey Institution of Harvard or the new Crocker Cancer Research Fund of Columbia. The Wistar Institute of Biology, affiliated with Pennsylvania, is perhaps the most important institution of its class. Then we have independent institutions endowed for research, of which the most noteworthy are the Smithsonian Institution, the Carnegie Institution of Washington and the Rockefeller Institute for Medical Research. The Smithsonian is of special interest, owing to its early and peculiar foundation, but its endowment is not large according to modern standards, and its energies are mainly taken up in directing government bureaus. It does some publication, but very little research work. The Carnegie Institution with its endowment of $12,000,000 has been a disappointment to those who hoped that it would act the part of a special providence for science and scientific men. It is at present conducting research institutions in various places and publishing the work accomplished. It holds a good position in physics, astronomy, botany and zoology, having in all its departments a total strength of 30.9 men. It has an endowment about equal to the part of the Harvard endowment which may be allotted to the natural and exact sciences, which supports the equivalent of 146 men, who teach as well as carry forward research, so its money, though well spent, does not seem to go so far. A considerable part of the income, has however, been used for construction, equipment and publication. The Rockefeller Institute stands high in pathology and physiology and is continually improving its position. It has been placed under the direct control of scientific men and appears to justify this procedure. The Marine Biological Laboratory at Woods Hole is also conducted by scientific men and although without endowment is an important center for research. The zoologists working there in summer would have a strength greater than any department in any science, including the geologists of the national survey.

Bureaus under the national government stand first in geology and anthropology, second in physics and third in chemistry and botany. Excellent work is accomplished by these and other bureaus, but it is probable that foreign governments which spend far less on science have in their service men of greater distinction. There is a wide-spread belief that the government should only cultivate utilitarian science.

In the opinion of the writer this is a mistaken point of view. Applied science can be left to commercial enterprise more safely than research in pure science. The work which is of value to the whole nation and to the whole world, but has not immediate commercial value to any individual or group, is the kind of work which requires public support. If the man of genius exists he should be given opportunity to use his genius to the best advantage of all. It is extremely difficult to find the men most competent to do research work and to place them under the most favorable conditions, but if the immeasurable importance to society were realized, the difficulties would be solved. It is possible to imagine a national research university to which the ablest men should be drawn, some permanently and some temporarily, there to be given all possible facilities for their work, together with such honorable consideration and such salaries that science and scholarship would attain their due place and be made attractive to the fittest. One can even dream of an international research university to the support of which each nation would contribute a part of the cost of the armaments which it would tend to make useless.

The figures here given show the advantage of statistics over general impressions. The writer is perhaps as well informed as any one in regard to the distribution of scientific men, but some of the figures came as a surprise to him. He knew, or thought he knew, that Harvard had gained and Columbia had lost, but he had no idea of the extent of the change. He supposed that Chicago had lost and that Yale had stood about stationary, whereas both institutions show decided gains. He had no idea that Princeton had among its instructors a larger proportion of scientific men of standing than Columbia, or that the proportion in different universities varied from one half to one sixtieth. And so in many other cases he had wrong impressions, and others probably had wrong impressions of the same or other kinds. We are apt to form general conclusions from striking individual cases without regarding all the conditions. Prominent men lost by or called to an institution attract attention rather than the gradual improvement in the performances of a considerable body of men. The eminent man that an institution loses is not as a rule supplied by a new man, but a large loss in one case is made up by small advances in many cases.

It may be hoped that an exposition of the true conditions will be of service to science. From the point of view of abstract philosophy it may not matter whether a scientific advance is made in Russia or America, at one university or another. But abstract philosophy influences conduct less than concrete loyalties. A man who cares as much for other people's children as for his own is not likely to care greatly for any of them. The president of a leading university has recently urged the importance of increasing salaries, not in order to attract better men to the academic career or to enable them to do better work, but in order that his professors may not be paid less than those of a sister institution. Such a point of view may seem rather naïve, but it is sound human nature and should be appealed to for the improvement of the conditions under which scientific work is done. If the loyalty of alumni could be transferred from football to scholarship, there would result a decided gain to scholarship. The fact that each state wants its university to be as strong as its neighbor's is one of the most potent factors in the advance of the state universities.

Individual conduct is in the main automatic response to chance circumstance. But the organism and the circumstances and especially their interrelations may be altered. Organic life consists of adjustments brought about by the slow processes of nature. We have now reached the extraordinary position from which it is possible to make such adjustments for our own welfare by foresight and scientific method. The individual can prescribe a life of reason more readily than he can follow it. But an environment can be formed in which desirable conduct becomes a reflex response. Reason can have no better use than to select individuals and to arrange circumstances so that science may be advanced and applied for the good of all.

22

FAMILIES OF AMERICAN MEN OF SCIENCE

Printed as a supplement to "American Men of Science: A Directory," (Third Edition) 781–808, 1921. Certain parts were published separately as follows: *Popular Science Monthly*, **86**: 504–515, 1915. *Scientific Monthly*, **4**: 248–262 and 368–377, 1917.

In a series of articles entitled "A Statistical Study of American Men of Science," printed in *Science* in 1906 and 1910 and as an appendix to "The Biographical Directory of American Men of Science," methods were explained by which the thousand leading scientific men of the United States had been selected and arranged in the order of the merit of their work. Studies were made of the measurement of scientific performance, of the origin and distribution of scientific men, and of the changes which occurred during an interval of several years. Data have now been gathered in regard to the families of the men of science previously selected. In our present state of ignorance a statistical study of any homogeneous and objectively chosen group should be of value, both as a contribution to psychological and vital statistics in general and for comparison with other groups which may be similarly studied. Scientific men form a desirable group for such study as, on the one hand, they may be assumed to be willing and competent to supply the information and, on the other hand, knowledge concerning the conditions favorable to scientific performance may have important practical applications.

Of one thousand one hundred and fifty-four scientific men from whom information in regard to their families was requested 1,036 replied and 118 did not. Of the replies 16 were blank, sometimes accompained by the explanation that the information was not readily attainable or the like, 7 were to the effect that the information would be sent later or the like, 13 were received too late, 25 were very imperfect, 975 were usable and in most cases complete. This is an unusually full reply to a questionnaire. For example, in answer to an inquiry in regard to noteworthy relatives addressed to 467 fellows of the Royal Society, Sir Francis Galton received 207 useful replies, and the completely available returns "scarcely exceeded 100." In such cases it is desirable that returns should be complete in order to avoid the selection of a special class. Thus, when people are asked whether they have noteworthy relatives, those having them are more likely to reply than others, and the percentage of positive replies may give no definite information in regard to the frequency. In the present case it appears, from examination of the names of the ten per cent who failed to reply, that there was no group that would affect appreciably the result of the inquiry.

I. Origin, Heredity and Performance

In the previous articles statistics were given in regard to the birthplace of the scientific men, and data are now at hand in regard to the nationality and race of their parents. Of the thousand scientific men first selected 126 were born abroad—34 in Canada, 38 in Great Britain and 19 in Germany. Table I gives the nationality of the parents of 917 leading scientific men. Six hundred and twenty-eight, or more than two thirds, have both parents of native American (United States) birth, 23 others have an American father and 42 an American mother, foreign men having American women more frequently than the reverse. In 165 cases both parents are foreign born and of the same nationality. Including Americans there are 124 marriages in which the nationality of the parents was mixed, but they were largely British. The American-born parents are mainly of British and New England descent; of foreign-born parents, 137 fathers and an equal number of mothers are English, Scotch, Irish or Canadian. Germany contributes 77 fathers and 66 mothers. Other nations contribute in all 51 fathers and 44 mothers—fairly equally distributed among Norwegians,

Table I.—Nationality of the Parents of American Men of Science

	Both parents	Father only	Mother only	Total families
American	628	23	42	**660.5**
English	48	36	28	**80**
Scotch	9	13	15	**23**
Irish	4	10	12	**15**
Canadian	14	3	7	**19**
German	54	23	12	**71.5**
Norwegian	6	0	0	**6**
Swedish	6	0	0	**6**
Danish	1	2	1	**2.5**
Russian	6	0	0	**6**
Dutch	3	3	5	**7**
French	6	6	2	**10**
Swiss	6	4	0	**8**
Italian	0	1	0	**0.5**
Japanese	2	0	0	**2**
Total	**793**	**124**	**124**	**917**

Swedes, Russians, Dutch, French and Swiss, with several from Denmark, Italy and Japan. The parents of American men of science are thus predominantly British-American, with an admixture of nearly 8 per cent of Germans and about 5 per cent from other nationalities.

Twelve and six tenths per cent of our leading scientific men are foreign born, 12.6 per cent are native born of foreign-born parents, and 7.1 per cent have one foreign-born parent. In the general population of the United States 14 per cent of the people are foreign born, 13.5 have both parents foreign born and 6.7 have one parent foreign-born. The foreign born and those of foreign-born parentage thus contribute less, but only slightly less, than the native population to scientific productivity. There is a great difference in the different nationalities. Those born in Great Britain contribute 1.2 per cent to the population and 3.4 per cent to our scientific men; Germany contributes 2.7 per cent to the population and 1.9 per cent to the scientific men; Russia 1.7 to the population and 0.6 to the scientific men; Italy 1.5 to the population and 0.1 to the scientific men. These differences are not, however, necessarily due to any racial superiority of the British and Germans. Men have been called from these countries to scientific positions here or have come to seek them, and in general a larger proportion of their immigrants have been from the educated classes. In my own science men so distinguished as Professor Münsterberg from Germany and Professor Titchener from England have accepted chairs of psychology in our universities. It is most unfortunate for us that this movement appears to have ceased. Between 1903 and 1910 only one scientific man of high distinction was called to this country, whereas nine leading scientific men returned to their native countries.

We could and should see to it that the foreigners coming to the United States contribute their share of men of performance. From the point of view of national selfishness nothing could be more profitable than to add to the community as many foreign men of distinction as would come for five or ten thousand dollars a year, and as many young men of promise as would come for one or two thousand dollars a year. Such men are already selected and their education is paid for. We have paid for the education of some 150,000 physicians to obtain at most 1,000 who are competent to advance medical science. The services of this thousand are probably worth as much as those of all the others combined, so if we divide equally the cost of bringing up and educating these physicians, the cost of a man competent to advance science is perhaps $500,000 and his value is far greater. Such men we can obtain from abroad free of cost beyond the payment for their living, which must be paid equally to those who are educated and selected at our own expense. Not only the men themselves, but their descendants also are assets to the country of incalculable value. From the point of view of the world at large, it is probably an advantage to bring men of distinction and of promise to this country, as this tends to promote friendly international relations and good-will, and because, the wealth being greater here and the competition less, we should be able to give better opportunity to the men. The war has placed on us great responsibility; we should provide for those debarred from advancing science, scholarship and art at home. If Great Britain can afford to cast ten billion dollars into the abyss, we are able to invest an equal sum to advance the arts of civilization.

While it is comparatively easy to determine the nationality of scientific men and of their parents, it is almost impossible to determine their race. Indeed, a consideration of the subject leads to a realization of the complexity of the racial descent of the peoples forming the nations of western Europe and America. There are 13.5 families stated to be Jews. Of 71.5 German families, 8 are Jews; of 6 Russian families, 5 are Jews; among 660.5 native American families, there is only one Jewish parent. There may be some unrecorded cases; the number of native-born scientific men of Jewish family is smaller than might have been anticipated. Two families are Japanese; none is known to be of Negro or of North American Indian descent.

TABLE II.—THE PERCENTAGE OF THE SCIENTIFIC MEN IN EACH OF FOUR GRADES ACCORDING TO THE NATIONALITY OF THEIR PARENTS

	No.	Percentage of each grade			
		I	II	III	IV
American	652.5	7.7	18.3	57.9	16.0
British	137	6.6	17.9	56.9	18.7
German	73.5	10.2	20.4	57.1	12.2
Others	48	8.3	20.8	56.3	14.6
Total	911	71	169	525	146
Per cent	.....	7.8	18.6	57.	16.0

The scientific men have been divided into four groups in accordance with the merit of their performance. These are: I. those among the leading hundred of our scientific men; II. those among the second and third hundreds; III. those below this rank in the thousand; and IV. those who in the second arrangement fell below the thousand. As shown in the previous paper, the first three groups cover about equal ranges of merit, and this also holds in a general way for the fourth group. In Table II is given the nationality of the parents of the scientific men in accordance with these grades. Those of American parentage are of average standing; those of British parentage are below and those of German parentage are above the average. Those of other nationalities are slightly above the average. Among the leading hundred men of science seven are of Jewish family. The Jewish race thus appears to show superior intellectual ability. The differences in the other nationalities and races are so small as to indicate practical equality. The slight superiority of the Germans is due to several men who have come to this country to fill scientific positions, half of whom are of Jewish descent.

TABLE III.—THE OCCUPATIONS OF THE FATHERS OF THE SCIENTIFIC MEN

	No.	Per cent	Percentage of each grade			
			I	II	III	IV
Professions..........	381	43.0	8.9	18.4	57.5	15.2
Clergymen........	89	10.1	5.6	19.1	60.7	14.6
Physicians........	66	7.5	9.1	18.2	50.9	22.7
Lawyers..........	58	6.6	10.3	24.2	51.7	13.8
Teachers.........	74	8.3	10.8	18.9	59.5	10.8
Others...........	94	10.6	9.6	13.8	61.7	14.9
Agriculture........	188	21.2	3.7	20.7	56.4	19.2
Manuf. and trade...	316	35.7	7.9	17.4	71.1	13.6
Total..........	885	....	7.5	18.5	58.5	15.5

The occupations of the fathers of 885 scientific men are given in Table III. Forty-three per cent belong to the professional classes; 21.2 per cent to the agricultural classes and 35.7 per cent to the manufacturing and business classes. In the United States in 1850, 3.1 per cent of white men having occupations were in the professions; 44.1 were engaged in agriculture, and 34.1 in trade, transportation, manufacturing and mechanical pursuits. The professional classes have thus contributed in proportion to their numbers about fourteen times as many scientific men as the others, the agricultural classes only half as many as the manufacturing and trading classes. The farm not only produces relatively fewer scientific men, but a smaller proportion of them are of high distinction and a larger proportion are in the lowest group. This traverses a common belief, as voiced, for example, by Dr. Charles W. Eliot, when he writes:

The country breeding gives a vigor and an endurance which in the long run outweigh all city advantages, and enable the well-endowed country boys to outstrip their city-bred competitors.[1]

[1] "Family Stocks in a Democracy," American Contributions to Civilization, 1898.

The writer showed, however, in the previous paper that in proportion to their population cities have produced twice as many scientific men as the country.

The four professions of divinity, medicine, law and teaching, with a fifth group composed of the remaining professions—engineering, fine arts, journalism, the government service, etc.—contribute numbers of scientific men not far from equal. According to the census of 1850, the numbers in the four learned professions were: Clergymen, 26,842; lawyers, 23,939; physicians, 40,765; men teachers, 30,530. For each thousand of their members, they contributed scientific men as follows:

Clergymen	3.3
Lawyers	2.5
Teachers	2.4
Physicians	1.6

Clergymen, therefore, have the best record, and physicians the worst. Yet at that period there was supposed to be a conflict between science and theology, and the work of the physician is, or should be, allied to, if not identical with, that of the man of science. But in the middle of the last century the clergymen were likely to be better educated and more closely identified with the colleges than the physicians. The lawyers and the teachers were equally productive, but college professors —of whom there were only 943 in 1850—are far before any other class. The group of "other professions" is too ill defined to permit statistical treatment. In the census of 1850, mechanics who ran engines were called engineers and included among the professions. It will be noted from the table that lawyers and teachers have contributed the largest percentage of scientific men of high distinction, but the differences are not so large as to be significant.

As it is much easier to determine nationality than race, so occupation can be stated more readily than social position. It would be desirable to know the social connections and incomes of the fathers of scientific men at the period when their sons were educated, but such information is not at hand. Men in the same profession have very different social environments; in manufacturing and trade a man may be an artisan or a multi-millionaire. It is, however, clear that a majority of scientific men come from the so-called middle and upper classes. Not very far from half of them are supplied by the professional classes, forming about one thirtieth of the population, and undoubtedly they tend to be sons of the more successful professional men. Under manufacturing and trade all sorts of occupations are included, but only a small part of the fathers belong to the class of artisans and still fewer to the class of clerks. Most of them own their own business, which may be

anything from a small shop in a university town[1] to the control of a
railway system. Not a single scientific man is recorded as coming
from the class engaged in domestic service, nor is any known to be the
son of a day laborer, even of the higher grades. Agriculture includes
agricultural laborers, but the fathers of the scientific men usually
owned their own farms, and were probably in the main the farmers of
the better class with relatives among professional men. Our farming
population belongs chiefly to a yeoman class, not to a peasant class,
such as forms nine tenths of the population of Russia.

The earlier studies of scientific men made by De Candolle and
Galton and the groups treated by Odin and Ellis yield results in regard
to the origin of men of performance comparable with those here given.
De Candolle[2] found that of 100 foreign associates of the Paris Academy
of Sciences, 41 came from noble and wealthy families, 52 from the
middle class and 7 from the working class. Galton[3] found that of 96
contemporary leading men of science none came from the artisan and
peasant classes. Odin[4] found that of 823 French men of letters, 65
per cent came from the nobility and governing classes, 23 per cent
from the professions, 12 per cent from the commercial and middle
classes and 16 per cent from the lower classes. Ellis[5] found that of 829
British men of genius 18.5 per cent came from the nobility and upper
classes, 41.3 per cent from the professions, 31.2 from the manufacturing
and commercial classes, 6 per cent from the yeomen and farmers and
2.5 from the artisan and laboring classes.

The working classes outnumber the nobility a hundredfold, but
produce only one quarter as many men of performance. If the working classes have equal ability and if they had been given equal opportunity, instead of a hundred scientific men of the rank of the foreign
associates of the Paris Academy there would have been forty thousand.
It may be that the peasant and artisan classes in European countries
are separated from the upper classes by an inferior heredity; but that
is scarcely the case in America. Five or ten generations back most of
us have ancestors of nearly the same average physical, intellectual and

---

[1] A notable case is of three brothers who have attained scientific distinction.
They obviously had inherited ability, but the opportunity to exhibit it in scientific
research was probably due to the fact that their father's shop was in a university
town.

[2] "Histoire des Sciences et des Savants depuis deux Siècles," Genève, 1873.

[3] "English Men of Science," London, 1874; New York, 1875.

[4] "Genèse des Grands Hommes," Paris et Lausanne, 1895. An excellent account of Odin's researches is given in Lester F. Ward's "Applied Sociology,"
Boston and New York, 1906.

[5] "A Study of British Genius," London, 1904.

social condition; any selection for ability within this short period must be slight and transient.

It is evident that what a man can do depends on his congenital equipment. How far what he does do depends on his environment and how far on his congenital equipment, or how far his congenital equipment depends on that of his parents and his family line of descent, we do not know. Most sociological writers and some biologists are confused in their use of the concept of heredity. When there is discussion of the relative influence on performance of heredity and environment, by heredity there is sometimes understood the original constitution of the individual and sometimes his resemblance to parents and other relatives. It is conceivable that the original constitution of son and father might be exactly the same and yet the individual be so plastic to environment that under different conditions there would be but slight similarity between their performances. It is also conceivable that there might be no similarity between the original constitution of son and father, and yet the performance of each be determined by his original constitution almost without influence from environment. Under which of these extreme hypotheses would the current sociologist call heredity strong or weak? The word heredity should be reserved for resemblance due to a common germ plasm and some other word found for the constitution of the fertilized ovum or zygote; perhaps the best that can be done is to use this uncouth word. We can then discriminate between the two distinct questions: What is the resemblance between the zygotes of two brothers? How far does the zygote of an individual determine his performance as an adult?

The distinctions are of vast importance for the organization of society. If men of performance could only come from superior family lines, this would be a conclusive argument for a privileged class and for a hereditary aristocracy. If the congenital equipment of an individual should prescribe completely what he will accomplish in life, equality of opportunity, education and social reform would be of no significance. Such an extreme position, though it is approached by men with so much authority as Sir Francis Galton, Professor Karl Pearson, Dr. F. A. Woods, Dr. C. B. Davenport and Professor E. L. Thorndike, is untenable. Equally extreme in the opposite direction is M. Odin's aphorism "Genius is in things not in men," or the not uncommon opinion that almost anything can be done with a child by training and education. It is a problem of degree and of circumstance, a scientific question that could probably be solved within a reasonable time, if as much intelligence and money were devoted to it as to one of the bureaus of the Department of Agriculture.

In the meanwhile we must do the best we can with the material at hand, even though the interpretation is in nearly all cases ambiguous. It is here shown that 43 per cent of our leading scientific men have come from the professional classes. We may conclude that more than one half of our men of science come from the one per cent of the population most favorably situated to produce them. The son of a successful professional man is fifty times as likely to become a leading scientific man as a boy taken at random from the community. My data also show that a boy born in Massachusetts or Connecticut has been fifty times as likely to become a scientific man as a boy born along the southeastern seaboard from Georgia to Louisiana. They further show that a boy is fifty times as likely to do scientific work as a girl. No negro in this country has hitherto accomplished scientific work of consequence. A boy from the professional classes in New England has a million chances to become a scientific leader as compared with one chance for a negro girl from the cotton-fields.

These great differences may properly be attributed in part to natural capacity and in part to opportunity. When it is asked how far the result is due to each of these factors, the question is in a sense ambiguous. It is like asking whether the extension of a spiral spring is due to the spring or to the force applied. Some springs can not be extended a foot by any force; no spring can be extended without force. The result depends on the relation between the constitution of the spring and the force applied. If the 174 babies born in Massachusetts and Connecticut who became leading scientific men had been exchanged with babies born in the south, it seems probable that few or none of them would have become scientific men. It may also be the case that few or none of the babies from the south transplanted to New England would have become scientific men, but it is probably true that a nearly equal number of scientific men would have been reared in New England. It is certain that there would not have been 174 leading scientific men from the extreme southern states and practically none from Massachusetts and Connecticut. If the stock of the southern states remains undiluted, it may, as social conditions change, produce even more scientific men per thousand of its population than New England has hitherto produced. In the first list of the thousand leading scientific men, Massachusetts produced 109 and Connecticut 87 per million of their population. Of the younger men added to the list in the second arrangement under comparable conditions, Massachusetts produced 85 and Connecticut 57. The other North Atlantic states failed in like measure, while the central states show a gain—Michigan from 36 to 74, Minnesota from 23 to 59, etc. These changes must be attributed to an altered environment, not to an altered racial stock.

Japan had no scientific men a generation ago and China has none now, but it may be that in a few years their contributions to science will rival ours.

A Darwin born in China in 1809 could not have become a Darwin, nor could a Lincoln born here on the same day have become a Lincoln had there been no civil war. If the two infants had been exchanged there would have been no Darwin in America and no Lincoln in England. Darwin was a member of a distinguished family line possessing high natural ability and the advantages of opportunity and wealth. Lincoln had no parental inheritance of ability or wealth, but he too had innate capacity and the opportunity of circumstance. If no infants had been born with the peculiar natural constitutions of Darwin and Lincoln, men like them could not have been made by any social institutions, but none the less the work they did might have been accomplished by others and perhaps their fame would have been allotted to others. There may have been in England other family lines equal in natural ability to the Darwins and in this country other individuals as well constituted as Lincoln, but undistinguished from lack of opportunity. It is still more probable that such conditions obtain in Russia and in China, in whose graveyards there may lie innumerable "mute inglorious" Miltons, Lincolns and Darwins.

The most exceptional ability may be suppressed by circumstances; but it can sometimes deal with them on equal or perhaps superior terms. Thus the writer has pointed out how widely distributed in race, age and performance are the most distinguished men who have lived.[1] When we turn from the most eminent men to those next in rank, we may doubt whether their natural ability has not been equaled by thousands who have not attained distinction. Among the two hundred most eminent men who have lived in the history of the world are: Napoleon III, Nero, Fox, Julian, Fénelon, Clive, Alberoni, Bentley and Gerson. It is quite conceivable that there are at present living in the United States hundreds or thousands of men having as great natural ability as these. There may be a hundred thousand men and women having the natural and specific ability of the thousand in this country who have accomplished the best scientific work.

President A. Lawrence Lowell has remarked that we have a better chance of rearing eaglets from eagles' eggs placed under a hen than from hen's eggs placed in an eagle's nest. But it is equally true that we have a better chance of raising tame eaglets in a chicken coop than in an eyrie. The difference between a man uninterested in science and a scientific man is not that between a chicken and an eagle, but that

[1] "A Statistical Study of Eminent Men," THE POPULAR SCIENCE MONTHLY, **1903.**

between an untrained chicken and a trick cock. Some cockerels can be trained better than others, but there are innumerable cockerels that might be trained and are not.

The son of a scientific man may on the average have the inherited ability which would make him under equally favorable circumstances twice, or ten times, or a hundred times, as likely to do good scientific work as a boy taken at random from the community. The degree of advantage should be determined. It surely exists, and the children of scientific men should be numerous and well cared for. But we can do even more to increase the number of productive scientific men by proper selection from the whole community and by giving opportunity to those who are fit. Galton finds in the judges of England a notable proof of hereditary genius. It would be found to be much less in the judges of the United States. It could probably be shown by the same methods to be even stronger in the families conducting the leading publishing and banking houses of England and Germany. As I write, the death is announced of Sir William White, the distinguished naval engineer, chief constructor of the British navy, president of the British Association. If his father had been chief constructor of the navy, he would have been included among Galton's noteworthy families of fellows of the Royal Society. The fact that his father-in-law was chief constructor of the British navy throws, if only by way of illustration, a light on the situation in two directions.

On the one hand, the specific character of performance and degree of success are determined by family position and privilege as well as by physical heredity; on the other hand, marriage, chiefly determined by environment, is an important factor in maintaining family lines. The often-quoted cases of the Jukes and Edwards families are more largely due to environment and intermarriage within that environment than to the persistence of the traits of one individual through several generations. The recently published "Kallikak Family" by Dr. H. H. Goddard demonstrates once again the heredity of feeble-mindedness. It would, however, have been a stronger argument for the omnipotence of heredity if the original ancestor had left by a healthy mother illegitimate children who established prosperous lines of descent, and a child by a feeble-minded wife who left degenerate lines of descent. Two experiments have been made on a large scale which seem fairly definite even though quantitative results can not at present be reached. The mulattoes may be assumed to have a heredity midway between negroes and whites, but their social environment is that of the negroes, and their performance corresponds with their social environment rather than with their heredity. Illegitimate children have perhaps a heredity as good as the average, but their performance falls far below the average. If performance were determined by heredity alone there might be expected to be among our thousand leading scientific men some forty mulattoes and some forty of illegitimate birth, whereas there is probably not one of either class.

At nearly the same time Agassiz came from abroad to Harvard and Brünnow to Michigan. We all know the list of distinguished naturalists trained under Agassiz—Brooks, Hyatt, Jordan, Lyman, Minot, Morse, Packard, Putnam, Scudder, Shaler, Verrill, Whitman, Wilder and many more, directly and indirectly. From Michigan have come, as is not so well known, one fourth of our most distinguished astronomers, including Abbe, Campbell, Comstock, Curtis, Doolittle, Hall, Hussey, Klotz, Leuschner, Payne, Schaeberle, Watson and Woodward. Certainly the coming of Agassiz and Brünnow was the real cause of greatly increased scientific productivity in America. Some, but not all, of those who worked under Agassiz would have become naturalists apart from his influence. The astronomers from Michigan must in the main be attributed to their environment. The men had the necessary ability, but if Brünnow had not gone to Michigan, they would not have become astronomers; if they had gone to the University of Pennsylvania, they would have been more likely to have become physicians than astronomers; if they had not gone to a university they would not have become scientific men.

It is certainly satisfactory if we can attribute the inferiority of scientific performance in America as compared with Germany, France and Great Britain to lack of opportunity rather than to lesser racial ability. In Germany scientific research has been made by the university rather than the reverse. In Great Britain also the universities have been potent, and, in addition, its leisure class has contributed greatly. Here prior to 1876 we had no university in which research work was adequately encouraged, and we have had no amateurs comparable to those of Great Britain. Professor Pickering found[1] that of the 87 scientific men who were members of at least two foreign academies, 6 were Americans as compared with 17 from Prussia, 13 from England and 12 from France. In so far as our scientific production is so measured, the reference is to a generation ago, when our universities were only beginning to develop and research work was only beginning to be appreciated. But it is a striking fact that of the six distinguished Americans, three are astronomers; and astronomy is the only science in which thirty years ago the facilities for research work in this country were equal to those of the leading European nations. Of the remaining three, two have not been engaged in teaching, and the third has been practically freed from teaching for his research work. We may hope

[1] THE POPULAR SCIENCE MONTHLY, October, 1908, and January, 1909.

that when conditions become as favorable for other sciences as they have been for astronomy, the United States will assume leadership in scientific productivity.

In order to answer questions such as the extent to which the scientific work accomplished in America is due to native endowment, whether such endowment is general or specific, how far it occurs in family lines, what part of those endowed are able to prove their ability, the influence of education and example, the effects of opportunity, encouragement and rewards, it is necessary to make a study of individual cases. A large mass of material is at hand concerning the relatives of scientific men who have shown scientific productivity or have attained distinction, but these data are not in order for publication and should be supplemented by answers to many enquiries. In the meanwhile the writer may say that it is his opinion that while we should welcome and support a eugenic movement tending to limit the birth of feeble-minded and defective children and encouraging the birth of those that are well endowed, it appears that under the existing conditions of knowledge, law and sentiment, we can probably accomplish more for science, civilization and racial advance by selecting from the thirty million children of the country those having superior natural ability and character, by training them and giving them opportunity to do the work for which they are fit. We waste the mineral resources of the country and the fertility of the soil, but our most scandalous waste is of our children, most of all of those who might become men and women of performance and genius.

Eugenics may become the most important of all applied sciences, but at present its scientific foundations must be laid by the study of comparative genetics, on the one side, and the study of human conduct, on the other. There is more immediate prospect of improving our civilization than our germ plasm. It is easier to decrease or eliminate typhoid fever by hygienic measures than to attain racial immunity, although this is not equally the case for tuberculosis and still less for cancer. We can increase to any desired extent from the existing population by proper selection and training the number of scientific workers in the United States. The number capable of exhibiting genius is limited, but many of them are lost through lack of opportunity. It is our business, it should be our principal business, to improve our civilization by giving opportunity to those who are fit, while at the same time investigating the conditions which will give us a better race.

II. Marriages and Number of Children

There are thousands of volumes containing vital statistics, but exact studies of definite groups of individuals have scarcely been made. It is often assumed that we must have vast numbers of cases, such as are obtained by a national census, in order to secure valid statistics, but in some directions better scientific results can be obtained by applying more careful methods to a limited number of cases. The difficulty in obtaining correct statistics is not the variable error, which decreases with the number of cases, but the constant errors, which can only be eliminated by proper methods. Thus, for example, I find that the parents of 871 scientific men had families of the average size of 4.65 children, with a probable error of 0.05. The chances are even that increasing indefinitely the number of cases would give a figure varying only between 4.6 and 4.7, and this is as close a determination as is needed. But a serious mistake would be made if it were assumed that the average family of the class from which the scientific men come were as large as 4.65. The fathers of 865 scientific men died at the average age of 70.6 years and their mothers at the average age of 70.2 years. The chances are even that this figure is correct within one third of a year, and this is all we need to know. It would, however, be incorrect to use these figures to prove that people of that class and generation lived to the age of seventy years or that the men lived longer than the women. In the census of 1880 there were found to be in the United States 170,000 more children in their second than in their first year. As over one tenth of all the children died in their first year, this result is incredible, and the large number of cases only makes the absurdity more obvious.

TABLE IV.—NUMBERS AND PERCENTAGES OF SCIENTIFIC MEN WHO ARE UNMARRIED IN ACCORDANCE WITH THEIR AGES

	Ages of scientific men					Total
	−39	40–49	50–59	60–69	70–	
Number..............	150	402	269	131	48	**1,000**
Unmarried............	27	42	19	12	3	**105**
Per cent..............	18.00	10.45	7.06	9.16	6.25	**10.5**

The table shows that of just one thousand leading scientific men for whom the information is at hand 105 are unmarried. 18 per cent of those under 40 years of age are single, 10.5 per cent of those between 40 and 50, and 7.5 per cent of those over 50. According to the census of 1900, 17.1 per cent of men 35 to 44 years old are single, 10.4 per cent of those from 45 to 54, and 7.8 per cent of those from 55 to 64. There is thus a tolerably close correspondence between the marriages of scientific men and of the general population, but the age groups of the census being five years older, a scientific man is more likely to be married than a man taken at random from the community. This is perhaps contrary to general opinion. A tradition of celibacy for the scholar has been inherited from the Roman Catholic Church, it being only within the time limits of these statistics that fellows of the colleges of the English universities have been permitted to marry. Professor Thorndike[1] found that only 12 per cent of those in "Who's Who in America" over forty years of age are unmarried. On the other hand, President Eliot[2] found 28 per cent of Harvard graduates 20 to 25 years out of college to be unmarried. There is a lack of satisfactory statistics of marriage conditions in different classes of the community. For different nations M. Bertillon[3] states the percentage of unmarried men over fifty years of age to vary from 16.3 in Belgium to 3.6 in Hungary, it being 7.5 in Germany and 10.1 in France.

Contrary to a wide-spread opinion, the marriage rate and the age at marriage have not varied considerably in the course of the past thirty years. The number of persons married annually for each thousand of the population in several countries has been as follows:[4]

	1881–1885	1910 (or 1909)
France	15	15.8
German Empire	15.4	15.5
Italy	16.1	15.5
England and Wales	15.2	15
Sweden	12.8	12

In England and Germany the rate was highest in the quinquennial period 1896–1900, reaching 16.1 and 18.8, respectively. The percentage of women between 15 and 49 years of age who are married has been:

	1880 (or 1881)	1900 (or 1901)
France	54.9	57.7
Italy	55.2	56.1
German Empire	51.9	52.8
England and Wales	51.4	49.2
Sweden	41.4	44.2

There has thus been no decrease in marriage corresponding to the de-

[1] "Marriage among Eminent Men," *The Popular Science Monthly*, 1902.
[2] Annual Report of the President of Harvard College for 1901–02.
[3] "La Depopulation de la France," Paris, 1911.
[4] Report of the Registrar-General (England and Wales) for 1910.

creasing birth rate which has occurred during this period. In France, where the birth rate is the lowest, the marriage rate and the percentage of women married are the highest.

The marriage rate varies from year to year with economic and social conditions, but the percentage of women of child-bearing age who are married proves that marriage is as usual now as it was a generation ago. The conditions, however, are extremely complicated, being influenced by birth rates, death rates, the age constitution of the people and immigration. The European nations with the exception of France have supplied great numbers of immigrants during the past thirty years; these are largely people of marriageable age with an excess of unmarried men. This circumstance makes it more significant that there has been no decrease in marriage in these nations. It explains in large measure the relations in France and England, the latter country having been left with an excess in its population of over a million women above fifteen years of age. The comparatively high birth rates and death rates of a generation ago, followed by the decreasing birth rates and death rates which have obtained in nearly all nations for the past forty years, give a large percentage of the population between twenty and forty years of age, and are favorable to a high marriage rate and to a large proportion of married people. It is significant of improved conditions regarding the health of married women that among 900 scientific men only 15 are stated to have children by a second wife and the number of children is only 29. The data also show that successive polygamy through divorce is unusual among scientific men.

TABLE V.—AGES AT MARRIAGE AND THE SIZES OF FAMILY

Age	15–19	20–24	25–29	30–34	35–39	40–	Av.	Med.
			Mother				22.88	22.29
Number	85	229	99	21	6			
Size	5.56	4.90	4.47	2.71	2.50	.....	4.74	
			Father				27.98	26.85
Number	5	123	175	88	27	22		
Size	6.40	5.27	4.57	4.60	3.96	4.00	4.74	
			Wife				26.63	25.65
Number	15	158	165	69	22	11		
Size	2.00	2.59	2.44	1.62	0.59	0	2.23	
			Scientific Man				29.50	28.40
Number	2	67	196	108	39	28		
Size	2.00	2.27	2.56	2.14	1.62	1.28	2.23	

In Table V data are given in regard to the age at marriage and the size of family of our leading scientific men and of their parents.[1] The

[1] The data are for the 440 cases in which the families of the scientific men

fathers married at the average age of 28 years and the mothers at the average age of 22.9 years. The median ages are naturally lower than the average ages, as marriage can be postponed beyond the average longer than it can precede this average. The distribution of ages is also shown in the table. Five of the fathers and 85 of the mothers married under the age of twenty, 137 of the fathers and 27 of the mothers beyond the age of twenty-nine, 298 of the fathers and 328 of the mothers between twenty and twenty-nine. The scientific men themselves married at the average age of 29.5 years and their wives were on the average 26.6 years old. The sons married about one and a half years later than their fathers and their wives nearly four years later than the mothers. There is a statistical anomaly in this comparison, especially as regards the mothers, for women who married late would have few children or none, and the average age of the mothers would thus be reduced as compared with the wives. The differences are partly due to the fact that all the scientific men and only part of the fathers belong to the professional classes; and there has probably been an increase in the age of marriage of the professional classes in this country; but the figures show that any such increase must be small.

Bertillon gives the following figures for the average age at marriage in the period 1896–1900:

	First marriages		All marriages	
	Men	Women	Men	Women
England........................	26.6	25.1	28.4	26.2
France........................	27.9	23.5	29.6	25.2
Italy........................	27.5	23.8	29.8	24.8
Prussia........................	....	....	29.3	26.2
Austria........................	....	....	30.9	26.8
Sweden........................	28.7	26.7	30.2	27.2
Norway........................	29.2	27.2	31.0	28.1

were "completed" and in which there were no remarriages either of the scientific men or of their fathers. The families were taken as completed when the wife was 45 or older, when there had been ten years of married life without a child or when the period since the birth of the last child added to the mother's age is at least 45. Some of the families are then not absolutely completed, but the births would be very few. None of the 11 women who were more than 39 at marriage had children, although newly married women of this age are more likely than others to bear them. A larger error is due to the selection of families, as those having few or no children would be more likely to be completed. The 211 incomplete families have on the average 1.90 children, which is about the same as for the completed families of parents of the same age.

The age of marriage is highest in the Scandinavian nations; it is lowest in the Sclave nations; it is as low in France, with its small birth rate, as elsewhere. In England in the case of first marriages the husband is one and a half years older than the wife, in France, nearly four and a half years older. The age of marriage for first marriages has increased in England by about three fourths of a year since 1896, before which date the registrar-general regards the records as inaccurate. The ages of the consorts at first marriages have increased from 26.59 and 25.08 in 1896 to 27.46 and 25.81 in 1911. The average age at which widowers marry has increased from 44.49 to 46.42; for widows from 40.58 to 41.74. In the quinquennial period 1876–80, 7.8 per cent of the husbands and 21.7 per cent of the wives were under twenty-one, in 1911 these percentages had decreased to 3.9 and 13.3. The professional and well-to-do classes marry later than the average; thus in England, the ages of the men and women are, respectively, about 32 and 27 years, as compared with about 26 and 24.5 years for the artisan and laboring classes. It thus appears that American scientific men marry at a somewhat earlier age than the professional classes in England and their wives are of about the same age.

The table shows that the size of family of the parents of the scientific men—the fraternity of the scientific men—decreases decidedly as the age of the mother at marriage increases. It is about five and a half when the mother is under twenty; it decreases to four and a half when she is between twenty-five and thirty and to scarcely over two and a half when she is between thirty and forty. The decrease would be somewhat greater if barren marriages were included; but it is altered in the opposite direction by the fact that the larger family has the better chance of giving birth to the scientific man. The decrease in the size of family with the advancing age of the father is less, and depends mainly on the fact that older husbands are likely to have older wives. The age of the wife tends to increase about one year as the age of the husband increases by two years. According to the New South Wales statistics, admirably compiled by T. A. Coghlan,[1] the size of the family is five when the mother marries at 21, and as the age of marriage increases to 24, 28 and 32, the size of the family decreases to approximately four, three and two. In the case of the scientific men the family is 2.59 when the mother was 20 to 24 years old at marriage and 2.44 when she was 25 to 29. It is only two in the fifteen cases when she was under twenty. A comparison of these figures with those for the larger families of the preceding generation is significant, as they seem to show the condition when the family is small and limited. Under these circumstances there is but slight difference in the number of

[1] "The Decline on the Birth Rate of New South Wales," Sydney, 1903.

children when a woman marries at ages from 15 to 29. After thirty, however, there is a marked decrease, the size of family being 1.6 for women marrying between 30 and 34 and only 0.6 for those marrying between 35 and 39. Less than half of those marrying between 35 and 39 had children and none of those who married at the age of 40 or older had children.

The families from which our scientific men come had on the average 4.7 children, and those scientific men who are married and whose families are complete have on the average 2.3 children, these figures including all the children born. Sir Francis Galton[1] found that a group of about 100 English scientific men (excluding barren marriages) had, on the average, 4.7 children, and their parents 6.3, and remarks: "This implies a diminution of fertility as compared with that of their parents, and confirms the common belief in the tendency to an extinction of the families of men who work hard with the brain." Mr. Havelock Ellis[2] found that 214 fertile marriages of British men of distinction produced, on the average, 5.45 children, while 276 "genius producing families" consisted, on the average, of 6.96 children, and remarks that "men of genius belong to families in which there is a high birth rate, a flaring up of procreative activity." He says further that this "might, indeed, have been anticipated. The mentally abnormal classes generally belong to families with a high birth rate"; and quotes data in regard to criminals and the insane. Thus two wide generalizations—that intellectual performance conduces to sterility and that genius is allied to insanity—are based on a curious statistical fallacy for which one would suppose Galton the least likely of men to be responsible.

In a population whose families remain of the same average size in successive generations, every one, whether he be a scientific man, a criminal or a tailor, is likely to come from a larger family than he has. If, for example, all families were of one or of seven children equally divided, the average family would be four in each generation, but the children would be seven times as likely to come from the larger family and would belong to a family which, on the average, would be 6.25. With an average family of three, the size of 100 families would be distributed approximately as follows:

Size of family	0	1	2	3	4	5	6	7	8	9	10
No. of families	18	10	20	22	13	6	4	3	2	1	1

When then we count up the average size of the family from which each of the 300 children come, it will be found to be 4.15. As our scientific

[1] "English Men of Science," London and New York, 1875.
[2] "A Study of British Genius," London, 1904.

men come from families of the average size of 4.7, one may conclude that the families of the class to which they belonged were of the average size of about 3.4. In one generation this family has been reduced to 2.3, owing either to a general fall in the birth rate or because scientific men have families which are smaller than those of the classes to which their parents belonged. Both factors are present; there is a general decrease in the birth rate and the educated classes have families smaller than the average.

In Table VI is given information in regard to the sizes of family of the parents of scientific men in accordance with their nationalities and their occupations. The Germans had families of the average size of 5.7, the British of 4.8 and the native Americans of 4.5. The probable errors show that these differences are not due to the limited number of cases. It is known that immigrants from foreign nations have larger families than native Americans, but these figures probably give the only information in regard to the families which produce scientific and other professional men. The disparity is not so great as in the so-called lower classes, but it is sufficient to indicate that in the professional classes descendants of recent immigrants from Germany and Great Britain will in part supplant the descendants of native Americans. It is, however, the case that immigrants are likely to become assimilated to native Americans in size of family as well as in other respects.

The parents of scientific men from the agricultural classes had families of the average size of 5, those engaged in manufactures and

TABLE VI.—THE SIZES OF FAMILY OF THE PARENTS OF SCIENTIFIC MEN IN ACCORDANCE WITH THEIR NATIONALITIES AND THEIR OCCUPATIONS

	No.	Size	
American	625	4.45	
British	131	4.83	
German	67.5	5.73	
Others	47.5	5.20	
Total	871	4.65	
Professions	381		4.51
Clergymen	88	4.77	
Physicians	65	4.22	
Lawyers	60	4.58	
Teachers	75	4.39	
Others	93	4.54	
Agriculture	185		5.09
Manufacturing and trade	311		4.59
Total	877		4.66

trade of 4.6 and those in the professions of 4.5. It was shown in the previous article that the agricultural classes contribute in proportion to their numbers only one thirtieth as many scientific men as the professional classes, and this disparity is increased by their larger families. Among the professions, physicians had the smallest families and clergymen the largest, but the differences are not large, the family of the clergyman being smaller than the family of the farmer. These figures do not, of course, give information in regard to families of the present generation, in which the differences are probably greater.

TABLE VII.—THE SIZES OF THE FAMILIES OF THE SCIENTIFIC MEN IN ACCORDANCE WITH THEIR NATIONALITIES

	No.	Size
American	544	2.19
British	49	2.43
German	19	3.21
Others	17	1.88
Total	629	2.23

In Table VII are given the figures for the children of the scientific men in accordance with their nationalities. The Americans have, on the average, a family of 2.19 children, the British of 2.43 and the Germans of 3.21. The German family is thus nearly 50 per cent larger than the American. The number of foreign families is, however, too small to give valid averages. It would be very desirable to obtain information in regard to the size of family and other vital statistics for different nationalities and social classes in our population. A single expert in the Bureau of the Census could collect and collate such data in the course of a couple of years at insignificant expense.

Table VIII gives the sizes of the families from which the scientific men have come and which they have in accordance with the geographical division in which they were born and in accordance with whether they were born in the country or in the city. The differences are small. When the parents lived in the country or in small places at the time of birth of the scientific man, they had on the average 4.68 children; and when they lived in towns which in 1900 had a population of 25,000 or over, the size of family was 4.6. The scientific men born in the country had on the average 2.31 children, those born in towns, 2.15. As it will take a long time to correct the common idea that children born in the country are more likely to attain success and distinction than those born in cities, attention may again be called to the fact that 34 per cent of these leading scientific men were born in cities having in 1860 about 12 per cent of the population of the country. The greater pro-

TABLE VIII.—THE SIZES OF THE FAMILIES FROM WHICH THE SCIENTIFIC MEN COME (THEIR FRATERNITIES) AND WHICH THEY HAVE (THEIR CHILDREN), IN ACCORDANCE WITH THE REGION OF THEIR BIRTH AND WHETHER BORN IN THE CITY OR IN THE COUNTRY

Divisions	Country born			City born			Total		
	No.	Fr.	Ch.	No.	Fr.	Ch.	No.	Fr.	Ch.
North Atlantic.............	206	4.40	2.34	124	4.18	2.22	330	4.32	2.29
South Atlantic.............	17	4.53	2.29	17	5.12	2.18	34	4.82	2.24
South Central.............	7	5.71	2.86	5	3.80	4.40	12	4.92	3.50
North Central.............	151	4.99	2.17	44	4.75	1.77	195	4.94	2.09
Western..................	5	6.00	4.00	5	6.20	1.60	10	6.10	2.80
Total..................	386	4.68	2.31	195	4.43	2.15	581	4.60	2.25

ductivity of cities in men of distinction is doubtless in part due to the fact that the abler and more enterprising people are drawn from the country to the cities, their children inheriting superior ability, and in part to the fact that the city-born children have an environment more favorable to education and to success in scientific work.

The number of families from the southern and western states is too small to give reliable information in regard to the number of children. The fraternities of the scientific men from the North Central States are larger than of those from the North Atlantic States, but their own families are smaller. The differences are small, but apparently significant. The scientific men born in the North Central States came from families of 4.9 and had families of 2.1, those from the North Atlantic States came from families of 4.3 and had families of 2.3. A generation ago the families of the Central States—at least those of this particular class—were larger than those of the Northeastern States; they are now slightly smaller. The fertile and wealthy state of Iowa had a smaller population in 1910 than in 1900. The increase in the population of the country is maintained by immigrants and the children of immigrants. The 87 scientific men born in Massachusetts had fraternities of 4.1 and families of 2.1 children, the 117 born in New York State had fraternities of 4.5 and families of 2.3 children.

The table shows the great preponderance of the North Atlantic and North Central States in the production of scientific men and the infertility of the south, concerning which statistics have been given by the writer in previous articles. The birth rate of leading scientific men per million of the population has been 107 in Massachusetts, 89 in Connecticut, 47 in New York, 23 in Pennsylvania, 32 in Ohio, 36 in Michigan, 45 in Wisconsin, 24 in Illinois, 12 in Missouri, 9 in Virginia, 5 in North Carolina, 3 in Georgia, 2 in Alabama, 1 in Mississippi and

Louisiana. In recent years, however, the North Central States have been gaining and the North Atlantic States have been relatively losing. Thus for younger men the birth rates in figures comparable to those given above have fallen to 85 in Massachusetts, 57 in Connecticut and 36 in New York, whereas they have risen to 35 in Ohio, 74 in Michigan and 54 in Wisconsin. These differences and changes the writer is disposed to attribute in the main to environment rather than to heredity. From the family stocks of Massachusetts, Michigan or Louisiana, we can obtain as many competent scientific men as we care to educate and support.

TABLE IX.—THE SIZES OF THE FRATERNITIES AND FAMILIES OF THE SCIENTIFIC MEN IN ACCORDANCE WITH THE INSTITUTION AT WHICH THEY ARE EMPLOYED

	No.	Fr.	Ch.
Larger universities	242	4.50	2.18
Smaller state institutions	89	5.04	2.62
Smaller private institutions	122	4.69	2.29
U. S. government	73	4.64	2.00
Commercial and private	61	4.72	2.44
Research laboratories, etc	56	4.52	2.41
Total	643	4.65	2.28

The distribution of the families among different kinds of institutions is given in Table IX. The fraternities of the scientific men are substantially the same in all cases. The only instance in which the departure from the average exceeds the probable error is for the smaller state-supported institutions, and the difference here may not be significant. In the case of the children of the scientific men, the size of family is probably influenced by the environment. The 61 men in the government service, most of whom live in Washington, have the smallest families, those in the smaller state-supported institutions the largest. The probable errors of the figures are about 0.1, so the differences are not likely to be due to chance. The 61 men in commercial work, or having no institutional affiliations, and the 56 men in research and related institutions have families larger than the average, while those in the larger universities have families smaller than average. In the larger private universities the situation, for those with 10 or more professors who supplied the information, is: Harvard, 42 families with an average of 2.2 children; Yale, 16 and 2.0; Chicago, 25 and 2.1; Johns Hopkins 12 and 2.1; Cornell, 29 and 2.3; Stanford, 13 and 2.4; Princeton, 10 and 2.5; Pennsylvania, 13 and 2.5; Columbia, 25 and 2.7. The smallest families are at Yale, Johns Hopkins and Chicago, the largest at Princeton, Pennsylvania and Columbia. The larger state universities have professors with the smallest families, the size of family being Michigan, 17 families with an average of 2.1 children; Minnesota, 10 and 1.8; Wisconsin, 15 and 1.7; Illinois, 15 and 1.6.

The figures given are for completed families and for all children born. The death rate for the children of scientific men is unusually small, 75 per thousand to the age of five years and about 120 to the age of marriage. The marriage rate for scientific men is high, 895 among the thousand being married. None the less it is obvious that the families are not self-perpetuating. The scientific men under fifty, of whom there are 261 with completed families, have on the average 1.88 children, about 12 per cent of whom die before the age of marriage. What proportion will marry we do not know; but only about 75 per cent of Harvard and Yale graduates marry; only 50 per cent of the graduates of colleges for women marry. A scientific man has on the average about seven tenths of an adult son. If three fourths of his sons and grandsons marry and their families continue to be of the same size, a thousand scientific men will leave about 350 grandsons who marry to transmit their names and their hereditary traits. The extermination will be still more rapid in female lines.

If the families of the scientific men should increase at the rate of the general population, the thousand leading scientific men would have some 6,000 grandchildren instead of fewer than 2,000. These well-endowed and well-placed people would probably have an average economic worth through their performance of not less than $100,000, and the money loss due to their non-existence is thus $400,000,000. The loss to the welfare of the nation and the world from the suppression of the social traditions and the germplasm is incalculable. Until democratic society learns that services for society must be paid for by society, and that the two most important services are scientific research and the bearing and rearing of children, the universities, on which three fourths of our scientific men depend for support, have great responsibilities. They to a certain extent profess that research is part of the work for which their professors are paid, but they do not acknowledge a similar obligation in regard to the children of professors. Columbia University gives, under certain faculties, scholarships to the sons of professors; Yale University has had a statute by which a married professor received a slightly increased salary; the provisions of the Carnegie Foundation benefit married professors. But these are slight acknowledgments of the obligations of our universities.

President Eliot tells us that "the welfare of the family is the ultimate end of all industry, trade, education and government"; but, in his book on "University Administration," he writes:

The general features of a good scale of salaries are as follows: The salary of an annual appointee at the start should be low, about the amount needed by a young unmarried man for comfortable support in the university's city or village. When, after a few years, this young man receives an appointment without limit of time, a somewhat higher salary should be given him, with a small advance each year for, say, three years. If this instructor so commends himself that the university desires his further service, he should receive, as assistant professor, a salary which will enable him to support a wife and two or three children comfortably, but without luxury or costly pleasures.

The scientific man receives his doctorate at the average age of twenty-seven years and is then eligible for an instructorship with a salary for an "unmarried man"; after "a few years" and then "three years" more he is to receive a salary which will enable him to support "two or three children." President Eliot also says:

The recent tendency of sons of well-to-do, and even rich, families, to go into the ministry, the medical profession, academic life, and the public service, is one in which all patriots may well rejoice. . . . It is a good deal safer to give a life office to a married man on whom marriage has proved to have a good effect, than to a single man who may shortly be married with uncertain results.

There might well be inscribed at Harvard and at other universities the words which President Eliot wrote for the Water-Gate of the Chicago World's Fair, changing one word, so that it would read:

TO THE
BRAVE WOMEN
WHO IN
UNIVERSITIES
AMID STRANGE
DANGERS AND
HEAVY TOIL
REARED FAMILIES
AND MADE HOMES

The vital statistics of the United States are entirely inadequate. Where registrations of deaths and births exist, they are imperfect, and the changing population, its age composition and the amount of immigration render them difficult to interpret. The only information concerning birth rates is given by the proportion of children as determined by the census,[1] but even this is unreliable. It might be supposed that it would be possible to determine the number of children by counting them, but this is not the case. The children reported in the census

[1] In January, 1917, was issued the first bulletin from the Bureau of the Census giving birth rates for ten states.

of 1850 were fewer than the survivors (with the comparatively small excess of immigrants) counted ten years later. There are always more children given as two years old than as one—in 1880 as many as 170,000 more. Nor can we have complete confidence in the compilations of the experts of the census. Thus in the case under consideration they give[1] figures showing that the white population of the United States increased from 1790 to 1800 by 35.7 per cent, adults over 20 by 50.9 per cent and children under 16 by 38.8 per cent, whence it follows that children from 15 to 19 decreased 22 per cent. This is of course absurd and is due to a gross error of some sort. However, the ratio of white adults twenty years of age and over to white children under 16, according to the census reports, is shown on the curve. The percentage of children under 16 years of age in the white population increased from 1790 to 1810 and was the same in 1820 as in 1790. In 1810 just half the white population consisted of children under 16; in 1900 the percentage of children had decreased to 35.7.

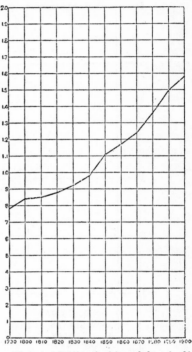

FIG. 1.—Ratio of white adults of self-supporting age to white children under sixteen years in the United States, according to the Bureau of the Census.

From a special study by Mr. Kuczynski,[2] it appears that the birth rate of the native population of Massachusetts has been 63 per thousand women of child-bearing age, as compared with 85 in France, 104 in England and 143 in Russia. Its birth rate per thousand of the population was 17, the size of family 2.61 and of the surviving family 1.92. Special statistics have been gathered for college graduates. President Eliot

[1] "A Century of Population and Growth," Bureau of the Census, 1909, pp. 80 and 103. An answer to a letter addressed by the writer to the director of the census partly explains the way this error was committed—but the explanation was marked "confidential!" It is, however, no violation of this confidence to state, as the information is available from official reports, that figures were not at hand prior to 1830 and that these were guessed—it appears very awkwardly—so as to give a regular curve.

[2] *Quarterly Journal of Economics*, November, 1901, and February, 1902.

in his report for 1901–02 stated that 634 married Harvard graduates of the classes from '72 to '77 had an average family of 1.99 surviving children. Only 71.9 per cent of the graduates were married, and the number of children for each member of the class was 1.43. If only 72 per cent of Harvard graduates are married at the average age of fifty, it is a serious indictment of the kind of men who go to

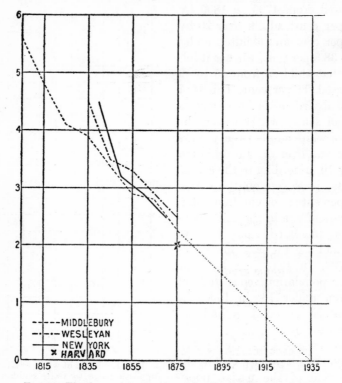

Fig. 2.—The decrease in the size of family of college graduates.

Harvard or of the influences under which they come. We have seen that 91 per cent of American men of science over 40 are married. Other data concerning the families of college graduates have been published by Professor Thorndike[1] and others.

Curves are here drawn for some of the data, which show that the gross size of the family of college graduates has decreased from 5.6 at the beginning of the century to 2.5 for classes graduating in 1875, while at that time the size for Harvard was about 2. A projection of these curves—which of course gives no scientific information—shows the curious result that if the decrease should continue at the same rate

[1] "The Decrease in the Size of American Families," Edward L. Thorndike, *Popular Science Monthly*, 1903.

students graduating in 1935 would have no children. The average college graduate has a family of about the same size as the scientific man of the same age. Data collected for the graduates of Yale,[1] in the classes 1869–86 twenty years after graduation and thus not quite complete, give the following results for different occupations:

Occupation	Marriages	Family
Clergy	119	2.2
Law	398	2.0
Education	163	2.0
Manufacturing	88	2.0
Medicine	108	1.7
Merchant	82	1.7
Miscellaneous	258	1.9

Graduates of colleges for women also have had families of about two, but half of them remain unmarried. The Harvard graduate thus has on the average three fourths of a son, the Vassar graduate one half a daughter.

Since this article was written and published in abstract elsewhere,[2] there have appeared two excellent articles on the size of family of college graduates. Johnson and Stutzmann[3] find that about half of Wellesley College alumnæ graduating from 1879 to 1888 married and had families averaging 1.56 children. John C. Phillips[4] gives data from the class reports of Harvard and Yale students compiled twenty-five years after graduation. Seventy-four per cent of Harvard graduates and 78 per cent of Yale graduates had married. The number of children born for each married graduate decreases from about 3 in the fifties to 1.8 in 1890. As Mr. Phillips points out, the decrease becomes slower between 1875 and 1890.

In Table X it is shown that the families of scientific men in which the mothers have had a college education are not appreciably smaller than others. If one regards only the total, it appears that when the mother had a college education the average family is about 2, when she had a partial college education 2.1 and when she had none 2.3, but these differences are chiefly and probably entirely due to the fact that the younger scientific men have the smaller families and at the same time are more likely to marry college graduates. If we divide

[1] *Yale Alumni Weekly*, 1907.

[2] Proceedings of the First National Conference on Race Betterment, January, 1914; *The Independent*, September 17, 1915.

[3] *Journal of Heredity*, 1915.

[4] *Harvard Graduates Magazine*, September, 1916.

the scientific men into three age groups, the differences become much less, and if the groups were subdivided still further they would probably disappear. This illustrates the possibility of statistical fallacies when a group is not homogeneous. Of the scientific men under fifty, 109 married college graduates and had families of the average size of 1.81, 33 married women with a normal school or partial college education and the average family was 1.79, 119 married women without a college education and the average family was 1.98. 54 per cent of scientific men under 50 have married women with a college education; for scientific men from 50 to 59 the percentage falls to 35 and for those 60 or older to 19.

TABLE X.—THE SIZES OF THE FAMILIES IN ACCORDANCE WITH THE EDUCATION OF THE MOTHER

	College	Partial	None	Total
Under 50				
No	109	33	119	**261**
Size	1.81	1.79	1.98	**1.88**
50 to 59				
No	58	20	145	**223**
Size	2.22	2.20	2.39	**2.33**
Above 59				
No	21	7	117	**145**
Size	2.57	3.43	2.69	**2.71**
Total				
No	188	60	381	**629**
Size	**2.02**	**2.12**	**2.35**	**2.23**

The figures result not only from the increasing numbers of women undergoing higher education, but also from an extension of common scientific interests and pursuits for men and women. A distinguished biologist has observed that "if marriages are made in heaven, Woods Hole may be regarded as a branch office." To the same biologist we owe the remark that "eugenics is an infant industry." There is truth in both epigrams. The percentage of men who have married women with whom they have been thrown into association as teachers or fellow students is large, and we are at present ignorant of the results of such marriages. Small as are the families of scientific men, it is here shown that they are not so because the mother is a college graduate. If both mother and father have common scientific aptitudes and interests, the physical heredity and social traditions should lead the children to follow similar scientific pursuits with an early start and favorable opportunities. I shall be able to give the percentage of fathers and sons, or of two or more brothers, who have engaged in scientific work, and it may be possible to determine the effect when the mother also has scientific interests and ability.

III. Vital Statistics and the Composition of Families

It has been claimed that children of older parents are physically and mentally inferior. Conversely, C. L. Redfield in a curious book entitled "Control of Heredity" and in various articles argues that men of distinction are likely to be born when their fathers are old and that their performance is due to inheritance of the experiences gained by their fathers. If the age of the parents affects the constitution of the children, this clearly is a matter of importance, particularly if the principles of eugenics are enforced either by law or by sentiment. But at present we have no scientific information on a problem which could be solved by statistical research.

The fathers of 865 leading American men of science were on the average 35 years old and their mothers were 29 years and 8 months old when their sons were born. The fathers married at the average age of twenty-eight years, being somewhat more than five years older than their wives. The scientific men are consequently born at an average interval of seven years after the marriage of their parents. The ages are given separately for the four groups into which the scientific men have been divided and are earlier for both fathers and mothers (group I in the table) of those more distinguished. The probable errors given in italics show that the differences may be due to chance, but that this is unlikely. It is the case, as shown below in Table XIV (p. 510), that the first-born son is the one most likely to become a scientific man, and the parents of first-born children are of course younger.

Table XI.—The Ages of the Parents at the Birth of the Scientific Men and at Death, According to the Standing of Their Sons

	No.	Age at birth of scientific man		No.	Age at death	
		Father	Mother		Father	Mother
I..........	64	34.02 ± .57	28.37 ± .50	62	70.18 ± 1.12	70.89 ± 1.36
II.........	160	34.54 ± .40	29.86 ± .31	154	70.85 ± .75	70.68 ± .78
III........	505	35.00 ± .23	29.72 ± .20	496	70.77 ± .38	69.96 ± .36
IV........	136	35.69 ± .53	30.09 ± .38	121	70.91 ± .92	69.45 ± .99
Total....	865	34.95 ± .18	29.70 ± .15	833	70.64 ± .30	70.20 ± .31

In Table XI is also given the average age at death of the parents, whence it appears that the fathers died at the average age of 70.6 years, the mothers at 70.2 years, the chances being even that these figures are correct within a third of a year. The average age of the scientific men being about fifty years, most of their parents are now no longer living. If, however, the deceased parents only had been included, the averages would have been too low, as the more long-lived parents would be those more likely to be living. The expectation of life has been added to the age of each of those still living, and the probable age at death used in the averages. The ages given do not mean that people of this class live to those ages, or that the men live longer than the women. A statistical error such as this has often been made, a distinguished scientific man having, for example, urged that it is one of the advantages of the scientific career that scientific men live much longer than the average, failing to note the circumstance that there are no scientific men who die when they are babies. The figures in the table mean that the fathers being on the average 35 years old when their sons are born have an expectation of life of 35.6 years, and will on the average die at the age of 70.6 years. The mothers, averaging 29.7 years old, have an expectation of life of 40.5 years. These expectations are about four years longer than those allowed by standard mortality tables, but the data are not exactly comparable. Although the parents of the more distinguished scientific men do not live longer than the others, they live longer after the births of their sons.

TABLE XII.—THE AGES AT DEATH OF THE FATHERS OF THE SCIENTIFIC MEN IN ACCORDANCE WITH THEIR OCCUPATIONS

	No.	Age at death
Professions...................	370	69.67 ± .45
Clergymen..................	94	71.68 ± .81
Physicians..................	66	67.20 ± 1.08
Lawyers....................	57	71.75 ± 1.19
Teachers...................	70	69.29 ± 1.07
Others.....................	83	68.25 ± .92
Agriculture..................	193	72.81 ± .62
Manufacture.................	330	70.65 ± .48
Total......................	**893**	**70.71** ± .29

Table XII shows that the farmers who were fathers of scientific men died at the average age of 72.8 years, the physicians at 67.2 years, a difference of over five years between the shortest and longest lived of the groups. The clergymen and lawyers lived one year less than the farmers, the teachers two and a half years less. Those engaged in manufacturing and trade died at the average age. According to the report of the English registrar-general (1908), the death rates per thousand during the years 1900–1902 for those between 45 and 65 in different occupations were: Farmers, 14.8; clergymen, 15.5; teachers, 15.8; lawyers, 18.3; physicians, 23.9.

Table XIII gives the ages at death of the mothers in accordance with the size of their families. The crude figures are subject to a statistical error, as mothers might have small families because they died early. This is eliminated by considering only those who survived the child-bearing age. In this case mothers of one child died at the average of 68.6 years; mothers of 12 children at the age of 80.6. There are included 759 families, but the number of families of different sizes is too small to give entirely valid averages. Still it is significant that the thirteen mothers of 11 and 12 children lived to the average age of 78 years; the 43 mothers of 9 and 10 children to the age of 75 years. It is probable that the women who were the more vigorous had the largest number of children and also lived to the greatest age; they might have lived as long or even longer if they had been unmarried. Though largely due to statistical selection, the fact remains that of 45 mothers of one child 10 did not survive the age of 45, whereas of 56 mothers of from 9 to 12 children not one died under this age. In view of these facts it may be doubted whether the practise of limiting the number of children is beneficial to the health and longevity of the mother.

TABLE XIII.—AGES AT DEATH OF MOTHERS OF THE SCIENTIFIC MEN IN
ACCORDANCE WITH THE SIZES OF THEIR FAMILIES

Size of family	1	2	3	4	5	6	7	8	9	10	11	12	Av.
Number..................	45	91	106	136	110	112	59	44	27	16	8	5	**759**
Age at death.............	61.7	67.9	69.3	71.7	69.1	71.5	73	70.7	77.6	70.5	76.2	80.6	**70.1**
No. dying under 45.......	10	17	11	10	11	3	2	4	0	0	0	0	**68**
Age at death of those surviving 45..............	68.6	74.2	73		74.4	72.5	72.5	74	73.6	77.6	70.5	76.2	80.6	**73.3**

Table XIV gives the numbers of scientific men who were first-born children, second-born children, etc., for each size of family. A scientific man is of course more likely to be a first-born child than a second-born, because there are families with only one child and consequently more first-born children. But it appears from the table that the first-born child is more likely than the others to become a scientific man. In families of two or more children, 284 are first-born and only 168 second-born; in families of three or more, 214 are first-born and 114 are third-born; in families of four or more, 159 are first-born and 81 fourth-born.

The first-born child has been reported to be more likely to be a man of genius, an idiot, a consumptive and various other things, but usually as the result of some statistical fallacy. If, for example, in our figures only families of two and eight are considered, there being on the average five children and one first-born, it looks at first sight as though the chances are one in five that an individual selected at random would be the first-born. But both families being represented, it has been argued that the chances are half that the individual is the first-born in the small family and one eighth in the large family, or on the average five sixteenths, nearly one in three. However, the family of eight is four times as likely to be represented in a random selection from the two families, so the chances of the individual being first-born are reduced to one in five. Finally—and this seems to have been overlooked —there are three times as many families of two as of eight, and there are in fact 16 chances out of 61, or a little over one in four, that the individual selected at random will be the first-born.

TABLE XIV.—THE ORDER OF BIRTH OF SCIENTIFIC MEN

	Order of birth												
	1	2	3	4	5	6	7	8	9	10	11	12	
1	63												63
2	70	52											122
3	55	39	31										125
4	53	33	32	29									147
5	47	13	18	17	23								118
6	30	17	16	19	21	14							117
7	16	7	8	7	9	14	7						68
8	7	3	5	4	8	5	4	8					44
9	5	1	2	4	4	4	0	3	5				28
10	1	1	2	0	1	2	0	0	0	5			12
11	0	1	0	1	0	1	0	0	1	1	1		6
12	0	1	0	0	0	0	0	1	0	1	1	1	5
	347	168	114	81	66	40	11	12	6	7	2	1	855

These errors have been eliminated by the method used in the table, but there are at least two other statistical errors that affect such data. When we are dealing with contemporary families the older children may be preferred. Thus children under fifteen are not likely to suffer from pulmonary tuberculosis or to be criminals, and the patient or the prisoner may be more likely to be the first-born child than the last born. This circumstance holds for the scientific men. They are on the average 38 years old when they attain their position, and the scientific population is rapidly increasing, so the earlier born children are more likely to be included. This factor, however, is small, as is shown by the fact that the second-born child is not appreciably more likely to be a scientific man than those later born. Probably a large statistical error is introduced by the fact that a man sometimes does not know of or ignores children who were born and died before he himself was born, and thus records himself as the first-born.

In so far as it may in fact be the case that the first-born child is more likely to be a scientific man, this is probably due to social rather than to physiological causes. Galton found the eldest son to be preferred, and perhaps this might be expected under a system of primogeniture. In this country where families are apt to improve their economic condition, the younger sons may be more likely to be sent to college than the older, but as to this there is no available information.

In Table XV the intervals are given between marriage and the birth of the first child and between the births of successive children for families of different sizes. When there is only one child it is born on the average 3.2 years after marriage, whereas in a family of five or more the interval is about a year and a half. In the standardized family of two the second child is born 4.2 years after the first, twice as long as for large families. The delay in the birth of children in small families might be due to the same physiological or pathological causes which make the family small, but in most cases it is probably due to voluntary control.

TABLE XV.—INTERVALS IN YEARS BETWEEN MARRIAGE AND BIRTH OF FIRST CHILD AND BETWEEN BIRTHS OF SUCCESSIVE CHILDREN

Size of family	No.	1	2	3	4	5	6	7	8	9	Av.
1	70	3.17	....	....	....	....	....	....	....	....	**3.17**
2	121	2.14	4.21	....	....	....	....	....	....	....	**3.17**
3	120	1.87	3.09	4.00	....	....	....	....	....	....	**2.99**
4	56	1.59	2.40	3.16	3.82	....	....	....	....	....	**2.74**
5	29	1.62	2.52	2.69	3.38	3.76	....	....	....	....	**2.79**
6	12	1.33	1.83	2.00	2.92	2.25	2.75	....	....	....	**2.18**
7	5	1.40	2.00	1.60	2.60	3.00	2.00	2.20	....	....	**2.11**
8	2	2.00	1.50	2.50	2.00	2.00	2.00	2.00	3.50	....	**2.19**
9	1	1.00	2.00	1.00	2.00	2.00	1.00	3.00	2.00	2.00	**1.78**

From Table XVI it appears that 478 scientific men reported 716 sons and 668 daughters. This difference falls within the limits of chance variation, and is not likely to be significant. In the families from which 832 scientific men come there were 2,537 sons and 1,527 daughters recorded. This disparity may at first strike the reader as inexplicable. Galton in his "Hereditary Genius" says: "I also found the (adult) families to consist on an average of not less than 2½ sons and 2½ daughters each. Consequently each judge has on an average of 1½ brothers and 2½ sisters. . . . 100 judges are supposed to have 150 brothers and 250 sisters." Nearly all those whom I have questioned about this statement think that it is correct. It seems to most people obvious that if there are equal numbers of boys and girls, a boy must on the average have one more sister than brother. However, a boy has as many brothers as sisters, owing to the sex composition of families. Thus in families of two, one fourth of the families will consist of two boys, one fourth of two girls and one half of a boy and girl. On the average, four boys will have among them two brothers and two sisters, and there is a similar equality for large families.

TABLE XVI.—DISTRIBUTION OF SONS AND DAUGHTERS

Size of family	No. of families	Family of parents		
		Sibs	Sisters	Brothers
(1)				
2	126	126	69	57
3	128	256	123	133
4	152	456	244	212
5	125	500	266	234
6	123	615	327	288
7	71	426	235	191
8	48	336	172	164
9	31	248	121	127
10	16	144	83	61
11	7	70	34	36
12	5	55	31	24
Total....................	832	3232	1705	1527

		Family of scientific men		
		Children	Sons	Daughters
1	81	81	42	39
2	136	272	153	119
3	130	390	199	191
4	63	252	130	122
5	41	205	104	101
6	15	90	46	44
7	5	35	16	19
8	4	32	10	22
9	3	27	16	11
Total....................	478	1384	716	668

Table XVII contains information in regard to deaths in the families of scientific men. For their brothers and sisters the percentage of deaths recorded under five years is 14.8, and under twenty-five years it is 22.5. For their children the percentages are 7.5 and 10.9. The death rate has thus decreased to half in a single generation, and for the children of the scientific men is probably the smallest known. As only completed families are considered, there are practically no children under five, but those under twenty-five who might die before reaching that age make the death rate too low in this group. It is

TABLE XVII.—DEATHS IN THE FAMILIES OF SCIENTIFIC MEN

	Size of family brothers and sisters		Total or average
	1 to 6	7 to 12	
Number of families....................	515	129	644
Brothers and sisters....................	1406	917	2323
% of deaths under 5....................	14.22	15.59	14.77
% of deaths under 25....................	22.28	22.63	22.51
	Children		
	1 to 4	5 to 9	
Number of families....................	416	67	483
Children.............................	1024	381	1405
% of deaths under 5....................	7.37	8.01	7.54
% of deaths under 25....................	10.66	11.55	10.93

difficult to see how more valid statistics can be obtained than those supplied by scientific men, the order of birth and the dates of birth and death having been given; yet it is undoubtedly the case that all deaths are not recorded, especially for the brothers and sisters who died in infancy. This error would, however, only emphasize the decrease in the deaths of the children as compared with the preceding generation. The number of deaths among a thousand children born is not directly comparable with death rates per thousand of the child population. When there are seventy-five deaths under the age of five among a thousand infants born to the scientific men, the annual death rate is somewhat larger than 15.

The decrease in the infantile death rate in recent years is so remarkable as to be almost incredible, and the existing differences in nations and social classes are appalling. In the families from which our scientific men come, the death rate for children under five is somewhat over 30 and in their own families it is somewhat over 15. The rate in the registration area of the United States in 1900 was 51.9. In the present registration area it was 32.9 in 1911, varying from 41.1 in

Massachusetts to 18.6 in Washington, from 74 in Fall River to 22.4 in Seattle. In or about 1900, the rates for the other nations were:

Russia	134.5
Spain	104.1
Austria	86.7
Germany	74.2
Italy	74.8
England	53.5
France	47.6
Sweden	37.5
New Zealand	23.2

The table indicates a small selective death rate against the larger families. When there were one to six brothers or sisters the percentage of deaths under five years was 14.2 as compared with 15.6 for larger families; when the number of children was four or less, the percentage was 7.4 as compared with 8 for families of five or larger. This small difference is probably due to the coinciding decrease in the birth rate and in the death rate. The larger families had a higher death rate not because they were larger but because they were earlier when the death rate was higher. Other statistics, such as those of Rubin and Westergaard for Copenhagen, show a selective death rate against the larger families. In the statistics with which we are concerned poverty and neglect are almost excluded.

TABLE XVIII.—THE RELATION BETWEEN THE SIZES OF FAMILIES OF THE PARENTS OF SCIENTIFIC MEN AND THE SIZES OF THEIR OWN FAMILIES

	Size of parents' families				Total or av.
	1, 2, 3	4, 5, 6	7, 8, 9	10, 11, 12	
Under 50	94	110	37	12	**253**
Size of family	1.69	1.99	1.81	2.41	**1.88**
50–59	74	93	33	5	**205**
Size of family	2.35	2.14	2.69	2.60	**2.32**
Above 59	43	61	31	4	**139**
Size of family	2.60	2.77	2.48	4.00	**2.70**
No of families	211	264	101	21	**597**
Av. size of families	**2.11** ± *.11*	**2.22** ± *.07*	**2.30** ± *.13*	**2.76** ± *.29*	**2.22** ± *.06*

In Table XVIII is shown the relation between the size of the family from which the scientific men come and the size of the family that they have, the scientific men being divided into three age groups. It will be noted that the size of family of the scientific men varies with their age at the time, being 2.7 children when they are above 59; 2.3 when they are between 50 and 59, and 1.9 when they are under 50. These differences are partly due to statistical selection, the families of the younger men being not absolutely complete, and the barren and smaller families being more likely to be included. They, however, in part represent the declining birth rate within a period of twenty years. There is shown a slight positive correlation between the number of brothers and sisters and the number of children. Thus when a man comes from a family of 1, 2 or 3 children, his family averages, 2.1, and as the size of the family from which he comes increases by groups of three, his own family increases to 2.2, 2.3 and 2.8. The probable errors show that the figures have a limited validity. The differences, however, may be due to the decreasing size of family, the older scientific men having larger families and coming from families which were larger because they were earlier. The inheritance of physiological fertility would depend partly and perhaps chiefly on the female, and the size of the modern small family is determined in the main by social and psychological causes. If the data here given were valid, they would show a slight correlation of fecundity in successive generations and a slight selective death rate against the larger family, which about balance each other. These conditions are those which must obtain in a state of nature, for unless there is a change in the environment, the number of individuals of a species can not considerably increase, and if they regularly decrease it will be exterminated. The relations which obtain in the families of scientific men are, however, probably due entirely to the decreasing death rates and birth rates of the past seventy-five years.

TABLE XIX.—THE STANDING OF SCIENTIFIC MEN AND THE SIZE OF FAMILY

	I	II	III	IV	Total or av.
Parents family					
No. of families	71	162	530	141	904
Average size	4.73	4.59	4.69	4.45	2.64
Own family					
No. of families	49	111	298	96	554
Average size	2.50	2.17	2.14	2.39	2.22

In Table XIX the scientific men are divided into four groups in accordance with their distinction, and the size of the family from which they came and which they have is given for each degree of distinction. The most distinguished group (I in the table) came from families of the average size of 4.7 and have families of the average size of 2.5, in both cases above the average. The eminent man is slightly more likely to have more brothers and sisters and appreciably more likely to have more children than his colleagues. The most eminent group is, however, about five years older than the others, and this about accounts for their larger families, so rapid has been the decline in the birth rate. The lack of correlation between the distinction of a scientific man and the size of his parents' family may be due to a combination of causes. On the one hand, the only child or the child from a small family may be more likely to have educational opportunities or inherited wealth; on the other hand, he may have inferior heredity and opportunity for forming character.

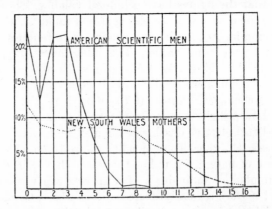

Fig. 3.—The percentage of families of American men of science of each size, compared with the data of Coghlan for New South Wales mothers in the decade 1891-1900.

The conditions are similar for scientific men who are unmarried or who have no children or but one, as compared with scientific men with larger families. There is but slight difference in their performance. The similarity may be due to a balance of various conditions, and is also in part accounted for by the fact that men marrying at the average age of 29.5 years have in large measure had such original ideas as they may hope to have and have in the main determined their careers. As a matter of fact those who are unmarried furnish fewer men than the average to the two more distinguished groups while those with six or more children supply a larger number. If the figures for scientific men with the largest families could be regarded as valid, it would be indicated that they are the ablest and most successful, but at the same time furnish the largest share to the group who have dropped out of the first thousand, perhaps owing to the circumstance that scientific work must be neglected to support the children. But the differences are too small and the families are too few to permit any conclusions except that under existing conditions there is no appreciable correlation between the distinction of a scientific man and the size of family from which he comes or which he has. This fact itself is, however, of considerable social significance. The material handicap of the larger family is balanced by improved character and greater efforts or by the superior quality of the men coming from and supporting the large family. In his study of "Heredity in Royalty" F. A. Woods finds that there is a direct correlation between intellectual and moral and size of surviving family. In this case the larger family is not a burden for the parents. It is reasonable to assume that if the cost of children could be borne by society for whose benefit they exist, there would be larger numbers of children having superior inherited ability.

IV. The Causes of the Declining Birth-Rate[1]

There is a biological adaptation which limits the average fertility of women to about twelve children, and social conditions have led to one half of the women of child-bearing age being unmarried. The further decrease of the average family to three or four—in the case of American scientific men or college graduates to two—must be due to infertility or to voluntary limitation. Both causes have been recognized since the time of the writing of the book of Genesis; both have doubtless increased in force in the course of the nineteenth century. It is generally believed that the principal cause of the small size of the modern family is voluntary limitation. A definite answer is supplied by information given to me by 461 leading scientific men, as shown in Table XX.

Table XX.—The Causes Limiting the Size of Families

Number of children	0	1	2	3	4	5	6	7	8	9	
Number of families......	102	58	98	100	54	31	12	2	3	1	**461**
Not limited..............	67	19	14	29	22	14	5	2	3	1	**176**
Voluntarily limited......	35	39	84	71	32	17	7	0	0	0	**285**
Health................	25	17	44	26	8	11	2	0	0	0	**133**
Expense..............	5	12	29	30	14	3	5	0	0	0	**98**
Other causes..........	5	10	11	15	10	3	0	0	0	0	**54**

Of these completed families 176 were not voluntarily limited, while 285 were so limited, the cause of the voluntary limitation being health

[1] From an article printed in the *Independent*, September 27, 1915, being the abstract of an address given at the First National Conference on Race Betterment. The writer had at that time made an extensive study of vital statistics, with special reference to birth-rates and related problems, but the collection of such statistics has been interrupted and their interpretation made difficult by the war.

in 133 cases, expense in 98 cases and various other reasons in 54 cases. Childlessness was involuntary in two thirds of the cases. In the standardized family of two children the condition was desired six times out of seven. In over one third of the 461 families the limitation was involuntary, due to infertility and other pathological causes, but if these had not obtained, voluntary limitation would have occurred later in

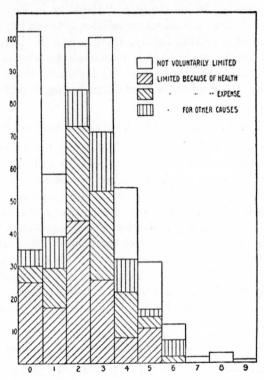

Fig. 4.—The number of families of American men of science of each size, showing the number voluntarily limited and the causes of the limitation.

nearly all cases. In seventy-one marriages prior to 1890 the average size of family including all children born was 2.9, and the limitation was voluntary in forty-eight per cent of the cases. In the decade of the 80's with 132 marriages the size of the family was 2.6, and the limitation was voluntary in sixty-four per cent of the cases. For 198 marriages contracted in the 90's, when no more children will be born, the average size of family was 2.0, and the limitation is voluntary in seventy per cent of the cases.

Neither the prevalence of the voluntary limitation of the size of family, nor the fact that the size of family is limited directly or indirectly through infertility or ill-health in more than three fourths of the cases, can be regarded with satisfaction. It is indeed evident that a limitation of the number of offspring was an essential condition of the evolution of a higher race and of the civilization to which it has attained. It might be as undesirable and be made as illegal for a man to have six children as to have two wives. But we are playing with edged tools when we substitute rationalism for fundamental instincts. In practise the family is not voluntarily limited for the welfare of the race, but to avoid risk and ill-health—real or fancied—expense and inconvenience, and to give the individual child greater advantages. There seem to be no existing conditions which will check the decreasing birth rate, while there are powerful forces tending to its decline below the danger point of the death rate.

23

THE ORDER OF SCIENTIFIC MERIT

Printed in *Science*, 46 : 541–547, 1922. Appears also in American Men of Science: A Directory, Fourth Edition, 1111–1117, 1927, under the title "The Order of Scientific Men and the Validity of Votes."

In selecting groups of one thousand American men of science for statistical study in 1903 and 1909, the workers in each of twelve sciences were arranged in the order of merit for their work by ten of their leading colleagues.[1] The average positions gave the order, and, as there were ten observations of the position of each individual, its probable error could be calculated.

As the writer of this paper is a psychologist and the ultimate object of the work is the study of behavior with a view to advancing scientific research, the psychologists may be used for illustrations of method. William James was placed first in 1903 by the independent judgment of each of the ten observers. The psychologist who stood second had an average position of 3.7 with a probable error of 0.5, the chances are even that his position was between 3.2 and 4.2. The psychologists who stood third, fourth and fifth were assigned, respectively, positions of 4.0, 4.4 and 7.5, with probable errors of 0.5, 0.6 and 1.0. It follows that the relative order of Nos. II, III and IV is not determined definitely, whereas the chances are some 10,000 to 1 that each of these stood below No. I and above No. V. The probable errors increase in size as the work of the men becomes less significant; it is on the average 0.65 places for the first ten of the fifty psychologists and 10.7 places for the last ten. Consequently No. XL on the list would have about one chance in four of falling out of the group of fifty, if the number participating in the arrangement had been very large.

The figures determine not only the validity of the positions, but also the differences in scientific merit among the psychologists, these varying inversely as the probable errors. As men who are about 6 ft. 2 in. tall are likely to differ from each other about ten times as much as men who are about 5 ft. 8 in. tall, so the more distinguished scientific men at the top of the list differ from each other about ten times as much as those toward the bottom, and a unit can be adopted for

[1] SCIENCE, November 23, November 30 and December 6, 1906, "American Men of Science," The Science Press, 1910.

measuring the differences. This method for converting relative positions into degrees of quantitative differences, which was first used by the writer[1] to measure subjective differences in the intensity of lights has proved to be of wide application.

For a third selection of our thousand leading men of science it seemed desirable, in order to avoid the inbreeding that might occur through selection by a limited group, to obtain a general vote from those competent, and, as before, the new methodological problems have proved to be of interest. The validity of votes appears not to have been considered, yet the problem is wide-reaching and is closely related to the drawing of balls from an urn, which has largely occupied students of the theory of probabilities.

If, for example, the council of the American Psychological Association, which consists of eight members, decides without consultation in favor of a given measure by a vote of 6 to 2, how likely is this to represent the majority opinion of the 432 members? We do not know the distribution of this "population," but if from an urn containing 216 white and 216 black balls, 8 are drawn, the chances are about one in nine that 6 will be white and about one in seven that 6 or more will be white. These may be regarded as approximately the chances that when the membership is about evenly divided a vote of that character will be obtained from the council; and on this basis the desirability of a plebiscite vote may be decided.

In 1916 Mr. Wilson was elected president by the vote in California, which was in his favor by 466,300 to 462,394, giving him a majority of 3,906. It might be supposed that this small majority would readily have been reversed by an indefinitely large electorate, but if the population were equally divided this would probably occur only once if an election were held every day for a hundred years.

If the members of a jury reached their decision without consultation and stood eleven to one for conviction, many would conclude that the chances are eleven to one that the defendant is guilty. As a matter of fact if the total population is divided in the same ratio and the legal fiction is followed that a man is proved guilty or innocent only by unanimous vote of twelve peers, the chance of obtaining a jury which without consultation will be unanimous for conviction are about one in three, of obtaining a jury unanimous for acquittal, only one in many billions. The practise of the courts must ultimately adjust itself to such conditions, and learn whether the unanimous vote of three or

[1] *Philosophische Studien*, 1902. See also "Studies by the Method of Relative Position," H. L. Hollingworth, in "The Psychological Researches of James McKeen Cattell," a review by some of his pupils, on the occasion of the twenty-fifth anniversary of his professorship. New York, 1914.

five jurymen without consultation is more or less valid than the unanimous vote of twelve after consultation. It must be decided on what probabilities a man shall be convicted and to what extent the chances of innocence shall be considered in imposing sentence.

When our rulers are selected and their legislation is determined by votes, it seems strange that knowledge concerning the variable and constant errors is so completely lacking. A decision of the supreme court, which may involve the welfare of hundreds of thousands of children or taxation amounting to billions of dollars, is equally binding whether the vote is unanimous or by a majority of one. It would apparently be as reasonable to require a three fourths vote of the supreme court to invalidate a law passed by both houses of the congress and signed by the president, as to require a unanimous vote of a jury to award petty damages.

The method of voting used to select scientific men might have useful applications in industry. For example, if a bank employs 100 clerks, some of whom will be promoted from time to time, all of them might be asked to check the fifty per cent and the five per cent most deserving of promotion. From the records an order of merit for promotion would be obtained, together with the relative value of the men to the bank and the salaries deserved. The data would also throw light on those voting, for the value of the judgment of each is measured by its departure from the average; if any were prejudiced or unfair in their treatment of friends or rivals this would be discovered. The combined judgment of associates is probably a more valid method of selection than the choice of a superior and would presumably lead to better service.

In like manner a group of factory workers or of laboring men might select a boss or leader by vote. If the employer would agree to take one of the five men receiving the most votes, the employees would understand and probably approve the method. Not only would a good selection free from favoritism be made, but the men would share in the control of their work and would be more loyal and more efficient.

The writer has proposed a compromise between the competitive and the semi-communistic systems for payment of the salaries of university professors, according to which, say, five super-professorships with relatively large salaries and large freedom should be established. The difficulty under our present method is that the appointments would be by favor of the administration. If, however, a vote of the teachers in the university, and perhaps of the students, were taken on the basis of desert for research, teaching and service, a method of selection would be used probably more accurate than the choice of the president and at the same time more conducive to cooperation and goodwill.

In the selection by votes of one thousand scientific men the same number for each of the twelve sciences was retained as in the two previous studies, this being nearly proportional to the total number of workers in each science. In the first edition of "American Men of Science" there were listed about 4,000 scientific men, in the second edition about 5,500, and in the present edition, published some fifteen years after the first, the number is about 9,600. The present writer was in 1888 the only professor of psychology in the world. The number

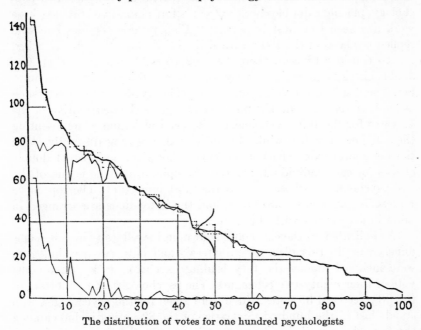

The distribution of votes for one hundred psychologists

of members of the American Psychological Association, which has a professional qualification, increased from 127 in 1903, when the first selection was made, to 432 in 1920. The average number of doctorates conferred in psychology during the five years prior to 1903 was 12.6; it was 40 in 1920. Competition for inclusion among our fifty leading psychologists or among our thousand leading men of science is thus much more severe at present than was the case when the selections were first made. There are now about 500 working psychologists and about 10,000 scientific men in the United States; the present selection consists approximately of those who form in each science the upper tenth in merit of their work.

In the case of the psychologists, here used as an example, those in the two earlier groups of fifty (except five no longer occupied with psychology or no longer residents of the United States), numbering 48, were asked to send the names of 10 or a smaller number of others whose work warranted their inclusion in such a group. Then those who received two or more nominations were in like manner asked to propose 10 or fewer names. The 52 who received the most votes were added to the original 48 to form a group of 100. These names were placed in alphabetical order on a list, which was sent to them all, with the request to "check ($\sqrt{}$) about 50 (namely, about one half) of the names to indicate those who have done the best work in psychology, placing a double check ($\sqrt{}\sqrt{}$) before about five of those whose work has been the most important." Eighty-three (besides one who replied too late) of the 100 returned the blank and, as each was asked not to consider himself, there were 82 votes. When more than five double checks were assigned they were weighted inversely as the number. The result of the votes can be conveniently shown by curves such as are here reproduced. The middle curve gives the distribution of the 82 votes for the 100 psychologists, the vertical ordinates representing the number of votes, while the individuals are ranged serially along the horizontal axis. The bottom curve shows the number of double checks for each individual, namely, the opinion that he is one of the five psychologists whose work is the most important. The top curve represents the sum of two votes, and the individuals are arranged in order in accordance with this vote.[1]

As indicated on the curve and shown on the tables (which it seems unnecessary in this place to print) two and only two psychologists were included among the fifty leading psychologists by unanimous vote of their eighty-two colleagues. The psychologist at the bottom of the fifty received 35 votes; three were given for the psychologist who stands last in the hundred. Sixty-two of the 82 voting include among the five whose work has been most important the two psychologists who received a unanimous vote for inclusion among the fifty and 20 do not. Such differences in judgment are legitimate and significant.

[1] Similar results have been obtained in each of the twelve sciences, the number of scientific men ranging from 175 chemists to 20 anthropologists. The returns, however, were most complete for psychology, the writer being personally acquainted with nearly all psychologists and a second request having been sent to those who did not reply to the first. There were in all some 130,000 votes to be collected, counted and tabulated. For the treatment of this material I am mainly indebted to my daughter, Miss Psyche Cattell. Dr. Dean R. Brimhall and Dr. Alexander Weinstein have also assisted in the revision of the material and in the computations.

I am under very great obligations to Professor Raymond L. Pearl, of the Johns Hopkins University, and to Professor H. L. Rietz, of the State University of Iowa, for their kindness in reading the manuscript of the paper and for the useful suggestions that they have made. This acknowledgment should not, of course, be construed as involving responsibility on their part.

Thus the psychologist placed eleventh is held by 22 of his colleagues to belong to the first five and by 21 not to belong to the group of 50, and similar conditions obtained for the one placed twentieth. The names could be guessed by one familiar with the situation. They are men of distinction whose more important work is by some judged not to fall within the field of psychology.

The attitude of those voting is of scientific significance, for it measures the validity of judgments. If we assume the average judgment of the 82 psychologists to be nearly correct, the departure from this average measures the competence of the individuals to form such judgments. There do not appear to be group differences dependent on distinction or age, but individuals, as shown in the previous study, differ in the ratio of about two to one. There will be an extraordinary change in our attitude toward political, social and business problems when we learn to look upon our observations, recollections, beliefs and judgments objectively, measuring the probability of their correctness and assigning probable errors to them.

The top curve represents the sum of the two votes and the order there given is the one used. A different weighting of the two votes would not considerably affect the order. The vote for the five leading psychologists in the main discriminates only the positions of the men in the upper quartile. In place of the double vote for the five and the fifty per cent of the 100 psychologists whose work has the most merit, a satisfactory distribution might be obtained by a vote for 25, or one fourth of the whole number. In view of the constant use of votes for elections and decisions, the problems involved deserve more complete investigation.

A probable error can be found for the positions of the individuals by a method that was apparently first used by the present writer. When eighty of those voting are divided into ten groups of eight each, we have the separate votes of each of these groups and from their variation the probable error of the average vote can be calculated. Thus the psychologist No. L, in the ten groups of eight votes each received, respectively, 4, 4, 2, 1, 4, 7, 4, 3, 2, and 2 votes. The probable error is 0.363, and for the group of eighty votes it is 3.63. The position on the curve assigned by each of the small groups can also be found and a probable error calculated from these ten positions.

The probable errors based on 80 votes (as a rule for each fifth individual) are indicated by the broken vertical line on the curve and when referred to the order of merit by the broken horizontal lines. The probable errors of the votes of the five psychologists last in the fifty are, respectively, 3.4, 2.8, 2.8, 3.1 and 3.6 an average of 3.14. The curve from No. X to No. C is nearly a straight line, the vote decreasing from 79 for No. *X* to 3 for No. *C*. Consequently the probable error of the vote when referred to the order is increased by about one sixth. The probable error of position at the bottom of the group of fifty is 3.6; there are thus only three or four for whom there would be as much as one chance in four of being dropped from the list if the arrangement were made by an indefinitely large electorate of the same character.

In the first study of the psychologists, the probable error at the lower end of the fifty was 10.7, that is, there were 10 or 11 for whom there was one chance in four that they should not be included on the list. There were then ten arrangements in order of merit; now there are eighty votes. The probable error decreases as the square root of the number of observations, and the probable errors in the two cases, other things being equal, should be about as 3:1, which is in fact almost exactly the case. The probable error of a single vote for the psychologists low in the group of fifty at the present time is thus the same as by order of merit in the group of 1903.

In the first study, however, we were concerned with the upper quartile, and we are now concerned with the upper decile of the group of American psychologists. If we assume distributions in accordance with the curve of error, the men who now stand at the bottom of the fifty in the present selection will be as able as those who stood about twenty in the first arrangement. An examination of the relative positions of the individuals who are in each of the two arrangements indicates that this tends to be the case. The probable error at the bottom of the fifty selected by votes should be in the neighborhood of those who stood about twenty in the first arrangements. This would make a single vote one half as valid (the ratio of the probable errors in the first arrangement for those near the bottom of the fourth hundred and in the tenth hundred of the thousand being 64:125) as a single judgment of order of merit. The figures given should, however, be regarded as indications of method rather than as exact determinations, for they are subject to various errors.

The average position of the survivors of the first group of psychologists in the arrangement of 1903 was (after deaths have been eliminated) 4; it is now for the same individuals 14.8. Those in the four following groups of ten have dropped, respectively, from 11.5 to 18.1; 20 to 27.4; 29.5 to 59.2, and 39.5 to 64.9. This drop in position is on the average less than would be expected if the 10,000 scientific men of to-day are as able and have as good opportunity as the 4,000 scientific men of 1903. The inference is that as the total number increases the proportion of men of distinction decreases. This may be due to the fact that men of special ability find their level apart from the size of the group or because the scientific career attracts less able men or gives them less opportunity than formerly. Both factors are probably present; it is apparent that the situation deserves further investigation. In the previous study it was shown that in the increased competition of a five-year period, those between 40 and 44 years of age remained on the average about stationary; those below 40 gained; those above 44 lost, the loss being in direct proportion to the age.

As the work of the men becomes more important, the differences between the individuals as measured by the probable error of position become greater, the distribution corresponding in a general way to the upper end of the curve of error. In the case of the votes there are complications, for the votes for different men do not have the same weight. The ten who receive the most votes receive nearly all the votes, and in the cases of the few who do not vote for them poor judgment or an error in checking is indicated. Some votes mean that a psychologist stands first or near the top of the list, whereas others mean that he is barely included. Consequently the order and the probable errors in the case of such a vote for one half of the group do not have great validity for the upper part of the distribution. The order is obtained in a satisfactory manner by the double vote, but this introduces further complications in the probable error. In all cases of votes, we have asymmetrical distributions and skew curves. The quantitative relations should be worked out in the first instance for less complicated material than that with which we are here concerned.

In nearly all cases in which probable errors have been applied to psychological data, the determinations are more exact than common sense would presuppose. Thus the writer found[1] that in grading traits of character by ten individuals on a scale of 100, a position was assigned with probable errors varying from 4.6 for physical health and cheerfulness to 3 for originality and efficiency. All other traits, such as energy, courage, judgment and integrity, were assigned positions with intermediate probable errors, the average being 4, which is nearly the same as the probable error of position as determined by 80 votes of the psychologists near the middle of the 100 in order of merit.

The comparatively small probable errors appear to be due to the fact that there are constant errors which affect the whole group. The psychologists who vote are subject to the same kind of influences, not making in fact independent judgments, but being influenced as a group by the knowledge of what others think and by all sorts of conditions, conventions and restrictions. If a similar vote were taken ten years hence the work of the same psychologists would be viewed from

[1] Address of the president of the American Society of Naturalists, SCIENCE April 10, 1903.

new standpoints and the positions would change to a much greater degree than the probable errors warrant. "Constant" errors are in fact more inconstant and variable than "variable" errors.

In the case of a vote (as in any series of measurements) there are two factors entering into the probable error, one dependent on the quantitative conditions prescribed in advance, the other on the behavior of the individuals. The former may be called the deductive probable error and when the latter is determined by experiment and added to it the whole is the inductive or actual probable error. Thus, if from an indefinitely large number of balls equally distributed between black and white, some are drawn, the most frequent distribution will be an equal number of black and white, but the average departure from equality will increase as the square root of the number drawn and the ratio of departure from equality will decrease as the square root of the number.

If large numbers of white and black balls are distributed in the ratio of 33 white to 47 black, and we draw 80 balls, the most probable number of white balls will be 33. The standard deviation from 33 in a large number of draws will be 4.40, and the quartile deviation or probable error will be 2.97; that is, in one case out of four there will be more than three white balls. The psychologist at the bottom of the fifty received 33 votes out of a possible 80. If an indefinitely large number of psychologists were distributed in this ratio the deductive probable error or error of sampling would be 2.97. The actual probable error, namely, 3.63, is composed of (the square root of the sum of the squares of the two) this deductive probable error and an error or deviation due to the groupings of the psychologists into different "species" with different points of view. The psychologists who stood XIL had a probable error of 3.1. The deductive probable errors are approximately the same for the two individuals, but it is more difficult to form a judgment regarding No. L than regarding No. XIL.[1]

The situation may be illustrated by an instance of general importance. Death rates, birth rates and marriage rates are continually used, but always without probable errors. Thus, for example, the Bureau of the Census issues weekly a bulletin that contains the death rates of the leading cities of the United States, but the figures have no meaning because one does not know whether the different rates are due to chance fluctuations with a limited population or to causes such

---

[1] In these cases the actual and the deductive probable errors have probable errors of the order of magnitude of the differences between them, and these differences have only moderate validity. The writer has purposely "not minded his p's and his q's," for it seems that equations are not becoming to one who is not a mathematician.

as a large proportion of infants or an epidemic of influenza.[1] If the average death rate is 12 per thousand, in a city of 100,000 population there will be about 23 deaths in a week. If black and white balls in indefinitely large numbers are distributed in the ratio of 23 black to 99.977 white and 100,000 are drawn, the most probable number of black balls is 23, but one time in four there will be more than 27. Thus the recorded death rate for a week for a city of 100,000 will normally fluctuate. If it is on the average 12, it will in half the weeks be approximately either as large as 15 or as small as 9.

If the death rate exceeds 15 in two consecutive weeks then the chances are fifteen out of sixteen that it is due to some cause such as an epidemic. The conditions are obviously of practical importance for physicians and health officers. The situation for death rates is nicely illustrated by the illustration that has been used of the distribution of black and white balls in an urn. If the population of the country were 100,000,000 and the death rate were 12 (as it should be, but is not), then 1,200,000 people would die during a year. Among 100,000,-000 black and white balls there are 1,200,000 black. But if we draw 100,000 (*i.e.*, take a town of that population) there will be a chance fluctuation as described above. It is also the case that the balls are not completely mixed, there being more black balls in some part of the urn than others. In some places we shall draw a larger proportion of black balls. When there is a negro population or a tenement house population or a large population of very young or very old people, there are relatively more black balls. There are temporarily more black balls in one place when there is an epidemic or the like. In that case we have the analogy of the black balls attracting one another.

This paper has been written to explain the methods used to select the thousand leading American men of science by votes. The psychologists have been taken as an example; if space and time permitted tables and curves might be given for the other sciences and a study of the data might yield results of interest. Such treatment must, however, be postponed or left to others. The object of the present paper will be accomplished if it makes clear that the scientific men have been selected and placed in the order of merit for their work by valid objective methods and that the methods used have wide application. In a subsequent paper the distribution of the scientific men will be considered with special reference to the changes that have occurred in the course of ten years.

[1] In the last report received (for the week ending September 2, 1922) the death rate of New Haven is given as 5.8 and of Houston as 13.9. In the same week a year ago the death rate of New Haven was 10 and of Houston 7.6. Without probable errors these figures give no useful information in regard to the conditions in the two cities.

24

THE SCIENTIFIC MEN OF THE WORLD

Printed in the Scientific Monthly, 23: 468–471, 1927. It appeared also in "American Men of Science: A Directory," Fourth Edition, 1130–1132, 1927.

There has for a long time been planned a study of the scientific men of the world on the lines of the statistical work on American men of science. International directories in the several sciences were taken up, those in psychology and zoology having been partly prepared, the latter in cooperation with Professor T. D. A. Cockerell. In connection with the third edition of the Biographical Directory of American Men of Science it was proposed to select by objective methods the thousand leading scientific men of the world. With such a list it would be possible to determine among other things the value of the contributions of each country to each science, both in quantity of work accomplished and in fundamental advances.

In order to obtain preliminary data I wrote in June, 1914, to the scientific academies of different countries asking for their membership lists. These were mailed from most of the German and other academies after war had begun. It was obviously impossible to continue the work at that time; it was indeed necessary to postpone the preparation of the third edition of American Men of Science. We have scarcely yet reached a situation where international cooperation and unprejudiced judgments are feasible; but the methods used enable us to measure validity of judgments and prejudice, so that the study might at the present time be of special interest from that point of view. We could, for example, measure the normal distortion of judgment through nationality, its excessive manifestation during war and its subsequent waning.

In connection with the study begun some years ago I counted up the scientific men of different countries in "Who's Who in Science," edited by H. H. Stephenson and published in England by Churchill. There has been no edition of the book since 1914, and the figures just before the war are no longer valid, but they have sufficient interest to warrant their publication, more especially in view of the recent widely quoted remark by Secretary Hoover to the effect that the United States is behind most European countries in its contributions to pure science and the statement of the National Research Endowment of the National Academy of Sciences to the effect that "the United

THE DISTRIBUTION OF SCIENTIFIC MEN ACCORDING TO "WHO'S WHO IN SCIENCE," 1914

	Medicine. Surgery	Chemistry	Engineering	Zoology	Mathematics	Geology. Mineralogy	Physics	Botany	Physiology. Pharmacology	Astronomy. Meteorology	Pathology	Anatomy	Agriculture. Forestry	Psychology	Geography	Anthropology	Total	Per million ca. 1860	Per million ca. 1920
United States	206	245	201	184	126	135	131	114	86	75	69	54	76	95	18	30	1845	58.7	17.4
Great Britain	252	295	349	118	86	90	104	78	53	64	51	37	59	30	42	21	1729	59.4	36.6
Germany	221	144	128	90	115	93	104	75	59	63	39	53	48	37	44	21	1334	35.0	22.3
France	109	52	23	32	32	27	39	16	33	16	39	24	8	12	16	16	504	13.7	12.3
Austria-Hungary	67	56	42	27	39	31	40	21	24	22	22	31	7	14	18	16	467	13.5	8.8
Asia	40	39	47	16	9	9	14	21	16	14	6	8	21	3	0	0	269		6.3
Italy	37	17	8	13	29	18	18	11	16	14	21	11	1	12	16	5	246	9.8	6.3
Switzerland	38	26	13	16	19	12	9	11	15	5	13	9	6	10	9	4	215	86.0	55.1
Norway	34	15	21	18	9	14	9	10	8	7	3	3	8	6	3	2	170	106.2	65.4
Holland	18	14	3	39	9	8	12	10	13	7	9	6	0	6	4	1	159	48.2	23.4
Canada	16	18	19	9	7	29	13	5	7	6	6	3	7	2	1	5	153	45.0	17.4
Australasia	12	11	30	10	10	19	8	8	4	8	2	4	10	3	1	3	145	120.0	19.4
Russia	19	17	10	12	12	10	9	9	5	8	7	8	0	6	3	3	136	2.0	1.3
Sweden	20	17	6	10	8	9	5	11	6	8	2	9	0	4	7	2	124	32.6	21.0
Denmark	11	11	14	9	7	4	3	9	8	3	4	4	4	2	4	0	97	60.6	29.4
Belgium	20	9	7	8	6	3	3	5	7	2	10	4	0	2	3	1	90	19.1	12.0
Africa	11	4	15	11	4	8	2	8	1	0	2	1	8	0	1	0	88		2.7
Spain	6	7	1	4	2	4	5	1	2	5	7	6	0	2	1	3	58	3.7	7.8
S. & C. America	5	2	3	5	7	8	2	3	1	10	3	0	3	2	1	2	52		
Portugal	6	2	1	3		4	4	3	3	1	4	4	0	2	2	1	47	13.0	7.8
Bulgaria	0	3	0	3	2	2	1	1	0	1	0	0	0	0	0	1	14	7.0	2.8
Roumania	0	0	0	1	2	0	1	0	1	1	0	1	0	0	0	0	8	2.9	.5
Greece	0	1	0	0	0	0	0	0	0	1	0	0	0	0	0	0	2	1.8	.4
Servia	0	0	0	0	1	0	0	0	0	0	0	0	0	0	0	0	2	2.0	.2
Malta	0	0	0	0	0	0	0	0	1	0	0	0	0	0	0	0	1	7.1	4.4
Total	1158	1006	941	638	546	537	536	429	369	351	320	280	266	250	201	127	7955		
U. S. per cent	.18	.24	.21	.29	.23	.25	.24	.27	.23	.21	.22	.19	.29	.38	.08	.24	.23		

States, which already occupies a leading position in industrial researches, should rank with the most enlightened nations in the advancement of pure science."

The scientific men whose biographies are included in "Who's Who in Science" and whose numbers are given in the table were probably selected somewhat at random, those of Great Britain and its colonial empire being the most completely represented and the United States coming next. Perhaps 800 from Great Britain and 1,200 from the United States would be a fairer basis for comparison with other countries than the 1,729 given from the former and the 1,845 from the latter. In that case Germany would be in the lead. The numbers from the non-English speaking nations may be regarded as comparable, though they doubtless vary with the sources of information.

If we take the figures as they stand, the United States, Great Britain and Germany were in 1914 far in advance of other nations in the numbers of their scientific men. France had 504, as compared with 1,334 from Germany; the then Austria-Hungary with 467 was nearly equal to France; Italy had 246. There then follow Switzerland with 215, Norway with 170 and Holland with 159. Sweden with 170 and Denmark 97.

According to the figures in the table referring to the several sciences, the United States stands higher in the so-called pure sciences than in medicine and engineering. We indeed stand first in all the natural and exact sciences except chemistry (largely an applied science) and geography. It is naturally gratifying to the present writer that psychology is the science in which we are most decidedly in the lead. We have 95 of the world's leading psychologists as compared with 30 in Great Britain, 37 in Germany and 12 in France. Geography is the science in which we are most deficient, 18 geographers being attributed to the United States, as compared with 44 to Germany and 42 to Great Britain. After psychology we are strongest in zoology, botany, agriculture and geology. This is what I guessed in a preceding discussion[1] of the subject, but I then added astronomy to psychology, zoology, botany and geology as the subjects in which we were probably in the van. The sciences in which we make relatively the poorest showing in the table, apart from the applied sciences and geography, are anatomy and astronomy. The differences in the percentages for the different sciences are, however, not large and would probably fall within the probable errors of sampling if these could be determined.

The figures in the table relate to a period preceding 1914. They do not have great validity even for that time, and the years that have since elapsed have been significant for international changes. The edition of American Men of Science published in 1910 contains about

[1] "Scientific Research in the United States," *Science*, February 12, 1926.

5,500 biographies of those who are supposed to have made contributions to science, the edition now in course of preparation will contain in the neighborhood of 15,000. The increase may to some extent be due to more complete representation, but in the main it measures the increase in the number of scientific workers. They have probably about doubled since the data were compiled for "Who's Who in Science." The increase has been much less elsewhere; indeed there may have been none in some nations, such as France and Italy. With the possible exception of Germany the United States is now far in advance of every other nation in the number of its scientific men and in the number of its contributions to science.

It does not follow that the number of great men of science and the significant contributions are proportional to the total number of workers and the total amount of publication, although this is perhaps the most probable situation if there is no information to the contary. It seems that England and ancient Greece have produced more than their share of the greatest men and this was indeed found to be the case in my study of the eminent men in the world's history.[1] It may be that at the present time Holland with 12 physicists attributed to it is making more important contributions to that science than the United States with 131. In psychology, which is the only subject on which I can speak with adequate information, we appear to lead in importance as well as in quantity of work.

In the last two columns of the table are given the numbers of scientific men in proportion to the populations of the different countries. The first column gives the numbers per million in 1860, which was about the average time at which they were born; the second column gives the numbers in relation to the present populations. In France, with a nearly stationary population, the figures in the two columns are of course nearly the same. In the United States and the British Dominions, with rapidly increasing populations, the proportion is much smaller in relation to the existing population than to the birth rate. For a given stock and civilization, if scientific productivity were wholly due to the innate constitution of the individual, the numbers should be proportional to the population at the time of their birth; if wholly due to opportunity it should be proportional to the existing population. An adequate study might contribute toward the solution of this problem.

Taking either the one figure or the other in the table, it is obvious that while in total productivity we may surpass every other nation, this is far from being the case in proportion to our population. This situation is still less creditable to us when wealth and opportunities

---

[1] "A Statistical Study of Eminent Men," *The Popular Science Monthly*, February, 1903.

for higher education are taken into consideration. It should, however, be noted that the lower figures can be attributed in part to the large Negro and immigrant populations and to an unproductive South. Our scientific men appear now to be increasing about four times as rapidly as the population, and the figures in the table have for this and other reasons (including redistribution of populations after the war) only a limited application. When allowance is made for disturbing factors, the number of scientific men of standing in proportion to the present population appears to be nearly the same in the United States, Great Britain and Germany, about half as large in France and a quarter as large in Italy. Norway and Switzerland have by far the largest proportion, followed among the smaller nations by Denmark, Holland and Sweden. I should have expected Holland to stand first, and it may, for the figures collected from the book have inconsiderable validity.

The greater relative productivity of the smaller cultural nations in science—the same situation probably holding in literature and in art—is a matter of considerable interest. It goes back to the Greek democracies and to the Italian states of the renaissance. In this country we had a local development in Massachusetts and Connecticut, in which, according to my statistics, the birth rate per million population of scientific men more highly selected than those on the international list was 109 and 87, respectively. If these figures are increased to make up for the number of scientific men given in the table, they become, respectively, 201 and 160, a much larger birth rate of scientific men than that of any foreign nation. It is probable that a similar situation now holds in California and in parts of the central west.

We apparently need regional cultivation of special fields with a group and a community interest in the work. The situation is difficult for with the increasing complexity of science and in our existing competitive system there must be support of research through taxation or gifts. But control from Washington, whether by the national government, or by a group of men who administer philanthropic funds, may do more to suppress research than to forward it, the rarer flowers of genius being particularly apt to wither when frost and sunlight are artificially controlled.

We are so ignorant of the causes of scientific productivity that it is possible for Galton to attribute it almost wholly to heredity in superior lines of descent, for Odin to claim that genius is in things, not in men. Yet it is a subject of fundamental importance both from the point of view of constructive science and for the applications of science to human welfare. The field is nearly untilled and for that very reason may prove to be fertile.

25

THE ORIGIN AND DISTRIBUTION OF SCIENTIFIC MEN

Printed in *Science*, **66**: 513–516. 1927.

The fourth edition of the Biographical Directory of American Men of Science, which will be published in December, contains an appendix describing the methods that were used to select the scientific men who are designated in the book as those whose contributions to science have been of the greatest value. There were added in the third and fourth editions (1921 and 1927) 601 names to the thousand first selected in 1903 and reselected in 1909. In the book there will be given a statistical study of the origin and distribution of these scientific men, and it may be worth while to print in SCIENCE some of the data.

In the production of the 601 scientific men New York leads with 67, followed by Ohio with 49, Massachusetts with 48, Illinois with 45 and Pennsylvania with 41. The group of states next following consists of Iowa 27, Wisconsin 24, Missouri 21. The position of the North Central States is noteworthy, and is further emphasized by the situation in states having a productivity between 10 and 20, namely, Indiana 18, Connecticut 16, Minnesota 14, Maryland 13, Michigan 13, California 11, Kansas 11. The number of scientific men coming from the South Atlantic, South Central and Western divisions is small, though there has been some gain since 1903.

Of the leading thousand scientific men selected in 1903, Massachusetts produced 134 and Connecticut 40. At the time of their birth Boston was the intellectual center of the country. New York in proportion to its population had then produced about half as many scientific men as Massachusetts and Connecticut, the North Central States about one third as many. The situation had changed for the list of 1910. Reduced to comparable figures the birth rate of leading scientific men per million of population had fallen in Massachusetts from 109 to 85, in Connecticut from 87 to 57. In Michigan it had increased from 37 to 74, in Minnesota from 23 to 59, in Wisconsin from 45 to 54. The intellectual fecundity of the North Central States, as compared with New England, has now further increased, extending westward and southward to Iowa, Missouri and Kansas.

If the 601 scientific men are increased to 1,000 proportionately distributed, which is approximately the result that would have been obtained if 1,000 had been selected, the gains or losses of each state may be found. The situation in New England is ominous for the future. Every state has lost and it appears that the rural population is becoming intellectually sterile. Of the thousand leading scientific men in 1903, Maine had produced 29, of whom 19 ranked in the first 500. Of 601 scientific men mostly born less than 50 years ago, the state has produced six; if a thousand had been selected the most probable number would have been ten. It has consequently lost 19, two thirds of its productivity. Massachusetts has lost 54. Analogous conditions obtain in all the New England States and southward along the Atlantic. The losses of New York, New Jersey and Maryland, in spite of, or it may be because of, their enormous increase in wealth, are startling. Pennsylvania and Delaware remain nearly stationary; there are small gains in most of the South Atlantic and South Central States.

The losses of the eastern states are counter-balanced by the gains of the central states, notably Illinois, Minnesota, Iowa, Missouri, Kansas and Nebraska. All the central states have gained except Michigan, though the gains in Ohio and Indiana are small. These three are the most eastern of the states and appear to be following in the wake of the Atlantic seaboard. Further to the west there tend to be moderate gains which predict a large future development. So indeed westward does the course of science take its way, but it is not gratifying if the eastern states do not equal the cultural nations of Europe before losing their leadership. This may indicate a waning of the world's great era in science.

Ten of the scientific men on the list of 1921 have died, giving an annual death rate of 4.7 per thousand, which is about normal for men of that age. Of the 591 remaining on the lists of 1921 and 1927, 122 live in New York, 57 in Massachusetts, 52 in Illinois and 47 in California. If the numbers are increased to 1,000 and proportionately distributed, it appears that in comparison with the thousand of 1906 Massachusetts has lost 49, whereas Illinois has gained 24 and California 23. Every New England state, as also New Jersey, Maryland, Virginia and North Carolina, have a smaller proportion of these leading scientific men than they had 21 years ago. New York has gained 11; Pennsylvania has lost two. Next to Illinois and California, Minnesota has the largest gain. The smaller gains or losses in other states show the real situation at the time and are significant, especially in view of the grouping by regions.

When we compare the birth places and residences we find that New York has acquired 55 more of the scientific men than it has produced, the individuals of course not always being the same. Massachusetts has gained 9, Connecticut 4, New Jersey 10 and Maryland

10, these representing men called to the universities. Illinois for the same reason has gained 7, Michigan 5 and Minnesota 4. In the other central states the loss has been large. One hundred and sixty, more than one fourth, of the scientific men were born in them and only 55 reside there. There are but few scientific men born in Washington while many are employed in that city by the government. Of the new group, three were born in the District of Columbia and 76 reside there. Eighty-six of the scientific men were born abroad, so they more than supply the excess in Washington and the balance remains nearly even for the different states.

In 1906 one half (501/1,000) of the leading scientific men of the United States resided in the North Atlantic States and somewhat more than one half (518/993) had been born there. In the short period of 26 years the proportion of those born in these states has fallen to one third (200/598) and the percentage of those residing there to 44.5 per cent (263/591). The cities of the eastern seaboard depend in large measure on Europe for their population, on the central west for their wealth and for their leaders. They will face a difficult situation when immigration is nearly cut off and centers of wealth and culture develop toward the west. It might be supposed that as wealth increases in the hands of a plutocracy, so scientific and other culture would increase in its centers. There has obviously been no change in native ability in the course of a few years. The only suggestion here made is that the state universities and denominational colleges of the central and western states are more nearly in touch with the people than the privately controlled universities of the east and have proved to be the better agencies for the selection and training of those having ability and ideal interests.

The eastern universities provide education for more men who become leaders in science than the states produce. As American students formerly went to Germany for advanced work, so in a later period they tended to congregate in the endowed universities of the Atlantic seaboard. The first degree of doctor of philosophy in the United States was given by Yale University in 1861, the first scientific man to receive it being Josiah Willard Gibbs in 1863. Prior to 1876, Yale had given 18 doctorates in the sciences, Harvard 4, Columbia and Cornell 2 each. Then was established the Johns Hopkins University, opening a new era of higher education and scientific research in the United States. In the following 20 years the Johns Hopkins conferred 179 doctorates in the sciences and 84 of the recipients (some had died) were on the list of 1,000 scientific men of 1910. During this period Columbia conferred 67 such degrees, Harvard 66, Yale 56, Cornell 33,

Pennsylvania 22, Clark (opened in 1888) 21, Chicago (opened in 1892) 8, all other universities 66.[1]

Up to and including 1910, the universities of the United States had conferred 2,513 doctorates for work in the sciences, the distribution being: Johns Hopkins 434, Chicago 276, Yale 271, Columbia 268, Harvard 267, Cornell 222, Pennsylvania 172, Clark 150, all others 453. Thus eight endowed universities awarded more than four fifths of these degrees. In 1926 according to data compiled for the National Research Council by Callie Hull and Clarence J. West there were 740 doctorates conferred in the sciences, the numbers for the leading institutions being: Chicago 78, Wisconsin 53, Johns Hopkins 50, Columbia 49, Illinois 44, Cornell 43, California 38, Yale 38, Harvard 35, Washington 32, Minnesota 30, Iowa 28, Ohio State 25. Thus Chicago in the central west is far in advance of the eastern privately controlled universities and the seven eastern universities which had conferred prior to 1910 nearly three quarters of all the degrees in 1926 conferred fewer than seven state universities of the north central states and California.

Of the institutions from which the 601 scientific men received their degrees, Harvard with 41 bachelors, 62 doctors of philosophy and three doctors of medicine, stands foremost as it did in 1903. It is, however, now surpassed by Chicago in the number of doctorates, as it was by the Johns Hopkins at the earlier period. After these three universities comes Columbia, followed by Yale, Pennsylvania, Cornell and California. The institutions whose graduates are in the twenties are Michigan, Minnesota, Princeton and the Massachusetts Institute; ranging from 18 to 12 are Wisconsin, Stanford, Indiana, Kansas, Illinois and Ohio State. The privately endowed universities still lead in the number of scientific men for whose education they were responsible usually some twenty to twenty-five years ago. They probably do not do so for the men graduated today, but we must wait another twenty years before the figures will be at hand. Many of the 41 bachelors who received degrees from Harvard and the 15 from Columbia and from Yale went to these universities from other institutions after they had planned their careers and the influence of the eastern endowed universities in the creation of scientific men is not large. The private colleges are also losing the influence that they formerly had. In the thousand of 1906 there were 23 graduates of Princeton and of Amherst, 16 of Wesleyan, 14 of Williams, 10 of Dartmouth and of

[1] These statistics concerning doctorates in the sciences are from an unpublished study. From 1898 to 1915 there was printed each year in SCIENCE an article on doctorates conferred by American universities, including the names of the recipients and the subjects of the theses in the natural and exact sciences.

Oberlin. For the contemporary list of 601 men the numbers are: Wesleyan 8, Princeton, Dartmouth and Williams 5, Amherst 4, Oberlin 2.

Another change that can not be regarded as wholly auspicious is the small number of the younger scientific men who have studied at foreign universities. In so far as this means such advance in our own institutions that it is needless to go abroad for special work it is gratifying. But it may result in lesser devotion to the ideals of scholarship and research that had their florescence in the German university of the nineteenth century. Of the thousand of 1906, 117 had studied in Berlin, 84 in Leipzig, 69 in Göttingen, 56 in Heidelberg, and a large proportion had received degrees from these and other German universities. Of the contemporary 601 only one has a degree from Berlin, none from Leipzig. This refers, of course, to men working in the period preceding the war. Perhaps now the various systems of unattached fellowships may lead to a larger international interchange of students. Before graduate students can afford to study abroad, we must, however, find a method by which younger scientific men receive positions in accordance with their ability rather than through the influence of the professors with whom they work.

The majority of scientific men still find their careers in universities. 358.5 (the decimal here and elsewhere referring to a divided position) of the 591 men hold academic positions and in the main earn their salaries by teaching. There are 95 connected with the research institutions that are the most notable development in scientific investigation of the present century. Sixty-two are engaged in industrial work, largely in the research laboratories of the corporations, where their work is not confined to applied science and will doubtless be more and more extended to the fundamental problems whose cultivation and by-products have an economic value far beyond their cost. Such work is besides only a proper return to society for the wealth acquired by monopoly. A public service corporation such as the American Telephone and Telegraph Company, whose profits are limited only by legal regulations, could easily and properly support and give the best facilities to scientific men engaged in research in physics, chemistry, mathematics and psychology. 74.5 of the men are employed by the government. Here again the work is largely but not wholly in applied science, and here again the most beneficial use of money collected by taxation would be the support of research that of all services is the most important for the nation and for the world.

Of these scientific men 60.7 per cent hold academic positions as compared with 73.8 per cent of those in the list of 1910. It has been recognized that there has been since the war a movement of scientific men from the universities to the research and industrial laboratories and we have here a measure of its extent. If the numbers are, as above explained, increased to a thousand we find that of this younger group the universities and colleges have lost 133. The research institutions have gained 88.5; the industrial laboratories and applied science 46; the government services 14.5. There is only one who may be classed as an amateur in the present list, as compared with 18 in 1910. We have never had in America a group of men, such as was represented in England by Darwin, Galton, Rayleigh and Huggins, who devoted themselves to scientific work without occupying a scientific position. The specialization of science and democratic institutions have now led to the practical disappearance of those who contribute significantly to the advancement of science without being professionally engaged in scientific or educational work. But we now have men who are professionally engaged in research.

The figures for the separate sciences show that nearly all mathematicians are teachers. Astronomy and pathology are especially well represented in the research institutions, geology and to a lesser extent physics, botany and zoology, in the government work, physics and chemistry in the industrial laboratories and applied science.

In treating the number of scientific men connected with different institutions we are in the main concerned with the present strength of the institutions rather than with changes in distribution, so all the scientific men are included. We have 1,176 instead of 1,000 as in the earlier lists. The competition for inclusion is now, however, more severe, for the list of 1906 included about one fourth of the scientific men of the country, whereas the present list includes only about one twelfth. The figures given are consequently relative. An increase of about 17.6 per cent means that an institution has remained stationary in its relation to other institutions.

Harvard has on its faculties 89.5 of these leading scientific men and has gained 23 since 1906. Under the existing system of university administration honor should be given to Mr. Eliot and Mr. Lowell for maintaining high academic traditions. In 1906 Harvard had 66.5 of our thousand leading scientific men, Columbia 60, and Chicago 39. Now of 1,176 leading scientific men Harvard has 89.5, Chicago 53.5, and Columbia 46.5. It should also be noticed that Harvard has 21 of the younger men of the group of 250, as compared with 15 at Chicago and 7 at Columbia. Following these three universities are Yale with 42.5 and California and the Johns Hopkins bracketed with 40.5. Cornell, which comes next, has lost relatively. There then follow the three state universities, Michigan, Wisconsin, and Illinois, of which Illinois has gained the most. Next come four endowed institutions, Stanford, Pennsylvania, Princeton and the Massachusetts Institute of Technology. Washington (St. Louis) is in the same group and has the largest gain. The only other universities having ten or more of these leading scientific men are Minnesota and the Ohio State. Apart from Columbia the universities that have lost most relatively are Missouri, Wesleyan, Syracuse, New York and Virginia.

The past twenty-six years have witnessed the development of endowed research institutions and the Carnegie Institution of Washington now stands next to Harvard and Chicago in the number of its scientific men of distinction. The Rockefeller Institute, limited to medical research, has also attained a high position. In this period the Carnegie Institution has grown from 7 to 47; the Rockefeller Institute from 3 to 19. The Boyce Thompson Institute, the Wistar Institute and the Mayo Clinic also show gains. The American Museum of Natural History and the New York Botanical Garden, with respectively 13 and 8 of the scientific men, rank before most universities and show a gain since 1906. It is of interest that these institutions can flourish under support and control partly private and partly public.

The industrial laboratories of the corporations, like the endowed institutions for research, have enjoyed a notable growth which is scarcely measured by the 11 men recorded for the General Electric Company, the 10 for the Bell Laboratories and other parts of the Telephone System and the 5 for the Eastman Kodak Company. Industrial research, like advances in engineering, is not always recorded in scientific papers, and is often a cooperative undertaking for which credit is not assigned to individuals. It is, however, to be noted that the number of leading scientific men under these three corporations has greatly increased and of 26 all but three belong to the group consisting mainly of younger scientific men.

The Bureau of Standards has during the period increased the number of leading scientific men in its laboratories from 8 to 23. The Geological Survey, with 28.5, is the strongest group in a single science, but relatively it has lost ground somewhat since 1906, as has also the Department of Agriculture. The Smithsonian Institute, with its government supported subsidiaries, has remained stationary, but this means a moderate relative loss. The U. S. Public Health Service has gained and some states and municipalities are now cooperating in this work.

In the book a table is printed showing the ten strongest departments in each science and their gain or loss since 1906. Harvard shows its leadership not only as a whole but in nearly every department. It stands first among universities in physics, chemistry, geology, botany, zoology, physiology and pathology, second in mathematics, third in astronomy and psychology, fourth in anthropology. There has been a gain since 1906 in every department except anatomy and psychology, though in several cases the gains are due only to the increased number of individuals on the present list. Chicago stands first in mathematics and second in zoology. Columbia stands first in psychology, but does not in any other science have a rank higher than fifth. The U. S. Bureau of Standards leads in physics and the Bureau of Ethnology in anthropology. By a wide margin the Carnegie Institution leads in astronomy, the U. S. Geological Survey in geology, the U. S. Department of Agriculture in botany and the Rockefeller Institute in pathology.

26

THE DISTRIBUTION OF AMERICAN MEN OF SCIENCE IN 1927

Printed in "American Men of Science: A Directory." Fourth Edition, 1118–1129, 1927.

In the fourth edition of the Biographical Directory of American Men of Science it seems desirable to add stars to the subjects of research of those who since the publication of the third edition have attained positions among our thousand leading men of science. A contemporary group was also wanted for studies of changes in distribution which make possible the measurement of movements in the history of science. It may be that in the future the development of science and the economic and social changes caused by it will be seen to be more important for civilization than any political or military event.

A determination of those who should be added to the list of our thousand leading men of science was consequently made in 1926. The 250 scientific men who had the greatest claim to be included among those previously selected were found and arranged in the order of merit. The methods of selection were similar to those used in the third edition, but were simplified by not undertaking to find the positions of the new names among the old or to determine those of the earlier group who in the competition would be dropped from it.

The simpler method was used mainly for economy, including the saving of the time of the large number of scientific men who have assisted. It is further the case that the selections can be made more accurately when only the new names are considered. It is easier to decide which 25 botanists among 50 have done the best work than to make the selection of 100 from 200. The former group is not only smaller, but also more homogeneous in age and performance.

The drawbacks of the simpler method are that it does not give us a contemporary list of the thousand leading men of science and makes only an approximation to the numbers that should be added in each science. It is, however, equally correct in so far as the stars in the book are concerned, for these indicate all those who have been included in the groups of a thousand in the four selections covering a period of 23 years. It has frequently been suggested that the stars should be removed in the case of those who do not maintain their positions. This would be scientifically correct, but needlessly invidious, as would be dropping from the membership of the National Academy of Sciences those who have not maintained their positions among our 250 leaders in science.

The names of those added, each of whom is probably among the thousand leading scientific men of the United States, are distributed among the sciences in accordance with the numbers found in 1903 as roughly proportional to the total numbers of those who had published research work in each science. The proportions were only approximate and there have been changes in the activity of the different sciences in the course of the past 23 years, so certain sciences are over or under represented. A more exact distribution could now be obtained by classifying the some 13,500 entries in the fourth edition of the Biographical Directory, but these were not ready when the selections were made, and for purposes of comparison it is better to retain in each science the same numbers as in the preceding studies. It may be that there should be more or fewer than 100 botanists among our thousand leading men of science, but the 100 botanists are those who are regarded as having done the best work in that science by the most expert contemporary judgment.

It is arbitrary to divide the whole range of science into twelve separate sciences. For example, anatomy, physiology, pathology and zoology might be combined into animal biology, or zoology might be divided into entomology, ornithology, parasitology, embryology, cytology, animal genetics, animal ecology, systematic zoology, animal behavior, etc. The separation of the sciences is conventional, each representing the subjects that can be mastered by an individual and in which there are groups of workers concerned with related problems. The number of sciences increases continually with the progress of science; the most fruitful fields for research are those in which two or more of the traditional sciences are involved.

If many sciences had been taken in this classification, then there would have been much overlapping, if but few, then scientific men would not have been acquainted with the whole field. In the present study the applied sciences of medicine, engineering, agriculture and education, as such, are not included, nor are the historical, social, political and philological sciences. Geography, mineralogy, geophysics and pharmacology have no separate places, apart from geology, physics, chemistry and physiology; workers in these sciences are discriminated against. It should be remembered that Canadians, though included in the Biographical Directory, are not considered in the selection, unless they were at the time residents of the United States.

In July, 1926, a memorandum similar to the following was sent to those (with the exceptions noted) in each science who had received a place in any one of the three preceding selections. Each scientific man was asked to nominate one fifth (or fewer) of the number included in the thousand in that science. Then each of those who received two or more votes was asked to make similar nominations. The memorandum for botany reads:

MEMORANDUM

For designation in the fourth edition of the Biographical Directory of American Men of Science it is necessary to obtain the names of those who should now be included among our hundred leading botanists and thousand leading men of science. The selection can be made most accurately and objectively by those included in this group in the previous editions and it is hoped that all or most of them will assist.

Will you therefore send the names of twenty or a smaller number of botanists who should probably be added? It is expected that a certain preference shall be given to those who are working in lines similar to your own, or with whom you have been personally associated. From all lists it will be possible to obtain an objective selection of those whose subjects of research should be starred in the new edition of the book.

There may be room for question as to the desirability of such a list, but the preponderance of argument appears to be in its favor. If it is prepared, this should be done with the greatest possible care, for it is a matter of importance to those concerned. The list will also be used for further statistical studies of the distribution and work of scientific men, which was the original object of the selection.

There is enclosed a list of those included in the three previous arrangements beginning in 1902, with the exception of those who have died and several no longer active. The names and addresses are wanted of twenty other men and women living in the United States who are of nearly the same rank in their contributions to science. The individual lists will be regarded as strictly confidential.

J. McKEEN CATTELL

3939 Grand Central Terminal
New York, N. Y.
July 21, 1926

The names with the addresses of those who received the most votes in each science were then arranged in alphabetical order, the number taken being twice as many as would be added to the thousand. Thus, for example, there are 100 botanists in the thousand and 25 were to be added. There were 334 botanists nominated and the 50 who received the largest number of independent nominations were placed with their addresses in alphabetical order on the list. This was then sent to botanists included in the previous thousands and to the fifty new names on the list with the following memorandum:

MEMORANDUM

The fifty botanists on this list are those who have received the most votes for inclusion among the hundred leading botanists and the thousand leading men of science of the United States whose subjects of research will be indicated by an asterisk in the fourth edition of the Biographical Directory of American Men of Science. In order that there may be a final and authoritative vote, please be so kind as to check (√)the names of about twenty-five of those whose work in botany has been of the greatest value and return the list to J. McKeen Cattell, 3939 Grand Central Terminal, New York, N. Y.

This list is from,——————————————————————————————

TABLE I.—THE NUMBER OF THOSE IN EACH SCIENCE WHO TOOK PART IN THE SELECTION OF THE 250 SCIENTIFIC MEN, AND THE NUMBER NOMINATED, TOGETHER WITH THE NUMBER OF VOTES FOR INDIVIDUALS

	Number asked to nominate	Number nominating	Number nominated	Number asked to vote	Number of ballots	Number selected	Largest vote	Vote just selecting	Smallest vote
Mathematics.........	136	109	91	135	95	20	89	35	12
Physics..............	238	147	204	231	161	37	136	57	14
Chemistry...........	340	208	450	264	193	44	161	67	26
Astronomy..........	70	60	45	74	60	13	58	24	7
Geology.............	226	145	251	146	117	25	90	45	13
Botany..............	293	179	334	154	134	25	98	53	29
Zoology.............	348	207	402	233	183	37	114	72	25
Physiology..........	98	74	103	66	54	10	42	25	8
Anatomy............	50	47	37	55	39	6	31	19	10
Pathology..........	156	82	190	99	65	15	46	30	4
Anthropology.......	29	29	27	36	29	5	23	13	4
Psychology.........	81	70	67	79	66	13	57	32	15
Total..............	2,065	1,357	2,201	1,572	1,196	250			

In Table I there is given the number in each science of those who took part in the selection together with information in regard to the votes. Two thousand and sixty-five scientific men received the blank printed above and 1,357 sent in nominations in the different sciences of those who should finally be added to the number designated and be included among the thousand leading scientific men of the United States. The 2,065 asked to make nominations consisted of 1,058 scientific men from the previous lists of a thousand and 1,007 who received two or more votes. A reply from two thirds of those addressed is satisfactory. It is unlikely that any scientific men who should be considered would not be proposed under these conditions, and any bad judgment, prejudice or favoritism is self-eliminating.

There were in all 2,201 nominations for the 250 places. Those asked to vote in the selection numbered 1,572, which included 1,072 on the previous lists of 1,000 and the five hundred nominees who received the most votes. The ballot was returned by 1,196 with the distribution among the sciences shown in the table. The last three columns give for each science the largest vote cast for an individual, the vote that just selected for inclusion in the 250 and the vote for the individual who received the fewest votes.

Thus, for example, the memorandum was sent to 154 botanists and was returned by 134; 98 votes were cast for the botanist who received the most, 29 for the one who received the fewest. The botanist who stood lowest among those included received 53 votes, the one next following 51. It is possible by methods previously proposed to calculate the probable errors of these numbers. The calculations have not been made again as the earlier work applies approximately to this case. It seems that time is often wasted in calculating probable errors and correlations by the method of least squares when only an approximation is wanted. The distributions are such as to make the methods inexact and constant errors are much larger and more disturbing than the variable error. The probable error of position of the botanists at the bottom of the list of those included in the 25 selected is about three places and there are four botanists not on the list who would have as much as one chance in four of being included among our leading 100 botanists and 1,000 leading men of science if the electorate had been indefinitely large. They would, however, have had positions near the bottom of the list.

The methods of selection are thus accurate and the degree of accuracy can be measured. Indeed the exact determination has a certain brutality in view of the human interests involved. All those who voted have competence, though in varying degree. Thus in the first study it was found that if we assume the average result to be correct, the validity of the judgments of the different individuals varied as about 2:1. This appears to be of interest because the validity of judgments was then for the first time measured and because the range of individual differences for normal individuals in other traits, such as time of reaction, accuracy of discrimination and correctness of memory, had been found in laboratory experiments to be about the same. There was no significant difference between the average judgments of those more or less eminent in science, nor between the older and the younger men. If what we mean by judgment could be further analyzed, differences might be found; thus the more eminent and the older groups might have had more experience but less information in regard to contemporary conditions.

A distinguished mathematician argues that his judgment has greater validity than the average of the judgments of 100 mathematicians less eminent and presumably less well informed, holding that when there is a difference of opinion he is likely to be right and the group wrong. He voted for nineteen of the forty, naming four of those not selected by the majority and failing to name five of those so selected. The chances are somewhat over 4 to 1 that if he had voted for 20, he would have voted for 80 per cent of the selected list. This is in fact a satisfactory agreement, giving what the probable error would predict. The variable error would lead us to assume that the combined vote of 100 mathematicians would be about ten times as correct as the vote of one of them, which would be reduced to five times if his judgment were twice as accurate as the average of the other individuals. The majority might, however, be subject to a constant error sufficiently large to outweigh the variable error.

A plebiscite vote may have no validity when the voters are uninformed and are moved by mob emotions. Thus when Cook claimed that he had reached the North Pole, and Peary was supposed to have been ungentlemanly because he questioned the claim, a newspaper in the Middle West obtained a vote of its readers on the two questions: "Did Cook reach the North Pole? Did Peary reach the North Pole?" The vote that Cook did reach the Pole was overwhelming and a smaller majority voted that Peary did not. It would not be feasible to determine whether man has descended from a lower order of animals by a popular vote in Kentucky. But it is also undesirable to leave the decision of every question to a Lenine or a Mussolini. The conditions are best when a democracy is sufficiently intelligent to choose its experts. It is the business of science to determine the validity of votes, judgments and decisions, a difficult task, but not more so than other problems of lesser human consequence which it has solved.

The 250 new names added in 1927 to the thousand of 1921 are about the number that would have won places to fill vacancies caused by deaths, to meet variation due to the probable error of selection, and as a result of competition with those on the list. There were on the list of 1910, 269 new names; on the list of 1921 (the interval having been prolonged by the war), 351 new names. The residences and positions of the scientific men are of January 1, 1906, 1910, 1921 and 1927. There is of course an interval between the time at which the selection of the names is begun and the completion of the final result. In the first arrangement this interval was about three years; in the last it has been reduced to five months. A statistical study of the names added in 1921 (whose subjects of research are prefixed by a star in the 1921 edition of the Biographical Directory) was made with the assistance of Miss (now Dr.) Psyche Cattell, Dr. Dean R. Brimhall and Dr. Alexander Weinstein, but the work was not published. The 351 names selected in 1920 and the 250 selected during the latter half of 1926 have now been combined and the 601 scientific men (with the residences and positions of January 1, 1927) are treated in the present study and compared with the list of 1906. In this compilation Jaques Cattell and Mrs. Quinta Cattell Kessel have assisted.

The increase since 1906 in the number of scientific men who have contributed by research to the advancement of science is notable. According to the sketches in the Biographical Directory there were about 4,000 in 1906, about 5,500 in 1910, about 5,500 in 1921, about 13,500 in 1927. The names may have been more completely selected in later editions, but this is perhaps counterbalanced by the greater difficulty in dealing with the larger numbers.

The question as to whether contributions to science, including notable advances, are increasing as rapidly as the number of scientific men is of fundamental importance. It appears that while scientific publication increases in proportion to the number of workers, the number of great men of science and of notable contributions does not so increase, if indeed there are as many such men and as many such contributions as there were 25 or 50 years ago. There are more than ten times as many scientific men as when Joseph Henry, Louis Agassiz and Willard Gibbs lived. We do not have thirty men so distinguished; do we have three? Are there ten contributions or is there one, to be later recognized, as in the case of the work of Willard Gibbs?

Among those high on the list of 1906 who are no longer living are: *Astronomy*, Simon Newcomb, G. W. Hill and E. C. Pickering; *Physics and invention*, S. P. Langley and A. Graham Bell; *Chemistry*, Ira Remsen, E. W. Morley, O. W. Gibbs and J. W. Mallett; *Geology*, G. K. Gilbert, C. R. Van Hise and Charles D. Walcott; *Botany*, W. G. Farlow; *Zoology*, W. K. Brooks, C. O. Whitman and Alexander Agassiz; *Physiology*, H. P. Bowditch, S. J. Meltzer and Jacques Loeb; *Anatomy*, Charles S. Minot and F. P. Mall; *Pathology and medicine*, William Osler, *Psychology*, William James. There are men of science now living who in 1906 stood equally high. The question is whether in this period there have arisen men to replace those who were then the leaders. We do not have three times as many, although the supply of scientific men is more than three times as great. Probably in some sciences we have now men of as high distinction as we had 21 years ago, in others not; in none do we seem to surpass obviously the earlier period. It appears that the situation is similar in England, Germany and France.

In Table II there is shown by states the birth place and residence

TABLE II.—BIRTHPLACE AND RESIDENCE BY STATES WITH THE ESTIMATED
INCREASE OR DECREASE SINCE 1906

	Birthplace		Residence	
North Atlantic				
Maine	6	−19	1	− 2
New Hampshire	7	− 3	3	− 3
Vermont	6	− 8	0	− 2
Massachusetts	48	−54	57	−49
Rhode Island	1	− 3	4	− 1
Connecticut	16	−13	20	−10
New York	67	−71	122	+11
New Jersey	8	−15	18	− 5
Pennsylvania	41	+ 2	38	− 2
South Atlantic				
Delaware	2	+ 1	1	+ 1
Maryland	13	− 4	23	− 9
Dist. Columbia	3	+ 2	77	+ 9
Virginia	8	0	3	− 5
West Virginia	4	+ 6	2	0
North Carolina	5	+ 3	2	− 3
South Carolina	4	+ 2	1	+ 2
Georgia	3	+ 2	0	− 1
Florida	0	0	0	0
South Central				
Kentucky	5	0	1	− 1
Tennessee	4	+ 1	3	+ 2
Alabama	2	+ 1	0	− 2
Mississippi	2	+ 2	0	0
Louisiana	1	+ 1	1	+ 1
Texas	1	− 1	8	+ 6
Oklahoma	1	+ 2	1	+ 2
Arkansas	2	+ 3	0	0
North Central				
Ohio	49	+ 7	20	− 1
Indiana	18	+ 2	5	− 4
Illinois	45	+33	52	+24
Michigan	13	− 5	18	+ 3
Wisconsin	24	+ 5	11	− 5
Minnesota	14	+19	18	+17
Iowa	27	+25	4	0
Missouri	21	+21	8	− 8
North Dakota	1	+ 2	0	− 2
South Dakota	3	+ 5	0	− 2
Nebraska	6	+ 8	2	− 6
Kansas	11	+11	5	+ 3

TABLE II.—BIRTHPLACE AND RESIDENCE BY STATES WITH THE ESTIMATED
INCREASE OR DECREASE SINCE 1906.—(*Continued*)

	Birthplace		Residence	
Western				
Montana	2	+ *3*	0	− *2*
Wyoming	2	+ *3*	2	+ *2*
Colorado	1	− *1*	2	− *5*
New Mexico	0	*0*	0	− *2*
Arizona	0	*0*	4	+ *5*
Utah	3	+ *5*	0	*0*
Nevada	0	*0*	0	*0*
Idaho	0	*0*	0	*0*
Washington	0	− *1*	1	+ *2*
Oregon	1	+ *2*	0	*0*
California	11	+ *7*	47	+*23*
Porto Rico	0	*0*	1	+ *2*
Canada	18	− *4*	3	+ *3*
Cuba	0	*0*	0	− *1*
West Indies	0	− *1*	0	*0*
Brazil	0	*0*	0	− *1*
England	21	+*10*	0	− *1*
Wales	0	− *1*	0	*0*
Scotland	4	− *2*	0	*0*
Ireland	1	− *1*	0	*0*
Australia	1	+ *2*	0	*0*
South Africa	1	+ *2*	1	+ *2*
Germany	7	− *7*	0	*0*
Austria	4	+ *1*	0	*0*
Norway	0	− *1*	0	*0*
Sweden	3	+ *2*	0	*0*
Denmark	1	*0*	0	*0*
Holland	3	+ *5*	0	*0*
Belgium	1	+ *2*	0	*0*
Switzerland	5	*0*	0	*0*
Italy	0	− *1*	0	*0*
Russia	8	+ *7*	0	*0*
Poland	2	+ *3*	0	*0*
Turkey	2	+ *3*	0	− *1*
Syria	2	+ *3*	0	*0*
India	0	− *4*	0	*0*
China	0	− *2*	0	*0*
Siam	0	*0*	1	+ *2*
Japan	2	+ *3*	0	*0*
Unknown	3		0	
Dead	0		10	
Total	**601**		**601**	

of the 601 scientific men of the lists of 1921 and 1927. In their production New York leads with 67, followed by Ohio with 49, Massachusetts with 48, Illinois with 45, and Pennsylvania with 41. The group of states next following consists of Iowa 27, Wisconsin 24, Missouri 21. The position of the North Central States is noteworthy, and is further emphasized by the situation in states having a productivity between 10 and 20, namely, Indiana 18, Connecticut 16, Minnesota 14, Maryland 13, Michigan 13, California 11, Kansas 11. The number of scientific men coming from the South Atlantic, South Central and Western divisions is small, though there has been some gain since 1903.

Of the leading thousand scientific men selected in 1903, Massachusetts produced 134 and Connecticut 40. At the time of their birth Boston was the intellectual center of the country. New York in proportion to its population had then produced about half as many scientific men as Massachusetts and Connecticut, the North Central States about one third as many. The situation had changed for the list of 1910. Reduced to comparable figures the birth rate of leading scientific men per million of population had fallen in Massachusetts from 109 to 85, in Connecticut from 87 to 57. In Michigan it had increased from 37 to 74, in Minnesota from 23 to 59, in Wisconsin from 45 to 54. The intellectual fecundity of the North Central States, as compared with New England, has now further increased, extending westward and southward to Iowa, Missouri and Kansas.

The situation is shown in the table by increasing the 601 scientific men to 1,000 proportionately distributed, which is approximately the result that would have been obtained if 1,000 had been selected. Under these conditions the gains or losses of each state are given. The situation in New England is ominous for the future. Every state has lost and it appears that the rural population is becoming intellectually sterile. Of the thousand leading scientific men in 1903, Maine had produced 29, of whom 19 ranked in the first 500. Of 601 scientific men mostly born less than 50 years ago, the state has produced six; if a thousand had been selected the most probable number would have been ten. It has consequently lost 19, two thirds of its productivity. Massachusetts has lost 54. Analogous conditions obtain in all the New England States and southward along the Atlantic. The losses of New York, New Jersey and Maryland, in spite of, or it may be because of, their enormous increase in wealth, are startling. Pennsylvania and Delaware remain nearly stationary; there are small gains in most of the South Atlantic and South Central States.

The losses of the eastern states are counter-balanced by the gains of the central states, notably Illinois, Minnesota, Iowa, Missouri, Kansas and Nebraska. All the central states have gained except

Michigan, though the gains in Ohio and Indiana are small. These three are the most eastern of the states and appear to be following in the wake of the Atlantic seaboard. Further to the west there tend to be moderate gains which predict a large future development. So indeed westward does the course of science take its way, but it is not gratifying if the eastern states do not equal the cultural nations of Europe before losing their leadership. This may indicate a waning of the world's great era in science.

Ten of the scientific men on the list of 1921 have died, giving an annual death rate of 4.7 per thousand which is about normal for men of that age. Of the 591 remaining on the two lists, 122 live in New York, 57 in Massachusetts, 52 in Illinois and 47 in California. If the numbers are increased to 1,000 and proportionately distributed, it appears that in comparison with the thousand of 1906 Massachusetts has lost 49, whereas Illinois has gained 24 and California 23. Every New England state, as also New Jersey, Maryland, Virginia and North Carolina, have a smaller proportion of these leading scientific men than they had 21 years ago. New York has gained 11; Pennsylvania has lost two. Next to Illinois and California, Minnesota has the largest gain. The smaller gains or losses in other states show the real situation at the time and are significant, especially in view of the grouping by regions.

When we compare the birthplaces and residences we find that New York has acquired 55 more of the scientific men than it has produced, the individuals of course not always being the same. Massachusetts has gained 9, Connecticut 4, New Jersey 10 and Maryland 10, these representing men called to the universities. Illinois for the same reason has gained 7, Michigan 5 and Minnesota 4. In the other central states the loss has been large. One hundred and sixty, more than one fourth, of the scientific men were born in them and only 55 reside there. There are but few scientific men born in Washington while many are employed in that city by the government. Of the new group, three were born in the District of Columbia and 77 reside there. Eighty-six of the scientific men were born abroad, so they more than supply the excess in Washington and the balance remains nearly even for the different states.

In 1906 one half (501/1,000) of the leading scientific men of the United States resided in the North Atlantic States and somewhat more than one half (518/993) had been born there. In the short period of 26 years the proportion of those born in these states has fallen to one third (200/598) and the percentage of those residing there to 44.5 per cent (263/591). The cities of the eastern seaboard depend in large measure on Europe for their population, on the central west for their wealth and for their leaders. They will face a difficult situation when immigration is nearly cut off and centers of wealth and culture develop toward the west. It might be supposed that as wealth increases in the hands of a plutocracy, so scientific and other culture would increase in its centers. There has obviously been no change in native ability in the course of a few years. The only suggestion here made is that the state universities and denominational colleges of the central and western states are more nearly in touch with the people than the privately controlled universities of the east and have proved to be the better agencies for the selection and training of those having ability and ideal interests.

The eastern universities provide education for more men who become leaders in science than the states produce. As American students formerly went to Germany for advanced work, so in a later period they tended to congregate in the endowed universities of the Atlantic seaboard. The first degree of doctor of philosophy in the United States was given by Yale University in 1861, the first scientific man to receive it being Josiah Willard Gibbs in 1863. Prior to 1876, Yale had given 18 doctorates in the sciences, Harvard 4, Columbia and Cornell 2 each. Then was established the Johns Hopkins University, opening a new era of higher education and scientific research in the United States. In the following 20 years the Johns Hopkins conferred 179 doctorates in the sciences and 84 of the recipients (some had died) were on the list of 1,000 scientific men of 1910. During this period Columbia conferred 67 such degrees, Harvard 66, Yale 56, Cornell 33, Pennsylvania 22, Clark (opened in 1888) 21, Chicago (opened in 1892) 8, all other universities 66.[1]

Up to and including 1910, the universities of the United States had conferred 2,513 doctorates for work in the sciences, the distribution being: Johns Hopkins 434, Chicago 276, Yale 271, Columbia 268, Harvard 267, Cornell 222, Pennsylvania 172, Clark 150, all others 453. Thus eight endowed universities awarded more than four fifths of these degrees. In 1926 according to data compiled for the National Research Council by Callie Hull and Clarence J. West there were 740 doctorates conferred in the sciences, the numbers for the leading institutions being: Chicago 78, Wisconsin 53, Johns Hopkins 50, Columbia 49, Illinois 44, Cornell 43, California 38, Yale 38, Harvard 35, Washington 32, Minnesota 30, Iowa 28, Ohio State 25. Thus Chicago in the central west is far in advance of the eastern privately

---

[1] These statistics concerning doctorates in the sciences are from an unpublished study. From 1898 to 1915 there was printed each year in SCIENCE an article on doctorates conferred by American universities, including the names of the recipients and the subjects of the theses in the natural and exact sciences.

controlled universities and the seven eastern universities which had conferred prior to 1910 nearly three quarters of all the degrees in 1926 conferred fewer than seven state universities of the north central states and California.

TABLE III.—INSTITUTIONS FROM WHICH FIVE OR MORE OF THE 601 SCIENTIFIC MEN RECEIVED THEIR DEGREES

	A.B. or B.S.	Ph.D.	M.D.	Total
Harvard	41	62	3	106
Chicago	20	68	4	92
Hopkins	12	40	20	72
Columbia	15	46	4	65
Yale	15	25	2	42
Pennsylvania	14	19	5	38
Cornell	16	21	0	37
California	20	13	1	34
Michigan	13	7	2	22
Minnesota	11	11	0	22
Princeton	5	16	0	21
Mass. Inst	16	4	0	20
Wisconsin	12	6	0	18
Stanford	11	6	0	17
Indiana	14	1	1	16
Kansas	13	2	0	15
Illinois	9	5	0	14
Ohio State	11	1	0	12
Brown	4	4	0	8
Iowa	4	4	0	8
Missouri	6	2	0	8
Wesleyan	8	0	0	8
Clark	0	6	0	6
George Wash	2	3	1	6
Nebraska	5	1	0	6
Dartmouth	5	0	0	5
C. C. N. Y	5	0	0	5
Wooster	5	0	0	5
Williams	5	0	0	5

Table III gives the institutions from which five or more of the 601 scientific men received their degrees. Harvard with 41 bachelors, 62 doctors of philosophy and three doctors of medicine, stands foremost as it did in 1903. It is, however, now surpassed by Chicago in the number of doctorates, as it was by the Johns Hopkins at the earlier period. After these three universities comes Columbia, followed by Yale, Pennsylvania, Cornell and California. The institutions whose graduates are in the twenties are Michigan, Minnesota, Princeton and the Massachusetts Institute; ranging from 18 to 12 are Wisconsin, Stanford, Indiana, Kansas, Illinois and Ohio State. The privately endowed universities still lead in the number of scientific men for whose education they were responsible usually some twenty to twenty-five years ago. They probably do not do so for the men graduated to-day, but we must wait another twenty years before the figures will be at hand. Many of the 41 bachelors who received degrees from Harvard and the 15 from Columbia and from Yale went to these universities from other institutions after they had planned their careers and the influence of the eastern endowed universities in the creation of scientific men is not large. The private colleges are also losing the influence that they formerly had. In the thousand of 1906 there were 23 graduates of Princeton and of Amherst, 16 of Wesleyan, 14 of Williams, 10 of Dartmouth and of Oberlin. For the contemporary list of 601 men the numbers are: Wesleyan 8, Princeton, Dartmouth and Williams 5, Amherst 4, Oberlin 2.

Another change that can not be regarded as wholly auspicious is the small number of the younger scientific men who have studied at foreign universities. In so far as this means such advance in our own institutions that it is needless to go abroad for special work it is gratifying. But it may result in lesser devotion to the ideals of scholarship and research that had their florescence in the German university of the nineteenth century. Of the thousand of 1906, 117 had studied in Berlin, 84 in Leipzig, 69 in Göttingen, 56 in Heidelberg, and a large proportion had received degrees from these and other German universities. Of the contemporary 601 only one has a degree from Berlin. There is none from Leipzig, which before had 39. This refers, of course, to men working in the period preceding the war. Perhaps now the various systems of unattached fellowships may lead to a larger international interchange of students. Before graduate students can afford to study abroad, we must, however, find a method by which younger scientific men receive positions in accordance with their ability rather than through the influence of the professors with whom they work.

The majority of scientific men still find their careers in universities. As shown in Table IV, 358.5 (the decimal here and elsewhere referring to a divided position) of the 591 men hold academic positions and in the main earn their salaries by teaching. There are 95 connected with the research institutions that are the most notable development in scientific investigation of the present century. The Smithsonian Institution (including government bureaus), museums, etc., are here placed under research institutions. Sixty-two are engaged in industrial work, largely in the research laboratories of the corporations, where their work is not confined to applied science and will doubtless be more and more extended to the fundamental problems whose cultivation and by-products have an economic value far beyond their cost. Such work is besides only a proper return to society for the wealth acquired by monopoly. A public service corporation such as the American Telephone and Telegraph Company, whose profits are limited only by legal regulations, could easily and properly support and give the best facilities to scientific men engaged in research in physics, chemistry, mathematics and psychology. 74.5 of the men are employed by the government. Here again the work is largely but not wholly in applied science, and here again the most beneficial use of money collected by taxation would be the support of research that of all services is the most important for the nation and for the world.

TABLE IV.—OCCUPATION OF THE 601 SCIENTIFIC MEN

	Teaching	Research institutions	Government work	Applied science	Amateur	Deceased	Total
Mathematics..............	49	0	0	1	0	0	50
Physics...................	48	6	13	22	0	1	90
Chemistry................	54	7	8	31	0	1	101
Astronomy................	13	19	1	0	0	1	34
Geology..................	27	3	22	3	0	4	59
Botany...................	28.5	13.5	14	0	0	2	58
Zoology..................	48.5	15	12.5	2	0	0	78
Physiology...............	22.5	3.5	1	0	0	0	27
Anatomy..................	10	2	0	0	0	0	12
Pathology................	26	16	3	1	0	1	47
Anthropology.............	5	8	0	0	1	0	14
Psychology...............	27	2	0	2	0	0	31
Total.................	358.5	95	74.5	62	1	10	601

Of these scientific men 60.7 per cent hold academic positions as compared with 73.8 per cent of those in the list of 1901. It has been recognized that there has been since the war a movement of scientific men from the universities to the research and industrial laboratories and we have here a measure of its extent. If the numbers are, as above explained, increased to a thousand we find that of this younger group the universities and colleges have lost 133. The research institutions have gained 88.5; the industrial laboratories and applied science 46; the government services 14.5. There is only one who may be classed as an amateur in the present list, as compared with 18 in 1910. We have never had in America a group of men, such as was represented in England by Darwin, Galton, Rayleigh and Huggins, who devoted themselves to scientific work without occupying scientific positions. The specialization of science and democratic institutions have led to the practical disappearance of those who contribute significantly to the advancement of science without being professionally engaged in scientific or educational work. But we now have men who are professionally engaged in research.

The figures for the separate sciences given in the table show that nearly all mathematicians are teachers. Astronomy and pathology are especially well represented in the research institutions; geology and to a lesser extent physics, botany and zoology in the government work; physics and chemistry in the industrial laboratories and in applied science.

Table V gives the number of scientific men connected with institutions where there are three or more. As we are here in the main concerned with the present strength of the institutions rather than with changes in distribution all the scientific men are included. They are divided in the table into three groups: (1) the scientific men of the list of 1910 who were retained in the list of 1921; (2) those added in 1921; and (3) those now added to the list. The numbers in the three groups, respectively, are 585, 341 and 250. We have consequently 1,176 scientific men instead of 1,000 as in the earlier lists. The competition for inclusion is now, however, more severe, for the list of 1906 included about one fourth of the scientific men of the country, whereas the present list includes only about one twelfth. The figures given in the table are consequently relative. An increase of 17.6 per cent means that an institution has remained stationary in its relation to other institutions.

Harvard has on its faculties 89.5 of these leading scientific men and its supremacy is unchallenged. Under the existing system of university administration honor should be given to Mr. Eliot and Mr. Lowell for maintaining high academic traditions. It is a remarkable circumstance that Harvard should have gained 23 scientific men of distinction during the period in which New England has been failing in the production of scientific men and the centers of scientific research have been moving westward. In 1906 Harvard had 66.5 of our thousand leading scientific men, Columbia 60, and Chicago 39. Now of 1,176 leading scientific men Harvard has 89.5, Chicago 53.5, and Columbia 46.5. It should also be noticed that Harvard has 21 of the younger men of the group of 250, as compared with 15 at Chicago and 7 at Columbia. Following these three universities are Yale with 42.5 and California and the Johns Hopkins bracketed with 40.5. Cornell, which comes next, has lost relatively. There then follow the three state universities, Michigan, Wisconsin and Illinois, of which Illinois has

TABLE V.—THE NUMBER OF THE SCIENTIFIC MEN CONNECTED WITH INSTITUTIONS
WHERE THERE ARE THREE OR MORE, TOGETHER WITH THE PROPORTIONAL GAIN
OR LOSS SINCE 1906

	1910	1921	1927	Total	
Harvard.....................................	47.5	21	21	**89.5**	+23
Chicago.....................................	25.5	13	15	**53.5**	+14.5
Carnegie....................................	19	13	15	**47**	+40
Columbia....................................	26.5	13	7	**46.5**	−13.5
Yale..	27.5	10	5	**42.5**	+16
California...................................	24.5	7	9	**40.5**	+13.5
Hopkins.....................................	22.5	10	8	**40.5**	+10
Cornell.....................................	18.5	12	4	**34.5**	+ 1
Michigan...................................	15	10	6	**31**	+11
Geological Survey...........................	13.5	6	9	**28.5**	− 3.5
Wisconsin...................................	18	5	5	**28**	+10
Dept. of Agr................................	12	9	6	**27**	− 5
Illinois.....................................	13.5	8.5	4	**26**	+20
Stanford....................................	13.5	6.5	6	**26**	+10
Pennsylvania................................	8.5	8	9	**25.5**	+ 8.5
Princeton...................................	12	7	5	**24**	+ 9.5
Smithsonian.................................	10.5	6	6	**22.5**	+ .5
Bur. of Stand...............................	9	8	5	**22**	+14
Mass. Inst..................................	13	3	4	**20**	+ .5
Rockefeller Inst.............................	8	6	5	**19**	+16
Minnesota..................................	4.5	9	5	**18.5**	+ 8.5
Wash. (St. Louis)...........................	8	6	2	**16**	+11
American Museum...........................	6	5	2	**13**	+ 5
Ohio State..................................	5	5	3	**13**	+ 3
General Electric.............................	3	6	2	**11**	+ 7
Bell Laboratories............................	0	3	7	**10**	*
Iowa State Univ.............................	4.5	3	1	**8.5**	+ 1.5
N. Y. Bot. Garden...........................	6	0	2	**8**	+ 2
Pittsburgh..................................	3.5	3	1	**7.5**	*
Brown......................................	3	3	1	**7**	+ 2
California Inst..............................	2	2	3	**7**	*
Cincinnati..................................	4	3	0	**7**	+ 1
Dartmouth..................................	5	0	2	**7**	+ 1
U. S. Health................................	1	3	3	**7**	*
Northwestern...............................	2	2.5	2	**6.5**	− 2.5
Bryn Mawr..................................	4	2	0	**6**	0
North Carolina..............................	4	1	1	**6**	+ 1
New York...................................	1.5	2	2	**5.5**	− 4
Clark.......................................	2	3	0	**5**	− 2
Eastman Kodak..............................	0	1	4	**5**	*
Indiana.....................................	4	1	0	**5**	− 1
Kansas.....................................	1	1	3	**5**	0
Missouri....................................	4	1	0	**5**	− 4
Western Reserve.............................	2	2	1	**5**	+ 1
Texas......................................	0	2	3	**5**	0
Rochester...................................	1.5	2	1	**4.5**	*
Boyce Thompson.............................	1	1	2	**4**	*
Virginia....................................	1	1	2	**4**	− 3
Amherst....................................	1.5	1	1	**3.5**	+ .5
Mayo Clinic.................................	0	1.5	2	**3.5**	*
Nat. Res. Council............................	2	1	0	**3**	*
Rice Institute...............................	0	2	1	**3**	*
Syracuse....................................	1	0	2	**3**	− 4
U. S. Navy..................................	1	1	1	**3**	− 5
Vassar......................................	3	0	0	**3**	0
Wesleyan...................................	1	2	0	**3**	− 4
Wistar.....................................	2	0	1	**3**	*

* Fewer than three in 1906.

gained the most. Next come four endowed institutions, Stanford, Pennsylvania, Princeton and the Massachusetts Institute of Technology. Washington (St. Louis) is in the same group and has the largest gain. The only other universities having ten or more of these leading scientific men are Minnesota and the Ohio State. Apart from Columbia the universities that have lost most relatively are Missouri, Syracuse, Wesleyan, New York and Virginia.

The past twenty-six years have witnessed the development of endowed research institutions and the Carnegie Institution of Washington now stands next to Harvard and Chicago in the number of its scientific men of distinction. The Rockefeller Institute, limited to medical research, has also attained a high position. In this period the Carnegie Institution has grown from 7 to 47; the Rockefeller Institute from 3 to 19. The Boyce Thompson Institute, the Wistar Institute and the Mayo Clinic attain places on the list. The American Museum of Natural History and the New York Botanical Garden, with respectively 13 and 8 of the scientific men, rank before most universities and show a gain since 1906. It is of interest that these institutions can flourish under support and control partly private and partly public.

The industrial laboratories of the corporations, like the endowed institutions for research, have enjoyed a notable growth which is scarcely measured by the 11 men recorded for the General Electric Company, the 10 for the Bell Laboratories and other parts of the Telephone System, and the 5 for the Eastman Kodak Company. Industrial research, like advances in engineering, is not always recorded in scientific papers, and is often a cooperative undertaking for which credit is not assigned to individuals. It is, however, to be noted that the number of leading scientific men under these three corporations has greatly increased and of 26 all but three belong to the two groups consisting mainly of younger scientific men.

The Bureau of Standards has during the period increased the number of leading scientific men in its laboratories from 8 to 22. The Geological Survey, with 28.5, is the strongest group in a single science, but relatively it has lost ground somewhat since 1906, as has also the Department of Agriculture. The Smithsonian Institution, with its government supported subsidiaries, has remained stationary, but this means a moderate relative loss. The U. S. Public Health Service has gained and some states and municipalities are now cooperating in this work.

In Table VI the ten strongest departments in each science are given, the men in them being weighted in accordance with the methods described in the previous study. Those on the lower part of the list being taken as a unit, a scale has been adopted of increasing weights

TABLE VI.—THE TEN STRONGEST DEPARTMENTS IN EACH SCIENCE TOGETHER WITH THEIR RELATIVE GAIN OR LOSS SINCE 1906

Mathematics			Physics		
Chicago	20.6	+ 6.6	Bur. Stand	26.2	+13.7
Harvard	15.6	+ 2.4	Harvard	22.4	+ 8.9
Princeton	10.7	+ 6.5	Gen. Electric	13.9	†
Illinois	10.4	+10.4	Chicago	11.3	+ 6.1
Columbia	7.9	− 1.8	Bell Tel	11.2	†
Yale	7.1	+ 0.2	Hopkins	10.1	+ 3.9
Cornell	6.7	− 0.1	Columbia	9.5	− 8.5
Michigan	6.0	†	Calif. Inst	9.0	†
Mass. Inst	5.7	+ 3.5	Cornell	7.9	− 2.0
California	5.3	†	Yale	7.8	†

Geology			Botany		
Geol. Surv	37.9	− 7.7	Dept. Agr	22.4	− 2.2
Harvard	10.7	+ 1.6	Harvard	15.0	− 0.1
Yale	8.5	− 0.7	Carnegie	12.0	+12.0
Carnegie	8.2	†	N. Y. Bot	12.0	− 1.5
Stanford	7.3	*	California	9.4	†
Chicago	6.8	− 1.9	Cornell	9.2	+ 2.0
Wisconsin	5.7	+ 1.5	Boyce Thomp	7.6	†
Hopkins	5.4	+ 2.3	Chicago	6.4	− 4.2
Michigan	4.0	†	Mo. Bot	6.3	+ 2.5
Smithsonian	4.0	†	Michigan	5.6	†

Anatomy			Pathology		
Chicago	4.5	*	Rockefeller	25.2	+20.6
Wistar			Harvard	15.1	+ 2.7
Minnesota			Hopkins	11.7	+ 1.2
Rockefeller			Chicago	8.8	+ 3.8
Hopkins			Columbia	6.2	+ 0.2
Michigan			Pennsylvania	5.1	0.0
California			Michigan		
Wisconsin			Stanford		
Columbia			N. Y. Univ		
Wash. (St. L.)			Wash. (St. L.)		

Chemistry			Astronomy		
Harvard	17.8	+ 4.0	Carnegie	19.8	+16.6
Yale	13.7	+ 4.5	California	11.0	+ 1.1
Mass. Inst	13.3	+ 0.2	Harvard	7.1	+ 0.6
Illinois	10.7	+ 9.7	Chicago	4.2	− 2.8
Cornell	9.5	− 0.1	Pittsburgh		
Columbia	9.3	+ 2.2	Princeton		
Gen. Electric	8.9	†	Wisconsin		
Carnegie	8.7	†	Yale		
Hopkins	8.4	+ 1.0	Michigan		
Princeton	7.8	†	Virginia		

Table VI.—The Ten Strongest Departments in Each Science Together with Their Relative Gain or Loss Since 1906.—(*Continued*)

Zoology			Physiology		
Harvard	25.5	+ 6.8	Harvard	12.0	+ 2.2
Chicago	14.2	+ 2.0	Hopkins	8.5	+ 1.3
Am. Mus	12.9	− 0.6	Yale	5.1	+ 0.2
Hopkins	12.8	†	W. Reserve	4.9	+ 4.9
Nat. Mus	12.0	†	Wash. (St. L.)	4.8	†
Columbia	11.2	− 5.5	Cornell	4.4	*
Carnegie	11.1	†	Chicago		
Penna	10.8	†	Columbia		
Yale	9.1	+ 3.1	Rockefeller		
Princeton	8.1	+ 4.5	Michigan		

Anthropology			Psychology		
Smithsonian	6.6	− 6.8	Columbia	14.2	+ 4.6
Am. Mus	5.4	*	Yale	6.7	†
California	4.0	*	Harvard	5.6	− 4.6
Harvard			Stanford	4.6	*
Columbia			Chicago	4.3	*
Field Mus			Cornell	4.0	*
Heye Mus			Princeton		
Chicago			California		
Carnegie			Iowa		
Penna			Michigan		

* Figure not given in 1906 because it was below four.
† Not included among the first ten institutions in the 1906 list.

up to 4 for the 25 at the head of the list. This scale corresponds in a general way with the range of merit and the average salaries received. The 250 men added to the list have been arranged in order of merit and interpolated in the list of 1921 in accordance with the distribution found in the previous arrangements. The probable errors of the figures given in the table, which are small, and the constant errors, which in some cases may be considerable, are discussed in the earlier publication. Owing to the possibility of injustice to certain departments there has been some hesitation as to the desirability of publishing the figures, but they are in the main correct and significant. The figures are omitted in cases where the strength of a department is less than 4 in order to avoid giving possible information in regard to the standing of individuals.

Harvard here shows its leadership not only as a whole but in nearly every department. It stands first among universities in physics, chemistry, geology, botany, zoology, physiology and pathology, second in mathematics, third in astronomy and psychology, fourth in anthropology. There has been a gain since 1906 in every department except anatomy and psychology, though in several cases the gains are due only to the increased number of individuals on the present list. Chicago stands first in mathematics and second in zoology. Columbia stands first in psychology, but does not in any other science have a rank higher than fifth. The U. S. Bureau of Standards leads in physics and the Bureau of Entomology in anthropology. By a wide margin the Carnegie Institution leads in astronomy, the U. S. Geological Survey in geology, the U. S. Department of Agriculture in botany and the Rockefeller Institute in pathology.

27

PRESBYOTA AND THE CAUSES OF DEFICIENT HEARING

Abstract of a paper presented before a meeting of the National Academy of Sciences at Urbana, Illinois, in October 1927, printed in *Science*: **66**: 404, 1927. The complete manuscript has not been found.

Presbyopia is well-known, but in so far as there is an analogous condition of the organ of hearing it has been so little considered that a new name must be invented for it. Oliver Wendell Holmes noted that in old age tones of high pitch, as the chirping of a cricket, can not be heard, and the upper limit of audible pitch is now measured by the Galton whistle and other methods. In the Bell Telephone Laboratories Dr. Harvey Fletcher, following work of Professor Seashore and others, has recently perfected an audiometer for measuring acuity of hearing for tones of different pitches, records from which are exhibited. Attention is here called to the fact that deficiency of hearing is due not only to failure to respond to the energy of the stimulus as measured by the audiometer, but also to the fusion of successive stimuli and that this condition may be normal after middle-life. Vision is a space sense; hearing a time sense. The inertia of eye and the fusion of visual sensations have been thoroughly investigated, but we have no corresponding information in regard to the fusion of auditory sensations. Sounds separated by one five-hundredth of a second can be discriminated, but with speech sounds given at longer intervals are fused. We can speak about as rapidly as we can hear—some twenty changes a second—and this may have evolutionary significance. In order to be heard by one of deficient hearing, or by an audience, it is necessary to speak not more loudly, but more distinctly and more slowly. The conditions are analogous to the loud speaker of the radio or to transmission on the telephone line, where increased loudness increases the distortion and blurring of the waves. As the muscular system of the eye controlling the curvature of the lens becomes flaccid with age, so the receptor in the ear may be expected to lose its elasticity with age. It does not respond to the more rapid vibrations and has greater inertia, so that a longer period is required to set it in motion and the motion may subside more slowly. There is consequently fusion of successive sounds, which are besides less distinctive because the higher overtones are lacking. A loss of acuity of hearing of 30 per cent is a small matter, for one can hear a conversation as well at six feet as at three, but the fusion of successive stimuli makes close attention necessary and explains the difficulty that older people experience in listening to an address or theater performance.

28

AN AFTER-IMAGE OF THE YELLOW SPOT

The abstract of a paper read before the National Academy of Science at Urbana, Illinois, in October 1927. The abstract was printed in *Science* **66**: 404. 1927. The original manuscript has not been found.

Loewe, Haidlinger, Clerk Maxwell and Helmholtz have described in detail the entoptic phenomena connected with fovea centralis and the yellow spot. If one looks at a blue surface or preferably through a blue glass or a solution of chrome alum, a dark spot appears in the center of the field of vision. Skilled observers may see a dark halo with a bright ring surrounding the spot. The observation here put on record is that after the retina has been fatigued by the blue light, if the eyes are turned to a white surface, say the clouded sky, a bright yellowish after-image of the yellow spot appears, comparable to the sun seen through the clouds. The yellow spot has been protected from the blue light by its pigment and is relatively more sensitive to the white light. Another observation that may be put on record is that about twenty-five years ago I obtained an after-image that still exists. The after-image followed exposure of the eyes for one minute to the clear sky through the cross-bar of a window. This positive after-image, which I can now see with closed eyes, may be due to permanent changes then caused in the retina, or it may be reinforced by attention. Newton describes an after-image of the sun that lasted three years.

29

THE DISTRIBUTION OF AMERICAN MEN OF SCIENCE IN 1932

Printed in *Science*, **77**: 264–270, 1933. It appeared also in American Men of Science: A Biographical Directory, Fifth Edition, 1261–1268, 1933.

The list of 250 names of those persons who were assigned stars for the first time in the Fifth Edition of the Directory has not been reproduced in this volume.

For the fifth edition of the "Biographical Directory of American Men of Science" there have been selected by objective methods 250 of those not included in the earlier selections who are regarded by their colleagues as among the leading scientific workers of the United States. The methods used were the same as in the fourth edition; there and in the earlier editions they were fully described and their validity was discussed in detail.[1]

The primary object of the work, begun more than thirty years ago, was to secure a group for scientific study. Still earlier there had been selected by objective methods the thousand most eminent men of history, and measurements had been made of nearly a thousand students of Columbia University. Each of the three groups is suited to scientific study, owing to its sociological interest and to the availability of the material. At that time but little attention had been paid to the measurement of individual differences, the present writer having in 1885 invented the term and published the first quantitative work on the subject.

Arguments may be advanced for and against giving the names of the scientific men selected for study. Each of them is probably among our thousand leading research workers, but there are others who deserve to be included. The situation is the same as in election to an academy of sciences or appointment to a university position, except that the determination of scientific merit is more exact. We also have

[1] In order to prevent misunderstandings that occur, it may be stated here: (1) The present writer has devised the methods and compiled the returns, but, apart from casting one vote for the psychologists, has had no part whatever in the selections. (2) Residents of North America are included in the book, but only residents of the United States in the selections for the stars. (3) The applied sciences as such are not included. (4) When an individual is selected in more than one science, he is assigned to the science in which he stands highest. (5) The subject of research given in the book is usually, but not always, the subject in which the star has been assigned.

an analogous problem in the measurement of the ability of a child
or a college student.

It is sometimes argued that all such determinations are undemo-
cratic. Democracy, however, does not consist in reducing all to a
common mediocracy, but in giving opportunity to each in accordance
with his ability and fitness. We long have had school grades, college
entrance examinations, requirements for the doctorate, qualifications
for a university position, honorary degrees, and societies of limited
membership. In so far as psychology is gradually developing quantitative methods to measure individual differences the results may at
times seem harsh and inconsiderate of the individual; but in the long
run truth is better than illusion.

While there are those who do not approve the selection of a group
of leading scientific workers, others urge that the stars should be
dropped when a position among the thousand is not maintained. The
competition in the earlier selections was less severe, for in 1903 there
were only about 4,000 Americans who had published research work,
whereas now there are more than 20,000. It is also true that some men
do not maintain the promise of their earlier work. A selection which
is correct at the time within the limits of the probable error may not
hold thirty years later. In order to make the situation definite and
to supply information that may be of historical interest, there will be
given in the new edition of the book an index number with the star,
showing the edition in which the individual was added to the list.

TABLE I.—DISTRIBUTION AMONG THE SCIENCES

Mathematics	756
Physics	991
Chemistry	2,561
Astronomy	239
Geology and Geography	903
Zoology	1,435
Botanical Sciences	1,187
Anthropology	111
Psychology	539
Social and Economic Sciences	23
Historical and Philogical Sciences	37
Engineering	1,245
Medical Sciences	2,207
Agriculture	769
Education	54
Total	12,877

The 250 individuals have been selected from more than 20,000;
consequently each of them stands first among more than eighty research workers, a somewhat severe selection. It is not feasible to give

at this time the number and distribution of the some 22,000 entries in the edition of the directory now in press. 12,877 names in the fourth edition were distributed, according to the sections of the American Association for the Advancement of Science, as shown in Table I.

If the applied sciences are omitted (though all those included in the book were understood to have advanced science by research) and the classification adopted in these studies is used, the number is 9,785 and the distribution is as shown in the first column of Table II.

TABLE II.—DISTRIBUTION AMONG THE FUNDAMENTAL SCIENCES

	All	Women	Per cent women
Mathematics	756	61	8.0
Physics	991	28	2.1
Chemistry	2561	117	4.6
Astronomy	239	23	9.6
Geology	903	32	3.5
Botany	1187	119	10.0
Zoology	1436	130	9.0
Physiology	460	48	10.4
Anatomy	206	11	5.4
Pathology	396	28	7.1
Anthropology	111	11	9.9
Psychology	539	117	22.0
Total	9785	725	7.4

TABLE III.—AVERAGE AGE IN THE DIFFERENT SCIENCES

Mathematicians	36.1
Physicists	36.0
Chemists	41.1
Astronomers	42.9
Geologists	49.4
Botanists	47.0
Zoologists	45.3
Physiologists	42.0
Anatomists	47.7
Pathologists	48.3
Anthropologists	41.8
Psychologists	44.0

In the group of 250 there are three women. There are two in the National Academy of Sciences with about the same number of members. There are 725 women included in the book distributed (all of them being assigned to the twelve sciences) as shown in Table II. The percentage of women in each science is also given. It ranges from

2.1 per cent in physics to 22 per cent in psychology. The preponderance in the latter subject is due in the main to the large number of teaching and clinical positions open to women.

The average age of the 250 in the group is 42.9 years. Distinction is attained at an earlier age in mathematics and the exact sciences than in the natural sciences, the average age in the different sciences being as shown in Table III.

In Table IV there is given under 1932 the distribution by states of the birthplace and residence of the 250 scientific men now added to the list. The numbers are multiplied by four in order to show comparisons with the earlier selections. There were 1,000 in 1903. The additions in 1910 were 269; in 1921 (the interval having been prolonged by the war) 351; in 1927, 250. The 601 names of 1921 and 1927 were considered together in the fourth edition of the directory. In the table all the figures are placed on the basis of a thousand entries, decimals being omitted.

While the numbers for most of the states are so small that they have only a limited validity, the general distribution of the scientific population in 1903 and its subsequent movements are clearly shown. Of the thousand scientific men of 1903, 134 were born in Massachusetts and 40 in Connecticut. This represents a birth rate of 108.8 per million population in Massachusetts, and of 86.9 in Connecticut, the population being based on the census of 1860. The birth rate is then reduced to about half in the surrounding states, being 47.2 in New York. There is a further reduction to one half in Pennsylvania, where it is 22.7, and this continues southward, the rate being 8.8 in Virginia, 5 in North Carolina, 2.8 in Georgia, 2.1 in Alabama, 1.3 in Mississippi and 1.4 in Louisiana. In the north central states the conditions are intermediate between New York and Pennsylvania and decrease southward.

The change in distribution of the birthplaces in the later selections is very significant for such a short period in the history of the nation. New England has lost its supremacy in the production of scientific men, the numbers from Massachusetts on the basis of a thousand, decreasing from 134 in 1906 to 100 in 1910, 80 in 1921–27, 72 in 1932. The corresponding figures for Connecticut are 40, 22, 27 and 16. The rural New England states fail even more in productivity. New York, New Jersey, Pennsylvania and Maryland also decrease. The gains are especially in the central west, the record for Illinois being 42, 52, 75 and 88. There are also large increases in other north central states: Minnesota, 4 to 32; Iowa, 20 to 32; Missouri, 14 to 40; Nebraska, 2 to 20; Kansas, 7 to 32. The more easterly states of Ohio and Indiana remain about stationary. Twelve states south of Virginia supplied

TABLE IV.—BIRTHPLACE AND RESIDENCE OF SCIENTIFIC MEN SELECTED AT FOUR
PERIODS

	Birthplace				Residence			
	1903	1910	1921–27	1932	1903	1910	1921–27	1932
North Atlantic								
Maine.................	29	22	10	8	4	7	2	4
New Hampshire........	15	11	12	...	8	4	5	
Vermont..............	18	11	10	8	2			
Massachusetts..........	134	100	80	72	144	160	95	100
Rhode Island...........	5	15	2	4	8	11	7	8
Connecticut............	40	22	27	16	43	60	33	56
New York.............	183	134	111	128	192	141	203	164
New Jersey............	28	15	13	12	35	19	30	44
Pennsylvania..........	66	52	68	48	65	48	63	28
South Atlantic								
Delaware..............	2	...	3	...	1	...	2	8
Maryland.............	26	7	22	4	47	48	38	32
District of Columbia....	3	4	5	8	119	97	128	76
Virginia..............	13	26	13	4	10	...	5	12
West Virginia..........	1	7	7	4	3	4	3	
North Carolina........	5	...	8	4	6	11	3	4
South Carolina........	5	11	7	4	...	...	2	
Georgia...............	3	4	5	8	1			
Florida...............	...	4						
South Central								
Kentucky..............	8	7	8	4	3	...	2	
Tennessee.............	6	7	7	4	3	...	5	
Alabama..............	2	7	3	4	2			
Mississippi............	1	4	3					
Louisiana.............	1	...	2	8	1	4	2	
Texas................	3	7	2	4	7	7	13	20
Oklahoma.............	...	...	2	...	...	...	2	
Arkansas.............	...	...	3					
North Central								
Ohio..................	75	86	81	72	34	37	33	40
Indiana...............	28	45	30	36	12	19	8	4
Illinois...............	42	52	75	88	63	104	86	96
Michigan..............	27	63	22	16	27	19	30	48
Wisconsin.............	35	41	40	20	23	48	18	28
Minnesota.............	4	19	23	32	13	11	30	36
Iowa.................	20	33	45	32	7	4	7	20
Missouri..............	14	19	35	40	21	22	13	40
North Dakota..........	...	...	2	...	2			
South Dakota..........	...	...	5	8	2	4		
Nebraska..............	2	4	10	20	9	15	3	4
Kansas...............	7	...	18	32	5	7	8	4

TABLE IV.—BIRTHPLACE AND RESIDENCE OF SCIENTIFIC MEN SELECTED AT FOUR PERIODS.—(*Continued*)

	Birthplace				Residence			
	1903	1910	1921–27	1932	1903	1910	1921–27	1932
Western								
Montana................	...	...	3	...	2			
Wyoming...............	...	...	3	4	1	...	3	
Colorado..............	3	...	2	16	8	7	3	
New Mexico...........	...	...	...	8	2			
Arizona...............	...	...	...	4	2	4	7	4
Utah..................	...	...	5					
Nevada................								
Idaho.................								
Washington............	1	...	...	12	...	...	2	
Oregon................	...	4	2	4	...	4		
California............	11	15	18	20	53	56	78	116
Territories and Dependencies								
Porto Rico............	...	...	...	...	1	...	2	
Alaska................	...	...	...	...	1			
Hawaii................	1	4	...	...	...	4	...	4
Philippines...........	...	4	...	...	3	7		
Panama................	...	...	...	...	...	4		
Foreign								
Canada................	34	33	30	36	2	...	5	
Brazil................	...	...	...	...	1			
Cuba..................	...	...	...	...	1			
West Indies...........	1							
England...............	25	...	35	8	1			
Scotland..............	9	15	7	12				
Wales.................	1							
Ireland...............	3	4	2					
Germany...............	19	22	12	36				
Austria-Hungary.......	6							
Austria...............	...	...	7	4				
Hungary...............	...	...	...	8				
Norway................	1	4	...	4				
Sweden................	3	7	5	8				
Denmark...............	2	...	2					
Holland...............	...	...	5	16				
Belgium...............	...	...	2	4				
Poland................	...	...	3					
Bulgaria..............	...	...	...	4				
Czecho-Slovakia.......	...	...	...	4				
Switzerland...........	8	...	8	8	...	4		
Italy.................	1							
Spain.................	1							
Russia................	6	11	13	12				

TABLE IV.—BIRTHPLACE AND RESIDENCE OF SCIENTIFIC MEN SELECTED AT FOUR
PERIODS.—(*Continued*)

	Birthplace				Residence			
	1903	1910	1921–27	1932	1903	1910	1921–27	1932
Foreign (*Continued*)								
Turkey................	...	...	3					
Syria..................	...	...	3					
India..................	4							
Mongolia..............	...	...	...	4				
China.................	2							
Japan.................	...	7	3	4				
Siam..................	...	...	...	...	...	...	2	
Dutch E. Indies........	...	...	...	4				
Australia..............	...	...	2					
South Africa..........	...	...	2	...	...	...	2	

only 35 men to the list of 1903; they show some improvement in the
subsequent selections, 58, 57 and 44.

The residence[1] of leading scientific men in the different states follows in general their production, but certain regions produce more than
they retain or obtain, while in others the reverse is the case. Massachusetts and Connecticut have had in residence even more scientific
men than they have produced. This holds also for New York and of
course in the greatest measure for the District of Columbia. Ohio
and Indiana, on the other hand, have in residence less than half as
many leading scientific men as they have produced. California gained
greatly in the last arrangement, being surpassed only by New York
and having a much larger percentage per million population.

On the list of 1903 there were 126 scientific men born in foreign
countries, contributed in very unequal measure by different nationalities, the number per million foreign-born population being: Switzerland,
68.9; England, 29.6; Germany, 7.1; Italy, 2.1; France, 0. The relative
numbers of scientific men born abroad in the subsequent selections
were 103, 144 and 172. There have been in the selections following the
war a large percentage of scientific men who migrated to this country
after having attained distinction at home.

Table V gives the institutions from which the 250 scientific men
received their academic degrees. Harvard is still in the lead by a wide
margin, having granted 19 bachelor's degrees, 39 doctorates of philosophy or science and 4 doctorates of medicine. Chicago comes next with
a total of 42 degrees, followed by Columbia with 29. There then follows

[1] The scientific men were selected in 1903; the residence is of January 1, 1906,
as given in the first edition of the directory.

TABLE V.—THE INSTITUTIONS WHICH GRANTED THREE OR MORE OF THE DEGREES

	A.B. or B.S.	Ph.D. or Sc.D.	M.D.	Total
Harvard	19	39	4	62
Chicago	13	28	1	42
Columbia	7	19	3	29
Cornell	9	11	..	20
Princeton	6	13	..	19
Johns Hopkins	2	10	6	18
Yale	5	12	..	17
Illinois	7	10	..	17
California	4	12	..	16
Michigan	8	1	..	9
Wisconsin	1	8	..	9
Minnesota	5	3	..	8
Brown	5	1	..	6
Virginia	2	4	..	6
Amherst	5	...	..	5
Ohio State	3	2	..	5
Washington (St. L.)	3	2	..	5
Kansas	4	...	..	4
Pennsylvania	2	2	..	4
Stanford	3	1	..	4
Texas	2	2	..	4
Dennison	3	...	..	3
Iowa	1	2	..	3
Missouri	3	...	..	3
Nebraska	2	1	..	3
Swarthmore	3	...	..	3
Elsewhere	82	4	2	88
Total	209	187	16	412
Berlin	...	3	1	4
Toronto	4	...	..	4
Edinburgh	2	...	1	3
Leiden	...	3	..	3
Munich	...	3	..	3
Zurich	1	2	..	3
Elsewhere	7	16	3	26
Total	14	27	5	46
Grand total	223	214	21	458

a group coming close together, Cornell, Princeton, the Johns Hopkins, Yale, Illinois, and California, with a drop to about half as many at Michigan and Wisconsin. These figures represent the situation for those who received their degrees on the average some twenty years ago. Since then the number of advanced degrees conferred by the state universities has increased with great rapidity. The 27 not recorded as having had a bachelor's degree had in practically all cases an equivalent education, in most cases abroad. Two men hold doctorates of both philosophy and medicine, leaving only 17 who do not hold one of these degrees.

In Table VI are given the institutions with which three or more of the scientific men are connected. Harvard has sixteen and California 15, followed by Chicago, Yale, Michigan, Columbia and Princeton. Seven of the men are connected with the Rockefeller Institute for Medical Research and six with the Carnegie Institution of Washington.

TABLE VI.—INSTITUTIONS WITH WHICH THREE OR MORE ARE CONNECTED

Harvard	16
California	15
Chicago	13
Yale	13
Michigan	11
Columbia	10
Princeton	10
Minnesota	9
Illinois	8
Johns Hopkins	8
Cornell	7
Rockefeller Institute	7
Stanford	7
Carnegie Institution	6
Washington (St. Louis)	6
Massachusetts Institute	5
U. S. Geol. Survey	5
Wisconsin	5
California Institute	4
Ohio State	4
Bell Tel. Labs	3
Iowa	3
Pennsylvania	3
Virginia	3
Elsewhere	69
Total	250

The movement from the universities to the research institutions, industrial laboratories and government service, which was notable shortly after the war, has apparently now ceased. In the list of 1927 fifteen of the 250 men were connected with the Carnegie Institution; nine with the Geological Survey; seven with the Bell Telephone Laboratories; six with the Department of Agriculture; five each with the Rockefeller Institute, the Bureau of Standards and the American Museum of Natural History; four with the Eastman Kodak Company and three with the U. S. Health Service.

There have been selected by the average space allotted to sketches

in biographical directories and encyclopedias the leading scientific men
of the United States who died prior to the present century. There are
not as many as a thousand reaching the standard of the 22,000 in the
present edition of the directory; it is necessary to include large numbers of physicians and inventors. Preparations have also been made
to select the thousand leading scientific men of the world now living
and the thousand most eminent who are no longer living. A study of
distribution among the sciences, in different nations and at different
periods, supplies the beginning of a quantitative study of history.
It is also proposed to print biographical sketches in a subsequent
edition of the directory. Some further study has been given to family
relationship among scientific workers. It is of interest to note the
considerable number of sons of scientific men who have attained high
standing in the course of the past twenty years.

The change in standing of a scientific man after a period of years
gives in quantitative units (with a probable error attached) his gain
or loss in the judgment of his colleagues. The efforts of a lifetime are
condensed into a single informing and dramatic figure. Data have
been published showing that men under forty years of age are likely
to gain in reputation; between forty and forty-five to remain about
stationary; after that age to lose and increasingly as they grow older.
The average gains or losses yield information concerning the effects
of different situations, for example, at one university or another, at
large or small institutions, in research institutions, in industrial
laboratories, in the government service, with much or little administrative work or teaching, etc. The data may ultimately give information concerning individual differences in relation to heredity and social
influences. But this is one of many studies that the present writer
has been unable to complete.

When the scientific men were arranged in 1903 in order of merit
it was stated that the lists would not be published within twenty
years. Nearly thirty years having now elapsed it may be useful to
make public a list that has considerable historical interest. The order
gives no information concerning the contemporary position, some of
those near the bottom of the selection in 1903 having now arisen to
the top and some of those then at the top having dropped. In the fifth
edition of the directory, to be published this month, the list will be
given in full. There are here printed in the order of merit for each
science the hundred men of science regarded in 1903 by their colleagues
as the most distinguished, the number in each science being approximately proportional to the total number of workers. The names of
those no longer living are given in italics with the years of birth and
death.

MATHEMATICS: *Eliakim Hastings Moore*, 62-32; *George William Hill*, 38-14; W. F. Osgood; *Maxime Bôcher*, 67-18; Oskar Bolza; F. Morley; Ernest W. Brown; H. S. White.

PHYSICS: *Albert Abraham Michelson*, 52-31; Carl Barus; Edward L. Nichols; *Arthur Gordon Webster*, 63-23; *John Trowbridge*, 43-23; N. I. Pupin; *Ernest Fox Nichols*, 69-24; *Samuel Pierpont Langley*, 34-06; *DeWitt Bristol Brace*, 58-05; Elihu Thomson; *Robert Simpson Woodward*, 49-24; *Charles Proteus Steinmetz*, 65-23; *Henry Smith Carhart*, 44-20; Edwin H. Hall; J. S. Ames.

CHEMISTRY: *Ira Remsen*, 46-27; *Edward Williams Morley*, 38-23; *Oliver Wolcott Gibbs*, 22-08; *Theodore William Richards*, 68-28; *Edgar Fahs Smith*, 54-28; *John William Mallet*, 32-12; Russell H. Chittenden; Arthur Michael; *John Ulric Nef*, 62-15; *Harvey Washington Wiley*, 44-30; *James Mason Crafts*, 39-17; *F. A. Gooch*, 52-29; C. L. Jackson; *William Francis Hillebrand*, 53-25; *William Olin Atwater*, 44-07; Arthur A. Noyes; *Albert Benjamin Prescott*, 32-05.

ASTRONOMY: *Simon Newcomb*, 35-09; *Edward Charles Pickering*, 46-19; *Lewis Boss*, 46-12; W. W. Campbell; *Seth Carlo Chandler*, 46-13.

GEOLOGY: *Thomas Chrowder Chamberlin*, 43-28; *Grove Carl Gilbert*, 43-18; *Charles Doolittle Walcott*, 50-27; *Charles Richard Van Hise*, 57-18; *Samuel Franklin Emmons*, 41-11; W. M. Davis; *John Casper Branner*, 50-22; *Nathaniel Southgate Shaler*, 41-06; *Clarence Edward Dutton*, 41-12; *Raphael Pumpelly*, 37-23.

BOTANY: *William Gilson Farlow*, 44-19; N. L. Britton; *John Merle Coulter*, 51-28; W. Trelease; *Charles Edwin Bessey*, 45-15; *Lucien Marcus Underwood*, 53-07; L. H. Bailey; *Roland Thaxter*, 58-32; D. T. MacDougal; B. L. Robinson.

ZOOLOGY: *William Keith Brooks*, 48-08; *Charles Otis Whitman*, 42-10; *Alexander Agassiz*, 35-10; E. B. Wilson; H. F. Osborn; *Charles Sedgwick Minot*, 52-14; E. L. Mark; T. H. Morgan; W. M. Wheeler; *Samuel Hubbard Scudder*, 37-11; Chas. B. Davenport; *David Starr Jordan*, 51-31; Edwin G. Conklin; C. Hart Merriam; *William Healey Dall*, 45-27.

PHYSIOLOGY: *Henry Pickering Bowditch*, 40-11; W. H. Howell; W. T. Porter; *Samuel James Meltzer*, 51-20.

ANATOMY: *Franklin Paine Mall*, 62-17; *George Sumner Huntington*, 61-27; H. H. Donaldson.

PATHOLOGY: William H. Welch; W. T. Councilman; Simon Flexner; *William Osler*, 49-19; Theobald Smith; *Theophil Mitchell Prudden*, 49-24.

ANTHROPOLOGY: Franz Boas; *Otis Tufton Mason*, 38-08.

PSYCHOLOGY: *William James*, 42-10; J. McKeen Cattell; *Hugo Münsterberg*, 63-16; *Granville Stanley Hall*, 46-24; J. Mark Baldwin.

BIBLIOGRAPHY OF THE WRITINGS OF JAMES McKEEN CATTELL ARRANGED IN CHRONOLOGICAL ORDER

Each Title Followed by an Asterisk is Reproduced in This Volume

1. Ueber die Zeit der Erkennung und Benennung von Schriftzeichen, Bildern und Farben.* (Translation.) *Philosophische Studien*, 2: 635–650, 1885.

2. Ueber die Trägheit der Netzhaut und des Sehcentrums. *Philosophische Studien*, 3: 94–127, 1885.

3. The Inertia of the Eye and Brain.* *Brain*, 8: 295–312, 1885.

4. Psychometrische Untersuchungen: I. Apparate und Methoden. *Philosophische Studien*, 3: 305–318, 1886. II. Die Reactionzeit. (Bound with I.) *Ibid.*, 3: 319–335, 1886. III. Die Unterscheidungszeit. *Ibid.*, 3: 452–472, 1886. IV. Die Wahlzeit. (Bound with III.) *Ibid.*, 3: 472–485, 1886. V. Einfluss der Aufmerksamkeit, Ermüdung und Uebung auf die Dauer psychischer Processe. (Bound with III.) *Ibid.*, 3: 486–492, 1886. VI. Die Association unter wilkürlich begrentzten Bedingungen. *Ibid.*, 4: 241–250, 1888.

5. Psychometrische Untersuchungen I–V. Inaugural-Dissertation zur Erlangung des Doctorgrades der philosophischen Facultät der Universität Leipzig. *Philosophische Studien*, 3: 305–335; 3: 452–492, 1886.

6. The Time Taken up by Cerebral Operations:* I. Apparatus and Methods. *Mind*, 11: 220–230, 1886. II. The Reaction-time. *Ibid.*, 11: 230–242, 1886. III. The Perception-time. *Ibid.*, 11: 377–392, 1886. IV. The Will-time. *Ibid.*, 11: 524–534, 1886. V. The Influence of Attention, Fatigue and Practice on the Duration of Cerebral Operations. *Ibid.*, 11: 534–538, 1886.

7. The Influence of the Intensity of the Stimulus on the Length of the Reaction Time.* *Brain*, 9: 512–515, 1886.

8. The Time it Takes to See and Name Objects.* *Mind*, 11: 63–65, 1886.

9. Experiments on the Association of Ideas.* *Mind*, 12: 68–74, 1887.

10. The Way We Read. (Read before the Aristotelian Society, Feb. 21, 1887. 4 pages.)

11. Review of Ladd, "Elements of Physiological Psychology." *Mind*, 12: 583–589, 1887.

12. The Psychological Laboratory at Leipzig. *Mind*, 13: 37–51, 1888.

13. The Time it Takes to Think. *Popular Science Monthly*, 32: 488–491, 1888. Also *Nineteenth Century*, 22: 827–830, 1887.

14. Grundzüge der Physiologische Psychologie von Wilhelm Wundt. *Mind*, 13: 435–439, 1888.

15. Recent Books on Physiological Psychology. *Brain*, 11: 263–266, 1888.

16. Die Association unter wilkürlich begrentzten Bedingungen. *Philosophische Studien*, 4: 241–250, 1888.

17. (With Sophie Bryant.) Mental Association Investigated by Experiment.* *Mind*, 14: 230–250, 1889.

18. Psychology at the University of Pennsylvania. *American Journal of Psychology*, 3: 281–283, 1890.

19. Mental Tests and Measurements.* *Mind*, 15: 373–381, 1890.

20. On the Origin of Music. *Mind*, 16: 386–388, 1891.

21. Review of Külpe, O., und Kirschmann, A., "Ein neuer Apparat zur Controle zeitmessender Instrumente." (*Phil. Stud.*, 8: 145–172, 1892) and Titchener, E. B., "Zur Chronometrie des Erkennungsactes." (*Phil. Stud.*, 8: 138–144, 1892.) *American Journal of Psychology*, 4: 596–597, 1891–1892.

22. (With George Stuart Fullerton.) On the Perception of Small Differences

with Special Reference to the Extent, Force and Time of Movement.* *Publications of the University of Pennsylvania*, No. 2, 159 pp. University of Pennsylvania Press, 1892.

23. Contributions from the Psychological Laboratory of Columbia College. *Proceedings of the American Psychological Association*, pp. 3–4, 1892; p. 26–27, 1893.

24. Tests of the Senses and Faculties. *Educational Review*, **5**: 257–265, 1893.

25. Mental Measurement. *Philosophical Review*, **2**: 316–332, 1893.

26. Aufmerksamkeit und Reaction.* (Translation.) *Philosophische Studien*, **8**: 403–406, 1893.

27. The Progress of Psychology. *Popular Science Monthly*, **43**: 779–785, 1893.

28. Errors of Observation in Physics and Psychology. *Proceedings of the American Psychological Association*, pp. 3–4, 1892. Also under the title "On Errors of Observation"* in the *American Journal of Psychology*, **5**: 285–293, 1893.

29. Survival of the Fittest and Sensation Areas. *Mind*, **2**: 505–509, 1893.

30. Review of Ebbinghaus, H., "Theorie des Farbensehens." (*Zeitsch. f. Psychol.*, **5**: 145–238, 1893.) *Psychological Review*, **1**: 324–325, 1894.

31. (With Charles S. Dolley.) On Reaction-times and the Velocity of the Nervous Impulse.* *Proceedings of the National Academy of Sciences*, **7**: 393–415, 1896. Also in *Psychological Review*, **1**: 159–168, 1894.

32. Chronoskop und Chronograph.* (Translation.) *Philosophische Studien*, **9**: 307–310, 1894.

33. Association, Reaction. (Review of Jerusalem and Wundt.) *Psychological Review*, **1**: 543–544, 1894.

34. The Spectrum Top. *Science*, **2**: 13, 1895.

35. The Sense of Equilibrium. *Science*, **2**: 99–100, 1895.

36. Consciousness and the Origin of Species. *Science*, **2**: 100, 1895.

37. Mr. Spencer on Tactual Perception and "Natural Selection," *Science*, **2**: 852–853, 1895.

38. The Rise of Psychological Teaching. *The New Review*, Sept. 19, 1895.

39. Review of the Recent Literature on Reaction-time. *Psychological Review*, **2**: 200–202, 1895.

40. On the Distribution of Exceptional Ability. (Abstract.) *Psychological Review*, **2**: 155–156, 1895.

41. Measurements of the Accuracy of Recollection.* *Science*, **2**: 761–766, 1895.

42. Contributions from the Psychological Laboratory of Columbia College. (Abstract of paper read.) Proceedings of the *American Psychological Association*, pp. 26–27, 1896.

43. Psychological Literature, Experimental; Review of Bourdon. *Psychological Review*, **3**: 110–111, 1896.

44. Address of the President before the American Psychological Association, 1895. *Psychological Review*, **3**: 134–148, 1896.

45. Review of Recent Literature on Evolution. *Psychological Review*, **3**: 437–443, 1896.

46. Science in America. *Science*, **4**: 205–207, Aug. 21, 1896 (unsigned).

47. (With Dr. Livingston Farrand.) Physical and Mental Measurements of the Students of Columbia University.* *Psychological Review*, **3**: 618–648, 1896.

48. (With L. Farrand and J. M. Baldwin.) Note on "Reaction Types." *Psychological Review*, **4**: 298–299, 1897.

49. (With J. LeConte.) Professor Cattell's Review of "Sight." *Science*, **6**: 737–739, 1897.

50. The Perception of Light. *Systematic Diseases of the Eye*, **1**: 505–538, 1897.

51. The Reaction-time of Counting. *Psychological Review*, **5**: 70–71, 1898.

52. The Biological Problems of To-day: Psychology. *Science*, N.S. **7**: 152–154, 1898.

53. (With J. Jastrow and J. M. Baldwin.) Physical and Mental Tests. *Psychological Review*, **5**: 172–179, 1898.

54. Professor Münsterberg on "The Danger from Experimental Psychology." *Psychological Review*, **5**: 411–413, 1898.

55. The Psychological Laboratory. *Psychological Review,* **5**: 655–658, 1898.

56. The Advance of Psychology, Address of the Vice-president and Chairman of Section H before the Section of Anthropology of the American Association for the Advancement of Science, Boston Meeting, Aug. 1898. *Proceedings,* **47**: 3–15, 1898.

57. The Time of Perception as a Measure of the Intensity of Light.* *Proceedings of the American Association for the Advancement of Science,* **48**: 95, 1899.

58. Relation of Time and Space in Vision. *Proceedings of the American Association for the Advancement of Science,* **48**: 95, 1899.

59. New Anthropometric Methods. *Proceedings of the American Association for the Advancement of Science,* **48**: 357–358, 1899.

60. The Depopulation of France. *Science,* **10**: 296–297, 1899.

61. The International Catalogue of Scientific Literature: Report from Columbia College. *Science,* **10**: 165, 1899.

62. (With J. M. Baldwin.) The Schedule for Psychology of the International Catalogue. *Science,* **10**: 297–298, 1899.

63. Methods of a Card Index. *Science,* **10**: 419–420, 1899.

64. Philosophy, Psychology and Physics. *Psychological Review,* **7**: 100–101, 1900.

65. On Relations of Time and Space in Vision.* *Psychological Review,* **7**: 325–343, 1900.

66. Vision with the Moving Eye. *Psychological Review,* **7**: 507–508, 1900.

67. Scientific Societies and Associations: Number 17 of the Monographs on Education in the United States, Ed. by Nicholas Murray Butler; Department of Education for the Paris Exhibition of 1900, pp. 3–27.

68. The American Association for the Advancement of Science. *Science,* N.S. **13**: 961–969, 1901.

69. The Visual Perception of Space. *Science,* N.S. **14**: 263–266, 1901.

70. The University President. *New York Evening Post,* Oct. 5, 1901.

71. The Time of Perception as a Measure of Differences in Intensity.* *Philosophische Studien,* **19**: 63–68, 1902.

72. The Relation of the American Society of Naturalists to Other Scientific Societies. (The Annual Discussion Before the American Society of Naturalists at the Chicago Meeting, 1902.) *Science,* N.S. **15**: 241–255, 1902; **15**: 299–300, 1902.

73. Concerning the American University. *Popular Science Monthly,* **61**: 17–182, 1902.

74. The Carnegie Institution. *Science,* N.S. **16**: 460–469, 1902.

75. The Academy of Sciences. (Address of the President of the New York Academy of Sciences.) *Science,* N.S. **16**: 965–974, 1902.

76. A Statistical Study of Eminent Men. *Popular Science Monthly,* **62**: 359–377, 1903.

77. Homo Scientificus Americanus. (Address of the President of the American Society of Naturalists, Annual Dinner, Washington, 1903.) *Science,* **17**: 561–570, 1903.

78. Statistics of American Psychologists.* *American Journal of Psychology,* **14**: 310–328, 1903.

79. The Limitations of Minor Logic. *Journal of Philosophy, Psychology and Scientific Methods,* **1**: 45–46, 1904.

80. The American Society of Naturalists. What Academic Degrees Should be Conferred for Scientific Work? William Trelease, David Starr Jordan, C. R. Van Hise, J. McKeen Cattell, John M. Coulter, J. H. Burrill. *Science,* **19**: 809–821, 1904.

81. The Conceptions and Methods of Psychology. *Popular Science Monthly,* **66**: 176–186, 1904.

82. Examinations, Grades and Credits.* *Popular Science Monthly,* **66**: 367–378, 1905.

83. The University and Business Methods. *The Independent,* Dec. 28, 1905.

84. University Control. *Science,* **23**: 475–477, 1906. (See also Nos. 101 and 104.)

85. A Statistical Study of American Men of Science.* *Science,* **24**: 658–665; **24**: 699–707; **24**: 732–742, 1906.

86. The New York Meeting of the American Association for the Advancement of Science. *Science,* **25**: 41–46, 1907. (Unsigned.)

87. The American College. *Science,* **26**: 368–373, 1907. Also published in the *Bulletin* of Lafayette College.

88. Reactions and Perceptions. In "Essays Philosophical and Psychological in Honor of William James" by his colleagues at Columbia University. New York: Longmans, Green, 1908, pp. 569–584.

89. The Carnegie Foundation for the Advancement of Teaching. *Science,* **29**: 532–539, 1909.

90. The School and the Family. *Popular Science Monthly,* **74**: 84–95, 1909.

91. The Length of Service Pensions of the Carnegie Foundation. *Science,* **31**: 384–386, 1910.

92. The Case of Harvard College. *Popular Science Monthly,* **77**: 604–614, 1910.

93. A Further Statistical Study of American Men of Science.* *Science,* **32**: 633–648; 672–688, 1910.

94. The Fifth Annual Report of the President of the Carnegie Foundation. *Science,* **33**: 334–336, 1911.

95. About Dismissing Professors. *Popular Science Monthly,* **78**: 305–307, 1911.

96. The Graduate College of Princeton University. *Popular Science Monthly,* **78**: 307–309, 1911.

97. Francis Galton. *Popular Science Monthly,* **78**: 309–312, 1911.

98. Doctorates Conferred by American Universities. *Science,* **34**: 193–202, 1911.

99. Science and International Good Will. *Popular Science Monthly,* **80**: 405–411, 1912.

100. A Program of Radical Democracy. *Popular Science Monthly,* **80**: 606–615, 1912.

101. University Control. *Science,* **35**: 797–808 and 842–860, 1912. See also Ref. Nos. 84 and 104.

102. Outworn Treaties. *New York Evening Post,* April 29, 1913.

103. Outworn Treaties and Newspaper Ethics. *New York Evening Post,* May 8, 1913.

104. University Control. New York: Science Press, 1913, pp. viii + 484. See also Ref. Nos. 84 and 101.

105. The Committee of One Hundred on Scientific Research of the American Association for the Advancement of Science. *Science,* **39**: 680–682, 1914; **40**: 846, 1914; **41**: 315–316, 1915; **45**: 57–58, 1917.

106. The Causes of the Declining Birth Rate. Address at the First National Congress on Race Betterment, Battle Creek Sanitarium, Jan. 8–12, 1914. *Proceedings. Nat. Cong. Race Betterment.*

107. Science, Education and Democracy. (Address of Vice-president and Chairman of the Section of Education of the American Association for the Advancement of Science, Atlanta, Ga., Dec. 31, 1913.) *Science,* **39**: 443–454, 1914.

108. Democracy in University Administration. (Read at the Conference on "The Relation of Higher Education to the Social Order," Yale University, Mar. 5, 1914.) *Science,* **39**: 491–496, 1914.

109. Research and Teaching in the University. *Science,* **40**: 628–630, 1914.

110. Families of American Men of Science.* *Popular Science Monthly,* **86**: 504–515, 1915.

111. The Scientific Monthly and the Popular Science Monthly. *Popular Science Monthly,* **87**: 307–308, 1915.

112. Scientific Journals and the Public. *Popular Science Monthly,* **87**: 308–309, 1915.

113. Science and National Welfare. *Popular Science Monthly,* **87**: 309–310, 1915.

114. Engineering Experiment Stations in the State Colleges. *Science*, **43**: 890–892, 1916.

115. For Peace. *New York Evening Post*, Jan. 25, 1917.

116. Our Psychological Association and Research. *Science*, **45**: 275–284, 1917.

117. Families of American Men of Science. *Scientific Monthly*, **4**: 248–262, 1917; **5**: 368–377, 1917.

118. Families of American Men of Science.* Supplement to "American Men of Science: A Directory" (Third Edition), 781–808, 1921. See also Nos. 110 and 117.

119. Memories of My Last Days at Columbia, 1918. Garrison-on-Hudson, N. Y., pp 24. (Privately Printed.)

120. The American Association for the Advancement of Science and Scientific Organization. *Science*, **49**: 112–114, 1919. (Unsigned.)

121. Carnegie Pensions. The Science Press, 1919, pp. vi + 253.

122. What the Trustees of Columbia University Have Done, 1918. Garrison-on-Hudson, N. Y., pp. 34. (Privately Printed.)

123. Academic Slavery. (Found in galley proof and dated May 18, 1917.)

124. Life Insurance and Annuities for Academic Teachers. *School and Society*, **8**: 541–549, 1918.

125. The Policies of the Carnegie Company. *School and Society*, **9**: 10–23, 1919.

126. Practical Psychology. (Address before the Section of Psychology at the Chicago Meeting of the American Association for the Advancement of Science, Dec. 29, 1920.) *Science*, **53**: 30–35, 1921.

127. In Memory of Wilhelm Wundt. *Psychological Review*, **28**: 155–159, 1921.

128. The Order of Scientific Merit.* *Science*, **56**: 541–547, 1922.

129. The Organization of Scientific Men. *Scientific Monthly*, **14**: 567–577, 1922.

130. The Psychological Corporation. In *Annals of American Academy of Political and Social Science*, **CX**: 165–171, 1923.

131. The Interpretation of Intelligence Tests. *Scientific Monthly*, **18**: 508–516, 1924.

132. Some Psychological Experiments. (Address of the Retiring President of the American Association for the Advancement of Science.) *Science*, **63**: 1–8 and 29–35, 1926.

133. Scientific Research in the United States. *Science*, **63**: 188, 1926.

134. Psychological Methods to Promote Highway Safety. *Scientific Monthly*, **22**: 301–308, 1926.

135. The Journal *Science* and the American Association for the Advancement of Science. *Science*, **64**: 342–347, 1926.

136. The Scientific Men of the World.* *Scientific Monthly*, **23**: 468–471, 1926.

137. The Origin and Distribution of Scientific Men.* *Science*, **66**: 513–516, 1927.

138. The Contribution of Science to the Nations: Science, The Declaration, Democracy. *Scientific Monthly*, **24**: 200–205, and 324–328, 1927.

139. The Distribution of American Men of Science.* In "American Men of Science," ed. by J. McK. Cattell and J. Cattell. New York: Science Press, 1927, pp. 1118–1129.

140. Encyclopedia of the Sciences. *Science*, **65**: 326–327, 1927.

141. Contributions that have been made by Pure Science to the Advancement of Engineering and Industry: Psychology. *Scientific Monthly*, **24**: 324–328, 1927.

142. An After-image of the Yellow Spot.* (National Academy of Sciences.) *Science*, **66**: 404, 1927.

143. Presbyota and the Causes of Deficient Hearing.* (National Academy of Sciences.) *Science*, **66**: 404, 1927.

144. An International Congress of Psychology in America. *Scientific Monthly*, **26**: 188–189, 1928.

145. The Scientific Men of Harvard and Columbia. *Science*, **67**: 136–138, 1928.

146. Early Psychological Laboratories. (Address at Wittenberg College.) *Science*, **67**: 543–548, 1928. Also in Appendix C of "Feelings and Emotions; the

Wittenberg Symposium," ed. by C. Murchison. Worcester, Mass: Clark Univ. Press; London: Oxford Univ. Press, 1928, pp. 427–433.

147. Book Reviews in *Science. Science,* **69**: 220–222, 1929.

148. Psychology in America. (Address of the President of the Ninth International Congress of Psychology.) *Science,* **70**: 335–347, 1929. Also in *Scientific Monthly,* **30**: 114–126, 1930.

149. The Usefulness of Psychology. *Science,* **72**: 284–287, 1930.

150. Education under the National Government. *School and Society,* **34**: 325–336, 1931.

151. President Butler's Athletic Record. *School and Society,* **33**: 138–141, 1931.

152. The Distribution of American Men of Science in 1932.* *Science,* **77**: 264–270, 1933.

153. Small Farm Doomed. *New York Herald Tribune,* March 22, 1933.

154. The Adrenal Glands in the Editor's Office. *Science,* **77**: 428–430, 1933.

155. Exemption of the Rich from Taxation. *The New York Times,* May 9, 1933.

156. The Need of Opportunity for Exceptional Ability. *Science,* **77**: 491–492, 1933.

157. A Bimetallic Dollar. *New York Herald Tribune,* Apr. 30, 1933.

158. For the Bimetallic Dollar. *New York Herald Tribune,* Oct. 3, 1933.

159. The Two Eagles. *School and Society,* **38**: 676, 1933.

160. The Future Control of School and Society. *School and Society,* **39**: 567–568, 1934.

161. A Scientific Approach to Emotional Problems. *Scientific Monthly,* **39**: 536–539, 1934.

162. Concerning Taxation. *The New York Times,* March 21, 1933.

163. Local Branches of the American Association for the Advancement of Science. *Science,* **80**: 576–578, 1934.

164. Retrospect: Psychology as a Profession. *Journal of Consulting Psychology,* **1**: 1–3, 1937.

165. University Presidents who have been Psychologists. *Scientific Monthly,* **45**: 473–477, 1937.

166. The *Scientific Monthly* and the American Association for the Advancement of Science. *Scientific Monthly,* **47**: 468–469, 1938.

167. The Founding of the Psychological Association and of the Hopkins and Clark Laboratories. *Psychological Review,* **50**: 61–64, 1943.